Principles of Genetics

Principles of

Irwin H. Herskowitz
Hunter College
The City University of New York

GENETICS

The Macmillan Company, New York
Collier-Macmillan Limited, London

To my wife, Reida

The Macmillan Company
866 Third Avenue, New York, New York 10022

Collier-Macmillan Canada, Ltd., Toronto, Ontario

Library of Congress catalog card number: 72–187072

Printing: 3 4 5 6 7 8   Year: 4 5 6 7 8 9

Preface

Most first courses in college biology provide a reasonably good introduction to genetics. Accordingly, students starting their first course in college genetics not only have some background in the origins and early advances in genetics, but also have some knowledge of the recent progress made through biochemical and microbial studies. Because of this prior exposure, the students also come to the course with enthusiasm and interest. It is feasible, therefore, to approach the subject in a highly structured manner.

The subject matter is contained in 37 chapters arranged in seven sections. In the first section the genetic material responsible for the uniqueness of organisms is identified as DNA or, less frequently, RNA, and the physical and chemical properties of these compounds are discussed. The next two sections take up, in turn, the role that this genetic material plays in the formation of more nucleic acid or protein, and the regular and irregular ways in which it varies qualitatively and quantitatively. The section that follows, the largest, deals with the recombination of genetic material. This section considers the various recombinational methods observed in organisms of all degrees of organismal complexity, from viruses and bacteria to multicellular plants and animals. The last three sections consider the interaction of gene products in the production of traits; the regulation of the synthesis, destruction, and action of genetic material; and the role of genetic material in evolution.

This book aims to elucidate the principles of genetics, many of which were recently discovered in molecular and microbial studies. Since principles are dealt with rather than history, no distinction is made between "classical" and "modern" genetics, and the presentation aims to be logical rather than chronological. The few names in the text—Watson, Crick, Mendel, Hardy, and Weinberg—are there simply because they are uniquely important, widely known, and commonly used.

After a brief introduction, each chapter contains a series of numbered conclusions or postulates, each of which is then proved, supported, or discussed. Each chapter ends with a summary, references, and questions and problems. The literature cited includes general references to the subject matter of the entire chapter followed by references to specific numbered sections. The references that were selected provide an entry into the current literature, give a more general presentation of the subject matter, or represent key papers in the discovery of major principles. Photographs of certain geneticists are included for the sake of personalizing the largely impersonal presentation.

The essential subject matter in each chapter can be covered, on the average, in one lecture period. Accordingly, the main contents of the text can be covered in the usual three-credit single-semester college course for undergraduates. A considerable amount of completely optional material, which contains no terms, facts, diagrams, or concepts needed to understand the remainder of the text, is included also. This dispensable information is restricted to (1) footnotes to the main text, (2) supplementary sections placed after the references of various chapters, and (3) a biometrical appendix following Chapter 37. The amount of this optional material used will depend upon the time available and the preparation and interests of the students and teachers.

I wish to thank my colleagues and students for many helpful suggestions, and my wife, Reida Postrel Herskowitz, for preparing the typescript. Little, Brown and Company, Publishers, kindly gave permission to use material from two texts of mine —*Genetics*, Second Edition, and *Basic Principles of Molecular Genetics*.

I. H. H.

Contents

Symbols and Abbreviations[1]

A	adenosine
ADP	adenosine 5'-diphosphate
Ala	alanine
Alanine tRNA or tRNA^{Ala}, etc.	the "uncharged" transfer RNA molecule that normally accepts alanine, etc.
Alanyl-tRNA^{Ala} or Ala-tRNA^{Ala}	the same, "charged," with alanyl residue covalently linked
Aminoacyl-tRNA	"charged" tRNA (tRNA carrying aminoacyl residues)
AMP	adenosine 5'-phosphate
Arg	arginine
Asp	aspartic acid
Asn	asparagine
ATP	adenosine 5'-triphosphate
C	cytidine
CDP	cytidine 5'-diphosphate
CMP	cytidine 5'-phosphate
CTP	cytidine 5'-triphosphate
Cys	cysteine
d	deoxy
DNA	deoxyribonucleic acid
DNase	deoxyribonuclease
DPN	diphosphopyridine nucleotide
fMet	formylmethionine
G	guanosine
Gal	galactose
GDP	guanosine 5'-diphosphate
Glu	glutamic acid
Gln	glutamine
Gly	glycine
GMP	guanosine 5'-phosphate
GTP	guanosine 5'-triphosphate
Hb	hemoglobin
His	histidine
I	inosine
Ile	isoleucine
Leu	leucine
Lys	lysine
Met	methionine
mRNA	messenger RNA
N	ribonucleoside
NAD	nicotinamide-adenine dinucleotide (diphosphopyridine nucleotide)
P	phosphate

P$_i$	inorganic orthophosphate
Phe	phenylalanine
poly N	polymer of ribonucleotides containing N
poly dN	polymer of deoxyribonucleotides containing dN
poly (N-N')	copolymer of ribonucleotides with N-N'-N-N'- in regular, alternating, known sequence
poly (dN-dN')	copolymer of deoxyribonucleotides with dN-dN'-dN-dN'- in regular, alternating, known sequence
poly (N, N')	copolymer of ribonucleotides with N and N' in random sequence
poly (A) · poly (B) or poly (A) · (B)	two chains, generally or completely associated
PP$_i$	inorganic pyrophosphate
Pro	proline
RNA	ribonucleic acid
RNase	ribonuclease
rRNA	ribosomal RNA
Ser	serine
Thr	threonine
tRNA	"uncharged" transfer RNA (RNA that accepts and transfers amino acids; amino acid-accepting RNA); see also entries following Ala
Trp	tryptophan
T	thymidine
Tyr	tyrosine
U	uridine
UDP	uridine 5'-diphosphate
UMP	uridine 5'-phosphate
UTP	uridine 5'-triphosphate
Val	valine

[1] Taken from "Abbreviations and Symbols for Chemical Names of Special Interest in Biological Chemistry" of the IUPAC-IUB Combined Commission on Biochemical Nomenclature, published in the Journal of Biological Chemistry, 241:527 (1966), Biochimica et Biophysica Acta 108, 1 (1965), and in Biochemistry, 5:1445 (1966).

Name	Formula	Mol. Wt.	% Composition			
			C	H	N	P
PURINES						
adenine	$C_5H_5N_5$	135.11	44.44	3.73	51.83	
2-aminopurine	$C_5H_5N_5$	135.11	44.44	3.73	51.83	
2,6-diaminopurine	$C_5H_6N_6$	150.15	39.99	4.02	55.97	
2,8-dioxyadenine	$C_5H_5N_5O_2$	167.13	35.93	3.01	41.90	
guanine	$C_5H_5N_5O$	151.15	39.72	3.33	46.33	
hypoxanthine	$C_5H_4N_4O$	136.11	44.11	2.96	41.16	
xanthine	$C_5H_4N_4O_2$	152.11	39.47	2.64	36.83	
PYRIMIDINES						
cytosine	$C_4H_5N_3O$	111.10	43.27	4.54	37.82	
5-hydroxymethylcytosine	$C_5H_7N_3O_2$	141.13	42.55	5.00	29.78	
5-methylcytosine	$C_5H_7N_3O$	125.13	47.99	5.64	33.58	
thymine	$C_5H_6N_2O_2$	126.11	47.61	4.79	22.21	
uracil	$C_4H_4N_2O_2$	112.09	42.85	3.59	24.99	
RIBONUCLEOSIDES						
adenosine	$C_{10}H_{13}N_5O_4$	267.24	44.94	4.90	26.20	
cytidine	$C_9H_{13}N_3O_5$	243.23	44.43	5.38	17.27	
2,6-diaminopurine ribonucleoside	$C_{10}H_{14}N_6O_4$	282.26	42.54	4.99	29.77	
guanosine	$C_{10}H_{13}N_5O_5$	283.26	42.39	4.62	24.72	
inosine	$C_{10}H_{12}N_4O_5$	268.24	44.77	4.51	20.88	
pseudouridine	$C_9H_{12}N_2O_6$	244.2	44.26	4.95	11.47	
5-methylcytidine	$C_{10}H_{15}N_3O_5$	257.26	46.69	5.87	16.33	
uridine	$C_9H_{12}N_2O_6$	244.20	44.26	4.95	11.47	
xanthosine	$C_{10}H_{12}N_4O_6$	284.24	42.26	4.26	19.71	
2′-DEOXYRIBONUCLEOSIDES						
deoxyadenosine	$C_{10}H_{13}N_5O_3$	251.24	47.80	5.21	27.87	—
deoxycytidine	$C_9H_{13}N_3O_4$	227.22	47.57	5.76	18.49	—
deoxyguanosine	$C_{10}H_{13}N_5O_4$	267.24	44.94	4.90	26.20	—
5-methyldeoxycytidine	$C_{10}H_{15}N_3O_4$	241.26	49.78	6.26	17.41	—
thymidine	$C_{10}H_{14}N_2O_5$	242.23	49.58	5.82	11.56	—
deoxyuridine	$C_9H_{12}N_2O_5$	228.20	47.36	5.30	12.27	—
RIBONUCLEOTIDES (5′)						
adenosine triphosphate	$C_{10}H_{16}N_5O_{13}P_3$	507.20	23.67	3.18	13.80	18.32
adenylic acid	$C_{10}H_{14}N_5O_7P$	347.22	34.58	4.06	20.17	8.92
cytidylic acid	$C_9H_{14}N_3O_8P$	323.21	33.44	4.36	13.00	9.58
guanylic acid	$C_{10}H_{14}N_5O_8P$	363.24	33.06	3.88	19.28	8.52
inosinic acid	$C_{10}H_{13}N_4O_8P$	348.22	34.48	3.76	16.09	8.89
uridylic acid	$C_9H_{13}N_2O_9P$	324.18	33.34	4.04	8.64	9.55
DEOXYRIBONUCLEOTIDES (5′)						
deoxyadenylic acid	$C_{10}H_{14}N_5O_6P$	331.22	36.25	4.26	21.14	9.35
deoxycytidylic acid	$C_9H_{14}N_3O_7P$	307.20	35.18	4.59	13.67	10.08
deoxyguanylic acid	$C_{10}H_{14}N_5O_7P$	347.23	34.58	4.06	20.17	8.92
deoxy-5-methylcytidylic acid	$C_{10}H_{16}N_3O_7P$	321.24	37.38	5.02	13.08	9.64
thymidylic acid	$C_{10}H_{15}N_2O_8P$	322.21	37.27	4.69	8.69	9.61

PART I

Identification and Properties of Genetic Material

Chapter 1

Genetic Material

All organisms contain information for their self-maintenance and self-reproduction. This book is devoted primarily to a consideration of the material basis of this information and its use in organisms. Let us investigate first the general nature of this informational material and then its specific type in several simple organisms. Details of its chemical and physical properties will be taken up in subsequent chapters.

1.1 The genetic material of an organism contains the information for the organism's self-maintenance and self-reproduction and for the formation of a unique set of proteins.

Typical of every organism on earth today are two properties: (1) the ability to maintain individuality for a period of time, and (2) the ability to produce offspring of the same kind. This self-preservation and self-reproduction in the face of an ever-changing environment depends at the molecular level upon the presence and arrangement of essentially three types of giant molecules, or *macromolecules*: *polysaccharides, proteins,* and *nucleic acids*. Lipids, which are involved in membrane structure and energy storage, are another important class of molecules. Simpler chemical substances —water, for example, which makes up the greatest bulk of most organisms—are usually also needed for structure, maintenance, and reproduction.

The polysaccharides and their derivatives store chemical energy that can be used

1

for maintenance and reproduction. Thus, these substances serve to prolong the period of time that a type of organism can exist. Although most organisms contain significant amounts of polysaccharides, some viruses (the simplest organisms) contain none at all. Composed entirely of protein and nucleic acid, such viruses persist, and may under appropriate conditions reproduce, in the absence of polysaccharides.

The proteins, on the other hand, play a more integral role in structure, maintenance, and reproduction; for all organisms contain these macromolecules. Moreover, the uniqueness of each kind of organism is associated with a unique set of protein molecules. Proteins are essential building blocks of membranes, which maintain the physical integrity of organisms, and are also enzymes, which catalyze metabolic reactions. Although the structure and metabolic activities of a cell are organized for its preservation, the protein components are continually being destroyed and replaced throughout the cell's existence. Therefore, an organism must possess initially and must retain during its existence instructions for producing proteins of correct kinds and amounts and at the correct times and places. Such information must also be transmitted to and maintained in its offspring.

The properties common to organisms must be based, therefore, on information that is preserved, replicable, and transmissible—information contained in *genetic material*. We can rule out carbohydrates as the usual genetic material because of their absence from a number of viruses. Because of their simple chemical makeup, viruses can be used to study whether proteins, nucleic acids, or both constitute genetic material.

1.2   Ribonucleic acid (RNA) is the genetic material of some viruses.

Tobacco mosaic virus (*TMV*) (Figure 1-1) is composed entirely of a characteristic protein complexed with a specific type of nucleic acid, *ribonucleic acid* (*RNA*). After a TMV particle enters a host tobacco cell and a suitable incubation period has elapsed, hundreds of TMV progeny are formed. Since uninfected tobacco cells do not (and cannot) synthesize the characteristic protein of TMV, the virus particle must contain the information required for this synthesis.

The RNA of TMV particles can be isolated by extracting the viral protein with a phenol and water mixture, a procedure that leaves the RNA in the aqueous (water) phase. When tobacco cells are exposed to the viral protein (phenol) fraction, they do not synthesize more viral protein or RNA. Cells exposed to the RNA fraction, however, produce hundreds of TMV progeny whose protein and RNA composition is identical to that of the infecting virus. Different strains of TMV and different strains of tobacco have been tested with the same result: Viral progeny identical to the parent type were produced when the nucleic acid (RNA) fraction was used. We conclude, therefore, that the RNA of TMV contains the information required for synthesis of both viral protein and more RNA—that RNA is the genetic material of the tobacco mosaic virus.[1]

[1] These experiments also prove that TMV protein plays no part—other than protecting the RNA and increasing the efficiency of infection—in the replication either of the RNA genetic material or of itself. This conclusion is tested by *reconstitution experiments*. Under appropriate conditions the separated protein and RNA of TMV can be recombined, the reconstituted virus having the infectiveness of the original virus. Using two genetically different strains, the standard (S) and Holmes rib grass (H), a highly infective virus containing the RNA of S and the protein coat of H can be constructed. The progeny obtained are typically S with both S RNA and protein coat. The reciprocal construct, a virus with H RNA and S protein, produces H progeny typical in both RNA and protein. Thus, only the RNA of a TMV particle specifies the RNA and protein of its progeny.

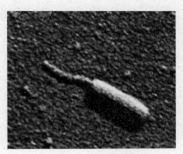

Figure 1-1 Electron micrographs of tobacco mosaic virus (TMV) showing its general configuration (top) and its hollow core (bottom). The middle photograph shows a particle whose protein has been partially removed by treatment with detergent, leaving a thinner strand of RNA. (Courtesy of R. G. Hart.) The hollow cylinder of the TMV particle is 3,000 Å long with a radius of about 80 Å. The outer dimensions are due to the aggregation in a gently pitched spiral or helix of about 2,200 identical protein subunits, each containing 158 amino acids in a single polypeptide chain (see Figure 6-1).

Poliomyelitis, influenza, and encephalitis viruses, as well as some *bacteriophages*, or *phages* (viruses that attack bacteria), are other organisms composed solely of RNA and protein. RNA isolated from such viruses, as with TMV, gives rise to progeny of the same kind. Thus RNA is genetic material in these organisms, too. The release of mature virus particles, or *virions*, from cells infected by viral nucleic acid is called *transfection*. (R)[2]

1.3 Deoxyribonucleic acid (DNA) is the genetic material of other viruses.

Some viruses consist only of a characteristic protein combined with *deoxyribonucleic acid (DNA)* rather than RNA. As before, we can obtain pure viral nucleic acid by phenol treatment. When DNA from ϕX174 (ϕ = phage)—a rather simple, spherical phage (Figure 1-2)—is mixed with *Escherichia coli* bacteria (with cell walls removed

---

[2] This symbol means that one or more references dealing with the material in this section can be found at the end of the chapter under Specific Section References.

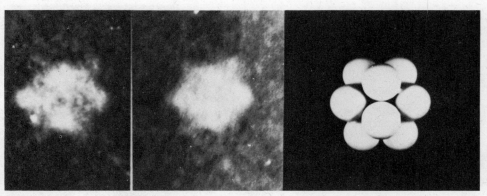

Figure 1-2   Electron micrographs of ϕX174. The phage seems to consist of a protein shell or coat, composed of 12 identical spherical protein subunits arranged in icosahedral symmetry, as shown in the model at the right, surrounding the DNA core. (Courtesy of R. W. Horne).

to facilitate penetration of certain chemicals), ϕX174 progeny are produced transfectively. Since the protein fraction of the virus transfers no such information, we conclude that DNA is its genetic material.

Other phages of *E. coli* (those of the T series) also contain DNA. Larger and structurally more complex than ϕX174, T phages contain their nucleic acid within a protein "head" (Figure 1-3A, B). Since DNA contains no sulfur and T-phage protein contains no phosphorus, the following experiment can be performed. The DNA of one phage sample is labeled by growing the viruses in bacteria containing radioactive phosphorus, ^{32}P; the protein of another sample is labeled by growing the phage in bacteria containing radioactive sulfur, ^{35}S. Labeled phage are then permitted to infect "cold" (that is, unradioactive) *E. coli*. In one sample all the ^{32}P (hence all the DNA) enters the bacterium; in the other only about 3 per cent of the ^{35}S (thus only a small fraction of the protein) enters. In both cases, and even if 80 per cent of the phage protein attached to the outside of the host cells is removed by the shearing action of a blender, a full yield of progeny phage results. These findings strongly suggest the hypothesis that DNA is the genetic material of T phages. (R)

1.4   Cells normally contain both DNA and RNA, which are often found in several different cell organelles.

Until recently, no virus was reported to contain both DNA and RNA; even the large and complex DNA virus vaccinia has no RNA. On the other hand, all uninfected cells (Figure 1-4) normally have both types of nucleic acid.

DNA is found in such cell organelles as the membrane-bound nucleus, the mitochondrion, chloroplast, and centriole of cells of higher organisms; and in the non-membrane-bound *nuclear areas* (Figure 1-5) of bacteria and blue-green algae. DNA is also found in less commonplace organelles such as yolk platelets, basal granules of cilia and flagella, and the mitochondrion-like kinetoplast of trypanosomes; it is attached to or present in the cell membrane of bacteria (and the nuclear membrane

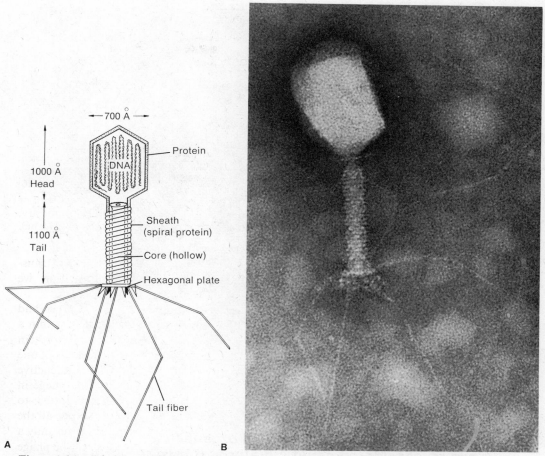

A   B

Figure 1-3A   Diagrammatic representation of the structures observed in intact and triggered T-even phages of *E. coli.*

Figure 1-3B   Electron micrograph of bacteriophage T4 showing its head (packed with DNA), to one end of which is attached a neck with a collar and a tail structure (0.1 μ long) containing 24 striations. At the base of the tail is the base plate, to which are attached six long tail fibers, kinked in the middle. These are the organelles of primary attachment to the host cell of this phage, *Escherichia coli.* Magnification 300,000 $\times$. (Courtesy of T. F. Anderson.)

of nucleated cells). DNA is reported to occur in microsomes (fragments of endoplasmic reticulum with small particles called *ribosomes* attached), in the cell membrane of lymphocytes and of red blood corpuscles which do not contain nuclei, and as part of avidin in egg white.

Although RNA has been detected wherever relatively large amounts of DNA are found in the cell—in the nucleus, mitochondrion, and chloroplast, for example—more than three-fourths of the RNA in a cell is located in ribosomes. Ribosomes are found in great numbers in the cytoplasm (in plastids, in mitochondria, and free or attached to the endoplasmic reticulum) and in the nucleus (inside and outside the nucleolus).(R)

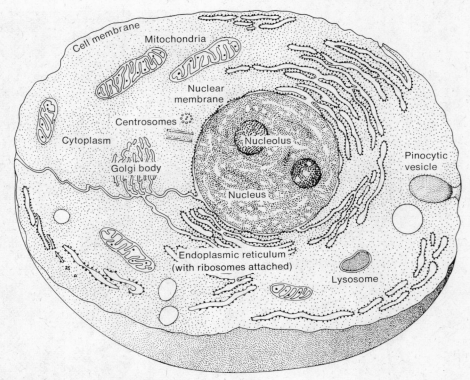

Figure 1-4 Diagrammatic cross section of a cell.

1.5   The DNA or RNA of a cell organelle can be considered genetic material if it is shown to contain information that is used for its own replication.

Because all ordinary organisms can multiply, their genetic material must also be able to multiply to assure informational continuity. The property of replicability, therefore, can be used by itself to identify genetic material. When a macromolecule of an organism is shown to contain information used for its own replication, we can regard it as genetic material.[3] This criterion, included when we earlier identified nucleic acid as genetic material in several viruses, can also be applied to cell organelles.

A thread containing DNA proved to be genetic material is called a *chromosome* ("colored body"), because it stains with certain dyes. A stained mass of chromosomes is called *chromatin*. A group of chromosomes made up of one chromosome of each kind normally present in the cell or organism is called a chromosome set, or *genome*. A basic set of RNA genetic material of organisms such as TMV is also called a genome.

---

[3] Except for *in vitro* syntheses, the terms "genetic material," "protein," and "organism" always go together. Although the current and subsequent definitions of genetic material exclude reference to its relation to protein, we shall describe how the two are necessarily related in an organism when we consider the origin and nature of the first organism in Section 37.2.

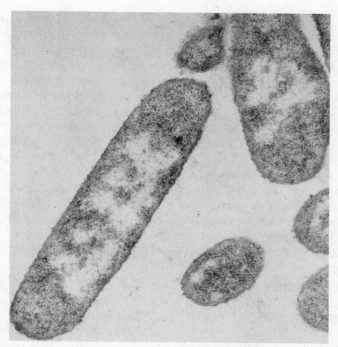

Figure 1-5   Thin section showing nuclear areas and the fine DNA-containing fibers within them. Original magnification 20,000 ×. Present magnification about 13,000 ×. (Courtesy of E. Kellenberger.)

1.6   Studying the properties of genetic material at the molecular level should be fruitful in discovering basic principles of genetics.

A virion ordinarily neither metabolizes nor replicates outside its host cell. Within a host, however, the virus preserves its information by utilizing its environment for the replication of its own nucleic acid, for the formation of its characteristic protein, and for the assembly of these molecules into viral progeny. For a more complete understanding of a virus's life activities, we would like to answer the following questions about genetic material:

What are the chemical and physical characteristics of DNA and RNA? Where and how do nucleic acids store information? How are DNA and RNA replicated? In what way does genetic material direct the synthesis of proteins? Do DNA and RNA contain other information? Once replicated, how is genetic material distributed? What are the consequences of chemical changes in genetic material and of errors in distribution and in replication? How did genetic material originate and evolve?

Answers to such molecularly oriented questions pertain not only to viruses but to the entire spectrum of organisms. In the following chapters we will consider properties of genetic material at the molecular level whenever possible and, in so doing, seek to discover and clarify the basic principles of genetics.

SUMMARY AND CONCLUSIONS

The uniqueness of organisms—their capacity for self-maintenance and self-reproduction—ultimately resides in the uniqueness of their protein and nucleic acid macromolecules. The production of both types of macromolecule requires the maintenance and replication of information contained in genetic material. Genetic material was identified as nucleic acid in viruses—RNA in some, DNA in others—because it contains information used in (1) its own replication, and (2) the synthesis of proteins characteristic of the organism. Because replicability is so essential to organisms, nucleic acids (for example, those of cell organelles) will henceforth be considered genetic material if they satisfy the first criterion, that is, if they are shown to contain information used for their own replication. The definition of genetic material will undergo change and additional clarification (in Chapters 5 and 26 for example), as we increase our knowledge of nucleic acid chemistry and function. Proof that DNA is genetic material in bacteria is presented in Chapter 11 (Section 11.1); in nuclei, in Chapter 14 (Section 14.6); and in extranuclear organelles, in Chapter 19.

Having identified RNA and (especially) DNA as genetic material in this chapter, the remainder of the book considers the following:

1. The physical–chemical nature of nucleic acids (Chapters 2 and 3).
2. How information in nucleic acid genetic material is used in the synthesis of more nucleic acid and of protein (Chapters 4 through 7).
3. The natural as well as the unusual variations that occur in the nucleic acids of organisms (Chapters 8 and 9).
4. The organization, transmission, and shuffling of the genetic material in phage and bacteria (Chapters 10 through 13), in nuclear chromosomes (Chapters 14 through 18), and in extranuclear chromosomes (Chapter 19).
5. How the products of the functioning of genetic material interact and the consequences of such interactions (Chapters 20 through 23).
6. How the genetic material regulates its own kind and amount (Chapters 24 and 25) as well as which portions of it are functional (Chapters 26 through 32).
7. The past, present, and future of genetic material, especially in populations (Chapters 33 through 37).

GENERAL REFERENCES

Journals
Annual Review of Genetics
Annual Review of Microbiology
Biochemical Genetics
Chromosoma (Berlin)
Cold Spring Harbor Symposia on Quantitative Biology
Evolution
Genetica
Genetical Research (Cambridge)
Genetics
Genetika
Hereditas
Heredity
Japanese Journal of Genetics
Journal of Molecular Biology
Nature (London)
Proceedings of the National Academy of Sciences (United States)
Science

Books

Adelberg, E. A. (Editor) 1966. *Papers on bacterial genetics,* second edition. Boston: Little, Brown and Company.

Cairns, J., Stent, G. S., and Watson, J. D. 1966. *Phage and the origins of molecular biology.* New York: Cold Spring Harbor Laboratory of Quantitative Biology. (Covering mostly 1945–1966).

Davis, B. D., Dulbecco, R., Eisen, H. N., Ginsberg, H. S., and Wood, W. B. 1967. *Principles of microbiology and immunology.* New York: Harper & Row, Inc.

Dunn, L. C. 1965. *A short history of genetics.* New York: McGraw-Hill Book Company. (Covers the period 1864–1939.)

Haynes, R. H., and Hanawalt, P. C. (Editors) 1968. *The molecular basis of life.* San Francisco: W. H. Freeman and Company, Publishers. (Readings from *Scientific American.*)

Herskowitz, I. H. 1965. *Genetics,* second edition. Boston: Little, Brown and Company. (A supplement contains Nobel prize lectures through 1962 dealing with genetics.)

Ingram, V. M. 1966. *The biosynthesis of macromolecules.* Menlo Park, Calif.: W. A. Benjamin, Inc.

Kennedy, D. (Editor) 1965. *The living cell.* San Francisco: W. H. Freeman and Company, Publishers. (Readings from *Scientific American.*)

King, R. C. 1968. *A dictionary of genetics.* New York: Oxford University Press.

Ravin, A. W. 1965. *The evolution of genetics.* New York: Academic Press, Inc.

Srb, A. M., Owen, R. D., and Edgar, R. S. (Editors) 1970. *Facets of genetics.* San Francisco: W. H. Freeman and Company, Publishers. (Readings from *Scientific American.*)

Stent, G. S. (Editor) 1965. *Papers on bacterial viruses,* second edition. Boston: Little, Brown and Company.

Sturtevant, A. H. 1965. *A history of genetics.* New York: Harper & Row, Inc.

Taylor, J. H. (Editor) 1965. *Selected papers on molecular genetics.* New York: Academic Press, Inc.

Watson, J. D. 1970. *Molecular biology of the gene,* second edition. Menlo Park, Calif.: W. A. Benjamin, Inc.

Zubay, G. L. (Editor) 1968. *Papers in biochemical genetics.* New York: Holt, Rinehart and Winston, Inc.

SPECIFIC SECTION REFERENCES

1.2   Fraenkel-Conrat, H., and Williams, R. C. 1955. Reconstitution of tobacco mosaic virus from its inactive protein and nucleic acid components. Proc. Nat. Acad. Sci., U.S., 41: 690–698. Reprinted in *Classic papers in genetics*, Peters, J. A. (Editor), Englewood Cliffs, N.J.: Prentice-Hall, Inc., 1959, pp. 264–271; and Bobbs-Merrill Reprint Series, Indianapolis: Howard W. Sams Company, Inc.

Gierer, A., and Schramm, G. S. 1956. Infectivity of ribonucleic acid from tobacco mosaic virus. Nature, Lond., 177: 702–703. Reprinted in *Papers in biochemical genetics*, Zubay, G. L. (Editor), New York: Holt, Rinehart and Winston, Inc., 1968, pp. 16–18.

1.3   Baltz, R. H. 1971. Infectious DNA of bacteriophage T4. J. Mol. Biol., 62: 425–437. (Transfection.)

Guthrie, G. D., and Sinsheimer, R. L. 1963. Observations on the infection of bacterial protoplasts with the deoxyribonucleic acid of bacteriophage ϕX174. Biochim. Biophys. Acta, 72: 290–297.

Hershey, A. D., and Chase, M. 1952. Independent functions of viral protein and nucleic acid in growth of bacteriophage. J. Gen. Physiol., 36: 39–54. Reprinted in *Papers on bacterial viruses*, second edition, Stent, G. S. (Editor), Boston: Little, Brown and Company, 1965, pp. 87–104; and Bobbs-Merrill Reprint Series, Indianapolis: Howard W. Sams Company, Inc. (This "Hershey–Chase" experiment was the first strong evidence for DNA as the genetic material of T phages.)

Mirsky, A. E. 1968. The discovery of DNA. Scient. Amer., 218 (No. 6): 78–88, 140. Scientific American Offprints, San Francisco: W. H. Freeman and Company, Publishers.

1.4   Baltus, E., Hanocq-Quertier, J., and Brachet, J. 1968. Isolation of deoxyribonucleic acid from the yolk platelets of *Xenopus laevis* oöcyte. Proc. Nat. Acad. Sci., U.S., 61: 469–476.

Bond, H. E., Cooper, J. A., II, Courington, D. P., and Wood, J. S. 1969. Microsome-associated DNA. Science, 165: 705–706.

Lerner, R. A., Meinke, W., and Goldstein, D. A. 1971. Membrane-associated DNA in the cytoplasm of diploid human lymphocytes. Proc. Nat. Acad. Sci., U.S., 68: 1212–1216.

Levinson, W., Bishop, J. M., Quintrell, N., and Jackson, J. 1970. Presence of DNA in Rous sarcoma virus. Nature, Lond., 227: 1023–1025. (Present with RNA in virion.)

Scientific American, Sept. 1961, Vol. 205, No. 3, *The living cell*, articles by J. Brachet and D. Mazia.

Swanson, C. P. 1969. *The cell*, third edition. Englewood Cliffs, N.J.: Prentice-Hall, Inc.

Alfred D. Hershey (1908–   ) in 1969, the year Dr. Hershey was the recipient of a Nobel prize.

QUESTIONS AND PROBLEMS

1. A growing crystal of table salt that can "reproduce" after fragmentation is not considered an organism. Why?

2. Does an organism that fails to reproduce contain genetic material? Explain.

3. How would you identify the genetic material of an organism from another planet?

4. If nucleic acid is the sole carrier of information of some viruses, why is their transmissive form not simply nucleic acid?

5. What can you conclude about the genetic material of T phages from the experiment described in Section 1.3?

6. Discuss the functional specialization of different kinds of macromolecules.

7. Does genetic material have to multiply just because organisms multiply? Explain.

8. Give a definition of genetics.

Chapter 2

Primary Structure

To determine what part of a nucleic acid contains information, what this information is, and how it is used, we will consider first the *primary structure* of nucleic acids, that is, the organization of component parts into single strands.

2.1 A nucleic acid is a polymer of nucleotides. Its monomeric units consist of a phosphate, a pentose sugar, and an organic base.

DNA and RNA are made up of many similar units, *nucleotides*, and are thus polymers of nucleotide monomers, or *polynucleotides*. Each nucleotide consists of one *phosphate* (PO_4) group, a *pentose* (a five-carbon sugar), and an *organic base* in which nitrogen and carbon atoms are arranged in one or two aromatic rings. The average molecular weight (MW) of a nucleotide is 330 (see the Table on page x for some physical and chemical characteristics of specific nucleic acid components).

2.2 The usual pentose of RNA is D-ribose (ribose); in DNA it is 2'-deoxy-D-ribose (deoxyribose).

Four of the five carbons in a pentose plus a single atom of oxygen can form a five-membered ring (Figure 2-1). (By convention, ring carbons are often omitted in structural diagrams, as in Figure 2-1a' and b'.) The pentose usually found in RNA is D-*ribose*, commonly called *ribose* (Figure 2-1a and a'), which has a hydroxyl (OH) group at positions 1', 2', 3', and 5'. (The positions of carbon atoms in the pentose are primed so they can be distinguished from the positions of carbons in an organic base.) Since the pentose usually found in DNA is a ribose which lacks oxygen at the 2' position, it is called *2'-deoxy-*D-*ribose,* or *deoxyribose* Figure (2-1b and b').

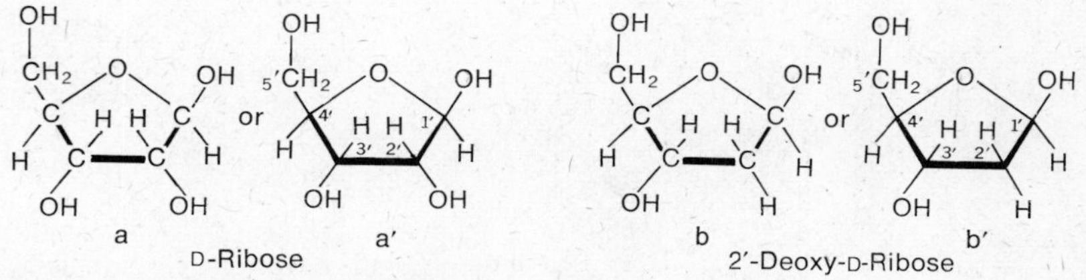

Figure 2-1 Pentoses found in nucleic acids.

2.3   The organic base of a nucleotide is either a pyrimidine or a purine. The most common pyrimidines are cytosine and uracil in RNA, and cytosine and thymine in DNA. The most common purines in RNA and DNA are adenine and guanine.

The structure of an organic base in a nucleotide is related to that of benzene, an aromatic hydrocarbon with a six-membered ring (Figure 2-2a, a′, and a″). The fundamental ring of the organic base is a *pyrimidine* ring, in which N replaces CH at positions 1 and 3 in the benzene ring (Figure 2-2b). Figure 2-2b′ and b″ are successive abbreviations of this formula corresponding to those used for benzene.

The other kind of organic base in nucleotides is a *purine*, which is closely related to a pyrimidine. A purine molecule consists of a pyrimidine ring whose 4 and 5 positions are shared with a five-membered imidazole ring (Figure 2-2c, c′, and c″). Hereafter, we will use the most abbreviated of these structural representations for pyrimidines and purines.

Figure 2-3 gives structural formulas for the most common pyrimidines in nucleic acids. All the derivatives shown have an oxygen at position 2 in the keto form ($O=C\!\!\big\langle$). The two pyrimidines found most often in RNA are *cytosine* and *uracil*. Cytosine has an amino (NH_2) group at position 6, whereas uracil has a keto oxygen at this position. Cytosine and *thymine* are the two pyrimidines usually found in DNA.

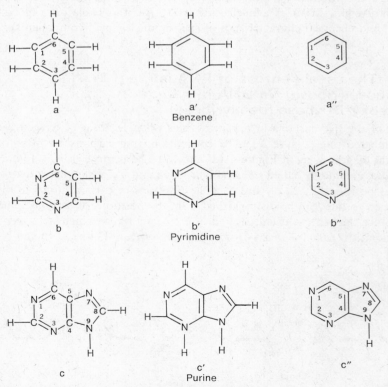

Figure 2-2   Relationships among certain ring compounds.

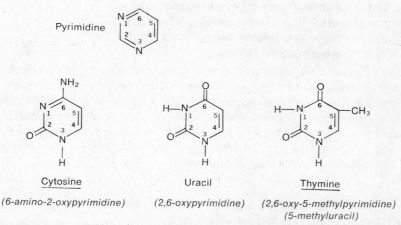

Pyrimidine

Cytosine
(6-amino-2-oxypyrimidine)

Uracil
(2,6-oxypyrimidine)

Thymine
(2,6-oxy-5-methylpyrimidine)
(5-methyluracil)

Figure 2-3   Pyrimidines. Names of pyrimidines occurring most often in DNA are underlined.

Since thymine is uracil with a methyl (CH_3) group at position 5, we can also call it 5-methyluracil. The pyrimidines differ primarily in the groups attached at the 5 and 6 positions.

In Figure 2-4 are structural formulas for the two most common purines in RNA and DNA: *adenine* and *guanine*. Adenine has an NH_2 group at position 6, whereas guanine has an O in keto form at this position and an NH_2 group at position 2. Purines generally differ most significantly in the groups at the 2 and 6 positions.

Purine

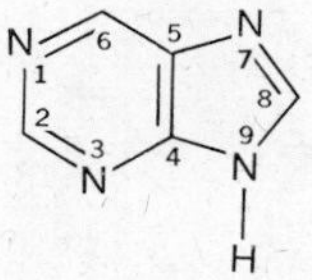

Adenine
(6-aminopurine)

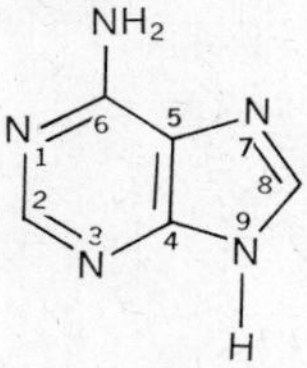

Guanine
(2-amino-6-oxypurine)

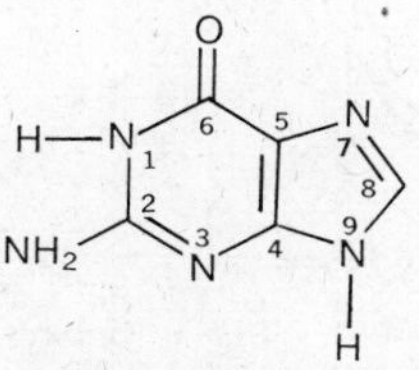

Figure 2-4   Purines occurring most often in RNA and DNA.

2.4 The combination of a pentose and an organic base is a nucleoside. Those in DNA are deoxyribonucleosides and those in RNA are ribonucleosides.

A purine or pyrimidine linked with a pentose is a *nucleoside*. The usual nucleosides in DNA, *deoxyribonucleosides*, are deoxycytidine (dC), deoxythymidine (dT), deoxyadenosine (dA), and deoxyguanosine (dG) (Figure 2-5). In RNA the usual nucleosides are cytidine (C), uridine (U), adenosine (A), and guanosine (G)—*ribonucleosides*. The linkage that forms a nucleoside is between the 1' position of the pentose and position 3 of pyrimidines or position 9 of purines. Each such linkage requires the removal of one molecule of water.

2.5 A nucleoside and a phosphate make up a nucleotide. Those in DNA are deoxyribonucleotides and those in RNA are ribonucleotides.

A *nucleotide* consists of a phosphate group joined to either the 3' or 5' carbon of sugar in a nucleoside. Since each of the three —O^- in PO_4^{3-} is ordinarily in —OH form, the union of phosphate and nucleoside ordinarily involves the removal of a molecule of water. The nucleotides in DNA are *deoxyribonucleotides* (Figure 2-6), or deoxyribonucleoside monophosphates. The 5'-monophosphates of dC, dT, dA, and

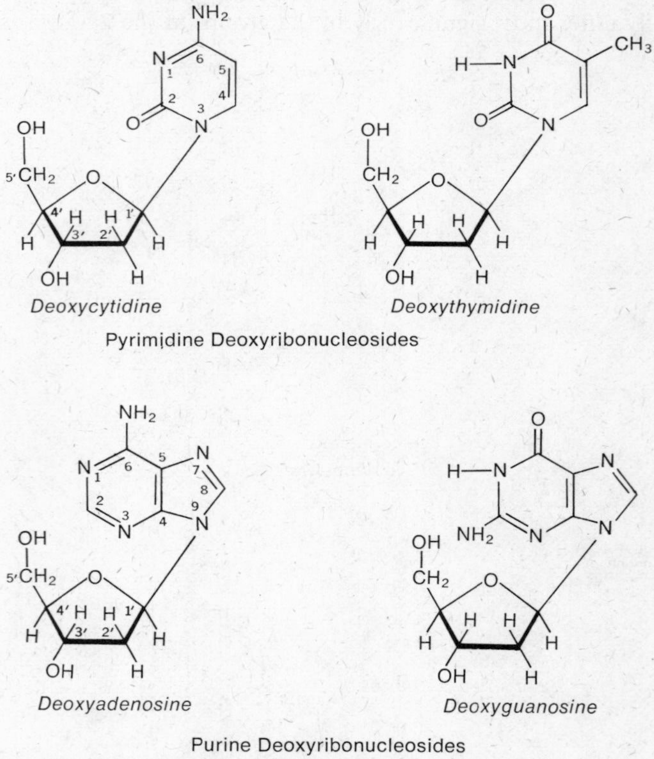

Deoxycytidine   Deoxythymidine

Pyrimidine Deoxyribonucleosides

Deoxyadenosine   Deoxyguanosine

Purine Deoxyribonucleosides

Figure 2-5   Common deoxyribonucleosides.

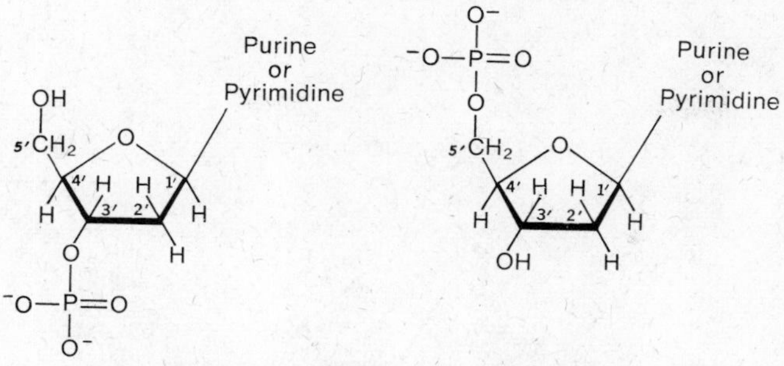

Deoxyribonucleoside 3′-monophosphate

Deoxyribonucleoside 5′-monophosphate

Figure 2-6 Deoxyribonucleotides.

dG are deoxycytidylic acid, deoxythymidylic acid, deoxyadenylic acid, and deoxyguanylic acid.

The nucleotides in RNA are *ribonucleotides*; the 5′-monophosphates of C, U, A, and G are cytidylic acid, uridylic acid, adenylic acid, and guanylic acid.

2.6 Nucleic acids are linear, polarized polymers with a pentose–phosphate backbone. This backbone imposes no restrictions upon the sequence of organic bases nor any limit to the length of the nucleic acid molecule.

DNA is a *polydeoxyribonucleotide*—a chain in which deoxyribonucleotides comprise the links. We can see how the links join by examining the two separate deoxyribonucleoside 5′-monophosphates shown in Figure 2-7. They can join if the topmost O^- of the right compound replaces the OH at position 3′ of the sugar in the left compound.[1] Since deoxyribonucleoside 5′-monophosphates can join by means of phosphate linkage to the 3′ position, polydeoxyribonucleotide chains of great length are possible (Figure 2-8). Linear, unbranched macromolecules, polydeoxyribonucleotides are of

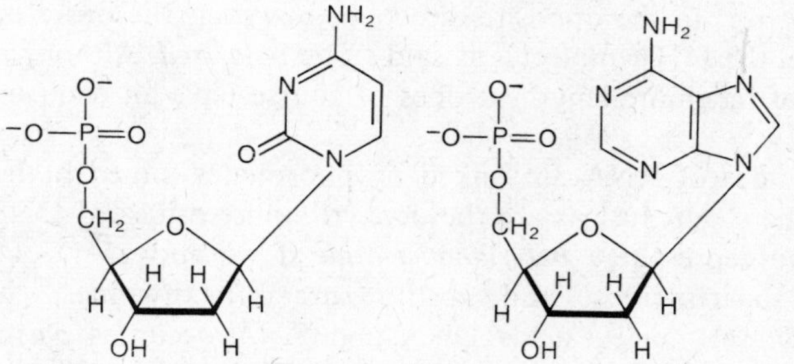

Deoxycytidine 5′-monophosphate
or
Deoxycytidylic acid

Deoxyadenosine 5′-monophosphate
or
Deoxyadenylic acid

Figure 2-7 Specific deoxyribonucleotides.

[1] Thus the union of two nucleotides also ordinarily requires the removal of a molecule of water.

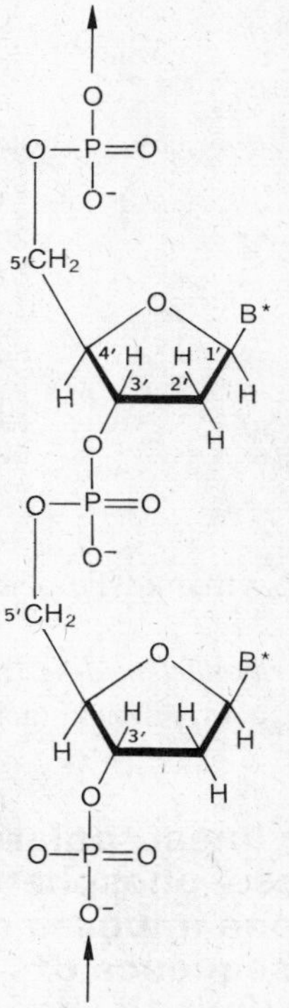

Figure 2-8   Polydeoxyribonucleotide.
*Pyrimidine or purine base of appropriate type (usually cytosine, thymine, adenine, or guanine).

indefinite length, with a backbone of sugar–phosphate linkages and with a linearity independent of the particular bases present at any point. In other words, the backbone of the chain is uninfluenced by the sequence of the bases, and vice versa. We notice further that this polymer of deoxyribonucleotides does not read the same in both directions. As indicated by the arrows, the two phosphates linked to each sugar are in a 3′5′ sequence; in the opposite direction, however, the order is 5′3′. Because of this difference, the DNA molecule is said to be *polarized*. Although a nucleic acid is theoretically of indefinite length, it does of course have an end, unless it is circular (Section 2.7).

Ribonucleosides of RNA are linked by phosphates joined both at the 3′ and 5′ positions of the sugar, just as are the deoxyribonucleosides of DNA. Consequently, Figure 2-8 can represent a *polyribonucleotide* if we add an O at each 2′ position (making each sugar D-ribose) and substitute uracil for thymine.

In summary, the nucleic acids DNA and RNA occur as *polynucleotides* (polydeoxyribonucleotides or polyribonucleotides). Each polynucleotide is made up of *mononucleotides* (deoxyribo- or ribonucleotides), which in turn are composed of phosphates joined to the 5′ carbon of *nucleosides* (deoxyribo- or ribonucleosides). These nucleosides consist of a *pentose* (deoxyribose or ribose) joined to a *pyrimidine* (usually cytosine or thymine for DNA; cytosine or uracil for RNA) or to a *purine* (usually adenine or guanine).

2.7   The DNA of certain phages is a single polynucleotide circle.

TMV RNA and other RNA's (see, for example, Figure 3-8), as well as the DNA's of certain viruses, are single polynucleotides with two ends. The DNA of mature ϕX174, however, has no ends (Figure 2-9). It is a single polynucleotide circle, a polymer of nearly 4,500 deoxyribonucleotides. Each nucleotide is approximately 10 Å (*angstrom units*) in diameter and contributes about 3.4 Å to the length of the chain. (R)

2.8   The complete base sequence is known for several RNA molecules.

The primary structure of several naturally occurring, relatively short, RNA molecules has been completely determined; the base sequence of one is given in Figure 2-10. This polyribonucleotide (in the form of a sodium salt) has a molecular weight of 26,600 and consists of 77 ribonucleotides. Although most nucleotide residues contain the common bases as found in A, U, C, and G, several other bases occur in minor quantities in such RNA molecules (these are discussed in Section 8.9). (R)

2.9   Different species differ in quantity of DNA per cell.

We expect that genetic differences among species can be correlated with differences in nucleic acid quantity. Figure 2-11 gives the DNA content per set of chromosomes, or genome, in various types of organisms. Although it is generally true that the higher an organism is on the evolutionary scale, the larger is its DNA content, it is perhaps

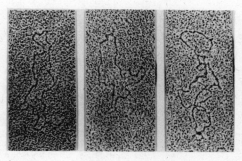

Figure 2-9   Electron micrograph of ϕX174 single-stranded circular DNA. The strand is about 1.7 nm and stained with uranyl salt. (Courtesy of A. K. Kleinschmidt, 1964. Science, 146: 254. Copyright 1964 by the American Association for the Advancement of Science.)

5'
G-G-G-C-G-U-G-U-MeG-G-C-G-C-G-U-A-G-DiHU-C-G-G-DiHU-A-G-C-G-C-DiMeG-C-U-C-C-U-U-I-
1   10   20   30
                                                                                              3'
G-C-MeI-Ψ-G-G-G-A-G-A-G-U-C-U-C-C-G-G-T-Ψ-C-G-A-U-U-C-C-G-G-A-C-U-C-G-U-C-C-A-C-C-A
        40   50   60   70   77

Figure 2-10   The nucleoside sequence of an RNA (alanine tRNA). The structures of the unusual ribonucleosides are shown in Figure 8-5. DiMe, dimethyl; Me, methyl; DiH, dihydro; Ψ, pseudouridine; I, inosine.

Organism	MW (daltons)	μg	Nucleotide pairs
Viruses			
ϕX174	0.9×10^{6a}	2.6×10^{-12a}	4500
T2 coliphage	130×10^6	2×10^{-10}	1.9×10^5
Polyoma			0.5×10^4
Bacteriophage λ			0.5×10^5
Bacteria			
Aerobacter aerogenes		2×10^{-9}	1.9×10^6
Escherichia coli	2.6×10^9	4.7×10^{-9}	4×10^6
Bacillus megaterium		25×10^{-9}	3×10^7
Fungi			
Saccharomyces cerevisiae		0.07×10^{-6}	7×10^7
Aspergillus			4×10^7
Porifera			
Tube sponge		0.06×10^{-6}	0.05×10^9
Coelenterate			
Jellyfish, Cassiopeia sperm		0.33×10^{-6}	0.3×10^9
Echinoderm			
Sea urchin, Lytechinus sperm	0.6×10^{12}	0.90×10^{-6}	0.8×10^9
Annelid			
Nereid worm, sperm		1.5×10^{-6}	1.4×10^9
Mollusks			
Limpet, Fissurella bandadensis sperm		0.50×10^{-6}	4.7×10^9
Snail, Tectorius muricatus sperm		0.67×10^{-6}	6.3×10^9
Insecta			
Drosophila	0.06×10^{12}		0.8×10^8
Crustacean			
Cliff crab, Plagusia depressa sperm		1.49×10^{-6}	1.4×10^9
Chordate			
Tunicate, Asidea atra sperm		0.16×10^{-6}	0.15×10^9
Vertebrates			
Diproan			
Lungfish, Protopterus		50×10^{-6}	47×10^9
Amphibia			
Frog		24.0×10^{-6}	23×10^9
Toad		7.5×10^{-6}	7×10^9
Necturus		3.7×10^{-6}	3.4×10^9
Amphiuma		84×10^{-6}	90×10^9
Elasmobranch			
Shark, Carcharias obscurus		2.8×10^{-6}	2.6×10^9
Teleost			
Carp		1.8×10^{-6}	1.7×10^9
Reptiles			
Green turtle		2.7×10^{-6}	2.5×10^9
Alligator		2.5×10^{-6}	2.4×10^9
Birds			
Chicken	6.5×10^{12}	1.2×10^{-6}	1.1×10^9
Duck		1.3×10^{-6}	1.2×10^9
Mammals			
Dog		2.7×10^{-6}	2.5×10^9
Man	1.5×10^{12}	3.0×10^{-6}	2.8×10^9
Horse		2.9×10^{-6}	2.8×10^9
Mouse	1.5×10^{12}	2.5×10^{-6}	2.4×10^9

[a]For double-stranded replicative form (see Section 4.4).

Figure 2-11 DNA content per chromosome set per typical nucleus, nuclear area, or acellular organism.

more meaningful to say that DNA content increases as the amount of information needed for maintenance and reproduction increases.[2] Two main methods of determining the amount of DNA in a nucleus are discussed in Section S2.9. (R)

2.10 The four most common bases occur in different proportions in the DNA of different species.

Percentages of adenine, thymine, guanine, and cytosine in DNA extracted from organisms of various species are given in Figure 2-12. We see a considerable variation in the relative frequencies of these bases—ranging from an organism relatively rich in adenine and thymine and poor in cytosine and guanine (sea urchin) to one in which adenine and thymine are much less abundant than cytosine and guanine (tubercle bacillus).

The chicken, salmon, and locust—certainly very different genetically—have very similar base ratios. Roughly the same relative frequencies of bases are also found in different members of a single species, when the total DNA in cells with large DNA content is analyzed. Likewise, the base ratios of normal (and neoplastic) tissues from different human beings are essentially identical. Assuming that DNA is the genetic material, the great variation within and among species, therefore, would be expected to be based upon the genome in one individual containing many DNA molecules which differ not only in base content but also in sequence from the DNA molecules of another.

	Adenine	Thymine	Guanine	Cytosine
Man (sperm)	31.0	31.5	19.1	18.4
Chicken	28.8	29.2	20.5	21.5
Salmon	29.7	29.1	20.8	20.4
Locust	29.3	29.3	20.5	20.7
Sea urchin	32.8	32.1	17.7	17.7
Yeast	31.7	32.6	18.8	17.4
Tuberculosis bacillus	15.1	14.6	34.9	35.4
Escherichia coli	26.1	23.9	24.9	25.1
Vaccinia virus	29.5	29.9	20.6	20.3
E. coli bacteriophage T2	32.6	32.6	18.2	16.6*

Figure 2-12 Base composition of DNA from various organisms.
*5-hydroxymethylcytosine.

[2] The amount of DNA per genome increases in the evolutionary scale, as expected if more information is needed as one ascends the scale and DNA is genetic material. Organisms rather closely related evolutionarily usually have similar DNA contents. Sometimes, however, related species are very different in their DNA content. Among Amphibia, for example, a toad has 7×10^9 base pairs, whereas *Amphiuma* has more than 10 times this amount, or 90×10^9 (Figure 2-11). Assuming that approximately the same qualitative amount of genetic information is needed in both species, the extra amount of DNA in one species might be due to extra multiples of all or part of the DNA information in the species having less DNA. The origin and function in one species of a multiple of all or part of the DNA in the genome of another are discussed in later chapters. We can suppose even now that a gross quantitative increase in DNA per genome is useful to make a species more adaptive to special circumstances.

2.11   The information content of a nucleic acid lies in its organic bases.

We expect successive portions of molecules of nucleic acids that are genetic material to be different and thus to contain different pieces of information. This linear differentiation cannot be due either to the pentose or phosphate, since one of each is present in every nucleotide. Therefore, all differences in information—genetic information—along the length of a polynucleotide strand must be due to the organic bases present and their sequence.

2.12   A gene is the smallest informational unit of genetic material. The nucleotide length of a gene depends upon the kind of information it stores.

As we have noted, the information for an organism's maintenance and reproduction is contained in genetic material. Let us define as a *gene* the smallest unit of genetic material that contains information used by an organism. We cannot, however, specify the length of a gene without specifying the particular tasks which the genetic material carries out and the ways in which it does so. Thus the nucleotide, the smallest unit of a nucleic acid macromolecule, may be only part of a gene. We can expect, therefore, that different kinds of tasks will require different amounts of information, and hence genes composed of different lengths of nucleotides. The various kinds of organismal information contained in genetic material—hence the different kinds of genes that occur—will be discussed again later (Section 26.3).

SUMMARY AND CONCLUSIONS

The primary structure of a nucleic acid is its nucleotide sequence. When the pentose in the sugar–phosphate backbone is ribose, the molecule is RNA; when it is deoxyribose, it is DNA. Since all pentoses have an asymmetrical shape, all nucleic acid molecules are directionally oriented; because any one of four usual organic bases can be attached to any pentose, the polarized molecule can have any base sequence (DNA has thymine as one of four alternative bases; RNA replaces this alternative with uracil). Naturally occurring nucleic acids are unbranched linear macromolecules; some of these have ends, whereas others—being circular—do not.

Anticipating proofs in later chapters that DNA is genetic material in cellular organisms, genome analysis shows that different types of organisms often differ (1) in amount of DNA, and/or (2) in the proportions of the four usual bases—adenine, guanine, cytosine, and thymine—these DNA's contain, as expected if different organisms require different amounts or kinds of DNA information. Since the information content of DNA resides in its organic bases, organisms whose DNA's are identical in amount and base composition can be very different because they differ in the sequence in which the bases are arranged. Whereas a genome contains an entire set of the nucleic acid genetic information of an organism, a gene is the shortest nucleotide (or base) sequence of a genome that contains information used for the maintenance or reproduction of the organism. The size of a gene is expected to depend upon the type of organismal information it contains.

GENERAL REFERENCES

Chargaff, E., and Davidson, J. N. (Editors) 1955 (Vols. 1 and 2). *The nucleic acids*; 1960 (Vol. 3). New York: Academic Press, Inc.

Felsenfeld, G., and Miles, H. T. 1967. The physical and chemical properties of nucleic acids. Ann. Rev. Biochem., 36: 407–448.

Mahler, H. R., and Cordes, E. H. 1968. *Basic biological chemistry*. New York: Harper & Row, Inc.

Miescher, F. 1871. On the chemical composition of pus cells. Translated in *Great experiments in biology*, Gabriel, M. L., and S. Fogel (Editors), Englewood Cliffs, N.J.: Prentice-Hall, Inc., 1955, pp. 233–239. (The discovery of nucleic acid.)

SPECIFIC SECTION REFERENCES

2.7 Sinsheimer, R. L. 1959. A single-stranded deoxyribonucleic acid from bacteriophage ϕX174. J. Mol. Biol., 1: 43–53. Reprinted in *Papers in biochemical genetics*, Zubay, G. L. (Editor), New York: Holt, Rinehart and Winston, Inc., 1968, pp. 37–48.

Sinsheimer, R. L. 1962. Single-stranded DNA. Scient. Amer., 207 (No. 1): 109–116. Scientific American Offprints, San Francisco: W. H. Freeman and Company, Publishers.

2.8 Cory, S., Marcker, K. A., Dube, S. K., and Clark, B. F. C. 1968. Primary structure of a methionine transfer RNA from *Escherichia coli*, Nature, Lond., 220: 1039–1040.

Holley, R. W. 1966. The nucleotide sequence of a nucleic acid. Scient. Amer., 214 (No. 2): 30–39, 138. Scientific American Offprints, San Francisco: W. H. Freeman and Company, Publishers.

Robert W. Holley (1922–   ). Dr. Holley was the recipient of a Nobel prize in 1968. (Photograph by D. K. Miller.)

2.9 Hennig, W., and Walker, P. M. B. 1970. Variations in the DNA from two rodent families (Cricetidae and Muridae). Nature, Lond., 225: 915–919. (Genome differences of 10 per cent within a rodent family.)

SUPPLEMENTARY SECTION

S2.9 The amount of cellular DNA can be measured histochemically and cytochemically.

Two main methods are commonly used in determining the amount of DNA present in a nucleus: the histochemical and the cytochemical.

The *histochemical method* employs whole tissues for the chemical extraction and measurement of DNA. Sometimes chemical analysis is made of masses of nuclei, from which most of the adhering cytoplasm has been removed by special treatment, to determine the average amount of DNA per nucleus. In the second, *cytochemical*, approach the DNA content of single nuclei, chromosomes, or chromosomal parts is determined. This method is based upon the finding that DNA is the only substance in the cell which stains under certain conditions. The *Feulgen technique* stains DNA purple, whereas the *methyl green method* stains DNA green. When properly applied, not only are these stains specific for DNA, but the amount of stain retained is directly proportional to the amount of DNA present. A given amount of dye bound by DNA will make a quantitative change in the amount of light of different wavelengths it transmits. These measurements can then be used to calculate the amount of DNA present. For example: a stained nucleus is placed under the *micro*scope; different appropriate wavelengths in the visible *spectr*um are sent through the nucleus, and a series of *photo*graphs is taken; its DNA content is *measured* by density changes of the nucleus. From the italicized portions of words comes the name of this procedure, *microspectrophotometry*.

A different application of microspectrophotometry utilizes another property of the purines and pyrimidines in DNA. These bases absorb ultraviolet light of wavelengths near 2,600 Å or 260 nm (*nanometers*, each unit equaling 10^{-9} meter). When other substances absorbing ultraviolet of these wavelengths are removed by enzymatic or other treatments, the quantity of DNA can be measured by its absorbence, using photomultiplier and photosensitive tubes. As one test of the validity of the absorbency, one can remove the DNA from the chromosome by the use of specific enzymes. These organic catalysts break the long DNA chains into short pieces which then can be washed out of the chromosomes and the nucleus. Such treatment produces the expected loss of absorbency.

QUESTIONS AND PROBLEMS

1. What is meant by the primary structure of a polymer such as a nucleic acid?
2. List similarities and differences between DNA and RNA.
3. Can one characterize DNA or RNA by molecular weight? Explain.
4. Discuss the ways DNA molecules terminate.
5. List specific features of the primary structure of a nucleic acid which might carry information.
6. What parts of a nucleotide are not factors in polarizing a nucleic acid? What parts do polarize the polymer? Explain.
7. What is the chemical distinction between
   a. a mononucleotide and polynucleotide?
   b. a nucleotide and a nucleoside?
   c. a pyrimidine and a purine?
   d. a ribose and deoxyribose sugar?
8. Express thymine as a derivative of uracil.
9. Draw the complete structural formula of a polyribonucleotide having the base sequence adenine, uracil, guanine, cytosine.
10. How could you proceed to measure the absorbency of ultraviolet light by chromosomal DNA? Chromosomal RNA?
11. Describe the role of dehydration in the synthesis of nucleosides, nucleotides, and nucleic acids.
12. List the physical properties of a specific DNA; of a specific RNA.

Chapter 3

Secondary, Tertiary, and Quaternary Structures

Because of its chemical and physical properties, a polynucleotide strand can interact with itself and other polynucleotide strands. The double coil that is formed when one strand winds on itself or when two strands wind about each other is the *secondary structure* of a nucleic acid (Figure 3.1). The result of a regular twisting and folding of a single strand or a double coil is its *tertiary structure*. And the interaction of two or more double coils gives rise to a *quaternary structure*. The present chapter describes these higher levels of organization in nucleic acids. In later chapters we will see how these levels of organization are related to the function of genetic material.

3.1   The DNA of most organisms contains an equal number of dA and dT nucleosides as well as an equal number of dC and dG nucleosides.

Since, as we have noted, the backbone of a DNA strand imposes no restrictions upon either the types or the frequencies of the bases present along the length of the strand, the nucleoside ratio, (dA + dT)/(dG + dC), can and does vary greatly from species to species. The numbers of dA and dT nucleosides in the DNA of organisms within a single species are, however, remarkably similar, as are the numbers of dG and dC (Figure 2-12). Since dA = dT and dG = dC in such species, dA + dG = dT + dC by simple algebraic addition. In other words, the total number of DNA purines equals the total number of DNA pyrimidines. Note that the primary structure of DNA cannot account for this significant regularity. (R)

3.2   As revealed by X-ray diffraction studies, DNA (but not RNA) usually shows more organization than can be explained on the basis of primary structure alone.

The basis for the dA = dT and dG = dC relationships will become clear (in the next section) after we discuss X-ray diffraction studies of crystalline DNA. A beam of X rays is bent or diffracted when it passes through matter. If this matter is completely heterogeneous in structure and orientation, the emergent beam will not form a regular diffraction pattern. But if the material is composed of molecules spatially

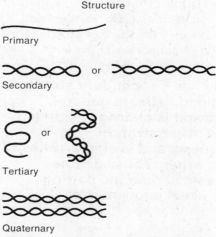

Structure

Primary

Secondary

Tertiary

Quaternary

Figure 3-1   Primary–quaternary levels of organization as applied to nucleic acids.

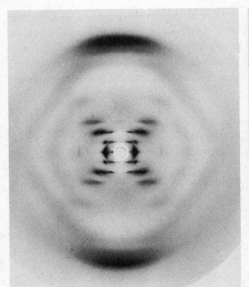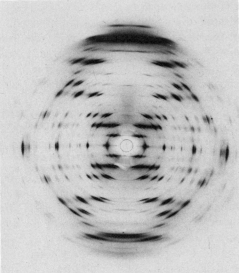

Figure 3-2   X-ray diffraction photographs of suitably hydrated fibers of DNA, showing the "B configuration." (Left) Pattern obtained using the sodium salt of DNA. (Right) Pattern obtained using the lithium salt of DNA. Analysis of these patterns gives details of nucleic acid structure. (Courtesy of Biophysics Research Unit, Medical Research Council, King's College, London.) DNA in the B configuration is "paracrystalline"; in the less-hydrated A configuration DNA is "crystalline" with paired bases tilted to the long axis, 11 base pairs per complete turn every 28 Å; DNA in the C configuration has 9.3 base pairs per turn.

arranged in a regular manner, the entering rays will be bent to form a pattern which is characteristic of that arrangement. From such patterns as those shown in Figure 3-2, crystallographers are able to "work backward" and recreate the object that scattered the X rays. Symmetrical patterns in diffraction pictures indicate a repeating unit structure in the sample. For instance, the black spots located symmetrically near the upper and lower edges in both photographs of Figure 3-2 correspond to nucleotides regularly spaced along a DNA chain. Other symmetrically arranged spots indicate other, larger, spacing regularities. Thus, in addition to its primary structure, DNA usually has a higher level of organization. On the other hand, X-ray diffraction patterns of most cellular RNA show only the spacings expected from its primary structure. Accordingly, most RNA does not possess higher levels of organization.

3.3   DNA usually has a secondary structure as a double-stranded helix. In general, adenine in one strand is hydrogen-bonded to thymine in the other strand; and cytosine in one strand is similarly linked to guanine in the other. Thus adenine : thymine and cytosine : guanine pairing accounts for the usual equivalences of these bases.

A simple model for the *secondary structure* of DNA, consistent with X-ray diffraction findings, was proposed by J. D. Watson and F. H. C. Crick in 1953 and has since been verified. They hypothesized that DNA usually contains two strands

(Figure 3-3) which are coiled around each other like the strands in a rope and which, therefore, cannot be separated unless one strand has two free ends. According to their explanation, a pentose–phosphate chain (corresponding to the ribbon in the illustration) forms the backbone of each strand on the outside of the double spiral. The rather flat organic bases (shown as horizontal bars) project into the center and lie perpendicular to the long axis of the fiber (the vertical interrupted line). Coiled right-handedly, that is, clockwise, the backbone completes a turn each 34 Å. Each nucleotide occupies 3.4 Å along the length of a strand. Consequently, there are 10 nucleotides per complete turn, with each successive nucleotide turning 36° in the horizontal plane.

Two DNA strands can form such a double coil, a *double helix*, with a uniform diameter of about 20 Å if a pyrimidine base on one strand is paired with a purine base on the other. A pair of pyrimidines (each a single ring) would be too short to bridge the gap between backbones, whereas two purines (each a double ring) would take up too much space. If cytosine (a pyrimidine) is paired with guanine (a purine) and adenine with thymine, the number of *hydrogen bonds* between the members of *base pair* is at a maximum.

Hydrogen bonds or *H bonds*, weak electrostatic interactions, can hold members of a base pair together and thus help to stabilize the double helix. In order for three H bonds to form between cytosine and guanine (Figure 3-4), cytosine : guanine, we should note that one base must be turned over relative to the other if we represent them initially as in Figures 2-3 and 2-4. The resulting bonds will involve the 6 NH_2 of

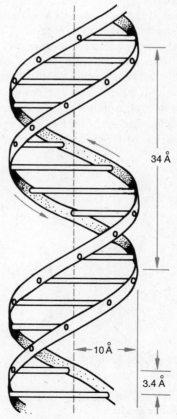

Figure 3-3   Double-stranded helix of DNA.

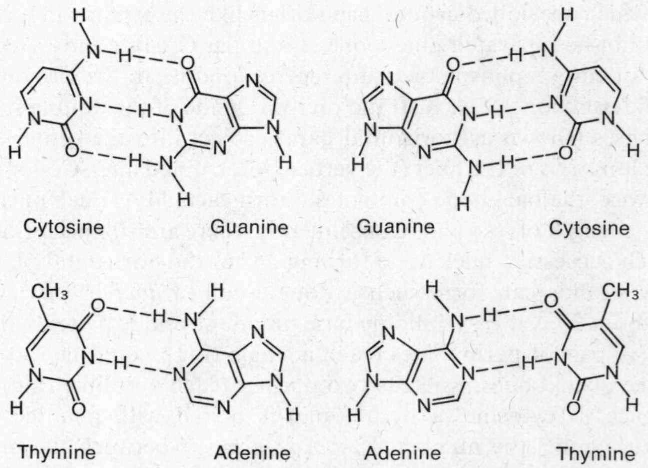

Cytosine   Guanine   Guanine   Cytosine

Thymine   Adenine   Adenine   Thymine

Figure 3-4   Base pairs formed between single DNA strands. Dashed lines represent hydrogen bonds.

cytosine and the 6 O of guanine, the 2 O of cytosine and 2 NH_2 of guanine, and the 1 N of cytosine and the 1 NH of guanine. The adenine : thymine base pair, joined by only two hydrogen bonds, is represented in the bottom half of Figure 3-3. The composition of the base pairs accounts for the equivalences of adenine and thymine and of cytosine and guanine found in most DNA's (Section 3.1).

Although the hydrogen bond is weak as compared with the covalent C—C bond, the great number of H bonds present along a double helix helps make the structure as a whole rather rigid even when moderately hydrated. Another structural characteristic involves the relationship between backbone and bases. We can see in Figure 3-5 that the region surrounding two base-paired nucleosides is separated into two areas by the point of attachment of each organic base to its respective pentose. If we were able to look "down" on a nucleic acid, that is, perpendicular to its long axis, we would see that the combination of larger areas determined by successive nucleoside

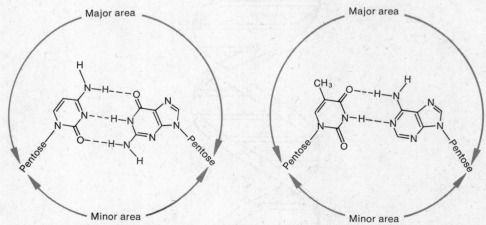

Figure 3-5   Major and minor areas surrounding base-paired nucleosides. A succession of these areas form major and minor grooves.

pairs constitutes a *major groove* and the combination of smaller areas a *minor groove* (Figure 3-6).

According to the Watson–Crick model, all the sugars of one strand face in one direction and all those of the second face in the other (Figure 3-7). Therefore, reading the figure from top to bottom, the phosphate linkages to sugar in the right chain are 3′5′, 3′5′, etc.; whereas they are 5′3′, 5′3′, etc., in the left chain. Thus we can say that the polarized chains of a double helix run in opposite directions (as indicated by the arrows). (R)

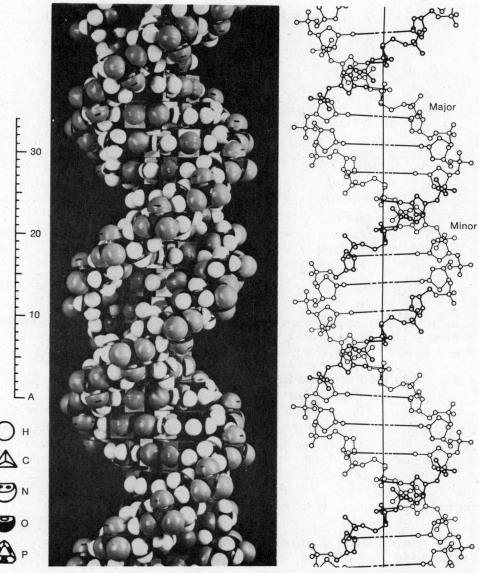

Figure 3-6   Molecular model of double-helical DNA. Left: space-filling model whose units represent different atoms. Right: its corresponding pentose–phosphate backbone, indicating the major and minor grooves. (Courtesy of M. H. F. Wilkins.)

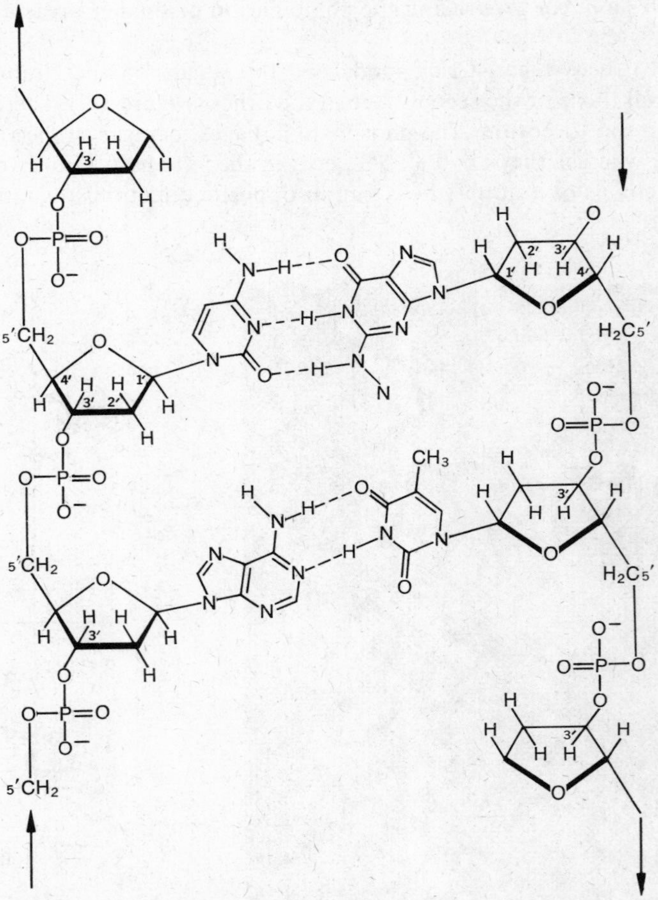

Figure 3-7 Two-dimensional representation of a DNA double helix showing the opposite directions of sugar–phosphate linkages in the two strands. See also the diagram of the backbone at the right of Figure 3-6.

3.4 The two strands in double-helical DNA are complementary.

When DNA has the secondary structure of a double helix, one helix can be considered the complement of the other. That is, if we know the sequence of bases in one strand, we know the base composition of the other. For example, if one strand contains the (deoxyribo)nucleoside sequence 5′ ATTGC 3′, the other strand will have 3′ TAACG 5′ in a corresponding region. The information in double helix DNA is therefore complementary, since the base sequence of one strand necessarily implies the base sequence, hence the information, of the partner strand.

3.5 Some DNA is normally single-stranded.

X-ray diffraction results which led to the double-helix hypothesis did not tell us that all DNA is two-stranded. Nor did they rule out the possibility that a double-stranded nucleic acid may be single-stranded at certain places or at certain times. What they did show was that a large part of the DNA of a wide variety of organisms is double-stranded. The DNA of ϕT2 and ϕT7, for example, is found to occur in the Watson–Crick double-helix configuration. But the DNA of mature ϕX174 is single-stranded (see Section 2.7), as proved both by the nonequivalence of dA and dT and of dC and dG and by X-ray diffraction photographs.

3.6   Some RNA is double stranded.

In contrast to TMV and many other viruses which contain single-stranded RNA as their genetic material, the infective forms of a wound virus obtained from sweet clover and a reovirus associated with the respiratory and enteric tracts of animals have double-stranded RNA as their genetic material. The RNA of these organisms is in a double-helical configuration[1] (like that of double-stranded DNA) in which A = U and C = G, with a molecular weight of 15×10^6 daltons (a *dalton* is a unit of mass equivalent to $\frac{1}{16}$ the mass of an oxygen atom). (R)

3.7   Double-stranded nucleic acids can be denatured and renatured.

Heating a double-stranded nucleic acid for 10 minutes at 100°C breaks all hydrogen bonds between base pairs, so that the two complementary strands usually separate (Figure 3-8). This process is one of melting, or *denaturation*. Naturally occurring double-stranded DNA, *native* DNA, with a high (dA + dT)/(dG + dC) ratio, becomes single-stranded (that is, it denatures) at a lower temperature than double-stranded DNA with a lower ratio. We should not be surprised by this difference, for dG and dC are linked by three hydrogen bonds, dA and dT by only two. Consequently, less energy is needed to break the hydrogen bonds of a DNA double helix rich in adenine and thymine than for one with high dG–dC content. Since organic bases absorb more ultraviolet light of 2,600 Å when they are separate than when they are in H-bonded pairs, denaturation, whether brought about by physical or chemical[2] means, is accompanied by an increase of up to 40 per cent in absorption at 2,600 Å— the so-called *hyperchromic effect*.

When the heated mixture is cooled *quickly*, the chains remain single as *denatured* DNA. Appropriate changes in molecular weight, density, and appearance under the electron microscope confirm the single-strandedness of the denatured polymer. A single strand of denatured DNA can base pair with itself by H bonds, if folding brings together complementary parts of the strand, to produce *stacking of base pairs*.[3] Short-range and long-range base-pair stacking involves adjacent and nonadjacent sequences of bases in a single strand, respectively. The less base-pair stacking occurs, the greater will be the hyperchromic effect of changing from a two-stranded to a single-

[1] Duplex RNA in solution apparently assumes the A type of DNA configuration (see the legend to Figure 3-1), with bases tilted relative to the long axis.

[2] DNA can be denatured *in vitro* by a large number of organic chemical substances, including urea, aromatic compounds, a variety of alcohols, and certain metallic ions. This finding, however, does not necessarily mean that such substances have this function *in vivo*, or that they reveal what is responsible for holding the strands in a DNA double helix together under *in vivo* or the usual *in vitro* conditions.

[3] Bases within a strand can also be associated by *free stacking*, which does not involve H bonding, is mainly temperature-dependent, and has almost no effect on UV absorbence. Evidence is increasing that although part of the conformational stability of ordinary duplex DNA is due to H bonding, another significant part is due to base-pair stacking, which is a hydrophobic reaction. Since uracil stacks most poorly with other bases and thymine resembles uracil, it is expected from base-pair stacking (as well as from H bonding) that DNA's rich in dA + dT are less stable than those rich in dC + dG.

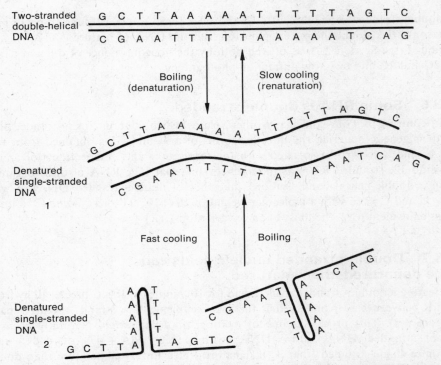

Figure 3-8 Denaturation and renaturation of two-stranded DNA: (1) has no base pairs, and therefore shows maximum hyperchromic effect and no evidence of secondary structure in X-ray diffraction photos; (2) has some short-range base-pair stacking, and therefore shows less than maximum hyperchromic effect and some evidence of secondary structure in the X-ray photos.

stranded condition, and the clearer will be the loss of the characteristic X-ray diffraction pattern indicating secondary structure.

When a hot mixture of denatured DNA is cooled *slowly,* however, base pairing occurs between complementary strands, and double-stranded DNA is formed. This *renatured* DNA is similar to the original DNA in ultraviolet absorption, X-ray diffraction pattern, molecular weight, density, and appearance under the electron microscope.

Denaturation and renaturation occur similarly for double-stranded RNA. Denatured RNA likewise shows a hyperchromic effect and can form a partial double helix by base-pairing with itself under certain conditions.[4] (R)

3.8 Some naturally occurring single-stranded RNA's have duplex regions.

Macromolecules can be characterized by their rate of sedimentation, measured in an ultracentrifuge and expressed in terms of *sedimentation units, s.* The number of s units for a macromolecule or particle varies directly with its size, although the relationship is not linear. Molecular shape influences s value—a given molecule precipitates faster and, therefore, has a larger s value when it is rolled up or globular than when it is extended or filamentous.

[4] Under certain conditions, polymers of single-stranded RNA containing only A, U, C, or inosinic acid are capable of base pairing after folding on themselves, thus forming regular double-helical structures.

We present next three examples of different types of single-stranded RNA (two of which are identified by their s values) which are partially duplex.

1. Each ribosome of *E. coli* seems to have a simple and homogeneous "5s" RNA molecule attached to it. The sequence of the 120 bases in this RNA has been determined (Figure 3-9). The figure also shows three regions where complementary bases are paired, giving the molecule secondary structure. Some properties suggest that there is even more base pairing than indicated in the figure.

2. Several regions of a 4s class of single-stranded cellular RNA's are base paired to give these molecules secondary structure (Figure 3-10). Note that despite the widely differing base sequence all four molecules have essentially the same cloverleaf shape.

3. The base sequence is known in a portion of the RNA molecule that comprises the genetic material of *E. coli* phage R17. Since the sequence can be written in the form of a simple loop with 18 typical base pairs in a sequence of 24 pairs of bases (Figure 3-11), it is probably in double-helix configuration *in vivo*.

3.9   Double-stranded nucleic acid hybrids can form if the two strands are sufficiently complementary.

Hybrid DNA–RNA duplexes (each composed of one DNA strand and one RNA strand) can be made by filtering single-stranded RNA through agar which contains

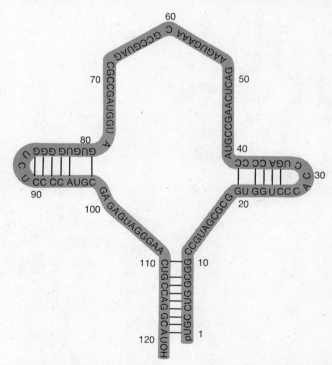

Figure 3-9   Nucleoside sequence of 5s RNA of *E. coli* showing regions of base pairing and, therefore, secondary structure. Solid line, standard base pair (G-C or A-U). (After G. G. Brownley, F. Sanger, and B. G. Barrell.)

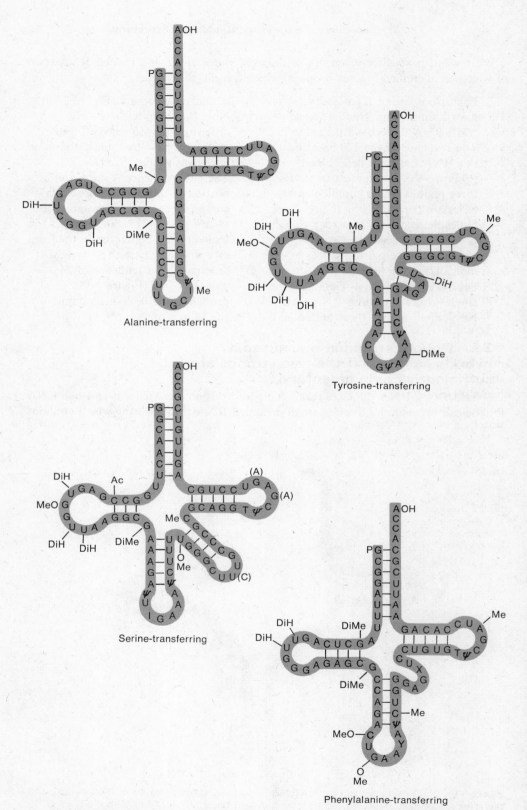

Figure 3-10 Cloverleaf secondary structure of four different 4s RNA molecules from yeast. The ability of 4s RNA's to transfer amino acids is described in Chapter 6.

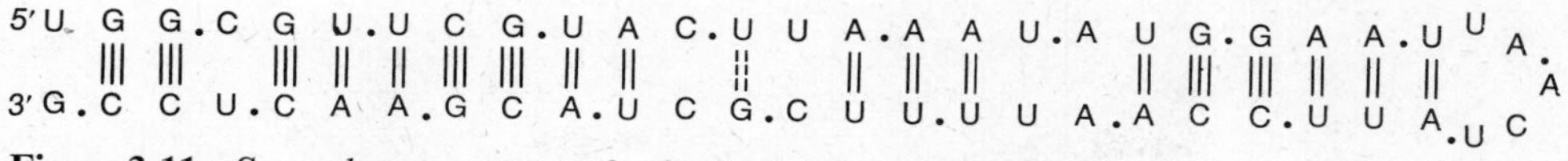

```
5'U  G  G.C  G  U.U  C  G.U  A  C.U  U  A.A  A  U.A  U  G  G.A  A.U  U  A
    |||  |||     |||  ||  ||  |||  |||  ||  ||      ::       ||  ||  ||          ||  |||  |||  ||  ||    .A
3'G.C  C  U.C  A  A.G  C  A.U  C  G.C  U  U.U  U  A.A  C  C.U  U  A.U C
```

Figure 3-11 Secondary structure of a fragment from φR17 RNA.

denatured DNA from the same organism. This hybridization shows that at least some RNA from a given organism is complementary to some of its own DNA. Hybrid DNA–DNA duplexes made up of single DNA strands from two different species can also be formed, if the genetic material of these species contains similar base sequences. We see therefore that hybridization can be a particularly useful technique in determining the similarity of RNA and DNA from the same or from different organisms. (R)

3.10   Molecules of nucleic acid are degraded either terminally or internally by nucleases, which can also be specific for the single-stranded or double-helical forms of RNA or DNA.

Before considering the tertiary structure of nucleic acids in the next section, we will need to consider the degradative effects that certain enzymes have on nucleic acid structure. *Nucleases* are enzymes that destroy nucleic acid primary structure (and hence all higher levels of organization, too) by causing breaks in the backbone of the polynucleotide chain. These breaks are usually the result of the enzymatic addition of water, or hydrolysis—a degradive action opposite to that which polymerizes nucleotides.

Nucleases may act on single and/or duplex nucleic acid; those that digest DNA are *deoxyribonucleases*, or *DNases*, whereas those that digest RNA are *ribonucleases*, or *RNases*. A nuclease may specifically attack a nucleic acid molecule terminally, that is, at the ends of the molecule only, being an *exonuclease*, or it may attack internally, being an *endonuclease* (Figure 3-12).[5] (R)

---

[5] There seems to be a nuclease for every purpose; some types of nucleases and their specificities are listed below:

1. *Exonucleases*
   a. Snake venom phosphodiesterase digests DNA and single-stranded RNA at the 3' position starting at the 3' end of the molecule (digestion occurring in the 3' to 5' direction), leaving the phosphate attached to the 5' position.
   b. *Bacillus subtilis nuclease* digests single-stranded DNA in the reverse, 5' to 3', direction.
   c. *Ribonuclease V (RNase V)* may be specific for single-stranded RNA (see Section 6.9).
2. *Endonucleases*
   a. *Endonuclease I of E. coli*, located primarily between the cell membrane and cell wall, digests duplex DNA by means of two-strand breaks.
   b. *Endonuclease II of E. coli* digests double-stranded DNA, via two-strand breaks in alkylated DNA and one-strand breaks in nonalkylated DNA.
   c. *Endonuclease III of E. coli* is a DNase that requires ATP (adenosine triphosphate) and *S*-adenosylmethionine.
   d. *Endonucleases induced by φT2 or by φT4* degrade primarily single-stranded DNA.
   e. *Endonuclease induced by φT4* produces one-strand breaks in double-stranded DNA.
   f. *Pancreatic DNase* produces one-strand breaks in duplex DNA at 3' positions.
   g. *Spleen phosphodiesterase* digests DNA at all 5' positions.
   h. *Lysosomal DNase* produces two-strand breaks in duplex DNA at 5' positions.

The determination of base sequence in nucleic acids has been aided enormously by the use of specific endonucleases which break the molecule into unique shorter pieces, each of which can be separated and have its base sequence determined through the use of specific exonucleases.

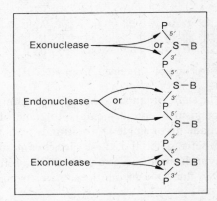

Figure 3-12 Different possible sites of cleavage (arrows) of the nucleic acid backbone by nucleases. P, phosphate; S, pentose; B, organic base.

3.11   Some double-helical DNA molecules are twisted in a regular manner, thus giving the nucleic acid a tertiary structure.

In boar sperm, bacteria, the polyoma virus (Figure 3-13), and several phages, double-stranded DNA occurs in circular form. In this form, we recall, the two complements cannot separate completely because of the absence of free ends. Superimposed on the right-handed coils of the polyoma duplex are additional coils which cause the double-stranded circle to fold back on itself (Figure 3-14A). The additional turns thus determine the *tertiary structure* of polyoma DNA. When an endonuclease induces single-strand breaks in such DNA, a site on the unbroken complementary strand opposite the breaks acts as a "swivel" and permits the unbroken strand to rotate and release the tertiary turns. Consequently, the duplex assumes an untwisted or unfolded circular configuration (Figure 3-14B, C).

That DNA has a tertiary structure in other organisms is indicated by the packing of long DNA molecules into containers of relatively small size (Figure 3-13) [for example, phage heads (Figure 3-15), bacterial cells, and nuclei] and by the coiling and uncoiling of chromosomes during nuclear division cycles without producing knots which would interfere with replication and strand movement.

Native DNA helices crystallize by chain folding (that is, by firehose folding) without being denatured irreversibly. It has been suggested that the DNA in the phage head is packed this way. (R)

3.12   4sRNA also has a tertiary structure.

Besides the short-range base-pair stacking that produces the cloverleaf secondary structure of 4sRNA (Figure 3-10), all of these RNA's seem to have bases of different loops participating in long-range base-pairing. These additional interloop base pairs result in a generalized tertiary structure for 4sRNA in which three arms of the cloverleaf are folded together (Figures 3-16 and 3-17). (Note that Ψ and A can base-pair.)[6] (R)

[6] A study of "phenylalanine tRNA" from yeast indicates that only four A residues (A35, A36, A38, and A76) are unpaired. This leads to a highly ordered tertiary structure for this 4sRNA, shown in Figure 3-17, in which four more A : U pairs are formed (A9 : U47, A21 : U59, A44 : U8, A73 : T54), as well as three more G : C pairs (G10 : C25, G45 : C48, G57 : C60). Although all 4sRNA's have the same general tertiary conformation, the details of their shape seem to depend upon the size of the dihydroU-containing loop and the central part (see Figure 3-16) so that each type of 4sRNA is unique. Different details of the tertiary structure of these RNA's are still being proposed.

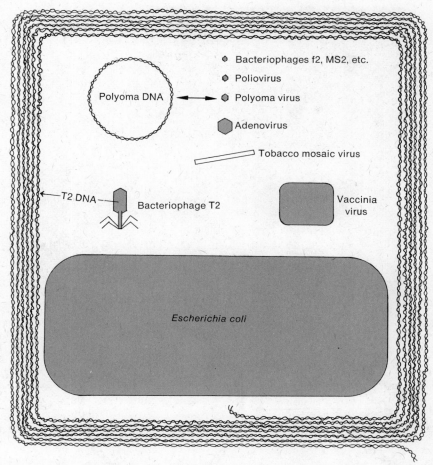

Figure 3-13 Sizes of virions, of the nucleic acids of some of them, and of a bacterium, all drawn to the same scale.

3.13 Native nucleic acids often occur in combination with basic proteins.

The acidic phosphate groups of nucleic acid tend to prevent the coming together or association of different parts of the same or different duplexes of nucleic acid. Such associations (necessary for the quaternary structure of nucleic acids—discussed in the next section) are made possible, however, when these acidic groups are neutralized by basic groups.

Nucleic acids are often found in combination with basic proteins. Such combinations are called *nucleoproteins*. In nucleated cells the DNA is usually combined with such basic proteins as *histone* or *protamine*. The amino groups of these basic proteins probably bond electrostatically to the phosphates of DNA. In some sperm the chromosome appears to contain a unit fibril about 40 Å in diameter composed of protamine and a single DNA duplex. In other nucleated cells, one DNA double helix and histone forms a chromosomal fibril about 100 Å in diameter. Nuclear chromosomes also contain varying amounts of *nonhistone* (*acidic*) *protein*. Further information about the biochemistry of these proteins and their relation to the functioning of DNA in nucleated cells will be presented in Chapter 27.

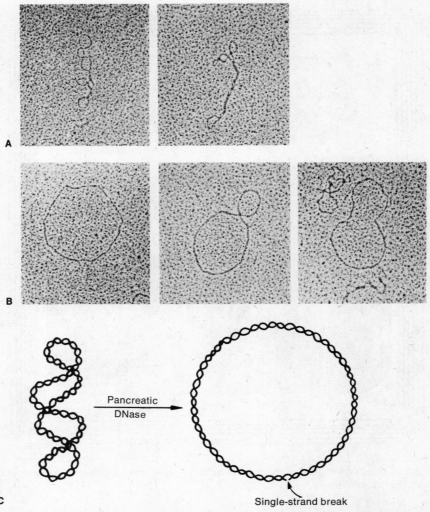

Figure 3-14   Electron micrographs of the twisted (A) and untwisted (B) forms of cyclic duplex DNA of polyoma (33,000 ×). (Courtesy of J. Vinograd.) Part (C) shows the conversion of the twisted to the untwisted form.

The DNA in bacteria and in phages seems to exist uncombined with typical basic protein, although bacterial and phage DNA may be combined with a less basic type of protein. In the latter case, the DNA-containing fibers have a diameter of about 25 Å. (R)

3.14   The nucleic acid in chromosomes containing more than one DNA double helix has a quaternary structure.

In cell nuclei of higher organisms, chromosomes that have replicated but not yet separated into daughter chromosomes contain at least two DNA double helices. The cells of several larval tissues of dipteran organisms have giant nuclei whose chromosomes are highly *polynemic*, or *polytene*; that is, they contain many DNA duplexes—

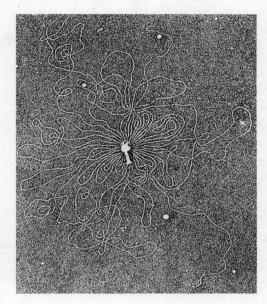

Figure 3-15 Electron micrograph of T2 phage with its DNA extruding from the head. The double-stranded strand is one filament of approximately 47 nm. (Courtesy of A. K. Kleinschmidt, 1962. Biochim. Biophys. Acta, 61: 861.)

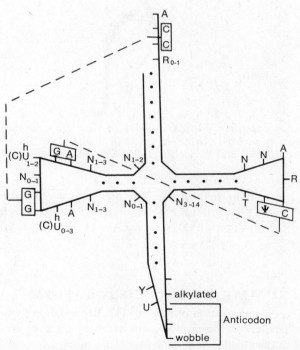

Figure 3-16 Schematic general cloverleaf structure of 4s RNA's. The dashed lines connect the eight bases that are proposed to form base pairs in the basic tertiary structure. Each base pair that is part of the secondary structure is indicated by a dot. Y, pyrimidine nucleoside; N, nucleoside; R, purine nucleoside; Ψ, pseudouridine; hU, dihydroU. Subscripts refer to the number of nucleoside units in each segment. (From F. Cramer, V. A. Erdmann, F. von der Haar, and E. Schlimme, 1969. J. Cell. Physiol., 74: No. 2, Suppl. 1, p. 172.)

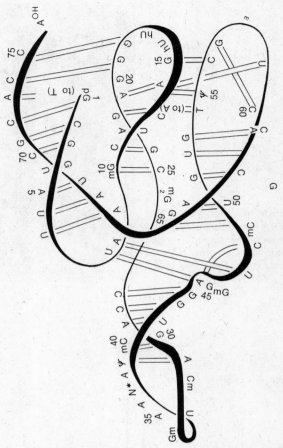

Figure 3-17 Tertiary structure proposed (in 1968) for a specific (phenylalanine-transferring) 4s RNA from yeast. m, methyl; other symbols as in Figure 3-16. (From F. Cramer, V. A. Erdmann, F. von der Haar, and E. Schlimme, 1969. J. Cell. Physiol., 74: No. 2, Suppl. 1, p. 169.)

sometimes over 1,000—lying side by side. The organization of two or more duplexes within a chromosome is the *quaternary structure* of the nucleic acids involved. Further discussion of the organization of DNA in nuclear chromosomes is postponed until Chapters 14 and 18.

SUMMARY AND CONCLUSIONS

The higher levels of organization of nucleic acids depend directly upon the chemical and physical properties of the components of their primary structure. The two components having the strongest influence are the organic bases and the phosphates. The organic bases can form H bonds and are hydrophobic, the former property leading to the formation of base pairs, the latter to their stacking in an aqueous medium. Since the negatively charged phosphates repel each other, it is understandable that the double helical secondary structure has the base pairs stacked internally and the phosphates located externally; the greatest stability being provided by the pairing of adenine with thymine and of cytosine with guanine; the strands of a duplex having opposite polarities due to the arrangement of the pentoses. The formation of H bonds between bases that would be distant from each other on the basis of primary structure at least partially explains the folding that is associated with tertiary structure. The neutralization of the acidic phosphate groups by basic groups such as those in the basic proteins histone and protamine also permits the folds and twists of tertiary structure as well as those associations between duplex regions which comprise nucleic acid's quaternary structure.

Although most naturally occurring DNA is double-stranded and RNA is single-stranded, several exceptions to both conditions are known.

Since H bonds broken by heating can reform upon cooling, one can destroy and create secondary structure in single and double strands of nucleic acid. This denaturation–renaturation technique applied between organisms produces hybrid DNA–DNA duplexes, especially when the two organisms are closely related by descent; this technique applied within an organism also shows, by the formation of hybrid DNA–RNA duplexes, that the base sequences in RNA are complementary to those in DNA. The basis for both kinds of observations will become clear in the next four chapters, which deal with the replication of nucleic acids and the transfer of information from one nucleic acid type to another.

GENERAL REFERENCES

Chargaff, E. 1968. What really is DNA? Remarks on the changing aspects of a scientific concept. Progr. Nucleic Acid Res. and Mol. Biol., 8: 297–333.

Chargaff, E., and Davidson, J. N. (Editors) 1955. (Vols. 1 and 2). *The nucleic acids*; 1960 (Vol. 3). New York: Academic Press, Inc.

Cohen, J. A. 1967. Chemistry and structure of nucleic acids of bacteriophages. Science, 158: 343–350.

SPECIFIC SECTION REFERENCES

3.1   Chargaff, E. 1955. Isolation and composition of the deoxypentose nucleic acids and of the corresponding nucleoproteins. In *The nucleic acids*, Vol. I, Chargaff, E., and Davidson, J. N. (Editors), New York: Academic Press, Inc., Chap. 10, pp. 307–371.

3.3   Crick, F. H. C. 1957. Nucleic acids. Scient. Amer., 197 (No. 3): 188–200, 278, 280. Scientific American Offprints, San Francisco: W. H. Freeman and Company, Publishers.

Watson, J. D. *The double helix*. 1968. New York: Atheneum. (A personalized account of the discovery of the double-helical nature of DNA.)

Watson, J. D., and Crick, F. H. C. 1953. Molecular structure of nucleic acids. A structure for deoxyribose nucleic acid. Nature, Lond., 171: 737–738. Reprinted in *Classic papers in genetics*, Peters, J. A. (Editor), Englewood Cliffs, N.J.: Prentice-Hall, Inc., 1959, pp. 241–243; and Bobbs-Merrill reprint series, Indianapolis: Howard W. Sams Company, Inc.

Watson, J. D., and Crick, F. H. C. 1953. Genetical implications of the structure of deoxyribonucleic acid. Nature, Lond., 171: 964–969. Reprinted in *Papers on bacterial genetics*, second edition, Adelberg, E. A. (Editor), Boston: Little, Brown and Company, 1966, pp. 127–132; in Bobbs-Merrill reprint series, Indianapolis: Howard W. Sams Company, Inc., and in *The biological perspective, introductory readings*, Laetsch, W. M. (Editor), Boston: Little, Brown and Company, 1969, pp. 126–131.

Watson, J. D., and Crick, F. H. C. 1953. The structure of DNA. Cold Spring Harb. Sympos. Quant. Biol., 18: 123–131. Reprinted in *Papers on bacterial viruses*, second edition, Stent, G. S. (Editor), Boston: Little, Brown and Company, 1965, pp.

James Dewey Watson (1928–) in 1969. Dr. Watson was the recipient of a Nobel prize in 1962.

Maurice H. F. Wilkins (1916–) in a recent photo. Dr. Wilkins was the recipient of a Nobel prize in 1962 for his X-ray diffraction studies of nucleic acids.

230–245; and *Papers in biochemical genetics*, Zubay, G. L. (Editor), New York: Holt, Rinehart and Winston, Inc., 1968, pp. 28–36.

3.6 Agol, V. I., Drygin, Yu. F., Romanova, L. I., and Bogdanov, A. A. 1970. Circular structures in preparations of the replicative form of encephelomyocarditis virus RNA. FEBS Letters, 8: 13–16. (First report of circular RNA duplexes.)

Millward, S., and Graham, A. F. 1970. Structural studies on reovirus: discontinuities in the genome. Proc. Nat. Acad. Sci., U.S., 65: 422–429.

3.7 Eigner, J., and Doty, P. 1965. The native, denatured and renatured states of deoxyribonucleic acid. J. Mol. Biol., 12: 549–580.

Studier, F. W. 1969. Conformational changes of single-stranded DNA. J. Mol. Biol., 41: 189–197. (Studies on stacking.)

Studier, F. W. 1969. Effects of conformation of single-stranded DNA on renaturation and aggregation. J. Mol. Biol., 41: 199–209. (Studies on stacking.)

3.8   Adams, J. M., Jeppesen, P. G. N., Sanger, F., and Barrell, B. G. 1969. Nucleotide sequence from the coat protein cistron of R17 bacteriophage RNA. Nature, Lond., 223: 1009–1014.

Lewis, J. B., and Doty, P. 1970. Derivation of the secondary structure of 5s RNA from its binding of complementary oligonucleotides. Nature, Lond., 225: 510–512. (Detection of unpaired base sequences.)

3.9   Marmur, J., Falkow, S., and Mandel, M. 1963. New approaches to bacterial taxonomy. Ann. Rev. Microbiol., 17: 329–372.

Spiegelman, S. 1964. Hybrid nucleic acids. Scient. Amer., 210 (No. 5): 48–56, 150. Scientific American Offprints, San Francisco: W. H. Freeman and Company, Publishers.

3.10   Altman, S., and Meselson, M. 1970. A T4-induced endonuclease which attacks T4 DNA. Proc. Nat. Acad. Sci., U.S., 66: 716–721.

Friedberg, E. C., and Goldthwait, D. A. 1969. Endonuclease II of E. coli, I. Isolation and purification. Proc. Nat. Acad. Sci., U.S., 62: 934–940.

Pogo, B. G. T., and Dales, S. 1969. Two deoxyribonuclease activities within purified vaccinia virus. Proc. Nat. Acad. Sci., U.S., 63: 820–827.

3.11   Vinograd, J., and Lebowitz, J. 1966. Physical and topological properties of circular DNA. J. Gen. Physiol., 49 (Suppl.) (No. 6, Part 2): 103–125; and Macromolecular metabolism, Boston: Little, Brown and Company.

Wang, J. C., Baumgarten, D., and Olivera, B. M. 1967. On the origin of tertiary turns in covalently closed double-stranded cyclic DNA. Proc. Nat. Acad Sci., U.S., 58: 1852–1858.

3.12   Cramer, F., Doepner, H., Haar, F. v.d., Schlimme, E., and Seidel, H. 1968. On the conformation of transfer RNA. Proc. Nat. Acad. Sci., U.S., 61: 1384–1391.

Levitt, M. 1969. Detailed molecular model for transfer ribonucleic acid. Nature, Lond., 224: 759–763.

Ninio, J., Favre, A., and Yaniv, M. 1969. Molecular model for transfer RNA. Nature, Lond., 223: 1333–1335.

3.13   Bram, S., and Ris, H. 1971. On the structure of nucleohistone. J. Mol. Biol., 55: 325–336.

Ikeda, H., and Tomizawa, J. 1965. Transducing fragments in generalised transduction by phage P1. II. Association of DNA and protein in the fragments. J. Mol. Biol., 14: 110–119.

Mokulskaya, T. D., Polonsky, Yu. S., Stolyarova, G. S., and Mokulsky, M. A. 1969. Studies on the structure and properties of the complex between DNA and internal protein of phage T2. In Structure and genetical functions of biopolymers, 2: 427–438. Moscow: Kurchatov's Institute of Atomic Energy. (In Russian with English summary.)

QUESTIONS AND PROBLEMS

1. What is meant by the secondary, tertiary, and quaternary structure of a polymeric molecule?

2. Why do we not ordinarily find guanine–thymine or adenine–cytosine base pairs in duplex DNA?

3. Is a double helix containing only A and G or C and T possible? Explain.

4. State three ways to determine whether a sample contains only single-stranded or only double-stranded nucleic acid.

5. What are the consequences of heating polyoma virus DNA for 10 minutes at 100°C?

6. Suppose you have three unlabeled cultures, two of one bacterial species and one of a distant relative. How can you tell which is which if all three cultures are accidentally killed by boiling?

7. Suggest a taxonomic use of the finding that the base ratio of a double-stranded nucleic acid can be determined by measuring its melting point.

8. A detective has the problem of identifying whether some blood found in a steam bath is human or canine. Suggest how he might determine its origin.

9. Suppose that 1,000 bases in a double-

stranded nucleic acid are uracil. If this RNA consists of 10,000 nucleotides, determine the approximate molecular weight of the duplex and the percentages of all the bases present.

10. Among the DNA molecules contained in a genome, why is it expected that many would differ in base sequence and content?

11. If a coil is right-handed (turns clockwise) when looked at from one end, is it also right-handed when seen from the other end?

12. At about 60°C double-stranded DNA will adsorb to a column of hydroxyapatite, a crystalline form of calcium phosphate, whereas single-stranded DNA will not. How can you apply this fact to determine how similar the DNA's are
a. in different organs of the same person?
b. in the same organ of different persons?

13. How could you remove all the noncircular (rod-shaped) DNA from a mixture of circular and noncircular DNA's?

14. Name a virion whose genetic material is
a. single-stranded DNA.
b. double-stranded DNA.
c. single-stranded RNA.
d. double-stranded RNA.

PART II

Replication, Transcription, and Translation of Nucleic Acids

Chapter 4

Replication of DNA

Since the genetic material of viral progeny is identical to that of their parent, a *replication* of nucleic acid must have taken place. Any synthesis that produces more of the same nucleic acid—DNA to DNA or RNA to RNA—we refer to as replication. The present chapter deals with the replication of DNA first *in vivo*, then *in vitro*. Chapter 5 starts with consideration of RNA replication, then takes up still other ways in which nucleic acid is synthesized.

DNA REPLICATION *IN VIVO*

4.1 Replication *in vivo* of double-stranded DNA results in two duplexes, each containing a parental strand and a newly synthesized complementary strand.

Let us consider an experiment designed to test the hypothesis that replication of double-stranded bacterial DNA *in vivo* involves the complete separation of parental strands and the formation of two duplexes, each containing a parental strand and a newly synthesized strand that is complementary to the parental strand. This mode of replication in which the members of a parental duplex separate to form old–new hybrid duplexes is called *semiconservative replication* (Figure 4-1), as distinguished from *conservative replication* (where the members of the parental duplex remain together), *dispersive replication* (where the parental contents are dispersed among strands that contain both old and new sections), and *nonconservative replication* (where both parental strands are destroyed).

We recall that each pyrimidine ring normally found in DNA contains two, and each purine double ring four, nitrogen atoms. Most of these atoms are ordinary "light" nitrogen, ^{14}N. However, if we grow bacteria in a culture medium whose only nitrogen is the "heavy" isotope ^{15}N, these bacteria will contain heavy DNA. We can actually see the difference between heavy and light DNA by means of a process called *density-gradient ultracentrifugation.*

When a solution of cesium chloride is centrifuged for many hours at great speed, a linear gradient of densities is found at equilibrium in the centrifuge tube such that the concentration of cesium chloride is greatest at the bottom and least at the top. Since the density of DNA lies within this gradient, DNA ultracentrifuged in such a tube assumes the position that corresponds to its own density. We expect, therefore, that heavy and light DNA will form different bands in the centrifuge tube. The nucleic acid can then be detected by its absorption of ultraviolet light of 2,600 Å.

To test the hypothesis, we grow bacteria on a heavy nitrogen medium for several generations so we can be certain that all DNA is heavy. Then, after synchronizing their multiplication, we allow the bacteria to grow for a single generation on a light nitrogen medium. DNA isolated from these bacteria forms a band whose position in the density gradient is exactly intermediate between the bands formed by heavy and light DNA. If we allow bacteria to grow for two generations on the light medium, isolated DNA takes two positions in the centrifuge tube—one intermediate between light

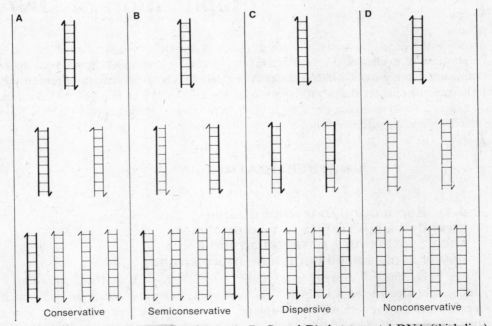

Figure 4-1 Four possible ways (columns A, B, C, and D) that parental DNA (thick line) may be distributed relative to offspring DNA (thin line) after DNA replication.

and heavy, and a second at the light position (compare with expectation in Figure 4-1B). Results of these and other generation times are shown in Figure 4-2.

These findings are consistent with our hypothesis of semiconservative replication of bacterial DNA.[1] Similar results have been obtained with DNA from the unicellular alga *Chlamydomonas*, man, and other higher organisms. Although these results (plus those described in the footnote) prove that replication yields semiconservative products, they do not reveal anything about the replication process.

4.2   The *E. coli* chromosome is a circular duplex of DNA, both strands of which seem to be synthesized in parallel starting at one point.

Electron micrographs reveal that the single chromosome in the nuclear area of *E. coli* (Figure 1-4) is a circle of double-stranded DNA. If we label DNA precursors radioactively to detect the position of newly synthesized DNA, we find that replication, as seen with the limited resolution provided by autoradiography, begins at the same point in both strands (Figure 4-3)—only one starting point per chromosome— and that synthesis of both strands proceeds in the same direction. The starting point of replication may differ in different *E. coli* strains. Within a strain, however, replication always starts at the same position.

The autoradiographs of *E. coli* confirm the conclusion of Section 4.1—that duplex replication involves the separation of parental strands and the formation of two duplexes, each with one parental strand and a newly synthesized complement, even though they too do not tell us how the replication process occurs at the molecular level. This semiconservative replication necessarily involves not only the unwinding of the parental duplex but also the rewinding of strands to form two new duplexes in circular form at the completion of replication. Since the parental duplex is in circular form and cannot completely strand-separate, it has been suggested that the point in the parental duplex where DNA synthesis starts serves as a "swivel" whose rotation permits uncoiling. Assuming that the duplex DNA circle of the polyoma virus (see Section 3.11) replicates the same way, it must also solve the same unwinding problems, having at least one breakpoint in the duplex. Our earlier discussion

[1] Although the results described for bacteria are consistent with the idea of semiconservative replication of double-stranded DNA, they do not automatically exclude other possible explanations. It might be claimed, for instance, that the double helix grows not by separation of strands followed by the synthesis of complementary ones, but by the addition of new double-strand material to the ends of the original double strand. This alternative explanation can be tested in two ways.

If the all-heavy molecules present initially grew by adding light material to their ends, they should be composed linearly of double strands that are successively heavy and light. It should then be possible for sonic vibrations, which do not produce strand separation, to fragment the macromolecules into smaller segments, some all-heavy and others all-light. This result should be detectable in the ultra-centrifuge tube by some of the sonicated hybrid DNA assuming the all-light and some the all-heavy positions. Whether or not it is sonically fragmented, however, the DNA remains in essentially the same hybrid position.

The second test of endwise DNA synthesis involves converting double-stranded, all-light and all-heavy DNA to the single-stranded condition and locating the positions of the two types of single strands in the ultracentrifuge tube. The "hybrid" double-stranded DNA is then made single-stranded and is ultracentrifuged. This preparation shows only two major components, one located at the all-light single-strand position and the other at the all-heavy single-strand position. This result also is inconsistent with the hypothesis being tested. Not only do the two tests eliminate the view that appreciable endwise synthesis of DNA occurs in bacterial DNA, but they offer additional support for the hypothesis of semiconservative replication of bacterial DNA.

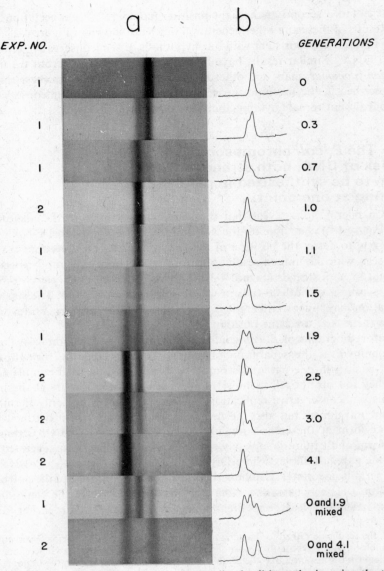

Figure 4-2 Test of the "chain separation after replication" hypothesis, using the technique of density-gradient centrifugation. DNA was extracted from heavy (^{15}N-labeled) bacteria grown for different generation times on light (^{14}N-containing) medium. The extracts were subjected to ultracentrifugation to position the DNA in the centrifuge tube according to its density. (Density increases to the right of the figure.) DNA absorption of ultraviolet light is indicated by the bands in different photographs under *a* and the height of the peaks in the corresponding densitometer tracings under *b*. The rightmost band in the bottom two frames and the band in the top frame represent heavy DNA. The leftmost band, seen clearly in all generation times after 1.5 generations, represents light DNA. The only other clear band is between the heavy and light ones. This band, which is the only one present after 1.0 generation, represents DNA that is hybrid in density. Note that at 1.9 generations, half the DNA is light and half is hybrid in density (see the row showing 0 and 1.9 mixed). (Courtesy of M. Meselson and F. W. Stahl, 1958. Proc. Nat. Acad. Sci., U.S., 44: 675.)

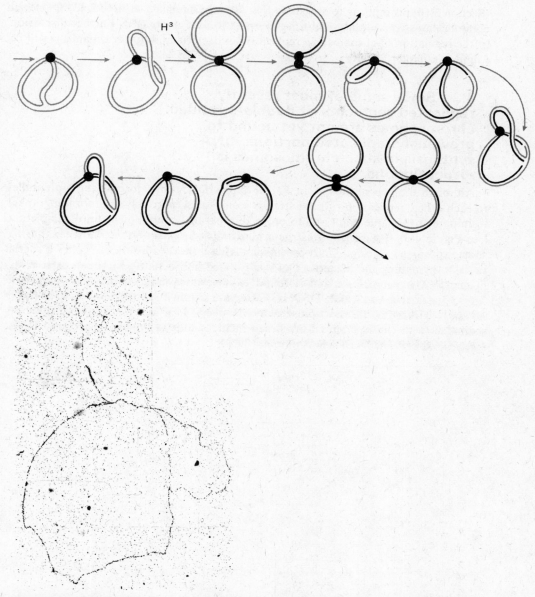

Figure 4-3 Replication of the *E. coli* chromosome. Below: Autoradiograph of the circular chromosome labeled with tritiated thymidine for two generations. Exposure time 2 months. Above: Diagrammatic representation of the chromosome, based on the assumption that each cycle of replication begins at the same place and proceeds in the same direction. gray, nonlabeled single DNA strand; black, labeled single DNA strand; ●, swivel; ^{3}H, tritiated thymine. (Courtesy of J. Cairns and the Cold Spring Harbor Laboratory of Quantitative Biology.)

(Section 3.10) prompts us to speculate that breakpoints may be produced by special endonucleases whose place and time of operation are controlled. Further discussion of the regulation of chromosome replication in bacteria and higher organisms will be found in Chapter 24. (R)

4.3 Since some of most recently replicated segments of double-stranded chromosomes are not yet bound to previously replicated portions, DNA synthesis in such chromosomes is discontinuous.

Although the two strands in an *E. coli* duplex DNA chromosome run antiparallel to each other, replication of both strands seems (as seen grossly in autoradiographs) to initiate at the same point and to proceed in parallel continuously until completion (see Figure 4-3). The finer, ultrastructural, details of replication can be studied using short exposures to labeled DNA precursors. After a short exposure of "cold" bacteria to ^{3}H—thymidine, the bacterial DNA is isolated and denatured. The most recently made DNA is radioactive and is found to have an average sedimentation rate of 7-11s; that is, the newly made DNA is shorter and sediments more slowly than parental DNA. If harvesting the short-pulsed DNA is delayed, however, the labeled material sediments with the heavier DNA, which includes long segments of progeny DNA synthesized previously as well as parental DNA.

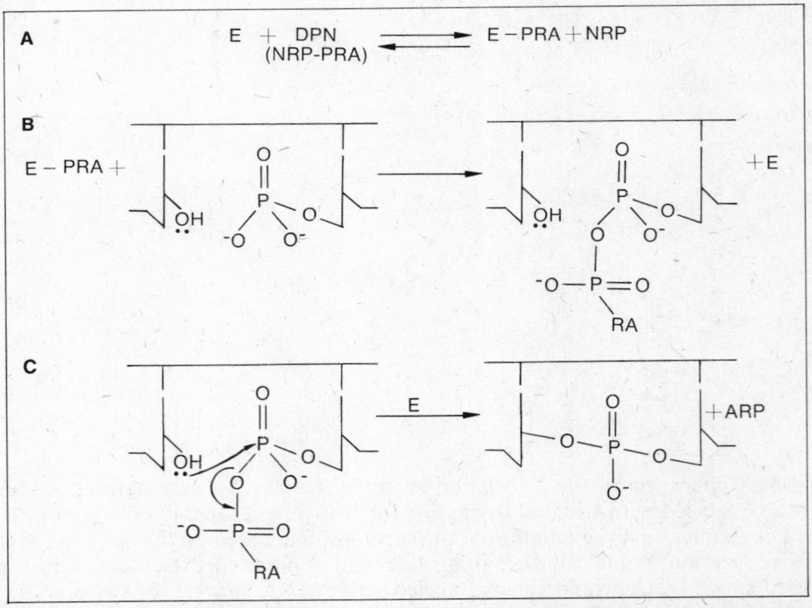

Figure 4-4 Postulated mechanism of the reaction catalyzed by the *E. coli*-joining enzyme, polynucleotide ligase. DPN is written as NRP-PRA to emphasize the pyrophosphate bond linking the nicotinamide mononucleotide (NRP) and adenylic acid (PRA) moieties of the DPN molecule. The designation E-PRA for enzyme-adenylate is not meant to imply that linkage of AMP to the enzyme is necessarily through the phosphate group. (A) Formation of ligase-adenylate intermediate; (B) formation of DNA-adenylate intermediate; (C) formation of phosphodiester bond. (From B. M. Olivera, Z. W. Hall, and I. R. Lehman, 1968).

These results support the hypothesis that at least some DNA synthesis is discontinuous and results in the production of short stretches of DNA. These short segments are subsequently connected to each other and/or to the older portion by 3′5′ *phosphodiester linkages*, in which one phosphate is joined to two pentoses—to the 3′ position of one and the 5′ position of the other. These phosphodiester linkages are assumed to be carried out *in vivo* by *polynucleotide ligases* (Figure 4-4), which *in vitro* unite one end of DNA bearing a phosphate group at the 5′ position to another end of DNA bearing a hydroxyl group at the 3′ position, both termini being properly aligned—as occurs when they are juxtaposed at the site where a single-strand break (or "nick") is present in duplex circular DNA. Different types of ligase and some details of how these operate are known.[2]

Support obtained for the above hypothesis makes it (1) unlikely that the short DNA pieces result from either fragmentation during collection or the action of an endonuclease, and (2) likely that it applies also to chromosomes of higher organisms, including mammals.

Figure 4-5 diagrams a recent version of this hypothesis in which both progeny DNA strands are synthesized by *DNA polymerase* as short segments which are subsequently bound together by polynucleotide ligase. Note that although synthesis of the new segments is represented as occurring antiparallel in this molecular model, it would appear to occur in parallel on a grosser, macromolecular level (as in the autoradiograph in Figure 4-3). (R)

4.4   Replication of single-stranded φX174 DNA requires two successive syntheses (by a DNA polymerase).

The double-stranded nucleic acid to double-stranded nucleic acid synthesis (as occurs in the replication of the DNA of the *E. coli* chromosome) is called a *two-complement synthesis* (Figure 4-6A). The DNA of mature φX174 is, we recall, in the

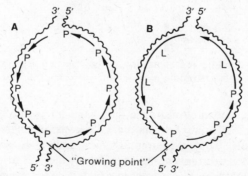

Figure 4-5   Hypothesized antiparallel synthesis of DNA in short strands (A) subsequently joined together (B). Arrows show direction of strand growth (5′ toward 3′). ∿, parental DNA; —, progeny DNA; P, DNA polymerase; L, polynucleotide ligase. (After A. Yudelovich, B. Ginsberg, and J. Hurwitz, 1968. Proc. Nat. Acad. Sci., U.S., 61: 1129–1136.)

[2] In uninfected *E. coli* and cells of rabbit bone marrow the ligase uses diphosphophyridine nucleotide (NAD or DPN) as a cofactor; the ligase present in *E. coli* after phage T4 or T7 infection uses ATP as cofactor. In all cases, the nucleotide ligation requires energy obtained by splitting the cofactor and involves an intermediary enzyme–adenylate complex (Figure 4-4), which in turn produces a DNA–adenylate intermediate.

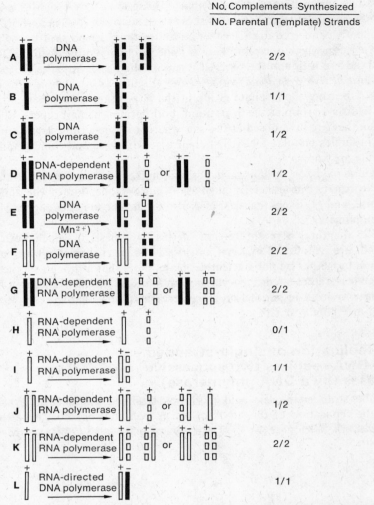

	No. Complements Synthesized
	No. Parental (Template) Strands

A DNA polymerase — 2/2

B DNA polymerase — 1/1

C DNA polymerase — 1/2

D DNA-dependent RNA polymerase — 1/2

E DNA polymerase (Mn^{2+}) — 2/2

F DNA polymerase — 2/2

G DNA-dependent RNA polymerase — 2/2

H RNA-dependent RNA polymerase — 0/1

I RNA-dependent RNA polymerase — 1/1

J RNA-dependent RNA polymerase — 1/2

K RNA-dependent RNA polymerase — 2/2

L RNA-directed DNA polymerase — 1/1

Figure 4-6 Diagrammatic representation of complementary synthesis. ▬▬ and ▬ ▬ ▬, old and new single DNA strands; ══ and ═ ═ ═, old and new single RNA strands.

form of a single-stranded circle. Once the phage enters an *E. coli* host, a DNA polymerase synthesizes a "minus" strand which is complementary to the "plus" parental strand (Figure 4-6B). Thus, the parental strand undergoes a *one-complement synthesis*. (This synthesis does not replicate the DNA.) As a result of phase 1 (see Figure 4-7), a "plus–minus" DNA helix is produced which is called the *replicative form* (RF). RF occurs as a double-stranded ring which has both strands closed (RFI) or has either the + or − strand open (RFII).[3] In phase 2, RFII undergoes a two-complement semiconservative synthesis to produce two progeny RFII, each composed of one old and one new strand. In phase 3, RFII with the + strand open undergoes a one-complement synthesis to produce a new open + progeny strand (dashed line, Figure

[3] One assumes that the single break required to convert RFI to RFII results from the action of an endonuclease.

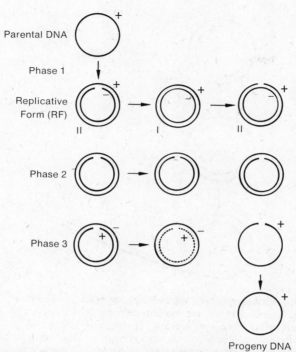

Figure 4-7 Synthesis of progeny single-stranded DNA of φX174 by parental single-stranded DNA. See the text for details.

4-6C), which displaces the old + from the + − duplex. The open + strand is closed before the progeny phage is matured.[4] We see, therefore, that the parental + to progeny + replication sequence requires two successive syntheses. (R)

4.5   Some double-stranded DNA uses a rolling circle in order to replicate.

The occurrence of double-stranded circular DNA in many organisms suggests that a basic mode of replicating DNA involves using single-stranded circular DNA to synthesize a complementary strand. According to the *rolling-circle model of DNA replication* (Figure 4-8), the DNA to be replicated starts as a covalent double-stranded circle (for example, starting with RFI of φX174). A single-strand break is postulated to occur (producing, for example, RFII of phase 3 in φX174 replication), and the liberated 5′ end becomes attached to a membrane (cell or nuclear). This 5′ end unwinds as a new copy of this strand is synthesized by chain elongation at its 3′ end, the new copy being the complement of the single-stranded circle which is rolling. If the single-stranded circle continues to roll, the linear complement can be extended an unlimited number of replicas. If the complement of the linear strand is to be made, this is presumed to be synthesized in the 5′–3′ direction in short segments joined together by polynucleotide ligase.

This model has been applied to the synthesis of one or both DNA complements

[4] The conversion of RFII to RFI and the circularization of open + strands of φX174 presumably require the action of a ligase.

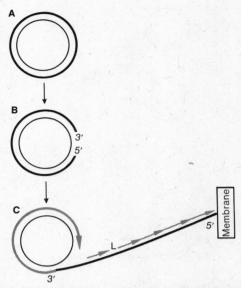

Figure 4-8 Rolling-circle model of DNA replication: (A) Covalent double-stranded circular DNA. (B) Single-stranded break in one complement (thick line). (C) 5′ end of the thick linear complement attaches to a membrane; it lengthens (shown as gray line) at its 3′ end in the 5′-3′ direction (indicated by thick arrowhead) by DNA polymerase synthesizing the complement of the rolling inner single-stranded circle. Polynucleotide ligase (L) joins short segments, complementary to the thick linear strand, synthesized in the 5′-3′ direction (indicated by thin arrowheads) by DNA polymerase.

of chromosomes of phages (φX174, λ, T4, and P22), bacteria, and higher organisms. Experimental support for its occurrence has already been obtained in phages and in bacteria behaving sexually. Such support includes finding that (1) replicating DNA is attached to a membrane, (2) that progeny DNA is attached linearly to parental DNA, and (3) that DNA strands occur that are longer than their circular complements. (R)

DNA REPLICATION *IN VITRO*

Whereas the previous sections of this chapter dealt with the synthesis of DNA *in vivo*, those remaining discuss it *in vitro*. Studies of nucleic acid synthesis *in vitro* (in this as well as the next chapter) are expected to provide useful information for the construction of models of mechanisms by which synthesis occurs *in vivo*. We must recognize, however, that *in vitro* mechanisms may be a biased sample of ways that nucleic acids are synthesized *in vivo*. But whether or not *in vitro* studies closely reflect the conditions *in vivo*, they are (at the very least) valuable in helping us to understand the origin of such mechanisms and to formulate hypotheses subject to experimental test.

4.6 Short strands of DNA that are synthesized *de novo* can serve as templates for further synthesis.

Before describing the synthesis of DNA using information in already formed DNA, we will consider the synthesis of DNA *de novo*, that is, in the absence of DNA.

DNA can be synthesized *in vitro* from suitable precursors in the presence of a DNA polymerase isolated from *E. coli*. This enzyme, *E. coli DNA polymerase* (DNA polymerase I), splits off the two terminal phosphates of a deoxyribonucleoside 5′-triphosphate (Figure 4-9) as *pyrophosphate (PP)*, and the remaining monophosphate joins by its phosphate to the free 3′ position of another deoxyribonucleoside 5′-monophosphate. Thus, in the absence of DNA, short strands of the nucleic acid can be formed after several hours of incubation in a system which contains deoxyadenosine 5′-triphosphate (dATP), deoxythymidine 5′-triphosphate (dTTP), Mg^{2+} ion, and *E. coli* DNA polymerase (Figure 4-10A). dA and dT occur in perfect alternation in such strands—called *copolymers* of deoxyadenosine and deoxythymidine, or poly (dA-dT). The mechanism for this *de novo* synthesis of DNA is not yet completely understood.

When a poly (dA-dT) strand becomes long enough to fold, it often base-pairs with itself. A single strand folded back on itself so that its free 3′ end is paired with an internal (rather than terminal) complement can grow by a *base-pairing synthesis* (Figure 4-10B). In such a synthesis the unpaired portion of the strand serves as a mold, or *template*, which attracts complementary precursors. As implied above, *E. coli* DNA polymerase can catalyze the addition of single nucleotides to the free 3′ position of DNA and thereby lengthen the polymer. Hence, the polymerase lengthens the poly (dA-dT) strand at its free 3′ position, this already formed DNA serving as a *primer* for its own lengthening. A portion of poly (dA-dT) that is not base-paired with itself can serve as template for the synthesis of a completely new complementary

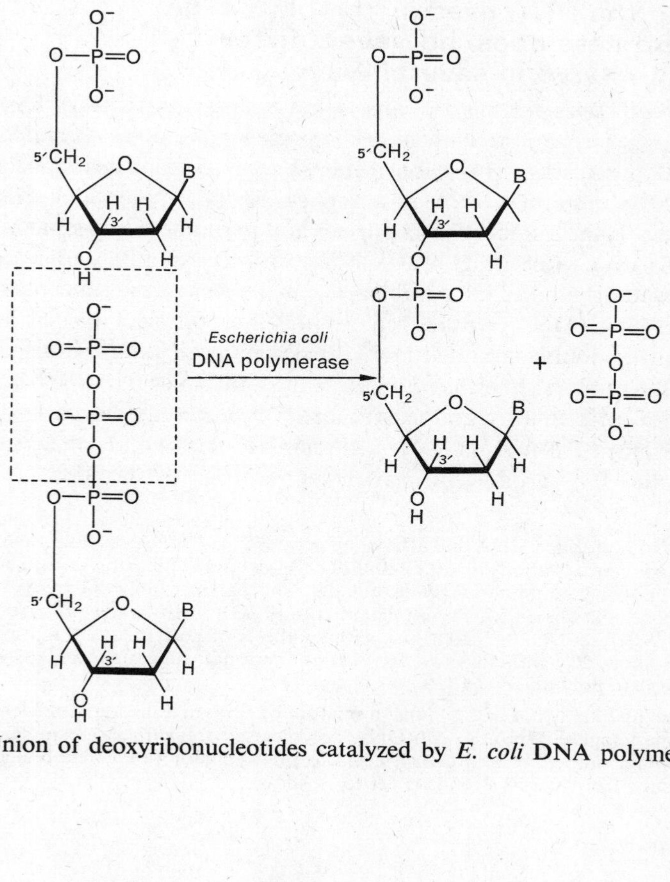

Figure 4-9   Union of deoxyribonucleotides catalyzed by *E. coli* DNA polymerase.

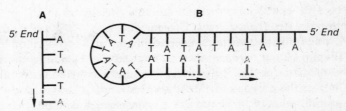

Figure 4-10 Synthesis of poly (dA-dT). Arrows show direction of growth: A, *De novo*; B, template base-pairing synthesis. T is lengthening the strand; A is initiating a new strand.

strand, since *E. coli* DNA polymerase can have multiple start points in single-stranded DNA.[5]

A "natural poly (dA-dT)" polymer has been discovered in the sperm of a certain crab. Comprising nearly 30 per cent of the total nuclear DNA content, this crab polymer consists mostly of dA and dT in strict alternation. dG and dC occur with a frequency of about 3 per cent.

DNA polymerase isolated from calf thymus, in contrast to the *E. coli* DNA polymerase, cannot form poly (dA-dT) *de novo*. Just like the *E. coli* enzyme, however, the calf thymus DNA polymerase can use the copolymer as template for making complementary DNA. (R)

4.7 DNA synthesized *in vitro* is very similar to the DNA used as template. The *in vitro* process does, however, differ from that *in vivo* in several ways.

Escherichia coli DNA polymerase can synthesize large quantities of DNA *in vitro* by the base-pairing, template mechanism in the presence of double-stranded DNA from any of several organisms, Mg^{2+} ions, and appropriate deoxyribonucleoside 5′-triphosphates.[6] The resulting DNA is a replica of the "parental" template in the following ways: (1) the numbers of its purines and pyrimidines are equal; (2) dA = dT and dC = dG; (3) its (dA + dT)/(dG + dC) ratio is essentially identical to that of the template, and (4) studies indicate that it has the same base sequences (see Section S4.7). Furthermore, DNA synthesized *in vitro* has physical properties similar to naturally occuring double-stranded DNA. Sedimentation rate and viscosity indicate that the *in vitro* product, like that *in vivo*, is of high molecular weight. An extensive *in vitro* synthesis of primarily double-stranded DNA can also be carried out starting with single-stranded DNA from ϕX174 as template. These and other studies indicate that most of the DNA product of *in vitro* synthesis is two-stranded.

[5] In the absence of preformed DNA and after a lag period, *E. coli* DNA polymerase—in the presence of Mg^{2+} and high concentrations of dCTP and dGTP—catalyzes the *de novo* formation of another double-stranded polymer containing only dC and dG. This polymer, poly dG · poly dC, is composed of two strands; one contains only dC's and the other only dG's, the two strands base-pairing to form a double helix. Whereas dA = dT after extensive synthesis of poly (dA-dT), most products of extensive poly dG · poly dC synthesis show 56 to 81 per cent dG, suggesting that poly dC is a better primer-template than poly dG.

[6] In the presence of Mn^{2+} (not Mg^{2+}) ions, a mixture of ribo- and deoxyribonucleoside 5′-triphosphates, and some template DNA, *E. coli* DNA polymerase can synthesize complementary strands *in vitro* that contain both ribo- and deoxyribonucleotides (Figure 4-6E). The biological or genetic significance of such RNA–DNA strands is yet to be shown.

Several significant differences, however, do exist between *in vitro* and *in vivo* synthetic processes. In *E. coli* there seems to be only one starting point in a template DNA strand for the synthesis of new strands *in vivo*. *In vitro*, several positions in a single DNA strand can be used as template starting points for the synthesis of new strands. Such differences may be the result of *in vivo* factors that are missing *in vitro* and from contaminants that are not present *in vivo*, as well as from changes incurred by DNA when it is isolated for use as a template in an *in vitro* synthesis. Moreover, *E. coli* DNA polymerase synthesizes DNA *in vitro* (1) that is branched (as seen in the electron microscope), (2) which does not strand-separate completely after prolonged heating (and which, therefore, renatures more readily than native DNA), (3) is made at a slower rate (by an order of magnitude) than it is *in vivo*, and (4) is not associated with the cell membrane (the site of DNA synthesis *in vivo*). Note that the enzyme *E. coli* DNA polymerase was named from its synthetic properties *in vitro*, not those proved to apply *in vivo*. Recent studies *in vivo* suggest that this enzyme may be used in *E. coli* primarily for the repair of damaged DNA (discussed in Section 9.8), and that one of the enzymes actually used for DNA replication in *E. coli* is DNA polymerase III. (R)

4.8 The DNA genetic material of ϕX174 can be replicated exactly *in vitro*.

Infective + strands of ϕX174 have been synthesized *in vitro* in the following manner. (Note that the process *in vivo* is certainly different in some respects.) Circular + strands are tagged with tritium while being synthesized in *E. coli*, then isolated and placed in an *in vitro* system containing *E. coli* DNA polymerase and a substrate of dATP, dGTP, dCTP, and $d\overline{BU}TP$ (in which 5-bromouracil, $\overline{BU}$, is used in the place of lighter thymine). One of the triphosphates has ^{32}P in its innermost phosphate. The polymerase synthesizes an open (*linear*) complementary − strand which is closed (circularized) by the addition of polynucleotide ligase, completing the preparation of half-synthetic RFI (see Figure 4-11A).

Isolation of the synthetic − circles labeled with both $d\overline{BU}$ and ^{32}P is accomplished by the plan outlined in Figure 4-11B. The duplex RFI circles are exposed to an endonuclease such as pancreatic DNase to an extent sufficient to produce one single-strand break in about one-half of the molecules, then the broken duplex molecules are made single-stranded by heat denaturation and rapid cooling. The resulting mixture contains (1) unbroken partially synthetic RFI duplexes, (2) circular and linear − strands labeled with ^{32}P and 5-bromouracil, and (3) circular and linear + strands labeled with tritium and thymine. When the mixture is fractionated by equilibrium density-gradient sedimentation in CsCl in the ultracentrifuge, three radioactive bands are obtained, the densest containing the − single-stranded DNA with $d\overline{BU}$. The material in this band is next subjected to velocity sedimentation in a sucrose gradient, in which the circular strand sediments faster than the linear one.

The next step is to prepare totally synthetic RFI (Figure 4-11C) using the isolated circular synthetic − strands marked with ^{32}P and $d\overline{BU}$ as templates for the synthesis of the open linear + strand by DNA polymerase. The substrate is changed, however; ^3H—dCTP is used as the radioactive label in the substrate and dTTP replaces $d\overline{BU}TP$. The RFII produced is converted to RFI by polynucleotide ligase, as before.

Using a procedure similar to the one employed earlier to obtain synthetic − circles from half-synthetic RFI, one can isolate synthetic + circular DNA. This DNA corresponds to the original + phage DNA. Since single nucleotide changes in the +

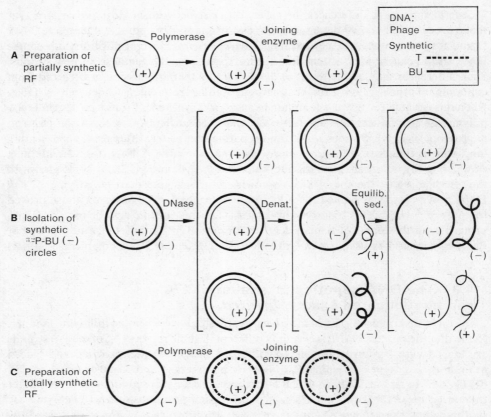

Figure 4-11 Schematic representation of the preparation of synthetic single-stranded (−) circles and completely synthetic RF [leading to the isolation of infective, completely synthetic, (+) circles] of φX174. See the text for details. (From M. Goulian, A. Kornberg, and R. L. Sinsheimer, 1967.)

strand are known to result in loss of infectivity, the finding that the synthetic + strand has the same range of infectivity as the naturally produced + strand demonstrates the precision of this *in vitro* enzymatic replication. (R)

SUMMARY AND CONCLUSIONS

The most common form of genetic material is duplex DNA. The replication of this DNA *in vivo* has the following general characteristics: (1) it most commonly occurs semiconservatively, producing two duplexes each composed of a parental strand and its progeny complement; (2) the synthesis is enzymatic, using a DNA polymerase (but, in *E. coli*, not necessarily the one called *E. coli* DNA polymerase); (3) there is usually a growing "point" at which synthesis of both complements occurs at nearby, if not exactly corresponding, positions; (4) the synthesis of one complement, if not both, is discontinuous, and (5) the newly synthesized fragments are joined by a polynucleotide ligase. An additional characteristic, to be more fully discussed and documented in bacteria and higher organisms in Chapters 14 and 19, is that during replication DNA is attached to a cellular membrane—plasma, nuclear, mitochondrial, etc. Considerable evidence is accumulating that a rolling single-stranded circle is used as template during the replication of DNA in bacteria under specific circumstances (certain phage infections or sexual activity).

We have made significant strides in understanding the steps that occur in the *in vivo* replication of single-stranded circular DNA such as occurs in ϕX174; a precise replication of this DNA *in vitro* has also been achieved. Other *de novo* and *in vitro* syntheses of DNA have enriched our knowledge of the problems that need be solved *in vivo*, besides providing us with synthesized DNA of specific types useful in the study of other genetic problems.

GENERAL REFERENCES

Kornberg, A. 1962. *Enzymatic synthesis of DNA.* New York: John Wiley & Sons, Inc.
Kornberg, A. 1968. The synthesis of DNA. Scient. Amer., 219 (Oct.): 64–70, 75–78, 144.
Replication of DNA in micro-organisms. 1969. Vol. 33, Cold Spring Harb. Sympos. Quant.
   Biol. New York: Cold Spring Harbor Laboratory of Quantitative Biology.

Arthur Kornberg (1918–   ) in 1964. Dr. Kornberg was the recipient of a Nobel prize in 1959. (Photograph by Stanford University.)

SPECIFIC SECTION REFERENCES

4.1   Meselson, M., and Stahl, F. W. 1958. The replication of DNA in *Escherichia coli*. Proc. Nat. Acad. Sci., U.S., 44: 671–682. (Density-gradient ultracentrifugation studies showing semiconservative replication.) Bobbs-Merrill Reprint Series, Indianapolis: Howard W. Sams Company, Inc. Reprinted also in *Papers in biochemical genetics,* Zubay, G. L. (Editor), New York: Holt, Rinehart and Winston, Inc., 1968, pp. 80–91.
   Oster, G. 1965. Density gradients. Scient. Amer., 213 (No. 2): 70–76, 119, 120.
4.2   Bourgaux, P., Bourgaux-Ramoisy, D., and Dulbecco, R. 1969. The replication of the ring-shaped DNA of polyoma virus, I. Identification of the replicative intermediate. Proc. Nat. Acad. Sci., U.S., 64: 701–708. (Needs DNA polymerase, endonuclease, and a ligase—see Section 4.3.)
   Cairns, J. 1964. The chromosome of *Escherichia coli*. Cold Spring Harb. Sympos. Quant, Biol., 28: 43–46. Reprinted in *Papers on bacterial genetics,* second edition, Adelberg, E. A. (Editor), Boston: Little, Brown and Company, 1966, pp. 397–402. (Replication photographed.)
   Cairns, J. 1966. The bacterial chromosome. Scient. Amer., 214 (No. 1): 36–44, 134. Scientific American Offprints, San Francisco: W. H. Freeman and Company, Publishers.

Champoux, J. J., and Dulbecco, R. 1972. An activity from mammalian cells that untwists superhelical DNA—a possible swivel for DNA replication. Proc. Nat. Acad. Sci., U.S., 69: 143–146.

4.3   Gefter, M. L., Hirota, Y., Kornberg, T., Wechsler, J. A., and Barnoux, C. 1971. Analysis of DNA polymerase II and III in mutants of *Escherichia coli* thermosensitive for DNA synthesis. Proc. Nat. Acad. Sci., U.S., 68: 3150–3153. (DNA polymerase III seems to be required for DNA replication in *E. coli*.)

Lindahl, T., and Edelman, G. M. 1968. Polynucleotide ligase from myeloid and lymphoid tissues. Proc. Nat. Acad. Sci., U.S., 61: 680–687.

Nuzzo, F., Brega, A., and Falaschi, A. 1970. DNA replication in mammalian cells, I. The size of newly synthesized helices. Proc. Nat. Acad. Sci., U.S., 65: 1017–1024. (Support for the same kind of DNA chain growth in mammals as in bacteria.)

Okazaki, T., and Okazaki, R. 1969. Mechanism of DNA chain growth, IV. Direction of synthesis of T4 short DNA chains as revealed by exonucleolytic degradation. Proc. Nat. Acad. Sci., U.S., 64: 1242–1248.

Olivera, B. M., Hall, Z. W., and Lehman, I. R. 1968. Enzymatic joining of polynucleotides, V. A DNA-adenylate intermediate in the polynucleotide-joining reaction. Proc. Nat. Acad. Sci., U.S., 61: 237–244.

4.4   Razin, A., and Sinsheimer, R. L. 1970. Replicative form II DNA of ϕX174; resistance to exonucleolytic cleavage by *E. coli* DNA polymerase. Proc. Nat. Acad. Sci., U.S., 66: 646–650.

Sinsheimer, R. L. 1968. Bacteriophage ϕX174 and related viruses. Progr. Nucleic Acid Res. and Mol. Biol., 8: 115–169.

4.5   Dressler, D., and Wolfson, J. 1970. The rolling circle for ϕX DNA replication, III. Synthesis of supercoiled duplex rings. Proc. Nat. Acad. Sci., U.S., 67: 456–463.

Eisen, H., da Silva, L. P., and Jacob, F. 1969. The regulation and mechanism of DNA synthesis in bacteriophage λ. Cold Spring Harb. Sympos. Quant. Biol. (1968), 33: 755–764.

Gilberg, W., and Dressler, D. 1969. DNA replication: the rolling circle model. Cold Spring Harb. Sympos. Quant. Biol. (1968), 33: 473–484.

4.6   Kornberg, A., Bertsch, L. L., Jackson, J. F., and Khorana, H. G. 1964. Enzymatic synthesis of deoxyribonucleic acid, XVI. Oligonucleotides as templates and the mechanism of their replication. Proc. Nat. Acad. Sci., U.S., 51: 315–323.

Smith, M. 1963. Deoxyribonucleic acids in crabs of the genus *Cancer*. Biochem. Biophys. Res. Commun., 10: 67–72.

4.7   Berg, P., Fancher, H., and Chamberlin, M. 1963. The synthesis of mixed polynucleotides containing ribo- and deoxyribonucleotides by purified preparations of DNA polymerase from *Escherichia coli*. In *Informational macromolecules*, Vogel, H. J., Bryson, V., and Lampen, J. O. (Editors), New York: Academic Press, Inc., pp. 467–483.

Schaller, H., Otto, B., Nüsslein, V., Huf, J., Herrmann, R., and Bonhoeffer, F. 1972. Deoxyribonucleic acid replication *in vitro*. J. Mol. Biol., 63: 183–200.

4.8   Goulian, M., Kornberg, A., and Sinsheimer, R. L. 1967. Enzymatic synthesis of DNA, XXIV. Synthesis of infectious ϕX174 DNA. Proc. Nat. Acad. Sci., U.S., 58: 2321–2328.

SUPPLEMENTARY SECTION

S4.7   Nearest-neighbor analysis indicates that the DNA synthesized *in vitro* by *E. coli* DNA polymerase has the same base sequences as the DNA used as primer-template.

Since different linear segments of DNA represent different informational units, the differences among genes lie in the sequence of their organic bases. Considering only the four usual deoxy-ribonucleotides, 16 different sequences of two nucleotides are possible. (The first nucleotide can be one of four, and so can the second, making possible 4 times 4, or 16 different linear arrangements in dinucleotides.) The base sequence in dinucleotides can be determined experimentally as follows: One of the four triphosphates added as substrate is labeled with ^{32}P in the innermost phosphate, the other three are not. Extended synthesis is permitted during which the labeled phosphate (P*) attaches to the 3′ of the sugar of the nucleotide which is its linear neighbor (refer to Figure 4.9). This linear neighbor can be identified by digesting the synthesized product with spleen phosphodiesterase, since this endonuclease produces deoxyribonucleoside 3′-monophosphates by breaking the polymer at all 5′ positions. Consequently, the P* is found joined at the 3′ position of the deoxyribonucleotide just anterior to the one on which it entered the DNA strand. The digest is then analyzed to see how frequently P* is part of dA 3′-P*, dT 3′-P*, dC 3′-P*, and dG 3′-P*. If the P* were originally in dAP*PP, we would then know the relative linear frequencies of dTdA, dAdA, dCdA, and dGdA. By carrying out this procedure three more times, labeling a different one of the triphosphates each time, the relative frequency of all 16 sequences can be determined.

Such *nearest-neighbor analyses* have been made of the DNA's synthesized using a number of different preformed DNA's. The values observed *in vitro* clearly follow those expected for complementary strands synthesized *in vitro* in opposite directions. What is already demonstrated via chemical analyses is independently proved via nearest-neighbor analysis—that the product of an extended synthesis has the same base frequencies as the natural two-stranded DNA used as primer-template. Moreover, each type of natural DNA proves to have unique and reproducible dinucleotide sequences, not predictable from its base composition. The accuracy of the *in vitro* synthesizing system in making progeny DNA like parental DNA is shown by the nearest-neighbor frequency being the same when native DNA is used as primer-template as when DNA synthesized from this native DNA is used.

QUESTIONS AND PROBLEMS

1. The nucleic acid synthesized using a parental duplex template may be (1) conservative, (2) semiconservative, (3) dispersive, or (4) nonconservative. Place each synthesis using a double-stranded template diagrammed in Figure 4-6 into one of these categories.
2. Give two pieces of evidence that the parental strands of double-stranded DNA are separated after *E. coli* DNA has replicated.
3. After a lag period during which dCTP and dGTP are incubated in the presence of Mg^{2+} and *E. coli* DNA polymerase, a double-stranded DNA is synthesized *de novo*. How can you prove that such duplexes are poly (dG) · poly (dC)?
4. What special problems are involved in replicating double-helical DNA that is circular rather than open?
5. Hypothesize how the problems mentioned in question 4 are resolved.
6. What clues does DNA synthesis *in vitro* provide about DNA synthesis *in vivo*?
7. What is meant by the statement that newly synthesized DNA is covalently linked to the primer but is not covalently linked to the template?
8. What effect does the absence or presence of preexisting DNA have upon DNA strand formation *in vitro*?
9. Does *E. coli* DNA polymerase take directions only from *E. coli* DNA? Explain.
10. Does strand separation occur during an extended synthesis of DNA *in vitro*? Explain.
11. Of what significance is the nearest-nucleotide-neighbor analysis?
12. If substrate depletion is prevented, what would you expect to happen to the (dA + dT)/(dC + dG) ratio when an extended synthesis is permitted to proceed for several hours?

Chapter 5

Replication of RNA and Transcription

When DNA or RNA is replicated, the information present in the parental sequence of organic bases is copied in the progeny sequence of organic bases; therefore, replication produces a new transcript of information, just as does copying over a set of lecture notes. Since uracil and thymine are, in a sense, equivalent (both being complements of adenine) transcription can also occur when DNA is used as template to synthesize RNA or RNA is used as template to synthesize DNA.

Despite the above view that transcription applies to all synthesis of nucleic acid that is complementary to nucleic acid, regardless which nucleic acid is the "parent" and "progeny," it has become customary to restrict the term to the complementary synthesis of one type of nucleic acid by the other type. Henceforth we shall, therefore, refer to *transcription* as the synthesis that proceeds from DNA to RNA, and to *reverse transcription* as the synthesis that proceeds from RNA to DNA.

Cells that do not divide (such as neurons) and organisms that do not reproduce (such as those that are sterile) nevertheless contain genetic material. Accordingly, since we cannot require a nucleic acid to have been replicated before identifying it as genetic material, we will call *genetic material* any replica of a nucleic acid that has been (or is expected to be) replicated or transcribed.

The present chapter discusses the *de novo* synthesis of RNA and RNA replication *in vivo* and *in vitro* before considering transcription and reverse transcription *in vivo* and *in vitro*.

5.1 RNA can be synthesized *de novo*.

Polynucleotide phosphorylase synthesizes RNA *de novo* from ribonucleoside *diphosphates* in an *in vitro* system. When different ribonucleoside diphosphates are involved, the final polymer contains ribonucleotides in a random linear array. Polynucleotide phosphorylase may serve *in vivo* to degrade rather than synthesize RNA.

RNA polymerase from *Azotobacter* can catalyze the *de novo* synthesis of RNA in the following reactions: ATP + UTP → (after a lag) poly (A)·poly (U); ITP + CTP → poly (I − C).

We should keep in mind that since the *de novo* synthesis of nucleic acids replicates no previous information, it is a nontranscriptional, nonreplicational process. Whether such RNA synthesis occurs *in vivo* is as yet unknown. (R)

5.2 Genetic RNA is replicated *in vivo* by RNA-dependent RNA polymerase.

Cells do not normally contain enzymes which catalyze the synthesis of RNA from RNA complements. They do acquire such enzymes, however, after infection by virions whose genetic material is double-stranded or single-stranded RNA. This type of enzyme, *RNA-dependent RNA polymerase* (sometimes called *RNA replicase*), results in the synthesis of progeny RNA.

Of course, both complementary strands are synthesized when virions containing double-stranded RNA reproduce (Figure 4-6K).[1] Both complementary strands are also produced during replication of single-stranded RNA genomes, for example, as found in TMV. Replication of the single-stranded genetic material of the RNA phage, ϕf2, seems to involve two enzymes—one that synthesizes a − strand complementary to the parental + strand (Figure 4-6I) and another that synthesizes + strands from the + − duplex (Figure 4-6J). Replication of the single-stranded RNA's of other viruses such as ϕQβ and ϕMS2, however, seems to involve only a single enzyme which synthesizes both − and + strands from their complements. Note that the RNA-dependent RNA polymerase of ϕQβ, *Qβ RNA synthetase*, requires two cofactors present in uninfected *E. coli* in order to function.

Since the single-stranded RNA of ϕR17 (3,500 nucleotides long) shows some secondary structure (Figure 3-11), an RNA polymerase must apparently be able to unfold this duplex structure during a synthesis that makes the complementary strand. (R)

5.3   RNA can be replicated *in vitro* by RNA-dependent RNA polymerase.

As genetic material, RNA seems to be confined to the genomes of viruses. The small size of these genomes encourages study of both their replication and primary structure.

In an *in vitro* system of Mg^{2+} ions and the ribonucleoside 5'-triphosphates of A, U, C, and G, the RNA-dependent RNA polymerase from cells infected with ϕQβ will not synthesize RNA with a template of (1) fragmented ϕQβ RNA, (2) carefully extracted RNA from ϕMS2, or (3) unbroken TMV RNA. If, however, the ϕQβ (+) RNA to be used as template is not fragmented, + RNA that is just as infective as the template is produced after two successive syntheses by the polymerase (Figure 4-6I, J). The RNA-dependent RNA polymerase isolated from *E. coli* infected with ϕMS2 shows a similar requirement for unfragmented ϕMS2 RNA as template for RNA synthesis.

These experiments indicate that there is a kind of specificity between phage RNA-dependent RNA polymerase and the RNA it uses as template.[2] Clues to this specificity have been found in the terminal nucleoside sequences of the viral RNA's. Thus, the 3' termini of ϕQβ RNA's + and − strands have almost identical nucleoside sequences

$$\ldots \text{CCACCC A—OH3' + strand}$$
$$\ldots \text{CCACCC C—OH3' − strand.}$$

The last residue (A or C) is apparently added on by the synthetase without using a complement and can be lost without affecting the infectivity of the RNA. The identity of the remaining 3' terminal sequence indicates that it serves as the *recognition gene*

---

[1] It should be noted, however, that the duplex + − RNA of reovirus does not strand separate in the infected cell, and + single-stranded RNA is made using an RNA polymerase contained in the virion. Thus, this is a conservative synthesis (Figure 4-6J, first alternative). The progeny + strand is then used to make a − complement, thereby completing replication of duplex progeny RNA.

[2] In contrast to the ϕQβ and ϕMS2 enzymes, however, another RNA-dependent RNA polymerase can use poly A, poly U, and poly C as templates in the *in vitro* synthesis of complementary RNA.

for $\phi Q\beta$ RNA synthetase, each 3' terminus apparently serving as a primer for the start of the synthesis of the complementary strand.[3] (R)

5.4   Double-stranded DNA is transcribed discontinuously *in vivo* to single-stranded RNA by DNA-dependent RNA polymerase.

In bacteria and all other cells cytoplasmic RNA is ordinarily single-stranded (see, however, Section 5.6), and is always the complement of one and the same strand of a given segment of double-stranded DNA. This asymmetrical synthesis is indicated by studies of RNA base content, which show A $\neq$ U and C $\neq$ G, and of DNA–RNA hybridizations, which show that a maximum of one half of the single strands of denatured duplex DNA can make hybrid duplexes with RNA. Therefore, cellular RNA is normally the result of *one-complement transcription*, from double-stranded DNA to single-stranded RNA (Figure 4-6D), catalyzed by normally present *DNA-dependent RNA polymerase* (sometimes called "transcriptase" to distinguish it from RNA-dependent RNA polymerase, or RNA replicase). The RNA is synthesized discontinuously,[4] producing segments ranging from 4s size up to 80s, perhaps larger.

DNA-dependent RNA polymerase is not only found in all cells, but seems to be a normal component of the virion of such DNA viruses as vaccinia and pox virus. (R)

5.5   Double-stranded DNA will also be transcribed to single-stranded RNA under certain *in vitro* conditions.

In the presence of preformed DNA and the ribonucleoside 5'-triphosphates of A, U, C, and G, DNA-dependent RNA polymerase can catalyze the synthesize of RNA *in vitro*. Double-stranded DNA is a more effective template than single-stranded DNA. If the "plus–minus" duplex ring DNA of ϕX174 is extracted carefully so that the duplex ring is not broken and it is then put into an *in vitro* system with DNA-dependent RNA polymerase, the RNA synthesized is complementary to only the − DNA strand. From this result we conclude that a one-complement transcription from a two-stranded template has taken place (Figure 4-6D, first alternative only).[5] (R)

5.6   Some duplex RNA occurs *in vivo* which is complementary to genetic duplex DNA.

After infection by vaccinia, whose virion genetic material is double-stranded DNA, duplex RNA which is complementary to the vaccinia DNA appears in the host chick

---

[3] We can assume, from the constant starting point of DNA replication in an *E. coli* chromosome, that there are also DNA recognition genes for DNA polymerase. Such genes are discussed later in Section 24.4.

[4] This implies the occurrence of recognition genes for starting and stopping the action of DNA-dependent RNA polymerase; we shall postpone consideration of such matters, however, until we consider the control or regulation of transcription in Sections 26.1 and 26.3.

[5] Under other conditions, described further in Section 26.10, the synthesized RNA has the same base ratio as the double-stranded primer-template DNA (we are considering T equivalent to U), indicating that a two-complement transcription has occurred from a two-stranded template (Figure 4-6G).

cell. Nucleated cells that are uninfected or infected with *Rous sarcoma virus* (*RSV*), whose virion genetic material is single-stranded RNA, also contain duplex RNA's which apparently are not single-stranded RNA's folded and base paired with themselves. The function of such virus-specific and normal duplex RNA's are as yet unknown; their biosynthesis and structure have started to be investigated. (R)

5.7   Reverse transcription occurs *in vivo*, from genetic RNA to genetic DNA; this DNA may then possibly be transcribed to genetic RNA.

The following evidence indicates that DNA is synthesized from RNA information *in vivo*. RNA–DNA hybridizations indicate that after infection with RSV the chick cell contains increased quantities of DNA which can base pair with the viral RNA. This "new" DNA appears to be the product of reverse transcription of RSV RNA and to contain information needed for replication of the virus. For if DNA synthesis is inhibited soon after the chick cells are exposed to the virus, no RSV progeny result. Moreover, Rous sarcoma virus as well as a large number of other single-stranded RNA viruses contain *RNA-directed DNA polymerase* (probably made using information contained in virion RNA) which uses single-stranded RNA to synthesize an RNA–DNA duplex *in vitro* (Figure 4-6L). (A nuclease is known that degrades such RNA–DNA hybrids.) The hybrid molecule might conceivably be used for making either duplex DNA or more of the single-stranded RNA. That synthesis may occur in the opposite direction also (from genetic DNA to genetic RNA) when RSV progeny are made is supported by finding, in the case of avian myeloblastosis virus (also having a single-stranded RNA genome in the virion) that complementary viral RNA is indetectable, yet viral RNA is bound to chick DNA in long polynucleotides. RNA-directed DNA polymerase activity has also been found in mammalian cells that are apparently not infected with tumor viruses. (R)

5.8   *In vitro* a conservative reverse transcription of double-stranded RNA produces double-stranded DNA.   ·

Poly (A)·poly (U) is a double-stranded RNA composed of two *homopolymers*, each containing a single type of base—poly A base-paired with poly U. An *in vitro* system of poly (A)·poly (U), *E. coli* DNA polymerase, Mg^{2+} ions, dATP, and dTTP produces double-stranded DNA. One strand of this DNA contains only deoxyadenylic acids and is, accordingly, poly dA; the other strand contains only deoxythymidylic acids, poly dT, the two strands base-pairing to make up poly (dA)·poly (dT). Clearly, then, poly (A)·poly (U) has served as a template.

Experimental evidence indicates that in this system no hybrid RNA–DNA duplexes are formed. Hence, complete strand separation of poly (A)·poly (U) apparently does not occur in the synthesis of poly (dA)·poly (dT); and both DNA strands may need to be synthesized simultaneously (Figure 4-6F). In a similar conservative synthesis, poly (G)·poly (C) probably can act as template for synthesis of poly (dG)·poly (dC). (R)

5.9   DNA polymerase probably acts in the major groove of duplex DNA, DNA-dependent RNA polymerase in the minor groove.

The site of polymerase activity in duplex DNA is indicated by studies dealing with the effect of *actinomycin D* on transcription. At low concentrations this drug binds to dG-containing sites in double-stranded DNA (and probably to G in double-stranded RNA as well) and suppresses the synthesis of RNA by DNA-dependent RNA polymerase.[6] Interference with DNA synthesis also occurs but at much higher concentrations. Experimental evidence suggests that actinomycin D lies in the minor groove of DNA, hypothesized to be the site of DNA-dependent RNA polymerase activity. The major groove may be the site for DNA polymerase action. It should be noted in this connection that phleomycin probably binds to adenine–thymine-rich DNA, inhibiting DNA polymerase but not DNA-dependent RNA polymerase. (R)

5.10   The mechanisms of template synthesis of nucleic acids are not yet fully known.

We have seen that the template synthesis of nucleic acids is a process which results in more copies of the information they contain. Let us now take a closer look at this process. When single-stranded genetic material (for example, the DNA of ϕX174 or the RNA of TMV) is used, the individual bases (through their conformation and H-bonding characteristics) serve as the template which together with the polymerases (through their conformation and other properties) must be primarily responsible for the ordering of nucleotides into a complementary strand which forms a duplex with the template.[7]

When nucleic acids are synthesized in the presence of double-stranded nucleic acids, however, we do not know whether the individual bases or the base pairs serve as the template. This is the situation in the three examples that follow:

1. *Semiconservative replication of duplex nucleic acid* (as occurs in the replication of *E. coli* DNA). The parental duplex may first denature, with the single strands then acting separately as templates to produce old–new base pairs. Or, positioning of new, free nucleotides may occur while the old nucleotides of the parent are still hydrogen-bonded to each other, the major area surrounding a base pair constituting the mold or template; afterward, the H bonds between parental strands break and reform to link parental strands with their newly synthesized complements. Evidence indicates that the pairing or positioning of bases occurs first, the correct sugar–phosphate backbone link then being

---

[6] Antibiotics such as rifamycin and its derivatives as well as streptovaricin seem to bind directly to DNA-dependent RNA polymerase, thereby inhibiting enzyme activity.

[7] In theory, synthesis may result in more copies of a strand without first producing a complementary strand (Figure 4-6H). In such instances, the polymerase or some agent attached to it might function as an adapter which accepts for incorporation into the new strand those nucleotides with the same bases as the template.

catalyzed by a DNA polymerase.

2. *Conservative synthesis of duplex nucleic acid* (as occurs when duplex RNA undergoes reverse transcription to duplex DNA *in vitro*). Without separating, the H-bonded base pair of a parental duplex may act as the template for both complementary nucleotides. Alternatively, the template might denature at the point of synthesis so that the separated bases can act as templates which bring complementary nucleotides of the new duplex close together. Hydrogen bonds would then form between the members of the new duplex and also reform between the strands of the parental duplex.

3. *Synthesis of one complement of a duplex nucleic acid* (as occurs when ϕX174 DNA in the $+$ $-$ replicative form is transcribed to $+$ RNA). If the duplex does not denature, the base pair can serve as the template for the synthesis of one complement; or the parental duplex may denature a piece at a time, followed by one-complement synthesis and renaturation.

We see, therefore, that the precise roles of polymerase and of single and double-stranded nucleic acids in semiconservative and conservative syntheses are not yet fully understood.

SUMMARY AND CONCLUSIONS

Although RNA can be synthesized *de novo in vitro*, the template mechanism of synthesizing complementary strands is used during the *in vivo* replication of both single- and double-stranded RNA's of virions. Template synthesis requires an RNA-dependent RNA polymerase, which, in some cases, recognizes a base sequence at the 3′ terminus as the primer for the synthesis of the complementary strand. Therefore, some genomes seem to contain unique RNA polymerase recognition genes a half-dozen or so nucleotides long.

Most of the RNA present in cells is the result of one (and the same) complement transcription of double-stranded DNA. Such synthesis is carried out by DNA-dependent RNA polymerase which starts transcription at various places in the DNA and subsequently ends it to produce RNA's differing in base sequence and length.

Some of the DNA in certain cells is produced by reverse transcription of viral genetic RNA. This DNA is probably genetic since it is a transcript which is probably transcribed to RNA or DNA or both. A considerable number of RNA viruses that attack nucleated cells contain an RNA-directed DNA polymerase, supporting the view that reverse transcription is a common part of the reproductive cycle of such viruses. This type of enzyme has been found in many nucleated cells; we do not know, however, to what extent such an enzyme (or duplex RNA) is a normal or abnormal cellular component.

The enzymatic synthesis of complements of a parental duplex template of nucleic acid requires the use of information provided by the parental bases. That is, the synthesizing enzymes must enter the grooves of the duplex—very likely DNA polymerase using the major and RNA polymerase the minor groove. Whether these enzymes use the conformation of grooves determined by the base pairs, or the conformation of grooves after base pairs have broken their H bonds, is as yet undetermined.

GENERAL REFERENCES

Hurwitz, J., and August, J. T. 1963. The role of DNA in RNA synthesis. In *Progress in nucleic acid research*, Davidson, J. N., and Cohn, W. E. (Editors), New York: Academic Press, Inc., Vol. 1, pp. 59–92.

Temin, H. M. 1972. RNA-directed DNA synthesis. Scient. Amer., 226 (No. 1): 24–33, 122.

Transcription of genetic material. Cold Spring Harb. Sympos. Quant. Biol., 35. 1971. New York: Cold Spring Harbor Laboratory of Quantitative Biology.

SPECIFIC SECTION REFERENCES

5.1   Krakow, J. S., and Karstadt, M. 1967. *Azotobacter vinelandii* ribonucleic acid polymerase, IV. Unprimed synthesis of rIC copolymer. Proc. Nat. Acad. Sci., U.S., 58: 2094–2101.

Michelson, A. M., Massoulié, J., and Guschbauer, W. 1967. Synthetic polynucleotides. Progr. Nucleic Acid Res. and Mol. Biol., 6: 83–141.

5.2   Schonberg, M, Silverstein, S. C., Levin, D. H., and Acs, G. 1971. Asynchronous synthesis of the complementary strands of the reovirus genome. Proc. Nat. Acad. Sci., U.S., 68: 505–508.

Shatkin, A. J., and Sipe, J. D. 1968. RNA polymerase activity in purified reoviruses. Proc. Nat. Acad. Sci., U.S., 61: 1462–1469.

Weissmann, C., and Ochoa, S. 1967. Replication of phage RNA. Progr. Nucleic Acid Res. and Mol. Biol., 6: 353–339.

5.3   Billeter, M. A., Dahlberg, J. E., Goodman, H. M., Hindley, J., and Weissmann, C. 1969. Sequence of the first 175 nucleotides from the 5′ terminus of $Q\beta$ RNA synthesized *in vitro*. Nature, Lond., 224: 1083–1086.

Gomatos, P. J., Krug, R. M., and Tamm, I. 1965. Reovirus RNA-directed synthesis of DNA. I. The reaction catalyzed by DNA polymerase from *Escherichia coli*. J. Mol. Biol., 13: 802–816. (Duplex RNA serves *in vitro* as template for synthesis of complementary, often double-stranded, DNA.)

Spiegelman, S., Haruna, I., Holland, I. B., Beaudreau, G., and Mills, D. 1965. The synthesis of a self-propagating and infectious nucleic acid with a purified enzyme. Proc. Nat. Acad. Sci., U.S., 54: 919–927.

5.4   Kates, J. R., and McAuslin, B. R. 1967. Poxvirus DNA-dependent RNA polymerase. Proc. Nat. Acad. Sci., U.S., 58: 134–141.

Munyon, W., Paoletti, E., and Grace, J. T., Jr. 1967. RNA polymerase activity in purified infectious vaccinia virus. Proc. Nat. Acad. Sci., U.S., 58: 2280–2287.

5.5   Chamberlin, M., and Berg, P. 1962. Deoxyribonucleic acid-directed synthesis of ribonucleic acid by an enzyme from *Escherichia coli*. Proc. Nat. Acad. Sci., U.S., 48: 81–94. Reprinted in *Papers in biochemical genetics*, Zubay, G. L. (Editor), New York: Holt, Rinehart and Winston, Inc., 1968, pp. 188–201.

Colvill, A. J. E., Kanner, L. C., Tocchini-Valentini, G. P., Sarnat, M. T., and Geiduschek, E. P. 1965. Asymmetric RNA synthesis *in vitro*: Heterologous DNA-enzyme systems; *E. coli* RNA polymerase. Proc. Nat. Acad. Sci., U.S., 53: 1140–1146.

Millette, R. L., and Trotter, C. D. 1970. Initiation and release of RNA by DNA-dependent RNA polymerase. Proc. Nat. Acad. Sci., U.S., 66: 701–708.

5.6   Colby, C., and Duesberg, P. H. 1969. Double-stranded RNA in vaccinia virus infected cells. Nature, Lond., 222: 940–944.

Duesberg, P. H., and Colby, C. 1969. On the biosynthesis and structure of double-stranded RNA in vaccinia virus-infected cells. Proc. Nat. Acad. Sci., U.S., 64: 396–403.

5.7   Baltimore, D. 1970. RNA-dependent DNA polymerase in virions of RNA tumour viruses. Nature, Lond., 226: 1209–1211.

Baluda, M. A., and Nayak, D. P. 1970. DNA complementary to viral RNA in leukemic cells induced by avian myeloblastosis virus. Proc. Nat. Acad. Sci., U.S., 66: 329–336.

Levinson, W., Bishop, J. M., Quintrell, N., and Jackson, J. 1970. Presence of DNA in Rous sarcoma virus. Nature, Lond., 227: 1023–1025. (Present in virion.)

Temin, H. M., and Mizutani, S. 1970. RNA-dependent DNA polymerase in virions of Rous sarcoma virus. Nature, Lond., 226: 1211–1213.

5.8   Lee-Huang, S., and Cavalieri, L. F. 1963. Polyribonucleotides as templates for poly-
          deoxyribonucleotides. Proc. Nat. Acad. Sci., U.S., 50: 1116–1122.
5.9   Wells, R. D., and Larson, J. E. 1970. Studies on the binding of actinomycin D to DNA
          and DNA model polymers. J. Mol. Biol., 49: 319–342. (Favors an intercalation
          model.)
5.10   Cassuto, E., and Chargaff, E. 1969. Role of base-pairing in the control of an enzyme
          reaction. Proc. Nat. Acad. Sci., U.S., 62: 808–812.
          Florentiev, V. L., and Ivanov, V. I. 1970. RNA polymerase: two-step mechanism with
          overlapping steps. Nature, Lond., 228: 519–522. (Hypothesis using single-stranded
          DNA as template.)
          Haskell, E. H., and Davern, C. I. 1969. Pre-fork synthesis: a model for DNA replica-
          tion. Proc. Nat. Acad. Sci., U.S., 64: 1065–1071. (Single-strand breaks that occur
          in parental DNA might permit unwinding and provide ends which can be used
          as primers for new DNA synthesis.)
          Riley, P. A. 1970. A suggested mechanism for DNA transcription. Nature, Lond., 228:
          522–525. (Hypothesis that uses the major groove and the base pair as the template
          for RNA synthesis.)

QUESTIONS AND PROBLEMS

1. Name two enzymes that synthesize nucleic acids by a template mechanism; by a non-template mechanism.
2. State specific different kinds of nucleic acid syntheses each of the following can catalyze:
    a. *E. coli* DNA polymerase.
    b. Calf thymus DNA polymerase.
    c. Polynucleotide phosphorylase.
    d. DNA-dependent RNA polymerase.
    e. RNA-dependent RNA polymerase.
3. What is the functional significance of the grooves of double-stranded DNA?
4. The two complementary strands of the DNA in a phage (SP8) that attacks *Bacillus subtilis* have distinctly different base compositions. Describe an experiment to test whether the phage DNA is used in the host for a one-complement transcription to RNA.
5. State the role of one-complement synthesis using a double-stranded template in the replication of the following viruses: ϕf2, ϕX174, TMV.
6. In reoviruses, actinomycin D inhibits RNA-directed incorporation of deoxyribonucleotides into DNA with DNA polymerase as catalyst to a lesser extent than the RNA-directed incorporation of ribonucleotides into RNA with RNA polymerase catalyst. How does this result compare with that expected from use of this drug on nucleic acid templates?
7. Defend the statement that genetic DNA and genetic RNA are intertranscribable.
8. Are all the nucleotides in a virion such as $\phi Q\beta$ genetic material? Explain.
9. Do you suppose some genetic material is single-stranded and replicated directly, without forming a complement? Explain.

Chapter 6

The Machinery and Mechanism of Translation

As noted in Chapter 1, the genetic material of a virus carries information both for the replication of this genetic material and for the production of the organism's characteristic proteins. The copying of DNA or RNA information into more nucleic acid involves a single language whose alphabet consists of organic bases. The formation of proteins from genetic information, however, requires a *translation* from the language of nucleic acids into the language of polypeptides, with an alphabet of some 20 amino acids. The present chapter describes the machinery and mechanism of translation.

The first five sections deal separately with each of the three main components of the machinery for translation. These components are the ribosome (see Section 1.4)—which is the site where translation takes place—and two types of RNA that attach to the ribosome—one type contains the information for determining which of the other type, carrying the amino acids to be polymerized into a polypeptide, shall bind to the ribosome. The procedure and mechanism of translation are then described in detail in the remaining sections, considering these and other factors simultaneously.

6.1   A ribosome consists of a smaller ribonucleoprotein subunit joined to a larger one. Ribosomal RNA (rRNA) is a transcript of chromosomal DNA. 5s RNA is also part of ribosomes.

Ribosomes come in two general sizes: "70s"—found in bacteria, mitochondria, and chloroplasts—and "80s"—found in the cytoplasm of plants and animals (Figure 6-1). Although there is some evidence that not all ribosomes of the "same" size are the same chemically, all are composed of a smaller plus a larger subunit. The 70s particle consists of a "30s" subunit joined to a "50s" subunit.[1] The 80s particle consists of a "40s" subunit joined to a "60s" subunit.

Both subunits are *ribonucleoproteins* in which the RNA contributes about two thirds of the weight and the protein one third. Whereas TMV and other plant viruses are ribonucleoproteins whose protein portion consists of a large number of identical

Ribosome Size Class	Ribosome Subunits	Number of Proteins Contained	RNA Class Contained
70s	30s + 50s	21 / 34	16s / 23s + 5s*
80s	40s + 60s	18 /	18s / 28s + 7s* } 5s*

Figure 6-1   General classes of ribosomes and their components.
*In the ribosomes of some, but not all, species.

[1] Under the electron microscope, the 50s subunit appears to have a pentagonal outline and a polydedral shape best approximated by an icosahedron.

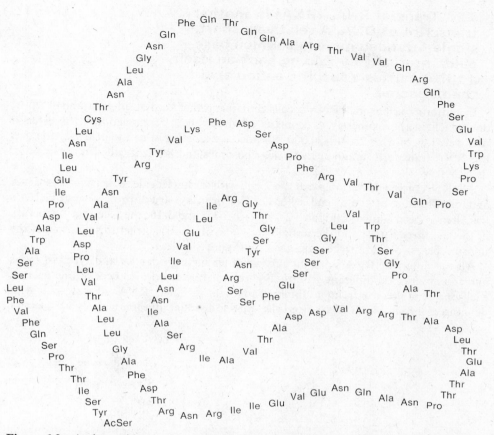

Figure 6-2   Amino acid sequence in the protein building block of tobacco mosaic virus (TMV). There are 158 amino acids in the subunit. (Courtesy of H. Fraenkel-Conrat.)

polypeptide subunits (Figure 6-2), a 30s ribosomal subunit contains 21 different polypeptide chains, each with a molecular weight of about 30,000—many of them basic proteins; 13 of these are present in only 1 copy. The 50s subunit contains 34 proteins, at least 12 of which are present in only 1 copy. Clearly, the protein structure of ribosomes is more complicated than that of RNA viruses.

Ribosomal RNA (rRNA) is primarily single-stranded (a short double-stranded region sometimes occurs; see Section 6.11). In the 70s ribosome, the 30s subunit has a "16s" RNA component (MW $0.55 \pm 0.10 \times 10^6$) and the 50s subunit contains a "23s" RNA (MW $1.15 \pm 0.20 \times 10^6$). The 16s and 23s RNA components consist of approximately 1,000 and 2,000 nucleotides, respectively. The 23s RNA is not merely two units of 16s RNA, though; evidence indicates that 16s and 23s RNA are transcripts of different segments of chromosomal DNA. The 40s and 60s subunits in 80s particles contain "18s" and "28s" RNA components. The difference between 70s and 80s ribosomes seems to be primarily in their rRNA.

Another piece of RNA, 5s RNA (see Section 3.8), is found in all 50s subunits in *E. coli* and in the 80s ribosomes of the toad *Xenopus*, although it is absent in the mitochondrial ribosomes of *Neurospora*. (R)

6.2 Transfer RNA (tRNA) is another transcript of DNA. A relatively short, single-stranded molecule which base-pairs internally by folding back on itself, a tRNA carries a specific amino acid to the ribosome.

In addition to ribosomal RNA's, cells contain another kind of single-stranded RNA, one which is approximately 4s, consists of about 70 to 80 nucleotides,[2] and has a relatively low MW of 25,000–30,000. Radioactive labeling of amino acids reveals that this RNA transports amino acids to the ribosomes and hence is called *transfer RNA,* or *tRNA.*[3]

All tRNA molecules terminate at the 3′ end with the nucleoside sequence —C—C—A and usually start at the 5′ end with G. The primary structure of several tRNA's has already been shown in Figures 2-10, 3-10, 3-15, and 3-16; the secondary structure in the last three listed; and the tertiary in the last two. The structures of some of the unusual bases found in tRNA are given in Figure 8-4.

All the different tRNA's are thought to differ in the sequence and types of bases and to comprise 20 different groups (Figure 6-3 shows two members of one group), each one capable of carrying a different amino acid. Since tRNA can base-pair with denatured chromosomal DNA from the same individual, it apparently is a transcript

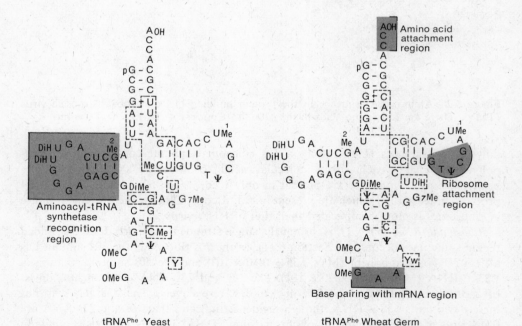

tRNA^Phe Yeast   tRNA^Phe Wheat Germ

Figure 6-3   Two tRNA members of the same Phe-carrying family, one from yeast and one from wheat germ. The areas boxed in dashed lines show regions of dissimilarity. (After B. S. Dudock, G. Katz, E. K. Taylor, and R. W. Holley.)

[2] The longest one so far sequenced has 87 nucleotides.

[3] It was formerly sometimes called *soluble RNA* or *sRNA* owing to its solubility under certain conditions.

of DNA. Base-pairing is best when the tRNA and DNA are from the same species—a fact which indicates that different species contain different sets of tRNA's. Since tRNA is a transcript of DNA, knowing the complete base sequence means that we know essentially the entire order of deoxyribonucleotides in the gene which specifies it; in fact, duplex DNA has been synthesized *in vitro* whose transcript is a tRNA. It has been reported in nucleated cells that tRNA comes in a pre-tRNA form, approximately 105 ribonucleotides long, which, unlike tRNA, has no methylated bases (methylation will be discussed in Chapter 8). Another form of pre-tRNA (a derivative of the first?) is apparently partially methylated. (R)

6.3   Activation of an amino acid precedes its attachment to a specific tRNA. A single enzyme (a different one for each kind of amino acid) catalyzes both processes.

Before attachment to a specific tRNA, an amino acid must be activated. This process involves linkage of the amino acid at its carboxyl ($-C \overset{O}{\underset{OH}{\big\langle}}$) end to the 2' or 3' hydroxyl group of adenosine 5'-triphosphate (ATP) and the removal of pyrophosphate (PP_i). We may summarize this reaction as follows: amino acid + ATP $\rightleftharpoons$ aminoacyl-AMP + PP_i, where AMP is adenosine monophosphate. Subsequently, the amino acid joins at its carboxyl end to the A-containing end of a tRNA: tRNA + aminoacyl-AMP $\rightleftharpoons$ aminoacyl-tRNA + AMP. Both the activation of a particular amino acid and its attachment to its specific tRNA are catalyzed by the same enzyme, *aminoacyl-tRNA synthetase*. At least one different enzyme exists for each kind of amino acid.

6.4   Different regions of the tRNA molecule have different functions.

When the primary structure of tRNA's for the same and different amino acids (Figures 3-10 and 6-3) are studied, as well as the behavior of fragments and of denatured and renatured tRNA's, it is possible to identify which chemical and functional features are held in common by all. As mentioned in Section 6.2, the —CCA terminus (common to all tRNA's) is the region where the amino acid is accepted for transport; the dihydro-U-containing loop seems to be the aminoacyl-tRNA synthetase recognition region (being different for each type of amino acid); the GTΨCG-containing loop seems to be the region (common to all tRNA's) responsible for attachment of the charged (amino acid-carrying) tRNA to the ribosome; the constant length from the —CCA terminus to the opposite loop of the cloverleaf is presumably associated with the correct positioning of amino acids for peptide bonding (discussed in Section 6.6); the loop opposite —CCA always serves as the region that base-pairs with another type of RNA, mRNA (see the next section). The reader is encouraged to locate these regions of special function in the diagram (Figure 3-10) showing tRNA tertiary structure. (R)

6.5   Messenger RNA (mRNA) is a single-stranded transcript of double-stranded DNA and serves as a carrier of polypeptide-specifying information from the genetic material to the ribosome.

After a T phage infects *E. coli*, the double-stranded DNA of the phage undergoes a one-complement transcription to RNA. Soon afterwards this RNA is found attached to a number of bacterial ribosomes. Since it carries information transcribed from phage DNA for the synthesis of one or more polypeptides on the ribosome, it is called *messenger RNA*, or *mRNA*. Messenger RNA is transcribed from DNA of normal cellular organelles also (see Section 5.4), being synthesized in the 5′ toward 3′ direction. Although rRNA and tRNA usually are used directly, as we have seen, mRNA functions indirectly, as a polypeptide-specifying message carrier. (R)

6.6   A ribosome with mRNA attached also has sites for attachment of two aminoacyl-tRNA molecules. These tRNA's function as adapters in the stepwise synthesis of a polypeptide, for when a portion of each base-pairs with mRNA their amino acids are properly aligned for peptide union.

Polypeptide initiation

In the absence of protein synthesis, the two subunits (30s and 50s) of the 70s ribosome are dissociated from each other. Protein synthesis, in *E. coli* for example, starts with the attachment of mRNA at its 5′ end to the 30s subunit. This combination binds an initiating aminoacyl-tRNA (described further in Section 7.12) to form an *initiation complex* in which a short segment of mRNA is base-paired with a short segment of the tRNA. The presence of GTP is needed as an *initiation factor* for binding the initiating charged tRNA, although the GTP is not hydrolyzed. The initiating aminoacyl-tRNA occupies what is called the *aminoacyl* or *A site*, or *site 1* on 30s (Figure 6-4A). Other initiation factors are f1, f2, and f3.[4]

The 50s subunit next joins this initiating complex (potassium is a requirement), thereby constituting the 70s ribosome and generating a second site, called the *peptidyl* or *P site*, or *site 2*. Initiation factor f2 also functions as a *translocase* that catalyzes the translocation of the initiating charged tRNA from the A to the P site. This translocation involves the hydrolysis of GTP and, presumably, a corresponding movement or translocation of the mRNA region with which the initiating tRNA is base-paired. Translocation frees site A to accept an aminoacyl-tRNA that bears complementary bases in the region for base-pairing with mRNA (Figure 6-4B).

One of the functions of the ribosomal subunits is apparently to make sure that the bound segment of mRNA is single-stranded (some phage RNA has secondary structure—Figure 3-11) and has its bases properly exposed for hydrogen-bonding with

---

[4] All are isolated only from the 30s subunit, having molecular weights of 8,000, 75,000, and 30,000, respectively.

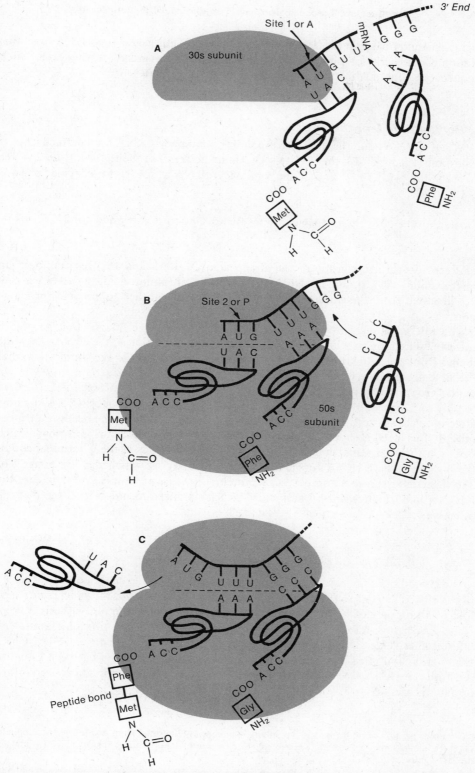

Figure 6-4 Schematic representation of the relationships between aminoacyl-tRNA's and mRNA at the ribosome in the formation of peptide linkages in *E. coli*. The mRNA moves in the 5′ direction with respect to the ribosome; the mRNA and aminoacyl-tRNA's pair in an antiparallel manner.

complementary bases in the tRNA's at the two sites. Thus we see that tRNA functions not only as a carrier of amino acids to the ribosome but as an adapter molecule which sequences amino acids according to instructions of the mRNA.

Polypeptide lengthening

When mRNA and the two corresponding aminoacyl-tRNA's are attached to a ribosome (Figure 6-4B), the —C—C—A-amino acid end of the tRNA at site 2 is free to reach the —C—C—A end of the aminoacyl-tRNA at site 1. An enzyme (or two)

located on the 50s subunit then catalyzes the formation of a peptide bond $-\overset{\overset{\textstyle O}{\|}}{C}-\overset{}{\underset{\underset{\textstyle H}{|}}{N}}-$

between the carboxyl group of the amino acid at site 2 and the free amino group of the amino acid at site 1.[5] No longer carrying an amino acid, the tRNA at site 2 is liberated from the ribosome and is free to accept another amino acid for transport.

The mRNA molecule then moves along or through the 30s subunit in the 5′ toward 3′ direction so that more of its message can be translated; the tRNA-dipeptide moves from site 1 to site 2 in the same direction (Figure 6-4C). We should note that the first dipeptide synthesized will have a free *N-terminal end* (the nitrogen of an amino group) and a bound *C-terminal end* (the carbon of the carboxyl group linked to tRNA). Directed by the bases of mRNA, an appropriate aminoacyl-tRNA can now attach to vacant site 1, and a peptide bond is formed as before. The result is a tripeptide. By this stepwise addition of amino acids, a polypeptide chain is formed which begins at the N-terminal end of its first amino acid and ends at the C-terminal end of the last. In a sense tRNA functions as the dictionary by which the "language" of nucleic acids is translated into that of proteins—that is, protein is synthesized in the NH_2 to COOH direction by aminoacyl-tRNA's translating mRNA in the 5′ to 3′ direction.

Polypeptide termination

We should note further that since the growing polypeptide chain appears attached to the ribosome (not to the messenger) only at its growing end, the polypeptide may fold to attain part of its three-dimensional configuration before its synthesis is complete. Just before release of a completed polypeptide from the ribosome and at all intermediate stages in its synthesis, the carboxyl end is joined to a tRNA. Chain termination and release are apparently aided by an enzyme which has been found to separate the tRNA from the polypeptide. In *E. coli*, chain termination needs three protein factors—S or T, R_1 and R_2.[6] (R)

---

[5] For every peptide bond formed, a phosphate is apparently liberated from guanosine triphosphate, GTP, by a ribosome-dependent GTPase; chain elongation requires three factors: Tu, Ts, and G, the last a tetramer of 80,000 MW.

[6] R_1 and R_2 each have a MW of 45,000, and each numbers 500 per cell (which, by comparison, also forms 30,000 ribosomes).

6.7   Depending upon the length of the mRNA molecule, several to many ribosomes can be joined to the same messenger. The successive ribosomes of such a polyribosome each bear a polypeptide chain at a successive stage of completion.

A 70s ribosome, with a diameter of approximately 230 Å, can accommodate only one mRNA and can make only one polypeptide chain at a given time. The 5' end of the messenger, the part synthesized first, is, as already noted, also the first to become attached to the 30s subunit (sometimes before the mRNA molecule has been completely synthesized.) Since some mRNA molecules may contain more than 1,500 nucleotides, each an average of 3.4 Å in length, such RNA is more than 5,000 Å long. It seems reasonable, therefore, that several ribosomes can use the same RNA molecule simultaneously. Since translation can begin at the 5' end of a messenger, we would expect ribosomes along the mRNA to carry polypeptides at successive stages of completion (Figure 6-5A). In support of this hypothesis is evidence that protein synthesis occurs among aggregates of several to many ribosomes in some organisms. Such aggregates, called *polyribosomes* or *polysomes*, are visible in electron micrographs (Figure 6-6) and may contain dozens of ribosomes when a long mRNA is being read.[7]

In a specific case in *E. coli* (see Section S6.7), a fixed number of approximately 20 closely packed ribosomes translate an mRNA in a wave just behind the transcribing DNA-dependent RNA polymerase (Figure 6-5B). The transcription and translation proceed at about 1,000 nucleotides per minute. (R)

6.8   Ribosomes dissociate into subunits between successive rounds of protein synthesis.

Those 70s ribosomes that have completely traversed an mRNA dissociate into their 30s and 50s subunit components as the completed polypeptide is released. The 50s subunits are free to combine at random with 30s subunits that enter into a protein initiation complex. Subunits are free to be used to translate the same message or others several times. The 80s ribosome seems to recirculate its 40s and 60s subunits in the same general manner. The dissociation of the 80s ribosome seems to require energy and to be inhibited by NaF.

Many antibiotics strikingly inhibit protein synthesis by acting at the level of translation; some prevent the formation of ribosomes from their subunits.[8] (R)

---

[7] The ribosomes in a polyribosome are arranged in a left-handed helix winding at an angle of about 70° around a column 220 Å in diameter.

[8] Streptomycin is reported to act in two ways: (1) inhibition of polypeptide chain initiation by prevention of the union of 30s and 50s to form the 70s ribosome, and (2) inhibition of chain lengthening in less time than it takes to add two amino acids to each active ribosome. Puromycin prevents chain lengthening because, although it looks like Tyr-tRNA at its NH_2 end and can, therefore, make one peptide bond, it has no COOH end to make a second peptide bond and permit the chain to lengthen.

A

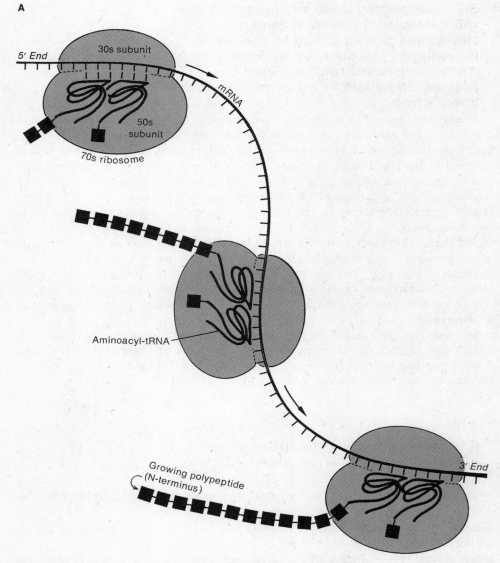

Figure 6-5A Schematic drawing of a polyribosome in *E. coli*. Arrows show the 5′→3′ direction mRNA moves during translation.

6.9   Different mRNA's survive for various lengths of time.

As noted earlier, transcription may be blocked by the drug actinomycin D. Studies of bacteria treated with this drug show that mRNA exists for about 2 to 5 minutes, on the average, before being degraded. The mRNA for hemoglobin, on the other hand, is among those which persist for a longer period (see also Section 30.9). The mechanism by which the nucleic acid is degraded is still unknown, but a ribonuclease[9]

[9] Ribonuclease V, an exonuclease, may be an mRNase since it needs the following to digest mRNA: GTP, ribosomes, translocation factors G and T, and the actual movement of ribosomes down an mRNA. Some evidence indicates that polynucleotide phosphorylase (see Section 5.1) also is able to degrade mRNA, particularly that of RNA phages.

B

Figure 6-5B   Electron micrograph of transcription and translation in *E. coli*. The vertical straight line visualizes bacterial DNA which is being transcribed in the top-toward-bottom direction. The upper arrow indicates a putative DNA-dependent RNA polymerase molecule at or very near the transcription initiation site; the lower arrow indicates a putative DNA-dependent RNA polymerase molecule whose partially completed RNA transcript (seen as a thin side branch) is loaded with ribosomes (seen as black dots) that translate the mRNA behind the polymerase, that is, as soon as the RNA is synthesized. Accordingly, the polyribosome becomes larger as the mRNA lengthens. (This preparation, like that in Figure 6-6, does not visualize the polypeptide chains being synthesized on the ribosomes.) (Courtesy of O. L. Miller, Jr., B. A. Hamkalo, and C. A. Thomas, Jr., 1970. Science, 169: 392. Copyright 1970 by the American Association for the Advancement of Science.)

is thought to be involved; for much, if not all, of a bacteria's RNase is found in latent form attached to the 30s particle. Moreover, in reticulocytes (immature red blood corpuscles), where mRNA shows little turnover, no latent RNase has been found on ribosomes. (R)

6.10   In cells with nucleoli, rRNA is a transcript of genes in the nucleolus organizer region of a chromosome.

Like many other sexually reproducing organisms, *Xenopus laevis* normally has two nucleoli in each nucleus of its *somatic* (body) cells. Each nucleolus is attached to a *nucleolus organizer region*, which occurs in each member of one chromosome pair. An abnormal *Xenopus* may have an "anucleolate" chromosome, apparently defective

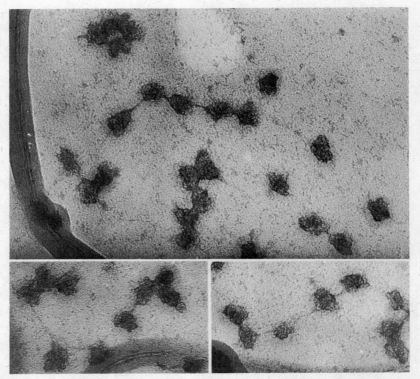

Figure 6-6 Electron micrographs of reticulocyte polyribosomes stained with uranyl acetate showing RNA connecting the ribosomes. (Courtesy of A. Rich.)

in the nucleolus organizer region, since organisms with one or two such chromosomes lack one or both nucleoli.

When no nucleoli are present, cells of the developing individual fail to synthesize rRNA. As we expect, such individuals die early in development because of their inability to make the needed ribosomes. An individual with one nucleolus, however, does produce 18s and 28s rRNA (in fact, as much as an individual with two nucleoli). It appears, therefore, that ribosomal RNA is a transcript of the DNA in the nucleolus organizer region. rRNA–DNA hybridization studies show that most, if not all, of the nucleolus organizer region is missing from anucleolate chromosomes. Since neither 18s nor 28s rRNA is made when both chromosomes in *Xenopus* are anucleolate, the DNA segments for these types of RNA appear to be close together in the same chromosome. Experiments with the fruit fly, *Drosophila*, give similar results.

Since the absence of the nucleolus organizer region has no effect on the amount of DNA that will base-pair with 5s RNA, it is concluded that the DNA transcribed to 5s RNA lies elsewhere in the genome. (R)

6.11   The RNA's in ribosomes of nucleated cells are cleavage products of longer pre-ribosomal RNA transcripts.

Nuclei from HeLa human-tissue culture cells can be fragmented in such a way that the chromosome fraction bearing the nucleolus organizer region of the chromosome

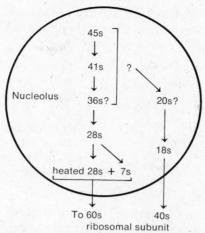

Figure 6-7 Origin of various types of nucleolar RNA in higher organisms. (After R. A. Weinberg, U. Loening, M. Willems, and S. Penman, 1967. Proc. Nat. Acad. Sci., U.S., 58: 1088–1095.)

and its associated nucleolus can be separated by centrifugation from the remaining nuclear chromatin. When the free nucleoli are subsequently subjected to acrylamide gel electrophoresis, RNA's of different sizes migrate at different rates and can be identified. Such studies reveal the metabolic relation between various species of nucleolar RNA. The largest type, 45s, is the precursor whose degradation products include 18s and 28s rRNA (Figure 6-7). 5s RNA also seems to be a cleavage product of a larger (but different) RNA precursor. (In *E. coli* the genes for 16s, 23s, and 5s rRNA seem to be transcribed together, in the sequence given, then degraded to the smaller units.)

The 28s rRNA fraction of HeLa, chick, and hampster cells is found, upon heating, to be composed of a 7s piece of RNA (about 130 nucleotides long) which is base-paired to a larger piece of RNA (about 5,000 nucleotides long) which when heated also is 28s. The 7s and heated 28s RNA's are derived from the same precursor (Figure 6-7). (R)

6.12 Some mRNA's of nucleated cells are cleavage products of longer pre-mRNA transcripts.

The mRNA located in the cytoplasm of nucleated cells is characterized by being about 6 to 30s. It also has a base ratio which reflects that of duplex DNA, in which the A and U as well as C and G residues are nearly equivalent in number. (This equivalence is understandable if a considerable portion of the total DNA sequence is sampled to make mRNA's of reasonable—1 to 3 hours—half-life.) This cytoplasmic mRNA seems to be derived mainly from *informational RNA* in the nucleus.

Informational RNA of the nucleus is characterized by being completely or largely restricted to the nucleus, giant-sized (60 to 90s), short-lived (with about a 30-minute half-life), and having a high-U nucleoside composition. Since it is short-lived, only a relatively small fraction of such RNA samples of DNA sequences exists at any instant, so that, as expected, C and G, for example, are unequal in amount. Over a cell's lifetime, informational RNA is apparently transcribed from many portions of the

DNA sequence. Some of this RNA is restricted to the nucleus; after digestion, some of the smaller fragments leave the nucleus to become cytoplasmic mRNA.[10]

Nuclear informational RNA has been found in

1. *Duck erythroblasts*, where giant 60s RNA yields 10s functional hemoglobin mRNA.

2. *HeLa cells*, where

	A	U	C	G
nuclear infor-mational RNA	21.3	31.0	26.4	21.1
cytoplasmic mRNA	28.0	28.1	24.3	19.5

3. *Chironomus larval salivary gland cells*, where it is manufactured in all nuclear chromosomes.

4. *Mouse liver and kidney cells* during regeneration of these organs.

5. *Bone marrow cells*, which contain 60 to 70s, nonribosomal, pre-mRNA.

6. *Amphibian embryo*.

We see in higher organisms, therefore, that just as rRNA and probably tRNA are shorter derivatives of longer RNA's, that at least some cytoplasmic mRNA's are breakdown products of longer strands of transcribed nuclear informational RNA, or pre-mRNA. Although some (if not all) nuclear informational RNA is pre-mRNA, we do not know the function of the portion that does not leave the nucleus and of the part which is so rich in U. We do not know whether all this RNA is single-stranded or if both complements of a DNA duplex are sometimes transcribed. (R)

6.13 Most proteins synthesized by organisms are translations of nucleic acids in a ribosome–aminoacyl-tRNA system, although some simple proteins are not. Single-stranded DNA can be translated *in vitro*.

The genetic material of single-stranded RNA viruses functions as messenger RNA (see Section 8.6 for an exception) by binding to ribosomes. Subsequently the characteristic protein of a virus (including coat protein and usually RNA-dependent RNA polymerase) is produced. Numerous additional results are consistent with the view that almost all polypeptide synthesis *in vivo* is the result of the translation of single-stranded nucleic acids in the ribosome–aminoacyl-tRNA system. It should be noted, however, that the acidic proteins in the calf thymus nucleus, which contain tryptophan and are associated with the RNA and DNA of chromosomes, may be synthesized by a system different from the ribosomal synthesizing mechanism, since tryptophan incorporation into polypeptides by an acidic protein extract is unaffected by tRNA, rRNA, and RNase.

The biosynthesis of certain antibiotic polypeptides definitely does not require the ribosomal system. For example, *gramicidin* is a decapeptide composed of a repeat of a pentapeptide which is synthesized by enzymes distinct from aminoacyl–tRNA synthetases. In this case, an amino acid is activated by forming a complex with enzyme and AMP (obtained from ATP which has released PP_i). The amino acid is

---

[10] In the case of nucleated cells, it is found that some of the complementary RNA made in the nucleus is used for translation in the cytoplasm. Evidence has been obtained that mRNA (or pre-mRNA) is transported from nuclear chromosome to cytoplasm complexed with a ribosomal subunit (40s presumably) or with protein.

then transferred to an acceptor (another amino acid in this case) and the enzyme and AMP released.

If an *in vitro* ribosome–aminoacyl-tRNA system is exposed to certain antibiotics, such as neomycin, denatured native DNA and certain chemically defined synthetic single-stranded DNA's can act like mRNA and be translated directly. Such single-stranded DNA's, *messenger DNA (mDNA)*, can also be translated directly without treating the system with antibiotic in a ribosome system obtained from calf thymus gland cell nuclei. Circular single-stranded DNA from ϕfd can also act directly as messenger, making long polypeptides when neomycin is present but not when the drug is absent. (Note that messenger nucleic acids do not need a 5' end to attach to a ribosome.) (R)

SUMMARY AND CONCLUSIONS

The great majority of organisms contain, in the base sequence of DNA genetic material, information which is first transcribed to mRNA and then is translated into the amino acid sequences of the various proteins that characterize each organism's individuality. The DNA also contains information for the translation machinery that enables base sequence to specify amino acid sequence. This machinery includes DNA-dependent RNA polymerase; the transcripts this produces—rRNA, 5s RNA, tRNA, as well as mRNA's whose translation produces ribosomal protein; aminoacyl-tRNA synthetases; and other proteins used or needed to produce factors for the initiation, lengthening, and termination of polypeptides. Although organisms (and their characteristic proteins) differ greatly, all employ a basically similar ribosome–tRNA system for the synthesis of all, or almost all, their proteins—that is, polypeptides are ordinarily synthesized at the ribosome in the $NH_2 \rightarrow COOH$ direction by aminoacyl-tRNA's translating mRNA in the 5' to 3' direction. Organisms whose genetic material does not contain information for all this machinery, such as DNA and RNA viruses, make use of their host's, as will be described further in Chapter 8.

Although the translation system is basically the same in all cellular organisms, some evidence indicates that differences occur in the r and tRNA's of different species (the chemical basis for this will again be discussed in Chapter 8). A striking variation occurs at the post-transcriptional level between organisms with and those without a nucleus. Cells with nuclei transcribe long nuclear, informational RNA's which are degraded into the shorter RNA's (t, r, and m) found in the cytoplasm. Evidence of such degradation leading to mRNA seems to be lacking in anuclear organisms such as bacteria. Anuclear as well as nuclear cells do, however, degrade different mRNA's after they have been translated a varying number of times.

The possibilities have not been excluded that significant amounts or types of protein, (1) besides antibiotics such as gramicidin, are synthesized outside the ribosome–tRNA system; and (2) are synthesized within such a system as translations of mDNA.

GENERAL REFERENCES

Anfinsen, C. B. (Editor), 1970. *Aspects of protein biosynthesis.* New York: Academic Press, Inc.

1964. *Synthesis and structure of macromolecules.* Vol. 28. Cold Spring Harbor Sympos. Quant. Biol. New York: Cold Spring Harbor Laboratory of Quantitative Biology.

1970. *The mechanism of protein synthesis.* Vol. 34. Cold Spring Harbor Sympos. Quant. Biol. New York: Cold Spring Harbor Laboratory of Quantitative Biology.

Watson, J. D. 1963. Involvement of RNA in the synthesis of proteins. Science, 140: 17–26. Reprinted in *The biological perspective, introductory readings.* Laetsch, W. M. (Editor), Boston: Little, Brown and Company, 1969, pp. 132–151.

SPECIFIC SECTION REFERENCES

6.1   Gould, H. J. 1970. Proteins of rabbit reticulocyte ribosomal subunits. Nature, Lond., 227: 1145–1147.

Kaltschmidt, E., and Wittmann, H. G. 1970. Ribosomal proteins, XII. Number of proteins in small and large ribosomal subunits of *Escherichia coli* as determined by two-dimensional gel electrophoresis. Proc. Nat. Acad. Sci., U.S., 67: 1276–1282. (There are 21 and 34 detected in the 30s and 50s subunits, respectively.)

Kurland, C. G. 1970. Ribosome structure and function emergent. Science, 169: 1171–1177.

Nomura, M. 1969. Ribosomes. Scient. Amer., 221 (No. 4): 28–35, 148. Scientific American Offprints, San Francisco: W. H. Freeman and Company, Publishers.

Spirin, A. S., and Gavrilova, L. P. 1969. *The ribosome*. Berlin: Springer-Verlag.

6.2   Agarwal, K. L., Büchi, H., Caruthers, M. H., Gupta, N., Khorana, H. G., Kleppe, K., Kumar, A., Ohtsuka, E., Rajbhandary, U. L., Van De Sande, J. H., Sgaramella, V., Weber, H., and Yamada, T. 1970. Total synthesis of the gene for an alanine transfer ribonucleic acid from yeast. Nature, Lond., 227: 27–34.

Bernhardt, D., and Darnell, J. E., Jr., 1969. tRNA synthesis in HeLa cells: a precursor to tRNA and the effects of methionine starvation on tRNA synthesis. J. Mol. Biol., 42: 43–56.

Dube, S. K., Marcker, K. A., and Yudelevich, A. 1970. The nucleotide sequence of a leucine transfer RNA from *E. coli*. FEBS Letters, 9: 168–170. (Its 87 nucleotides makes this tRNA the longest so far sequenced. It makes a four-leafed clover.)

6.4   Dudock, B. S., Katz, G., Taylor, E. K., and Holley, R. W. 1969. Primary structure of wheat germ phenylalanine transfer RNA. Proc. Nat. Acad. Sci., U.S., 62: 941–945.

6.5   Brenner, S., Jacob, F., and Meselson, M. 1961. An unstable intermediate carrying information from genes to ribosomes for protein synthesis. Nature, Lond., 190: 576–581. Reprinted in *Papers on bacterial viruses,* second edition, Stent, G. S. (Editor), Boston: Little, Brown and Company, 1965, pp. 402–409. (An early report of mRNA.)

Geiduschek, E. P., and Haselkorn, R. 1969. Messenger RNA. Ann. Rev. Biochem., 38: 647–676.

Gross, F., Hunt, H., Gilbert, W., Kurland, C. G., Risebrough, R. W., and Watson, J. D. 1961. Unstable ribonucleic acid revealed by pulse labelling. Nature, Lond., 190: 581–585. (An early report of mRNA.)

Hurwitz, J., and Furth, J. J. 1962. Messenger RNA. Scient. Amer., 206 (No. 2): 41–49.

6.6   Dintzis, H. M. 1961. Assembly of the peptide chains of hemoglobin. Proc. Nat. Acad. Sci., U.S., 47: 247–261. Reprinted in *Papers in biochemical genetics*, Zubay, G. L. (Editor), New York: Holt, Rinehart and Winston, Inc., 1968, pp. 282–296.

Goldstein, J., Milman, G., Scolnick, E., and Caskey, T. 1970. Peptide chain termination, VI. Purification and site of action of S. Proc. Nat. Acad. Sci., U.S., 65: 430–437.

Kuechler, E., and Rich, A. 1970. Position of the initiator and peptidyl sites in the *E. coli* ribosome. Nature, Lond., 225: 920–924. (mRNA and newly made polypeptide are located deep in the ribosome.)

Lengyel, P. 1970. The process of translation as seen in 1969. Cold Spring Harbor Sympos. Quant. Biol., 34: 828–841.

6.7   Morse, D. E., Mosteller, R. D., and Yanofsky, C. 1970. Dynamics of synthesis, translation, and degradation of *trp* operon messenger RNA in *E. coli*. Cold Spring Harbor Sympos. Quant. Biol., 34: 725–739.

Rich, A. 1963. Polyribosomes. Scient. Amer., 209 (No. 6): 44–53, 178. Scientific American Offprints, San Francisco: W. H. Freeman and Company, Publishers.

Weiss, P., and Grover, N. B. 1968. Helical array of polyribosomes. Proc. Nat. Acad. Sci., U.S., 59: 763–768.

6.8.   Colombo, B., Vesco, C., and Baglioni, C. 1968. Role of ribosomal subunits in protein synthesis in mammalian cells. Proc. Nat. Acad. Sci., U.S., 61: 651–658.

Kaempfer, R. O. R., Meselson, M., and Raskas, H. J. 1968. Cyclic dissociation into stable subunits and re-formation of ribosomes during bacterial growth. J. Mol. Biol., 31: 277–289.

Modelell, J., and Davis, B. D. 1968. Rapid inhibition of polypeptide chain extension by streptomycin. Proc. Nat. Acad. Sci., U.S., 61: 1279–1286.

6.9   Kuwano, M., Schlessinger, D., and Apirion, D. 1970. Ribonuclease V of *Escherichia coli* requires ribosomes and is inhibited by drugs. Nature, Lond., 226: 514–516. (This enzyme digests mRNA, but not rRNA, in the 5′-3′ direction, and requires active translation for its action.)

McClatchy, J. K., and Rickenberg, H. V. 1967. Heterogeneity of the stability of messenger ribonucleic acid in *Salmonella typhimurium*. J. Bact., 93: 115–121.

6.10 Brown, D. D., and Gurdon, J. B. 1964. Absence of ribosomal RNA synthesis in the anucleolate mutant of *Xenopus laevis*. Proc. Nat. Acad. Sci., U.S., 51: 139–146.

Brown, D. D., and Weber, C. S. 1968. Gene linkage by RNA–DNA hybridization. I. Unique DNA sequences homologous to 4s RNA, 5s RNA, and ribosomal RNA. J. Mol. Biol., 34: 661–680.

6.11 Doolittle, W. F., and Pace, N. R. 1971. Transcriptional organization of the ribosomal RNA cistrons in *Escherichia coli*. Proc. Nat. Acad. Sci., U.S., 68: 1786–1790. (Supports the view that the genes for 16s-23s-5s are transcribed together, in this sequence, then degraded to the smaller units.)

Leaver, C. J., and Key, J. L. 1970. Ribosomal RNA synthesis in plants. J. Mol. Biol., 49: 671–680. (Cytoplasmic rRNA is produced by selective cleavage of larger pre-rRNA molecules.)

Perry, R. P. 1967. The nucleolus and the synthesis of ribosomes. Progr. Nucleic Acid Res. and Mol. Biol., 6: 219–257.

Rogers, M. E., Loening, U. E., and Fraser, R. S. S. 1970. Ribosomal RNA precursors in plants. J. Mol. Biol., 49: 681–692.

6.12 Daneholt, B., and Svedhem, L. 1971. Differential representation of chromosomal HRNA in nuclear sap. Exp. Cell Res., 67: 263–272. (80–90s nuclear RNA is found in *Chironomus*.)

Davidson, E. H. 1968. *Gene activity in early development*, pp. 308–312. New York: Academic Press, Inc.

Willems, M., Musilova, H. A., and Malt, R. A. 1969. Giant nucleoplasmic RNA in the switch-on of compensatory renal growth. Proc. Nat. Acad. Sci., U.S., 62: 1189–1194.

6.13 Bretscher, M. S. 1970. Ribosome initiation and the mode of action of neomycin in the direct translation of single-stranded fd DNA. Cold Spring Harbor Sympos. Quant. Biol., 34: 651–653.

Lipmann, F. 1971. Attempts to map a process evolution of peptide biosynthesis. Science, 173: 875–884. (Synthesis of certain polypeptide antibiotics is enzymatic but does not use m or tRNA or ribosomes.)

SUPPLEMENTARY SECTION

S6.7   In *E. coli* a fixed number of about 20 closely packed ribosomes can translate a particular mRNA in a wave just behind the transcriptase, the transcription and translation proceeding at about 1,000 nucleotides per minute.

Under appropriate conditions, the addition of indole-3-proprionic acid to the culture medium of *E. coli* causes the initiation of synthesis of an mRNA, about 8,700 nucleotides long, whose translation produces five specific enzymes needed for the synthesis of tryptophan. The addition of large amounts of tryptophan prevents further initiations of this transcription, although "tryptophan" mRNA's whose synthesis was already begun are completed. Determination of the amount of two of the specific enzymes produced

at different times reveals the following temporal relationships between transcription and translation.

Soon or immediately after the start of transcription by the transcriptase—other studies show that DNA-dependent RNA polymerase transcribes at the rate of approximately 1,000 nucleotides per minute—the partially synthesized mRNA is continuously loaded until after about 25 seconds it bears a cluster of about 20 ribosomes, the first ribosome of this polysome being close behind the polymerase, which is at the growing point of the mRNA (Figure 6-8). (About the time the ribosomes have been loaded on the mRNA, a new mRNA synthesis is initiated.) No more ribosomes attach to the first mRNA, those attached proceeding to translate it at a uniform speed of about 1,350 nucleotides per minute and require about 6.5 minutes for the complete transit. The mRNA is apparently degraded at the 5′ end by exonuclease before the 3′ end is synthesized.

Such a degradation (see Section 6.9) explains the lack of ribosome attachment at the 5′ end soon after the initiation of mRNA synthesis.

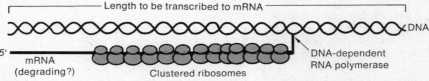

Figure 6-8 Transcription and translation at about 3 minutes from the initiation of transcription of "tryptophan" mRNA in *E. coli*. The mRNA is about half-synthesized. The ribosomes (about 20) are clustered close together just after the DNA-dependent RNA polymerase, ribosome attachment at the 5′ end having ceased some time earlier.

QUESTIONS AND PROBLEMS

1. Isolated protein-synthesizing ribosomes sometimes have DNA "attached." Explain the presence of this DNA and its mode of attachment to the ribosome.

2. Design an experiment which shows that protein is synthesized in the cytoplasm; in the nucleus.

3. How many different sizes of RNA are found in ribosomes? How are these related in their origin?

4. Knowing that the DNA-containing vaccinia virus replicates in the cytoplasm of human-tissue culture cells, design an experiment to show that mRNA can be made from a cytoplasmic DNA template.

5. The DNA of HeLa human-tissue culture cells can be collected, fragmented, and separated into two portions: with and without attached nucleoli. How would you test these portions for the presence of DNA complementary to rRNA? What results would you expect?

6. Design an experiment to show that synthesis of polypeptide chains begins at the N-terminal end.

7. List the elements needed for translation in *E. coli*.

8. State one evidence that the genes for rRNA of different species differ in the sequence or the number of bases.

9. Define the term "messenger nucleic acid."

10. Would you expect an artificial amino acid—one not found in protein—to be transported by tRNA? Explain.

11. What can you conclude from each of the following observations:
    a. Small amounts of RNase cannot destroy the RNA in ribosomes, but can digest part of ribosome-attached mRNA.
    b. When polypeptide-synthesizing ribosomes are treated with RNase, the protein being synthesized remains attached to the ribosome.
    c. Under a variety of *in vitro* conditions, the rate of protein synthesis is proportional to ribosome concentration.
    d. Although the ribosomal RNA's from *Pseudomonas aeruginosa* and *Bacillus megatarium* are indistinguishable, the DNA is 64 per cent dG + dC in the former, and 44 percent in the latter.

12. Discuss the hypothesis that ribosomes are viruses.

13. Since 17 leucine molecules occur in reticulocyte hemoglobin, how can you explain J. R. Warner's finding an average of 7.4 leucine molecules per ribosome in a polysome synthesizing hemoglobin protein?

14. To what do you attribute the difference between polysomes composed of 5 or 6 ribosomes (in reticulocytes making hemoglobin protein) and 50 to 70 ribosomes (in a mammalian cell infected by poliomyelitis virus)?

15. Although the average cell of the adult rat liver probably divides less often than once a year, it synthesizes an amount of protein equivalent to its own content every 6 or so days. In bacteria, on the other hand, the time required to double the protein content is roughly equal to the generation time. Compare the turnover of messenger RNA in bacteria with that expected in adult rat liver cells.

16. When native RNase is treated with urea and sulfhydryl reagents, its disulfide bands are broken and the enzyme unfolds into an inactive linear form. When O_2 is bubbled slowly through a solution of this denatured enzyme, the disulfide bonds reform and enzymatic activity resumes. What do these results tell you about the genetic basis for the folding of polypeptides?

17. How might you obtain DNA which, if it could be visualized, appears "cloverleaf"?

Chapter 7

The Code for Translation

The translational information present in mRNA must reside exclusively, or primarily, in the sequence of its organic bases (see Section 2.11). A single nucleotide, nucleoside, or organic base of ribosome-bound mRNA cannot correspond to a single amino acid, however, since the usual four bases could correspond to, or code for, only 4 amino acids, and translation must account for the specification of some 20 amino acids. The nucleoside "letters" of mRNA—A, U, C, G—must, therefore, be grouped into "words" so that translation into the language of proteins may occur. Let us consider now the size of a "word," or coding unit, or *codon*, of a messenger nucleic acid—that segment which base-pairs with an aminoacyl-tRNA. The codons for translation *in vitro* will be discussed before considering those *in vivo* later in the chapter.

7.1 Synthetic polyribonucleotides used as mRNA are translated into polypeptides in an *in vitro* ribosome–aminoacyl-tRNA system.

We can study the mechanism of protein synthesis *in vitro* by using the following cell-free system: a suspension of ruptured *E. coli* cells, 5'-triphosphates of A, G, C, and U, and the 20 amino acids usually found in protein (Figure 7-1). When radioactively labeled amino acids are added to the system, we can readily detect incorporation into polypeptides. If RNase or DNase is added, the synthesis is stopped. Evidently the RNase stops the synthesis by degrading the mRNA present in the *E. coli* suspension, so genetic information is no longer available to be read. The DNase acts by degrading DNA so that no new mRNA can be made.

Since the mRNA present in the *in vitro* system is responsible for directing polypeptide synthesis, it is interesting to see the effect of adding synthetic polyribonucleotides of known composition to the system as synthetic mRNA. When poly U is added, phenylalanine is incorporated into protein, and a polypeptide consisting only of phenylalanines (polyphenylalanine) is produced. Hence, we conclude that some sequence of U's codes for phenylalanine *in vitro*.

When poly U is mixed with poly A so that the two strands base-pair with each other, the amount of phenylalanine incorporated is diminished. The synthetic messenger thus seems to be most effective *in vitro* when it is single-stranded, as we expect of mRNA *in vivo*. When single-stranded poly A is used in the *in vitro* system, polylysine is produced; when poly C is used, polyproline is made. Poly G does not work well as messenger in this system. Its effectiveness is reduced probably because G–G interactions that occur when the polymer folds back on itself interfere with the ability of guanine to base-pair with cytosine in a tRNA.

Polyribonucleotides containing two, three, or four different ribonucleotides can also be synthesized[1] and tested *in vitro* for their effects on amino acid incorporation into

---

[1] We recall from Section 5.1 that the enzyme which catalyzes the synthesis of such mixed polymers, polynucleotide phosphorylase, arranges the bases linearly in a random array.

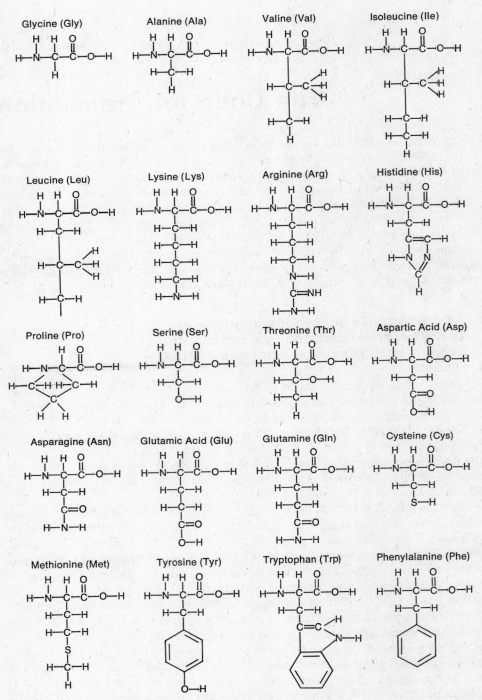

Figure 7-1 Twenty of the most common amino acids.

protein. Some amino acids require the presence of two different nucleotides in the synthetic polynucleotide in order to be incorporated. Consequently, the codon must contain at least two nucleotides. No amino acid requires the presence of all four types of organic bases in the synthetic polynucleotide for incorporation. Hence, we hypothesize that either doublets or triplets of synthetic mRNA nucleotides are translated into amino acids. In other words, the *in vitro* codon is either a doublet or a triplet.

When poly dA, poly dT, poly (dC-dA), and poly (dT-dG), are used directly as mDNA in an *in vitro* system treated with neomycin (see Section 6.13), the same amino acids are incorporated as when the corresponding RNA polymer is used as mRNA, except for occasional mistakes and the complete failure of poly dA to serve as messenger. (R)

7.2   The *in vitro* codon is a triplet whose base sequence can be determined by the binding of specific aminoacyl-tRNA's to ribosomes carrying specific ribonucleotide triplets. Codons are read unidirectionally.

The incorporation of amino acids into protein *in vitro* requires that long polynucleotides (for example, a poly U of 500 to 1,000 nucleotides) be used as messenger. It is not surprising, therefore, that a single dinucleotide or trinucleotide cannot stimulate amino acid incorporation. However, short polyribonucleotides can be synthesized (or isolated) and tested *in vitro* for their ability to cause the binding of specific aminoacyl-tRNA's to ribosomes. (By convention, a triribonucleotide of U with a 3'-terminal phosphate is represented as UpUpUp and one with a 5'-terminal phosphate, pUpUpU.) When pUpUpU, pApApA, and pCpCpC are tested, they are found to direct the binding of Phe-, Lys-, and Pro-tRNA, respectively. Dinucleotides bring about no binding.[2] The simplest explanation for these results is that *in vitro* codons are triplets.

Since a polynucleotide containing U and G in random sequence, poly (U,G), incorporates valine into protein, the codon for valine includes U and G. The order of the bases in the codon can be investigated by using poly (U,G), dinucleotides, the trinucleoside diphosphate GpUpU, and its sequence isomers UpGpU and UpUpG. The binding of radioactive ^{14}C-Val-tRNA to ribosomes is found to be directed both by poly (U,G) and GpUpU but not by UpGpU, UpUpG or dinucleotides. Moreover, the binding of Val-tRNA is specific—GpUpU has no effect on the tRNA's of 17 other amino acids. From these results, we conclude that a codon is read undirectionally, that one for valine is GUU, and that Val-tRNA apparently carries the complementary *anticodon* CAA (AAC, when read from the 5'- toward the 3'- end of the tRNA). The anticodon is a triplet of bases in the loop of the tRNA cloverleaf opposite the termini (see Figures 7-2, 3-10, and 3-15). (R)

---

[2] An additional finding is that trinucleotides with a 5'-terminal phosphate are more active than those missing a 5'-terminal phosphate. Trinucleotides with a 3'- (or 2'-) terminal phosphate are also inactive.

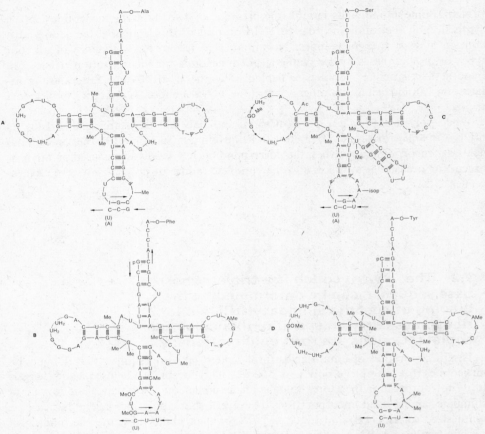

Figure 7-2 Complete structure of transfer RNA's of yeast. (A) Ala-tRNA; (B) Phe-tRNA; (C) Ser-tRNA (two species); (D) Tyr-tRNA. In each instance the proposed anticoding triplet in the bottom loop is shown in complementary juxtaposition to possible messenger coding triplets, arrows showing 5′-3′ direction. *Indicates suggested deletion of bases in Ser-tRNA; Ψ, pseudouridine; A-isop, 6-aminoisopentenyladenosine; I, inosine; Me, methyl. (After T. H. Jukes, 1966. Biochem. Biophys. Res. Commun., 24: 744.)

7.3 *In vitro* codons for all amino acids are known. The code for translation is degenerate. Some triplets code for no amino acid (that is, are nonsense codons); some are ambiguous under special circumstances.

From studies such as those described above, the *in vitro* coding ability of all 64 triplets of the general type BpBpB, where each B can be A, U, C, or G, has been determined (Figure 7-3). We note from the table that the code is *degenerate*; that is, more than one triplet can be translated as the same amino acid. The major degeneracy occurs at the third position, the 3′ end of the codon triplet. For example, when the first two bases are specified, the same amino acid may be coded for whether the third base is (1) U, C, A, or G (G*U*U, G*U*C, G*U*A, and G*U*G, for example, all code for valine), (2) either pyrimidine (both AG*U* and AG*C* code for serine), or (3) either purine (both CA*A* and CA*G* code for glutamic acid). Degeneracy may also occur in

SECOND RIBONUCLEOSIDE

FIRST RIBONUCLEOSIDE	U	C	A	G	THIRD RIBONUCLEOSIDE
U	○UUU ⎫ Phe .UUC ⎭ .UUA○★ ⎫ Leu ○UUG ⎭	UCU ⎫ .UCC ⎪ Ser ○★UCA ⎪ .UCG★ ⎭	○★UAU ⎫ Tyr .UAC ⎭ UAA non UAG non	UGU○★ ⎫ Cys UGC○ ⎭ UGA non ○.UGG Trp	U C A G
C	★CUU○ ⎫ CUC ⎪ Leu CUA ⎪ ○CUG ⎭	CCU ⎫ CCC ⎪ Pro ★.CCA ⎪ CCG ⎭	CAU★ ⎫ His CAC○★ ⎭ ○CAA ⎫ Gln ○★CAG ⎭	.CGU ⎫ CGC ⎪ Arg ○CGA ⎪ CGG○ ⎭	U C A G
A	.AUU○ ⎫ AUC ⎪ Ile AUA○★ ⎭ .AUG○★ Met	.ACU ⎫ ○ACC ⎪ Thr ACA○ ⎪ .ACG ⎭	★.AAU○★ ⎫ Asn .AAC○ ⎭ ○★AAA ⎫ Lys AAG○★ ⎭	★AGU ⎫ Ser AGC○ ⎭ AGA○ ⎫ Arg AGG★ ⎭	U C A G
G	GUU★ ⎫ GUC○★ ⎪ Val GUA○★ ⎪ GUG○★ ⎭	.GCU ⎫ GCC○ ⎪ Ala GCA○ ⎪ .GCG ⎭	GAU ⎫ Asp GAC ⎭ ○.GAA ⎫ Glu ○GAG ⎭	GGU○ ⎫ GGC○ ⎪ Gly ○GGA ⎪ GGG ⎭	U C A G

Figure 7-3 *In vitro* mRNA codons for amino acids. non, nonsense or chain-terminating codons; ambiguities are not indicated; *in vivo* codons in normal φR17 (·), *E. coli* (○), and φT4 (×) indicated to the left of codon; *in vivo* mutant codons indicated to the right of codon.

the first position. Arginine is coded by *A*GA and by *C*GA; leucine by *C*UG and *U*UG.

Three triplets (UAA, UAG, and UGA) do not code for any amino acid *in vitro*, or do so only under certain conditions. Such "no-amino-acid sense" or *nonsense* codons seem to have another informational function—to serve as signals to stop the translation of mRNA. As mentioned in Section 6.8, polypeptide chain termination in *E. coli* needs three soluble factors: S or T, R1, and R2. R1 recognizes UAA and UAG; R2 recognizes UAA and UGA.

The *in vitro* code is sometimes *ambiguous*; that is, a single codon may be translated into different amino acids. Although UUU is translated into phenylalanine under "usual" *in vitro* conditions, it is also translated into isoleucine and to a lesser extent serine and leucine when the ribosome is treated with streptomycin. Low temperature, ethyl alcohol, or high Mg^{2+} ion concentration also causes ambiguity. It has been found that a single protein in the 30s subunit, P10, is responsible for inhibition of protein synthesis (see the footnote to Section 6.8) as well as misreading of codons when ribosomes are exposed to streptomycin, certain other antibiotics, ethyl alcohol, or high Mg^{2+} concentrations. (R)

7.4   Since the base in the first position of the anticodon is often able to base-pair with more than one base in the third position of the codon, base pairing between these positions shows "wobble," and degeneracy is observed in the third position of the codon.

As seen in Figure 7-2 the first position of the anticodon apparently is often occupied by an unusual ribonucleoside; for example, by inosine (I) in the case of Ala-tRNA,

Ser-tRNA, and, although not shown, Val-tRNA; and by 2′-O-methylguanosine (containing methylated ribose; see Figure 8-5) in the case of a Phe-tRNA. Since the anticodon of Ala-tRNA (IGC) can recognize three codons *in vitro* (GCU, GCC, and GCA), it is reasoned that extraordinary base pairs can form by H bonding between the first position of the anticodon and the third position of the codon. That such "wobble" base pairings may be possible at this position but not at the other two is supported by the tertiary structure of tRNA (see Figure 3-15), where the first anticodon position is located at the apex of the molecule. The standard and wobble base pairings for the pairing of the codon and the anticodon at the third codon position are shown in Figure 7-4 and also in Figure 7-2. The *wobble hypothesis*, therefore, explains a considerable portion of the degeneracy found at the third codon position *in vitro*. (R)

7.5 Genetic changes can produce sense, missense, and nonsense codons.

Despite the rupture and fragmentation of *E. coli* in the production of *in vitro* synthesizing systems, the *in vitro* transcription and translation processes seem to accurately reflect these processes *in vivo*. For when phage T4 DNA is placed in an *E. coli* system *in vitro*, transcription and translation will produce two enzymes coded in the phage DNA, T4 β-glucosyl transferase and T4 lysozyme. What would be the expected translational consequences, *in vitro* and *in vivo*, of the addition or subtraction of a single nucleotide in such phage (or other genetic) DNA's? In each case there would be a corresponding change in the mRNA, causing the mRNA triplet codons for that region to be read out of phase. For example, with a deletion of b, the message abc def g. . . . . becomes acd efg . . . . The mRNA triplets that the tRNA's now read include nucleotides from triplets which previously had been in adjacent codons.

The triplets that result after such a phase shift (change in reading frame, or *frameshift* change) fall into three categories (Figure 7-5): (1) *sense* codons, which are translated into the same amino acid because the new triplet is identical or synonomous

Ribonucleoside

Anticodon	Codon
U	A G
C	G
A	U
G	U C
I	U C A

Figure 7-4 Normal and wobble base pairs between the codon and anticodon in the first anticodon position.

	5'Original 3'			
	...GGG	UGU	NNN	NNN ...
	... Gly	Cys	X	X ...

Single nucleoside addition producing

1. Sense	...GGG	UGU	UNN	NNN ...
or	...GGG	UGC	UNN	NNN ...
	... Gly	Cys	X	X ...
2. Missense	...GGG	UGG	UNN	NNN ...
	... Gly	Trp	X	X ...
3. Nonsense	...GGG	UGA	UNN	NNN ...
	... Gly	Non		

Figure 7-5 Types of codons produced by insertion of a single nucleoside (underlined) in mRNA. The translational product is indicated below each mRNA sequence. N, any nucleoside; X, any amino acid; Non, polypeptide chain termination.

with the old one; (2) *missense* codons, which are translated into a different amino acid; and (3) *nonsense* codons, which are translated into no amino acid and are, therefore, translation terminators. Although sense codon change produces no chemical change in the coded protein, missense and nonsense codons produce chemically changed protein of normal and shorter lengths, respectively, whose functional effect depends upon the nature and location of the changes in the protein. Thus, a nonsense codon appearing near the 3' end of an mRNA for a protein (and permitting the synthesis of almost the entire protein before acting as a terminator) is expected to produce less of a detrimental effect on the functioning of the protein than one appearing near the 5' end of the mRNA (and permitting synthesis of only the N-terminal portion of the protein).

7.6   Messenger RNA is translated unidirectionally in successive triplet codons *in vivo*.

Phage T4 has also been used extensively and productively to study the nature and consequences of the genetic code *in vivo*. One region of T4 DNA is of particular interest to us, because it has been used to demonstrate *in vivo* much of what was already found *in vitro*.

The *rII* region of T4 DNA is composed of two adjacent polypeptide-coding genes, *A* and *B*. Genetic changes can be induced at different sites in the *B* gene by chemical agents such as acridine dyes, which act by causing the addition (+) or loss (−) of one or more whole nucleotides (the mechanism of this is discussed in Section 9.5). Such changes can produce missense and nonsense codons that result in no functional product for gene *B*.

If acridines induce changes as described above, + − or − + doubly defective organisms might have some functional *B* activity (provided that the two defects in the *B* gene are near each other and no nonsense codons occur between the two defects), since the reading of nucleotides placed out of phase by the defect nearest the 5' end of the mRNA should once more be in phase due to the compensating defect nearer the 3' end. Such phages do indeed possess some *B* function (Figure 7.6). In this example one gene defect is suppressed by a separate defect in the same gene; that is, the defect produced second acts as an *internal suppressor* of the first defect. It should be possible, moreover, to increase the number of defects of the same type (all − or all +) until the number of nucleotides subtracted from or added to the *B* gene equals the number in a codon. At this point, the nucleotides beyond the last defective codon would again be in phase for correct translation, and some *B* activity might be restored. Accordingly, phages carrying two, three, four, five, and even six different − (or +) defects in the *B* gene have been constructed. Some of the three or six − (or +) defectives do have *B* activity; the combination of four − and one + also shows *B* activity. No activity is found, however, if the defects fail to add up to three or an integral multiple of three.

These results demonstrate that *in vivo* mRNA contains no punctuation in its sequence of amino acid–coding nucleotides; the nucleotides are used in successive, nonoverlapping, groups; and a codon is most probably three successive nucleotides. Other support for the code being nonoverlapping and triplet *in vivo* comes from the following physical evidence: (1) that α and β chains in hemoglobin, about 150 amino acids long, are each coded by an mRNA of approximately 450 nucleotides; and (2) the protein coat of the satellite tobacco necrosis virus (STNV), approximately 300 amino acids long, is coded by a single-stranded genetic RNA of about 1,000 nucleotides.

One particular strain of φT4, carrying deletion number 1589, lacks adjacent parts of both the *A* and *B* genes (Figure 7-6). Phages with this deletion show no *A* activity

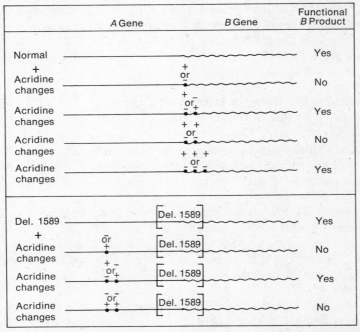

Figure 7-6 Effect of acridine-induced changes in the *A* and *B* genes of the *rII* region of φT4 on functional product of gene *B*. Brackets show portions of *A* and *B* lost in deletion 1589.

but partial *B* activity. When single + (or −) acridine-induced defects in the *A* region are introduced into deletion 1589 phages, the partial *B* activity is always lost. In other words, the partial activity of the *B* gene is stopped by defects in the *A* gene. (When deletion 1589 phage are made doubly defective in the *A* region, some + − double defects can, but − − or + + combinations cannot, maintain partial *B* activity.) These findings show that in a deletion 1589 phage, if the reading is out of phase due to a nucleotide addition or subtraction in *A*, all subsequent codons (that is, those in gene *B*) will be misread. (Thus, deletion 1589 "connects" the *A* and *B* genes.) These results and others prove that the codons in *rII* mRNA are always read unidirectionally—from *A* to *B*.

7.7   Many of the codons *in vitro* have already been proved to have the same amino acid meanings *in vivo*.

Codons used *in vivo* have been identified two ways: (1) by comparing amino acid sequences, before and after frame-shift changes, with possible *in vitro* codon sequences; and (2) by aligning a known amino acid sequence with a known nucleotide sequence to make the best fit using *in vitro* codons.

Changes in amino acid sequence

An internal change in the sequence of amino acids in a protein can be due to two frame-shift changes in the genetic material coding for the protein—for example, the first change can be a deletion of a nucleotide and the second the addition of one some distance away. Figure 7-7 shows a change in the sequence of five amino acids in the protein lysozyme coded by such a doubly defective phage. A study of the *in vitro* codons of Figure 7-3 reveals that these missense changes are explained most simply by sequence 2 having a deletion of the DNA coding for A at the left and an insertion of DNA coding for G about 15 nucleotides later to the right. The assignment of unique base sequences for the two amino acid sequences permits one to recognize that 9 of the *in vitro* codons designate the same amino acids *in vivo*.[3]

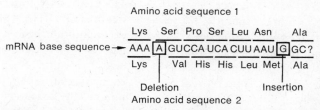

Figure 7-7   Identifying codons *in vivo* using a double phase-shift change in the gene coding for lysozyme that causes the amino acids to change from sequence 1 to sequence 2. Horizontal arrow shows direction of reading the mRNA.

[3] It should be noted that the five codons known for the normal phage (see Figure 7-3) end in A or U—the phage having an adenine–thymine-rich DNA; on the other hand, the five codons known for normal *E. coli* (also entered in Figure 7-3) end in all four possibilities—the bacterium having DNA in which all four bases are equally frequent.

Alignment of amino acid and nucleotide sequences

Phage R17 is an *E. coli* RNA virus of some 3,300 nucleotides. The RNA codes for only three proteins; one is the phage coat protein whose amino acid sequence is known. Using the *in vitro* code one can write a set of possible nucleotide sequences corresponding to the amino acid sequence of the coat protein. When this sequence is compared with the base sequence of a pure portion of the RNA of the phage, it is clear that this fraction of the RNA codes for a specific part of the coat protein (amino acids 82 through 99) (Figure 7-8). The 17 codons used *in vivo* are also entered in Figure 7-3. Since four amino acids are each specified by two codons, the phage code is degenerate. All these *in vivo* codons have the same translational meanings they have *in vitro*.

The nucleotides in this segment of the phage genetic material show secondary structure (see Figure 3-11, where the phasing of the codons is indicated by dots). Since the third position is often degenerate *in vitro*, it is interesting that the alternative chosen *in vivo* is the one that makes a base pair, even though the degenerate *in vitro* code would permit base substitutions to remove two thirds of these base pairs without changing the amino acid. Perhaps maximum base pairs is one of the functions of degeneracy *in vivo*. (R)

7.8   A significant portion of the degeneracy in the *in vivo* code is explained by different codons binding different tRNA's carrying the same amino acid.

It has been found that the frequency of some amino acids in the protein of different organisms remains nearly constant even though the $(dA + dT)/(dC + dG)$ ratio varies greatly. This finding suggests that the *in vivo* code must contain more than one triplet for each of these amino acids; that is, it must be degenerate. Although the wobble hypothesis is expected to apply *in vivo*, explaining some degeneracy, the possibility exists that the *in vivo* code is also degenerate because the tRNA's are—that is, different codons are served not merely by a single wobbly tRNA but by different tRNA's carrying the same amino acid. This possibility is supported by the following three lines of evidence.

1. Leu-tRNA of *E. coli* can be separated into three types, each with different coding properties *in vitro* and, presumably, *in vivo*. The first type responds preferentially to poly (U,G), the second type preferentially to poly (U,C), and the third to poly U and copolymers rich in U, including poly (U,C).

The discovery that leucine is carried by different tRNA's provides an explanation of how six different triplets can code for the same amino acid, the wobble hypothesis explaining at most three codons and none of the degeneracy in the first two positions of a codon.

2. Two different Leu-tRNA's

CA UGG CGU UCG UAC UUA AAU AUG GAA UUA ACU AUU CCA AUU UUC GCU ACG AAC UCC G
···Ala · Ala · Try · Arg · Ser · Tyr · Leu · Asn · Met · Glu · Leu · Thr · Ile · Pro · Ile · Phe · Ala · Thr · Asn · Ser · Asp ···
80   90   100

Figure 7-8 Nucleotide sequence of a fragment from the coat protein gene of ϕR17 RNA, indicating the corresponding amino acid sequence of the coat protein. (See J. M. Adams, P. G. N. Jeppesen, F. Sanger, and B. G. Barrell, 1969.)

contribute leucine to separate sites in a chain of hemoglobin synthesized *in vitro*, indicating that each tRNA also responds to a distinct codon *in vivo*. Similar results have been obtained with two Ser-tRNA's. In one case the degeneracy is proved to reside in different anticodons; the same Ser-tRNA synthetase charges both types of Ser tRNA.

3. Since 29 tRNA's specific for 16 amino acids have been detected in *E. coli* and up to now about 60 different tRNA's have been isolated, it appears that tRNA degeneracy *in vivo* is ordinarily extensive. (R)

7.9 The *in vivo* code may be occasionally degenerate because of translational errors.

Two kinds of errors made at the translational level can also result in degeneracy (Figure 7-9A, where Leu has acquired a new codon in each case). In one case, a nonwobble base-pairing error is made (and Leu replaces Phe); in the other, an amino-acyl-tRNA synthetase places the wrong amino acid on a tRNA (and Leu replaces Phe). Such degeneracies would only be occasional—being part of the background of metabolic errors in amino acid sequence of proteins originating in errors at the translational level.

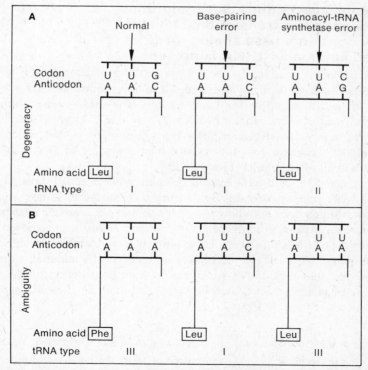

Figure 7-9 Several possible types of abnormal nonwobble degeneracy and ambiguity. The examples of degeneracy are also examples of ambiguity since they involve codons for phenyl-alanine.

7.10   The *in vivo* code may be occasionally, perhaps routinely, ambiguous.

After certain changes in ribosomes (see Section 7.3), a given codon may be translated *in vitro* into different amino acids on different occasions. This ambiguity can result, for example, if the wrong tRNA anticodon base-pairs with the mRNA (Figure 7-9B). The UUU codon, for example, is translated *in vitro* both by Phe-tRNA and one type of Leu-tRNA. Ambiguity can also result if the aminoacyl-tRNA synthetase makes an error and links an incorrect amino acid to the tRNA. One such error occurs when a Phe-tRNA synthetase of *Neurospora crassa* attaches phenylalanine to the wrong tRNA of *E. coli*. Degeneracy and ambiguity go together when, in response to a given codon, one amino acid is substituted for another.[4]

The factors causing ambiguity *in vitro* would presumably also operate if they occur *in vivo*. Determinations of amino acid sequence in a polypeptide of hemoglobin in the rabbit and mouse suggest that significant ambiguity may occur *in vivo*; even when this polypeptide is apparently coded by a normal gene, an amino acid normally present at a given position is sometimes replaced by another having a similar codon *in vitro*. Proof of routinely occurring ambiguities *in vivo* needs further support and confirmation. (R)

7.11   Nonsense codons can sometimes make sense at the translational level if (1) they contain a base analog, or (2) a modified aminoacyl-tRNA is present.

When 5-fluorouracil is added to the culture medium of *E. coli*, it is sometimes incorporated into mRNA being synthesized. Since 5-fluorouridine (fU) is similar in structure to U, it can substitute for U. When this *base-analog* substitution occurs, there is a much greater chance that a tRNA will "mistake" fU for C than if U were present. If, for instance, the original triplet is UAA (a nonsense codon, which prevents translation of the messenger past that point), then a reading of fUAA as CAA, a sense codon, will allow translation to continue.

The RNA phage f2 uses the translation machinery of its *E. coli* host to produce the coat and other proteins it codes. Some genetically variant ϕf2 have a particular nonsense codon which does not allow the phage to make a complete coat protein in certain strains of *E. coli*; in other, genetically different, *E. coli* strains, however, complete phage coat protein is produced. These latter bacterial strains are able to "suppress" the nonsense triplet of the phage because their genetic material codes for the synthesis of a new aminoacyl-tRNA which can, at least sometimes, read the nonsense triplet as sense or missense. Such bacteria, we say, contain an *external suppressor* of the phage nonsense codon. (R)

---

[4] Amino acid substitution may occasionally occur following an error of transcription. If, for example, a DNA duplex has the sequence $\frac{dTdTdT}{dAdAdA}$ and instead of UUU the mRNA synthesized is UUG through a transcriptional error, the end result (of a correct translation) would be a substitution of Leu for Phe.

7.12   In *E. coli* the mRNA segment coding for each polypeptide apparently starts with the initiator codon AUG which is translated into N-formyl-methionine; subsequent noninitiator AUG codons are translated into methionine.

We have already noted in Section 7.3 that termination of a polypeptide results when any one of three nonsense codons is present. The existence of terminator codons suggests that there may also be special codons for initiation of a polypeptide. We shall consider now evidence for such initiator codons.

In an *in vivo* synthesis, the coat protein of normal ϕf2 and the fragment of coat protein produced by ϕf2 with a nonsense codon both start (at the N terminus) with the amino acid sequence Ala-Ser-Asn-Phe-. When the synthesis occurs *in vitro*, however, this sequence is preceded by *N-formylmethionine (fMet)*, that is, methionine with

$$\overset{\text{O}}{\underset{\|}{}}$$

a formyl (—C—H) group[5] attached to the amino group. This result suggests that, at least in *E. coli*, all polypeptides synthesized start with *N*-formylmethionine, which is subsequently digested enzymatically (either the entire fMet or just the formyl group is removed).

Two Met-tRNA's are known that differ in a number of bases and hence tertiary conformation. Met-tRNA$_F$ with anticodon CAU can be formylated; Met-tRNA$_M$ with anticodon C$^+$AU (where C$^+$ is probably N$_4$-acetylated C) cannot. These results indicate that a unique mRNA sequence signals the initiation of all polypeptide chains made in *E. coli*. The initiator or start signal is the codon for methionine, AUG, (or GUG), to which only formylated or to-be-formylated Met-tRNA$_F$ responds (see Figure 6-4). Only Met-tRNA$_M$, on the other hand, responds to AUG located internally in an mRNA segment coding for a polypeptide. Since the *N*-formylmethionine incorporated at the N terminus has a blocked amino group, the formation of a peptide bond with the carboxyl group of another amino acid is prevented.[6]

Among the important consequences of the above findings are (1) that proteins are synthesized in only one direction—from the amino toward the carboxyl end—as noted previously; and (2) that regardless of the codon that terminates the first polypeptide, two polypeptides coded in the same mRNA cannot become linked linearly because the amino group which begins the second is blocked and cannot form a peptide bond.

The relationship between the codons for polypeptide chain initiation and those for chain termination can be studied using *E. coli* ϕR17, a close relative of ϕf2. As mentioned earlier (Section 7.7), this RNA phage also codes for three proteins: A protein (needed for ϕ maturation), coat protein, and an RNA-dependent RNA poly-

---

[5] The formyl group of fMet is supplied by N^{10}-formyltetrahydrofolate, whose synthesis requires a source of tetrahydrofolate.

[6] *In vitro* a peptidyl-tRNA (for example, diphenylalanyl-tRNA), whose NH$_2$ group of the amino acid bound to tRNA is also blocked, can also serve as initiator of polypeptide synthesis under special conditions. An enzyme has been found that has no effect on fMet-tRNA or unsubstituted aminoacyl-tRNA's, but which cleaves N-substituted aminoacyl-tRNA's. Such an enzyme assures the *fidelity* of protein synthesis by correcting incorrectly charged tRNA's (and perhaps serves to release the terminal amino acid in a protein under synthesis from its tRNA).

merase. Since these proteins are needed in different amounts, one might expect that there are three sites on the RNA where ribosomes can bind to initiate protein synthesis. This expectation is realized in experiments in which radioactive ϕ RNA is used to initiate protein synthesis; since the RNA not bound to the ribosome is unprotected, it can be degraded; the remaining RNA, which occurs in three fragments, is then base-sequenced. AUG's that code for fMet are found in all three segments of ϕR17 RNA, no terminator codons occurring directly before these AUG's. These initiator AUG's are probably not base-paired (being, therefore, in single-stranded regions); other internal AUG's are present but are probably buried by secondary structure (being base-paired). Similar results are reported for ϕQβ.

The preceding discussion of polypeptide synthesis in *E. coli* seems to apply generally to all *procaryotes*—cellular organisms like bacteria and blue-green algae without a nucleus but with a nuclear area. Mitochondria and chloroplasts resemble procaryotes in containing not only 70s-type ribosomes, but fMet tRNA's. As might be expected, therefore, phage f2 RNA is translated into coat protein that has fMet at the N terminus in a protein-synthesizing system isolated from chloroplasts. (R)

7.13   Similarly, in nucleated cells Met is incorporated into protein by Met-tRNA$_F$ responding to the initiator codon, AUG, and by Met-tRNA$_M$ responding to internal AUG's.

Using the 80s ribosomal protein-synthesizing machinery from mouse acites tumor-cell cytoplasm, the proteins synthesized in such an *in vitro* system start at the N terminus with Met, which is later cleaved off. This Met is brought to the ribosome by Met-tRNA$_F$ in response to an initiator codon, AUG, or possibly also GUG. Although this Met-tRNA$_F$ can be formylated *in vitro*, it is not formylated *in vivo* (contrary to the comparable type in procaryotes such as *E. coli*). Met-tRNA$_M$, which responds to internal AUG codons, cannot be formylated. Thus, protein initiation is similar in procaryotes and *eucaryotes*—cellular organisms having a nucleus—except that in the cytoplasm of cells of the latter type of organism the protein does not have its N terminus blocked from forming peptide linkage by a formyl group. Note that the factors required for polypeptide chain elongation in eucaryotes are similar to those required in procaryotes (Section 6.8). (R)

7.14   DNA is colinear with the polypeptide it codes.

Although DNA and the polypeptides it specifies are both linear polymers, we would like to know whether the linearity of the polypeptides is strictly dependent upon the linearity of the corresponding DNA, that is, whether *colinearity* or *congruence* exists. We can test for this possibility by using 10 ϕT4 strains each of which produces incomplete head protein of a different length. The position of the defect in the phage DNA (which, via correspondingly defective mRNA, stops the translation of head protein with a nonsense codon) can be determined for each of these strains and the defective positions arranged in a linear map.[7] When the head protein of each defective strain is analyzed, the length of the polypeptide segment synthesized is found to be directly proportional to the distance from one end of this genetic map. The DNA of the phage is, therefore, colinear with the polypeptide it codes. (R)

7.15   The genetic code is essentially universal in present-day organisms.

We have seen that the machinery and the type of code for translation are, apparently, very similar in all organisms, even though these are widely divergent in genetic content and appearance, and have no common ancestor in recent history. Is the genetic code basically identical in all present-day organisms? Is it universal, so that codons generally have the same translational meanings in all organisms? An affirmative answer is supported by the six lines of evidence that follow.

1. TMV infects a variety of plants, including zinnia (belonging to the Compositae) and tobacco (Solanaceae). When TMV–RNA is used for infection the amino acid sequence of the coat protein of the progeny is the same whether the host is zinnia or tobacco.
2. The polypeptides of rabbit hemoglobin can be synthesized using mRNA from rabbit reticulocytes in the cell-free protein synthesizing system of *E. coli*.
3. ϕf2 RNA directs the synthesis of phage coat protein not only in extracts of its normal host, *E. coli*, but also in extracts of *Euglena gracilis*, a green unicellular alga.
4. When SV40 virus DNA, which normally infects monkey cells, is placed in an *in vitro E. coli* system, transcription and translation produce two viral coat proteins which seem normal when tested electrophoretically.
5. Synthetic polynucleotides have many of the amino acid incorporation properties in certain animal cell-free systems that they have in bacterial cell-free systems.
6. Finally, a marked correlation exists in a variety of organisms between dC + dG content and the percentages of certain amino acids incorporated into protein.

All these results support the hypothesis that, although modifications occur, there is only one basic genetic code for polypeptide synthesis in present-day organisms. (R)

SUMMARY AND CONCLUSIONS

The universal use of the ribosome and aminoacyl-tRNA's in translation, discussed in the last chapter, is paralleled in various features of the genetic code for translation *in vivo* which apply apparently universally to both procaryotes and eucaryotes. These features of the code, most of which have also been observed *in vitro*, include

---

[7] Through studies of electron micrographs of DNA–DNA hybrids between phages whose DNA's are defective in different places (see Section 9.5), it is possible to place the defects in a uniquely spaced linear sequence (that is, to arrange them in a genetic DNA map; see Section 10.3). Since it is also possible to arrange the genetic defects in the same sequence on the basis of studies of genetic recombination (by making a genetic recombination map; see Section 10.3); the chemical and recombinational genetic maps are apparently colinear. In the present case congruity was studied between the recombinational map of a gene and the polypeptide coded by the gene.

1. A message (usually, if not always, contained in mRNA) that is read unidirectionally in successive, nonoverlapping triplets.

2. A code that contains nonsense codons that are probably involved in polypeptide termination.

3. A code that uses a special initiator codon (probably only AUG) which places Met at the N terminus of all (?) polypeptides before it is or is not removed enzymatically.

4. A code that exhibits degeneracy—that is, more than one codon is translated into the same amino acid—because the same amino acid is bound to (a) one tRNA showing wobble or (b) more than one type of tRNA (owing to the normal presence of two or more different tRNA's for a given amino acid, or to errors made by aminoacyl-tRNA synthetase or in codon–anticodon base pairing).

5. A code that is probably, at least occasionally, ambiguous—that is, the same codon is translated into different amino acids at different times.

6. A code in which genetic material is colinear with the polypeptide it codes.

7. A code which, together with its degeneracies and ambiguities, is essentially universal in all organisms; that is, codons generally have the same translations in all organisms.

It should be noted that DNA seems to contain, in its base sequence, information that is used for purposes other than translation; for example, we have already implied in Chapter 5 the existence of recognition genes for starting and stopping the action of RNA (and in a footnote, DNA) polymerases. We have at present very little knowledge about the nature of the genetic "code" for such information.

GENERAL REFERENCES

Sadgolpal, A. 1968. The genetic code after the excitement. Adv. Genet., 14: 325–404.

Speyer, J. F. 1967. The genetic code. In *Molecular genetics,* Part II, Taylor, J. H. (Editor), New York: Academic Press, Inc., Chap. IV, pp. 137–191.

Ycas, M. 1969. *The biological code.* New York: American Elsevier Publishing Company, Inc.

1967. *The genetic code,* Vol. 31. Cold Spring Harbor Sympos. Quant. Biol. New York: Cold Spring Harbor Laboratory of Quantitative Biology.

1970. *The mechanism of protein synthesis,* Vol. 34. Cold Spring Harbor Sympos. Quant Biol. New York: Cold Spring Harbor Laboratory of Quantitative Biology.

SPECIFIC SECTION REFERENCES

7.1　Morgan, A. R., Wells, R. D., and Khorana, H. G. 1966. Studies on polynucleotides, LIX. Further codon assignments from amino acid incorporations directed by ribopolynucleotides containing repeating trinucleotide sequences. Proc. Nat. Acad. Sci., U.S., 56: 1899–1906.

Nirenberg, M. W., and Matthaei, J. H. 1961. The dependence of cell-free protein synthesis in *E. coli* upon naturally occurring or synthetic polyribonucleotides. Proc. Nat. Acad. Sci., U.S., 47: 1588–1602. (The first cracking of the code.)

7.2　Smith, M. A., Salas, M., Stanley, W. M., Jr., Wahba, A. J., and Ochoa, S. 1966. Direction of reading of the genetic message, II. Proc. Nat. Acad. Sci., U.S., 55: 141–147.

7.3　Bennett, T. P. 1969. Elements of protein synthesis: a student model. San Francisco: W. H. Freeman and Company, Publishers.

Crick, F. H. C. 1966. The genetic code: III. Scient. Amer., 215 (No. 4): 55–62, 150. Scientific American Offprints, San Francisco: W. H. Freeman and Company, Publishers.

Nirenberg, M. W., Leder, P., Bernfield, M., Brimacombe, R., Trupin, J., Rottman, F., and O'Neal, C. 1965. RNA codewords and protein synthesis, VII. On the general nature of the RNA code. Proc. Nat. Acad. Sci., U.S., 53: 1161–1168.

7.4   Crick, F. H. C. 1966. Codon–anticodon pairing: the wobble hypothesis. J. Mol. Biol., 19: 548–555. Reprinted in *Papers in biochemical genetics*, Zubay, G. L. (Editor), New York: Holt, Rinehart and Winston, Inc., 1968, pp. 362–369.

7.5   Crick, F. H. C., Barnett, L., Brenner, S., and Watts-Tobin, R. J. 1961. General nature of the genetic code for proteins. Nature, Lond., 192: 1227–1232. Reprinted in *Papers on bacterial viruses*, second edition, Stent, G. S. (Editor), Boston: Little, Brown and Company, 1965, pp. 388–401, and in *Papers in biochemical genetics*, Zubay, G. L. (Editor), New York: Holt, Rinehart and Winston, Inc., 1968, pp. 159–164. (As revealed by the functioning of *rII* changed by acridines.)

Fraenkel-Conrat, H. 1964. The genetic code of a virus. Scient. Amer., 211 (No. 4): 47–54, 142. Scientific American Offprints, San Francisco: W. H. Freeman and Company, Publishers.

Reichmann, M. E. 1964. The satellite tobacco necrosis virus: a single protein and its genetic code. Proc. Nat. Acad. Sci., U.S., 52: 1009–1117.

7.7   Adams, J. M., Jeppesen, P. G. N., Sanger, F., and Barrell, B. G. 1969. Nucleotide sequence from the coat protein cistron of R17 bacteriophage RNA. Nature, Lond., 223: 1009–1014.

Jeppesen, P. G. N., Artgesinger Steitz, J. A., and Spahr, P. F. 1970. Gene order in the bacteriophage R17 RNA: 5'-A-protein-coat protein-synthetase-3'. Nature, London., 226: 230–237.

Ocada, Y., Amagase, S., and Tsugita, A. 1970. Frameshift mutation in the lysozyme gene of bacteriophage T4: demonstration of the insertion of five bases, and a summary of *in vivo* codons and lysozyme activities. J. Mol. Biol., 54: 219–246. (Close correlation between bases at third position and DNA base ratio indicates many *in vitro* codons are used *in vivo*—already 13 and 20 codons are known to be used in *E. coli* infected by wild and variant T4, respectively.)

Streisinger, G., Okada, Y., Emrich, J., Newton, J., Tsugita, A., Terzaghi, E., and Inouye, M. 1967. Frameshift mutations and the genetic code. Cold Spring Harbor Sympos. Quant. Biol., 31: 77–84.

Marshall W. Nirenberg (1927–   ) in 1968, the year he was the recipient of a Nobel prize.

H. Gobind Khorana (1922–) in 1971. Dr. Khorana was the recipient of a Nobel prize in 1968.

7.8   Sundharadas, G., Katze, J. R., Söll, D., Konigsberg, W., and Lengyel, P. 1968. On the recognition of serine transfer RNA's specific for unrelated codons by the same seryl-transfer RNA synthetase. Proc. Nat. Acad. Sci., U.S., 61: 693–700.

7.10   Rifkin, D. B., Hirsh, D. I., and Konigsberg, W. 1967. A possible ambiguity in the coding of mouse hemoglobin. Cold Spring Harbor Sympos. Quant. Biol., 1966, 31: 715–718.

von Ehrenstein, G. 1967. Translational variations in the amino acid sequence of the α-chain of rabbit hemoglobin. Cold Spring Harbor Sympos. Quant. Biol., 1966, 31: 705–714.

7.11   Brenner, S., Stretton, A. O. W., and Kaplan, S. 1965. Genetic code: the "nonsense" triplets for chain termination and their suppression. Nature, Lond., 206: 994–998. Reprinted in *Papers in biochemical genetics*, Zubay, G. L. (Editor), New York: Holt, Rinehart and Winston, Inc., 1968, pp. 416–420.

Champe, S. P., and Benzer, S. 1962. Reversal of mutant phenotypes by 5-fluorouracil: an approach to nucleotide sequences in messenger-RNA. Proc. Nat. Acad. Sci., U.S., 48: 532–546. Reprinted in *Papers in biochemical genetics*, Zubay, G. L. (Editor), New York: Holt, Rinehart and Winston, Inc., 1968, pp. 165–178.

Engelhardt, D. L., Webster, R. E., Wilhelm, R. C., and Zinder, N. D. 1965. *In vitro* studies on the mechanism of suppression of a nonsense mutation. Proc. Nat. Acad. Sci., U.S., 54: 1791–1797.

7.12   Capecchi, M. R. 1966. Initiation of *E. coli* proteins. Proc. Nat. Acad. Sci., U.S., 55: 1517–1524.

Clark, B. F. C., and Marcker, K. A. 1968. How proteins start. Scient. Amer., 218 (No. 1): 36–42, 150.

Lengyel, P. 1967. On peptide chain initiation. In *Molecular genetics*, Part II, Taylor, J. H. (Editor), New York: Academic Press, Inc., Chap. V, pp. 194–212.

Steitz, J. A. 1969. Polypeptide chain initiation: nucleotide sequences of the three ribosomal binding sites in bacteriophage R17 RNA. Nature, Lond., 224: 957–964.

7.13   Brown, J. C., and Smith, A. E. 1970. Initiator codons in eukaryotes. Nature, Lond., 226: 610–612.

Jackson, R., and Hunter, T. 1970. Role of methionine in the initiation of haemoglobin synthesis. Nature, Lond., 227: 672–676. (The N-terminal Met is cleaved off early in α and β chain synthesis.)

Smith, A. E., and Marcker, K. A. 1970. Cytoplasmic methionine transfer RNA's from eukaryotes. Nature, Lond., 226: 607–610.

Wigle, D. T., and Dixon, G. H. 1970. Transient incorporation of methionine at the N-terminus of protamine newly synthesized in trout testis cells. Nature, Lond., 227: 676–680.

7.14   Sarabhai, A. S., Stretton, A. O. W., Brenner, S., and Bolle, A. 1964. Co-linearity of the gene with the polypeptide chain. Nature, Lond., 201: 13–17.

Yanofsky, C. 1967. Gene structure and protein structure. Scient. Amer., 216 (No. 5): 80–94, 167. Scientific American Offprints, San Francisco: W. H. Freeman and Company, Publishers.

Yanofsky, C., Carlton, B. C., Guest, J. R., Helinski, D. R., and Henning, U. 1964. On the colinearity of gene structure and protein structure. Proc. Nat. Acad. Sci., U.S., 51: 266–272. Reprinted in *Papers on bacterial genetics*, second edition, Adelberg, E. A. (Editor), Boston: Little, Brown and Company, 1966, pp. 177–183; and in *Papers on biochemical genetics*, Zubay, G. L. (Editor), New York: Holt, Rinehart and Winston, Inc., 1968, pp. 400–407. (A proof of colinearity.)

7.15   Laycock, D. G., and Hunt, J. A. 1969. Synthesis of rabbit globin by a bacterial cell-free system. Nature, Lond., 22: 1118.

Okada, Y., Nozu, Y., and Ohno, T. 1969. Demonstration of the universality of the genetic code *in vivo* by comparison of the coat proteins synthesized in different plants by tobacco mosaic virus RNA. Proc. Nat. Acad. Sci., U.S., 63: 1189–1195.

QUESTIONS AND PROBLEMS

1. Amino acid incorporation into protein can be studied *in vitro* with synthetic copolymers, polynucleotides in which two different bases alternate, serving as mRNA.

    a. The copolymer of U and C, poly (U-C), codes for a polypeptide in which serine and leucine alternate strictly (Ser-Leu co-polypeptide).

    b. Poly (U-G) codes Cys-Val copolypeptide.

    c. Poly (A-C) codes Thr-His copolypeptide.

    d. Poly (A-G) codes Arg-Glu copolypeptide.

    e. The polymer of ApApGp codes polylysine, polyarginine, and polyglutamic acid.

    How can a given nucleic acid code *in vitro* for two or more kinds of polypeptides? Determine from the above results *in vitro* codons for each amino acid incorporated and compare your results with the codons in Figure 7-3.

2. Short synthetic polyribonucleotides of types (1) ApApApApApCpAp . . . pApApA and (2) ApApApApCpAp . . . pApApA direct the synthesis *in vitro* of short polylysine molecules (1) with Asn at the N terminus and (2) with Thr at the N terminus, respectively. What can you conclude from these results about

    a. codons for specific amino acids?

    b. the direction of translation of mRNA?

    c. the starting position of mRNA translaation *in vitro*?

3. Devise experiments that permit the collection of essentially pure Phe-tRNA; Lys-tRNA.

4. Work out the relative frequencies of the codons UUU, UUA, AAU, UAC, AAA, and CCC in a polymer synthesized by poly-

nucleotide phosphorylase from the disphosphates of U, A, and C in the relative amounts of 6, 1, and 1, respectively.

5. Are the nucleotides comprising a codon or an anticodon adjacent? Justify your answer.

6. If you added 5-fluorouracil to the culture medium of a bacterium and all protein synthesis ceased within several minutes, what could you conclude?

7. What might be the translational consequence of base substitution in the codon that specifies *N*-formylmethionine?

8. In molecular terms, what is the nature of mRNA for *rII* region of φT4 that (a) has deletion 1589? (b) is wild type, that is, contains no deletion?

9. What can you deduce about the number of nucleotides missing in otherwise normal deletion 1589 phage? What would be the resulting activity of gene *rIIB* if one of a large number of different multinucleotide deletions in the *rIIA* gene were present in addition to deletion 1589?

10. Some deletion 1589 phage that is also defective in the *rIIA* gene (1) shows no *B* activity in *E. coli* host strain KB unless fU is added to the culture medium, and (2) shows *B* activity in *E. coli* host strain KB-3 even in the absence of fU. What is the translational effect (a) of the defect in *rIIA*, (b) of fU, and (c) of changing the host?

11. How are eucaryotes similar, if not identical, to procaryotes with regard to translation machinery and the genetic code for translation?

12. Discuss the physical–chemical basis of degeneracy.

PART III

Variation of
Nucleic Acids

Chapter 8

Regularly Occurring
Variation

   We have already noted in a general way that nucleic acids in organisms vary both quantitatively and qualitatively. For example, increasing quantities of DNA per genome are programmed in different species as one proceeds up the evolutionary scale (Section 2.9 and Figure 2-11), and considerable variation occurs in the types of bases found in tRNA (Section 2.8 and Figure 2-10). After having considered the replicative, transcriptional, and translational properties of polynucleotides (Chapters 4 through 7), we can more fully appreciate how such variations change the amount and kinds of information present in an organism.

   This part of the book presents a more comprehensive view of the variations that occur in naturally occurring nucleic acids, providing information that will be useful in understanding the groups of chapters that follow. This chapter deals with all nucleic acid variations that occur regularly because they are (or are expected to be) coded or programmed in genetic material; Chapter 9 deals only with genetic variations that occur irregularly, whether or not they are caused directly or indirectly by genetic material.

8.1   Various quantitative and qualitative changes in DNA within an organism occur regularly and are programmed genetically. Some of these changes occur normally and depend upon cell functioning; other regular changes occur abnormally as a result of infection.

Besides the usual changes in the DNA content which take place when a cell replicates its DNA and undergoes division, other examples occur in which intracellular DNA is normally programmed to undergo quantitative and qualitative change. In these cases,[1] cells performing special functions have special kinds or amounts of DNA. Such changes in DNA are normally produced in the course of development and their origin and function will be studied in detail in later chapters.

Abnormal changes in normal nuclear DNA information involving (1) gain, (2) loss, and (3) shift in its location can also occur regularly after infection by microorganisms such as bacteria and viruses. Infection and cure of DNA viruses are themselves circumstances in which abnormal DNA information is regularly added to and lost from cells. Abnormal change in DNA content due to infection is also discussed in later chapters.

8.2   Quantitative and qualitative variation in cellular RNA normally accompanies cellular maintenance, growth, and repair. Viral RNA is also regularly gained and lost.

All cellular maintenance, growth, and repair utilizes protein—either or both as structural elements and as enzymes. Accordingly, since new proteins need be produced to perform new functions or to replace protein molecules that have become defective, the cell must anticipate these metabolic needs by forming sufficient ribosomes; this involves producing rRNA, which, we recall, accounts for some 70 per cent of the cell's RNA. Protein synthesis requires synthesis of RNA's of transfer and messenger types also. Since RNA's are constantly undergoing degradation, the cell normally has an ever-changing population of them.

When a virus has RNA as its genetic material, RNA information is regularly gained

---

[1] Seven examples follow:

1. Digestive (salivary gland) and excretory (Malphighian tubule) cells of insect larvae often have from 2 to 1,000 times the DNA in an ordinary somatic cell, due largely, if not entirely, to an increase in the multiple of DNA genomes present.
2. In nuclear chromosomes of certain insect larvae, moreover, certain DNA regions are replicated several more times than others.
3. In the nucleus of the amphibian oocyte, the nucleolus organizer region of the chromosome is replicated to produce an extra 1,000 times or so more of these regions than occurs in ordinary somatic cells.
4. In other cases, as in *Ascaris* and *Sciara*, special cells discard nuclear DNA and apparently have a reduction not only in

quantity but in kind of DNA information.
5. The red blood cell that loses its nucleus loses all the DNA information that organelle contains.
6. The number of replicas of the DNA in chloroplasts and mitochondria changes, of course, depending upon the number of such organelles present in a cell, which depends in turn upon the metabolic activity of the cell.
7. Amphibian eggs contain yolk platelets which contain 10 times the amount of DNA detected in the egg's mitochondria, and, therefore, considerably more DNA than do corresponding cells in a yolkless condition.

or lost when such a virus infects or leaves the cell. When a DNA virus infects, the host cell also gains, then perhaps later, loses, whatever RNA is regularly transcribed from the viral genome. (R)

8.3   Genetic DNA and genetic RNA contain nonrandom, sometimes repeated, base sequences.

Certain general regularities and irregularities may be expected in nucleic acid base sequence from a knowledge (1) of the *in vivo* amino acid code, and (2) that all tRNA's have portions of their base sequence in common.[2] The following gives specific examples of the nonrandom distribution of bases in genetic DNA and genetic RNA.

Genetic DNA

In general, all ribosomal RNA's are purine-rich relative to the base ratio of most duplex DNA. Thus, in the nucleolus organizer region for example, the *sense strand* of the DNA duplex that codes for rRNA must be pyrimidine-rich. Similarly, since bacterial mRNA is AG-rich, the sense DNA strand is pyrimidine-rich in these regions also. (Note, however, that HeLa cells do not have AG-rich mRNA.) Poly A which hybridizes with nuclear DNA has been found attached to mRNA's of HeLa, mouse ascites tumor, and globin-synthesizing rabbit cells. The duplex DNA transcribed to poly A must be poly dA · poly dT.

We have already mentioned (Section 4.6) a specific example of nonrandom sequences of purines and pyrimidines in the natural poly (dA-dT) fraction of the DNA of certain crabs, whose amount is relatively constant from tissue to tissue and from crab to crab. Since this DNA has a base composition that differs from most of the DNA of the crab, it is collected in a separate, small (or satellite) band in the ultracentrifuge, and is called *satellite DNA*. Satellite DNA's also occur in mammalian cells. Base-sequence analysis of mouse satellite DNA shows it contains a repeat of six successive pyrimidines, probably five thymines followed by one cytosine. The satellite DNA of the guinea pig repeats the sequence

$$5'\ dCd\,Cd\,CdTdAdA\ 3'$$
$$3'\ dGdGdGdAdTdT\ 5'.[3]$$

Genetic RNA

Another specific example of runs of bases is found in reovirus whose virion RNA, only 75 per cent duplex, is composed of numerous double-stranded and single-stranded

---

[2] Despite the base sequence similarities among DNA's of different organisms, each organism has some unique sequences that code for their unique proteins. This is evidenced by each DNA having a unique set of dinucleotide frequencies—as described in Section S4.7.

[3] Further evidence of nonrandom sequences of bases along DNA strands comes from studies of runs of bases: 70 per cent of the bases are distributed so that three or more pyrimidines (and hence purines) occur in successive linear nucleotides; linear sequences of five successive thymines exist; and 4.9 per cent of a given DNA contains sequences of eight or more pyrimidines in succession. The frequencies of runs of one to eight pyrimidines in bacterial DNA's, however, do not differ significantly from those expected from a random distribution of bases, although such DNA's have relatively too few runs of three deoxycytidylic acids. On the other hand, mammalian DNA has significantly more runs of one to eight pyrimidines than expected on the basis of a random distribution of bases. Such results suggest that mammalian DNA may contain *silent regions* which are not transcribed and translated into amino acid information, but have other meaning (including, for example, sequences which function as recognition genes for polymerases).

segments. Ten duplex segments each end with single-stranded 5' ends composed of six successive purines, probably guanines. Analysis of all the bases in the single-stranded portions shows they contain roughly 90 per cent A residues. (R)

8.4   At least a small percentage of nuclear DNA is redundant for the base sequences transcribed to t, r, and 5s RNA's.

About 0.26 per cent of the total DNA present is transcribed to tRNA in wheat embryos, *Drosophila*, and *E. coli*. This probably means in *E. coli* that the redundancy in base sequences is mostly for portions of singly occurring genes for different types of tRNA which can be considered to be derivatives of each other. In higher organisms, however, whose DNA content is about 1,000 times that in *E. coli* there must be many genes that produce the same type of tRNA and, therefore, are completely redundant.

Because rRNA is complementary to about 0.3 per cent of the total nuclear or nuclear area DNA in wheat embryos, pea seedlings, *Drosophila*, HeLa cells, mice, and bacteria, it appears that the number of these genes too is directly proportional to the total DNA present in the nuclear region. This number is about 6 in *E. coli*, hundreds in an ordinary amphibian somatic cell,[4] and thousands in an amphibian oocyte (to be discussed further in Section 24.11).

About 20,000 genes in a *Xenopus* cell and more than 1,500 genes in the rat liver cell[5] code for 5s RNA. (R)

8.5   The DNA in nuclei has large amounts of partially redundant (as well as nonredundant) base sequences.

When duplex DNA in low concentration is heat denatured and cooled slowly the renaturation or annealing obtained depends upon the frequency of identical and near-identical sequences (Figure 8-1). Bacterial DNA, for example that of *E. coli*, seems to have no protein coding genes repeated; annealing rate is, therefore, slow while the reformed duplex, being precise in its pairing, has a high stability to heating. Such DNA has almost completely *nonredundant sequences* or is *nonredundant DNA*.

Poly (dA-dT), whether artificial or natural as in certain crabs, has the same base sequence repeated over and over; it has only or almost only *completely redundant sequences*, and comprises *redundant DNA*. In the same low concentration as above, redundant DNA anneals quickly and has a high stability to heating. Mouse satellite DNA (Section 8.3), comprising 10 per cent of the DNA present, seems to be redundant DNA composed of about 2×10^7 copies of a sequence 8 to 13 base pairs long.

All eucaryotic (that is, nucleated) multicellular organisms tested, plants as well as

---

[4] In *Xenopus* there is normally a large amount of complete redundancy for rRNA genes—about 450 genes for 28s and 18s RNA per genome, all clustered together in one chromosome (see Figure 24-2A). The genes for 5s RNA appear to be partially clustered elsewhere.

[5] As determined from RNA–DNA hybridization experiments, the number of genes per adult rat liver cell is 300 for rRNA, 13,000 for tRNA, and 1,660 for 5s RNA. Since, on the average, such a cell synthesizes 650 ribosomes, 11,000 molecules of tRNA, and 650 molecules of 5s RNA per minute to maintain steady-state concentrations of these entities, the individual genes for rRNA, tRNA, and 5s RNA are transcribed approximately twice a minute, once a minute, and once every $2\frac{1}{2}$ minutes, respectively.

DNA	Organisms	Annealing Rate	Heat Stability
Nonredundant	Bacteria; all eucaryotes tested	Slow	High
Redundant	Crab sperm; mouse "satellite"	Fast	High
Partially redundant	All eucaryotes tested	Fast	Low

Figure 8-1   Characteristics of DNA's of different degrees of redundancy.

animals, have large amounts of DNA's that, under the same conditions, anneal quickly but have a low stability to heating. This result is interpreted to mean that such DNA's contain genes that occur as families in which each member repeats most but not the entire base sequence. A family contains 50 to 2 million related base sequences. Thus, this DNA shows partial homology in internal base sequence, being *partially redundant DNA*. For this reason annealing can occur quickly but because the pairing is imperfect the partial duplex is easily heat denatured.[6]

The relative amounts of nonredundant and partially redundant DNA varies considerably in different eucaryotic organisms. The per cent of DNA that is nonredundant is 70 per cent in the mouse, 55 per cent in *Xenopus*, and less than 20 per cent in the salmon; the values for partially redundant DNA are about 15 per cent in the mouse, 45 per cent in *Xenopus*, and 80 per cent in salmon, wheat, onion, and the salamander *Amphiuma*.

Since the genes for t, r, and 5s RNA's discussed in the previous section, usually comprise less than 1 per cent of the total genetic material, they can only account for a fraction of 1 per cent as nonredundant, redundant, and partially redundant DNA. There is, therefore, no need to suppose that the bulk of partially redundant DNA is used for such translational machinery or, in fact, to code for amino acids. The possible, perhaps regulatory, function of partially redundant DNA is discussed in Sections 30.2 and 30.7. (R)

8.6   Part of the variation in types of bases present in viruses is due to the types of pyrimidines incorporated when the polynucleotide is formed.

Naturally occurring DNA's vary considerably in the types of bases they contain. This variability is due to changes in bases that occur before they are incorporated into DNA (discussed in this section) or after (discussed in the next section).

No example is known in which one purine completely replaces another during DNA synthesis *in vivo*. In the DNA of some viruses, however, one of the usual pyrimidines is replaced completely by another pyrimidine. For example:

1. In *Bacillus subtilis* phages PBS1 and PBS2, uracil occurs in place of thymine.
2. The infectious bovine rhinotracheitis virus contains 5-bromouracil— thymine modified by substitution of a bromo group for the methyl group at position 5.
3. In phage SP8 of *B. subtilis*, thymine is replaced completely by 5-hydroxy-methyluracil.
4. In the DNA of a phage of

[6] Denaturation temperature is reduced 1°C for approximately each 1.5 per cent noncomplementary bases.

Xanthomonas oryzae, cytosine is completely replaced by a new pyrimidine base, 5-methylcytosine (Figure 8-2).

5. In *T-even phages*, that is, ϕT2, T4, or T6, the hydrogen at position 5 of cytosine is replaced by a hydroxy-methyl (CH_2OH) group. The result is *5-hydroxymethylcytosine* (Figure 8-3) which completely replaces cytosine in the phage DNA.

We see from the above that the replacement pyrimidines have changes only at the 5 position (in the case of thymine—demethylation, replacement of —CH_3 by —Br, or replacement of —H in the methyl by —OH; in the case of cytosine—replacement of —H by —CH_3 or —CH_2OH). (R)

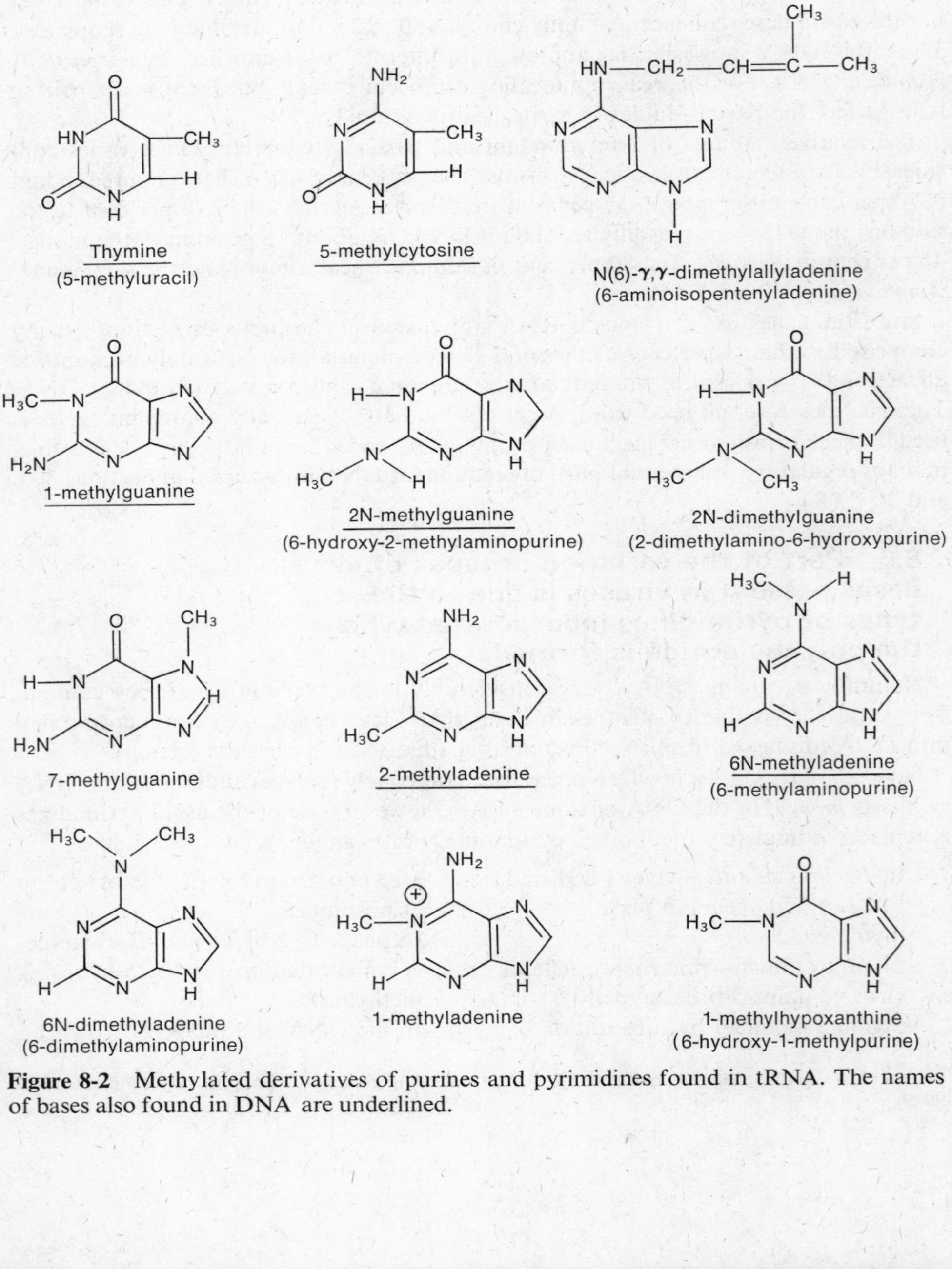

Figure 8-2 Methylated derivatives of purines and pyrimidines found in tRNA. The names of bases also found in DNA are underlined.

8.7   Part of the variation in the bases found in naturally occurring DNA is due to chemical changes occurring after polynucleotide formation.

In the case of T-even phages, glucose residues are added to some of the hydroxy-methylcytosines already incorporated in DNA, in a species-specific pattern (Figure 8-3). Another pyrimidine, 5-methylcytosine, occurs in the DNA of higher organisms such as mammals, fish, insects, and cereal grains but not at all or in lesser amounts in many microorganisms—e.g., bacteria, actinomycetes, yeasts, algae, and protozoans.

DNA may contain a variety of purines. In contrast to the pyrimidines, however, variant purines do not occur in appreciable quantity in naturally occurring DNA. For example, 6-methyladenine occurs with a frequency of up to 0.7 per cent of all bases in some bacteria and their phages, but is not found in DNA of actinomycetes, yeast, and higher plants and animals. Trace amounts of 2-methyladenine, 1-methylguanine, N^2-methylguanine, and 6-dimethylaminopurine are also reported to occur in DNA (see Figure 8-2).

All the preceding variations of cytosine, adenine, and guanine found in DNA involve methylation. In the presence of appropriate enzymes, DNA can be methylated *in vitro* to form 5-methylcytosine (from cytosine) and 6-methylaminopurine (from adenine). After being synthesized, the DNA of different organisms is methylated to different extents and in different patterns determined in part by species-specific *DNA methylases*. These enzymes are Mg^{2+} and SH-dependent and use *S*-adenosylmethionine as the methyl donor. That the reaction requires an intact secondary structure of DNA is indicated by the inhibition of methylation by heat denaturation of DNA, or exposing it to actinomycin D. In *E. coli*, which has some of its adenines and cytosines methylated, methylation occurs *in vivo* only of the newly made complements close to the replication point of DNA. (R)

8.8   Most organisms seem to modify the chemistry of the usual bases to provide a unique conformation to their DNA's.

The species-specific modification of DNA described in the two previous sections gives each organism's DNA a conformational individuality not otherwise achieved by sequencing the four usual bases. Such individuality apparently permits self- (1) DNases, (2) DNA polymerase, and (3) DNA-dependent RNA polymerases to distinguish

R=		T2	T4	T6
H		25	0	25
α-glucosyl		70	70	3
β-glucosyl		0	30	0
β-(1-6)-glucosyl-α-glucosyl		5	0	72
		100	100	100

Figure 8-3 Percentages of glucosylated 5-hydroxymethylcytosine deoxyribonucleoside (dHMC) in T-even phage DNA. (After I. R. Lehman and E. A. Pratt.)

between normal self-DNA and abnormal self- or foreign DNA's, thereby rendering these appropriately resistant or sensitive to the action of these enzymes.

The biochemical pathways leading to the synthesis and postsynthesis modification of DNA reveal the details of how the DNA's of bacteria (as described in Section S8.8a for *E. coli*) and their phages (as described for T-even phages of *E. coli* in Section S8.8b) attain unique conformations. As already indicated, this end result is apparently accomplished in *E. coli* DNA by methylating the DNA in a unique pattern; and in T-even phage DNA by (1) incorporating 5-hydroxymethylcytosine (and not cytosine) during DNA synthesis and, after DNA synthesis, by (2) glucosylating some of these bases, and (3) methylating others in a unique pattern. We find that DNA viruses, which have much less genetic information than their hosts, utilize the genetically coded materials and machinery of their hosts to replicate their own genetic material, which has a unique base sequence and, apparently, a unique conformation. Host DNase will not degrade viral DNA if the conformation of this DNA (however unique) is compatible with the unique conformation of the host's DNA. As expected, gene-directed changes in phage DNA conformation can result in the digestion of phage DNA by bacterial DNase (as illustrated with T-even phages in Section S8.8c). (R)

8.9 Naturally occurring t and rRNA's vary in types of bases they contain due to modifications made after transcription. These RNA's also contain some methylated riboses.

1. *mRNA* does not seem to contain unusual types of bases; on the other hand, tRNA and rRNA do, the evidence favoring the view that all the minor bases originate through the modification of ordinary bases sometime after transcription.

2. *tRNA* has some 2 per cent of its purine and pyrimidine bases methylated; the derivatives found are shown in Figure 8-2. (Note that in uracil and cytosine, methyl groups link to carbon; in adenine, to carbon and nitrogen; in guanine, to three different nitrogens.) The tRNA of different species is methylated to different extents and in different patterns due in part to species-specific *tRNA methylases*—six of which are already known.[7] The methyl donor for all RNA methylases is *S*-adenosylmethionine, as it is for DNA methylases. tRNA methylases seem to be restricted to the nucleolus of eucaryotes and to act exclusively on tRNA. Methylated tRNA is more highly organized (in tertiary structure presumably) than nonmethylated tRNA as shown by the lesser UV absorbency of the former; moreover, yeast aminoacyl-tRNA synthetase will not charge nonmethylated tRNA with amino acid. We have already mentioned (Section 6.2) that pre-tRNA is nonmethylated. Other nonmethyl-ated bases that occur in tRNA are described by name and structure in Figure 8-4.

3. *rRNA* is not as extensively methylated as tRNA, although methylated bases occur in 80s ribosomes in HeLa cells, and in the RNA's of both subunits of the 70s ribosome. Two types of *rRNA methylases* have been found, one

---

[7] Embryonic and tumor tissues seems to have a high tRNA methylase capacity, owing to the absence of a natural inhibitor.

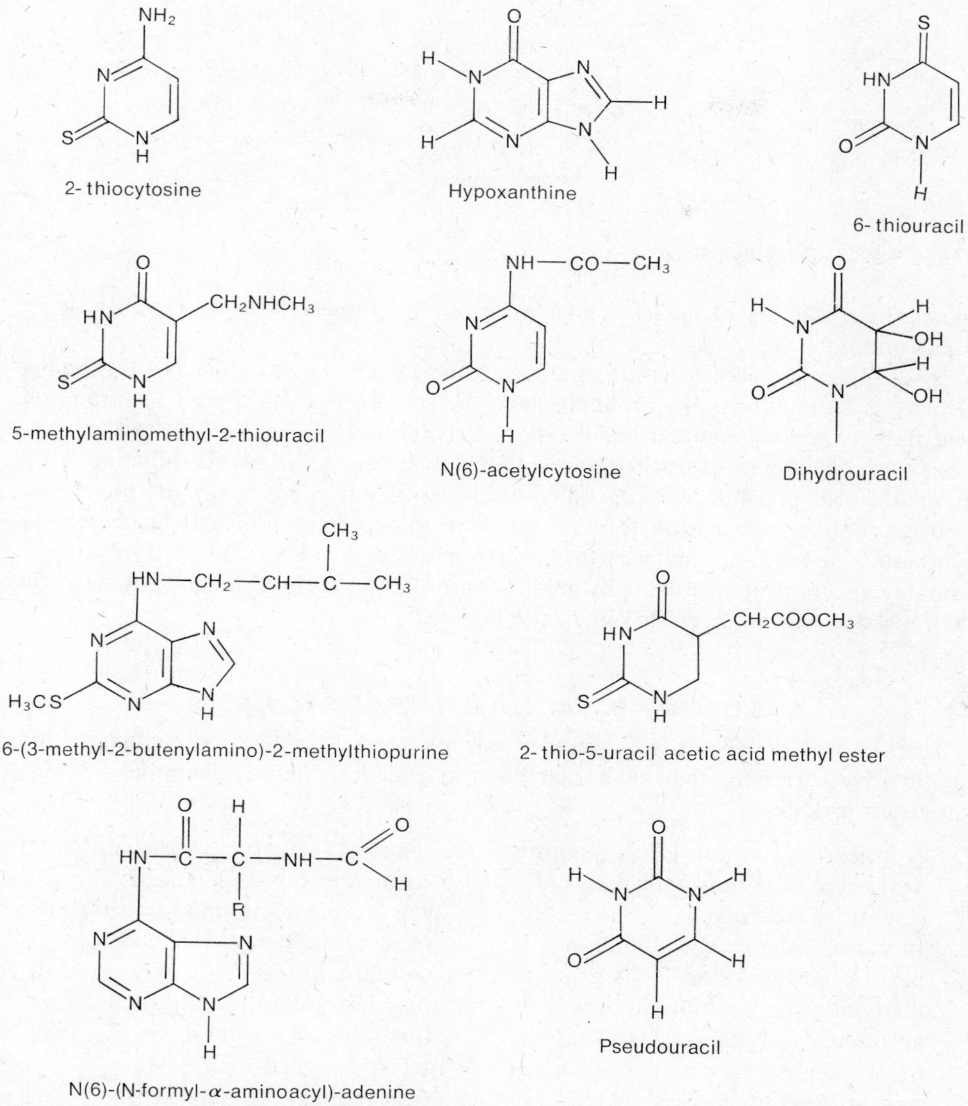

2- thiocytosine

Hypoxanthine

6- thiouracil

5-methylaminomethyl-2-thiouracil

N(6)-acetylcytosine

Dihydrouracil

6-(3-methyl-2-butenylamino)-2-methylthiopurine

2- thio-5-uracil acetic acid methyl ester

N(6)-(N-formyl-α-aminoacyl)-adenine

Pseudouracil

Figure 8-4 "Nonmethylated" minor bases found in tRNA. The ribonucleoside of hypoxanthine is inosine (I); of pseudouracil, pseudouridine (Ψ).

for methylating adenine, the other, cytosine; these cannot methylate TMV RNA or synthetic RNA polymers, although they can methylate tRNA. Methylation of rRNA probably occurs when the rRNA is in ribonucleoprotein. It should be noted that nascent rRNA can be translated, although mature rRNA, being methylated and showing secondary structure, cannot unless it is heated and neomycin is present.

Another kind of methylated compound that occurs both in tRNA and rRNA is 2'-O-methylribose (Figure 8-5), which is found joined to all four major bases. In addition, 2'-O-methylpseudouridine occurs in tRNA. Methylated pentoses seem to

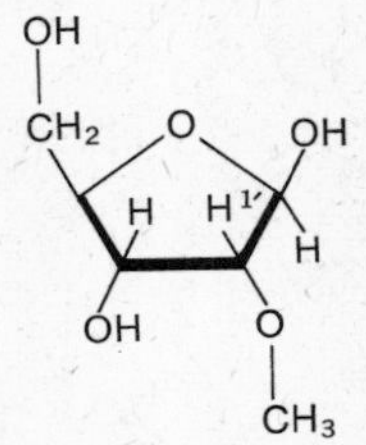

Figure 8-5   2′-*O*-methylribose.

increase the stability of nucleic acids which become more resistant to hydrolysis by alkali and nucleases.

By changing the conformation and base-pairing characteristics of RNA (especially tRNA), base modifications probably have the following advantages: (1) formation and stabilization of secondary and tertiary structure; (2) prevention of their translation; (3) protection against self-RNases; and (4) performance of special functions such as amino acid or ribosome attachment and also wobble. RNA viruses, like DNA viruses, contain information for the utilization of host material and machinery to synthesize their genetic material (as described in Section S8.9). Viral RNA is presumably also in proper (nonmethylated?) conformation with the host RNA so it can be translated and not degraded by host RNase. (R)

SUMMARY AND CONCLUSIONS

The DNA's and RNA's that occur in cells are normally subject to qualitative and quantitative variations that have their basis in genetic material. Examples of these variations include

1. A general increase in DNA quantity as the type of organism increases in somatic complexity.
2. Increases and decreases in all or part of the DNA and RNA genetic material present within an organism at different stages of its existence. Such changes occur both as a normal part of development and as the result of infection, and result in corresponding changes in the nucleic acids transcribed within the organism.
3. The organic bases in genetic nucleic acids are arranged in nonrandom, sometimes repeated, sequences.
4. Some of the repeated sequences are due to repeats of the same or similar genes coding for t, r, and 5s RNA's.
5. Most nuclei contain 15 to 80 per cent of their DNA in runs of similar, if not identical, base

sequences—that is, as partially redundant DNA. The possibility exists that the nonrandom runs and most of the partial redundancy so common in the DNA of eucaryotes may have other (perhaps regulatory) functions than to be transcribed to RNA's needed or used for translation.
6. The chemistry of some DNA bases, sometimes modified before DNA synthesis (for example, hydroxymethylation of cytosine in T-even infected *E. coli*), is usually modified after DNA synthesis (methylation; sometimes glucosylation). The type and pattern of change serves to confer a unique conformation upon the DNA of each organism.
7. t and rRNA's are also changed chemically after synthesis, enabling

these molecules to assume a more suitable conformation and perhaps preventing them from being translated.

8. Viruses, which have relatively limited genetic information, utilize their host's materials and machinery to produce genetic material which contains unique base sequences and, apparently, a unique conformation; but which also complies conformationally with the host's DNA or RNA (and is, therefore, functional and not degraded upon infection).

GENERAL REFERENCES

Borek, E., and Srinivasan, P. R. 1966. The methylation of nucleic acids. Ann. Rev. Biochem., 35 (Part I): 275–298.

Britten, R. J., and Kohne, D. E. 1968. Repeated sequences in DNA. Science, 161: 529–540.

Britten, R. J., and Kohne, D. E. 1970. Repeated segments of DNA. Scient. Amer., 222 (No. 4): 24–31, 130.

Chargaff, E. 1968. What really is DNA? Remarks on the changing aspects of a scientific concept. Progr. Nucleic Acid Res. and Mol. Biol., 8: 297–333.

Cohen, S. S. 1968. *Virus-induced enzymes.* New York: Columbia University Press.

SPECIFIC SECTION REFERENCES

8.2 Kolodny, G. M. 1971. Evidence for transfer of macromolecular RNA between mammalian cells in culture. Exp. Cell Res., 65: 313–324. (All major cytoplasmic species of RNA are transferred.)

Stroun, M., Anker, P., and Auderset, G. 1970. Natural release of nucleic acids from bacteria into plant cells. Nature, Lond., 227: 607–608. (Bacterial RNA found in shoot cells is either taken up directly or transcribed from bacterial DNA taken up directly.)

8.3 Blumenfeld, M., and Forrest, H. S. 1971. Is *Drosophilia* dAT on the Y chromosome? Proc. Nat. Acad. Sci., U.S., 68: 3145–3149. (About 4 per cent of total DNA is poly [dA–dT] and poly dA · dT).

Lim, L., and Canellakis, E. S. 1970. Adenine-rich polymer associated with rabbit reticulocyte messenger RNA. Nature, Lond., 227: 710–712.

8.4 Quincey, R. V., and Wilson, S. H. 1969. The utilization of genes for ribosomal RNA, 5s RNA, and transfer RNA in liver cells of adult rats. Proc. Nat. Acad. Sci., U.S., 64: 981–998.

Spardari, S., and Ritossa, F. 1970. Clustered genes for ribonucleic acids in *Escherichia coli*. J. Mol. Biol., 53: 357–367.

8.5 Southern, E. M. 1970. Base sequence and evolution of guinea-pig α-satellite DNA. Nature, Lond., 227: 794–798. (The sequences are short and repeated many times.)

Thomas, C. A., Jr., Hamkalo, B. A., Misra, D. N., and Lee, C. S. 1970. Cyclization of eucaryotic deoxyribonucleic acid fragments. J. Mol. Biol., 51: 621–632. (After treatment with exonuclease, shear-broken fragments of DNA form circles by base pairing when obtained from eucaryotes but not procaryotes, indicating tandem redundancy in the former.)

8.6 Kuo, T., Huang, T., and Teng, M. 1968. 5-Methylcytosine replacing cytosine in the deoxyribonucleic acid of a bacteriophage for *Xanthomonas oryzae*. J. Mol. Biol., 34: 373–375.

8.7 Billen, D. 1968. Methylation of the bacterial chromosome: an event at the "replication point"? J. Mol. Biol., 31: 477–486.

Lark, C. 1968. Studies on the *in vivo* methylation of DNA in *Escherichia coli* 15T⁻. J. Mol. Biol., 31: 389–399.

Vanyushin, B. F., Tkacheva, S. G., and Belozersky, A. N. 1970. Rare bases in animal DNA. Nature, Lond., 225: 948–949. (Mostly amounts of methylated bases.)

8.8 Luria, S. E. 1970. The recognition of DNA in bacteria. Scient. Amer., 222 (No. 1): 88–102, 146.

8.9 Muto, A. 1968. Messenger activity of nascent ribosomal RNA. J. Mol. Biol., 36: 1–14.

SUPPLEMENTARY SECTIONS

S8.8a Bacterial genes code for the enzymes that synthesize the raw materials to make DNA and to modify it after synthesis.

We have already noted that the amount and kinds of genetic material in a cell are increased by the event of viral infection. In order to better understand the changes that occur in nucleic acids after a cell has been infected with virus, we shall consider first the synthesis of the nucleotides used to make DNA in a normal, uninfected bacterial cell like *E. coli.*

The pathways for synthesizing the four most common deoxyribonucleoside 5′-triphosphates: dATP, dGTP, dTTP, and dCTP are summarized in Figure 8-6. In uninfected *E. coli* the *ribo*nucleoside 5′-diphosphates of A, G, C, and U are converted by *deoxyribosidase*, or *reductase*, to the corresponding *deoxyribo*nucleoside 5′-diphosphates. ATP supplies energy for this reduction (loss of O from the 2′ position). Uracil is converted to thymine by *thymidylate synthetase*, which adds a methyl group to the pyrimidine at its 5 position. Since this enzyme can act only when the uracil is in the form of deoxyuridine monophosphate (dUMP), dUDP (and dUTP) must first be changed to this form in order to be used. The resulting dTMP is phosphorylated by a specific dTMP kinase in the reaction

$$dTMP + ATP \xrightleftharpoons{\text{dTMP kinase}} dTDP + ADP.$$

All four deoxyribonucleoside 5′-diphosphates become triphosphates through the action of other specific phosphorylating enzymes, *nucleoside diphosphate kinases*, which catalyze the following general reaction:

$$dXDP + ATP \xrightleftharpoons{\text{nuceloside diphosphate kinase}} dXTP + ADP,$$

where X is the nucleoside C, A, G, or T.

The conformation of *E. coli* DNA is changed by methylation immediately after its synthesis, as mentioned in Section 8.7. We should note that all the reactions in the pathways that synthesize gene components, DNA, and methylated DNA require enzymes, which are themselves coded in genes.

Bessman, M. J. 1963. The replication of DNA in cell-free systems. In *Molecular genetics*, Part I, Taylor, J. H. (Editor), New York: Academic Press, Inc., Chap. 1, pp. 1–64. (Includes viral DNA synthesis.)

S8.8b T-even phages destroy, use, and replace bacterial genetic material and gene synthesizing machinery to synthesize a variant type of phage-specific DNA.

After infection by T-even virulent phage, all DNA and RNA synthesis in the bacterial cell seems to be directed by the phage DNA. This is possible because the T-even phage genome codes for new enzymes, which (1) carry out syntheses unique to viral DNA production, (2) bypass host enzymes antagonistic to this process, (3) speed up synthesis of viral DNA by supplementing the action of the host's enzymes, and (4) degrade the host's DNA. The following examples demonstrate how DNA synthesis is sequestered genetically in the T-even-phage-*E. coli* system.

Changes in nucleotide raw materials. Instead of containing cytosine, as does *E. coli* DNA, T-even DNA contains 5-hydroxymethylcytosine (HMC = hydroxymethylcytidine) to which glucose is sometimes attached (Figure 8-3). Within several minutes after infection by a T-even phage, dCMP in the pathway of phage DNA synthesis is converted to dHMCMP by a *hydroxymethylase.* This enzyme is newly produced, since uninfected cells or cells infected with T5 (which has no dHMC in its DNA) have no hydroxymethylase activity. Through the action of specific monophosphate and diphosphate kinases (likewise produced only in T-even infected cells). dHMCMP is phosphorylated to dHMCTP. In T2-infected cells another new enzyme appears which splits pyrophosphate from dCTP and *orthophosphate* (P) from dCDP to form dCMP, the substrate for making dHMCMP. This enzyme, *dCTP-dCDPase*, has a high dephosphorylating activity but has no effect upon dHMCTP. Consequently, it is not surprising that dC is not found in the DNA of T-even phages.

Changes in DNA synthesis. In cells infected with T-even phages, a DNA polymerase uses the dHMCTP, dATP, dGTP, and dTTP to make phage DNA. This enzyme has a component that is phage-induced since it shows an especially high level of activity in phage-infected cells. Since the DNA polymerases from uninfected and T2-infected cells are different in various characteristics, a new DNA polymerase, *T2 DNA polymerase*, apparently is formed in T2-infected *E. coli.*

Changes in the DNA polymer. The proportion of dHMC that has glucose attached to it differs in the different T-even phages (Figure 8-3). The glucose residues are added to dHMC in already-

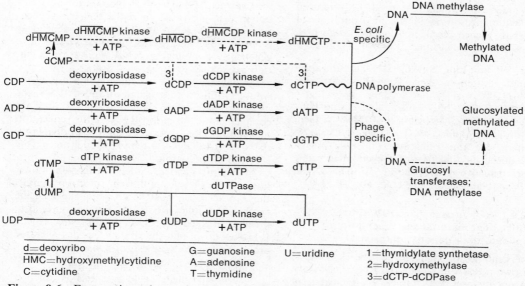

d = deoxyribo   G = guanosine   U = uridine   1 = thymidylate synthetase
HMC = hydroxymethylcytidine   A = adenosine   2 = hydroxymethylase
C = cytidine   T = thymidine   3 = dCTP-dCDPase

Figure 8-6 Enzymatic pathways leading to DNA synthesis in *E. coli*. Interrupted arrows denote reactions occurring and wavy line denotes reaction blocked in cells infected with T-even phages. (After M. J. Bessman, 1963.)

formed DNA by *glucosyl transferases*, which transfer glucose from uridine diphosphate glucose (not shown in Figure 8-6) to the dHMC. Since such enzymes are not found in uninfected cells, they must be coded in the phage DNA. The DNA of T-even phages also codes for a new thymidylate synthetase and a *DNA methylase* which converts some adenine to 6-methyladenine in the completed DNA polymer.

Other phage-specific changes. The DNA of ϕT4 also apparently codes for (1) a DNase that is thought to destroy host DNA; (2) a *polynucleotide kinase* that catalyzes the transfer of orthophosphate from ATP to the 5′-hydroxyl termini of DNA, RNA, short polynucleotides, and even nucleoside 3′-monophosphates; (3) a *DNA ligase*; and (4) a heat-labile factor that combines with host ribosomes to cause ϕT4 mRNA to be preferentially translated. All T phages code for *phage-specific tRNA's.*

Adesnik, M., and Levinthal, C. 1970. RNA metabolism in T4-infected *Escherichia coli.* J. Mol. Biol., 48: 187–208. (Synthesis of stable host RNA ceases 2 minutes after infection.)

Hsu, W.-T., and Weiss, S. B. 1969. Selective translation of T4 template RNA by ribosomes from T4-infected *Escherichia coli.* Proc. Nat. Acad. Sci., U.S., 64: 345–351.

Scherberg, N. H., and Weiss, S. B. 1970. Detection of bacteriophage T4- and T5-coded transfer RNAs. Proc. Nat. Acad. Sci., U.S., 67: 1164–1171. (Five identified from T4 and 14 from T5 phage-infected *E. coli.*)

S8.8c Changes in the genetic material in the host can prevent the occurrence of normally occurring changes in the bases of phage DNA, thereby changing its conformation.

A strain of *E. coli* and one of *Shigella dysenteriae* are both defective in the biosynthesis of uridine diphosphoglucose, the glucosyl group donor in the DNA-glucosylating reaction that occurs in T-even phages. Accordingly, ϕT2 obtained from normal hosts that infect either of the two strains produce T2 progeny with nonglucosylated DNA. The nonglucosylated T2 progeny can productively infect the defective *Shigella* strain, but not the *E. coli* one, where enzymes attack and digest the entering nonglucosylated phage DNA. Growing the nonglucosylated T2 on normal *Shigella* restores the progeny DNA to its normal glucosylated pattern.

Another example of a failure to modify the bases of phage DNA is due to the simultaneous presence of another phage. Phage T3 codes for the enzyme *S*-adenosylmenthionine-ase (*Sam-ase*) which prevents DNA (and RNA) methylation by digesting the methyl donor. When *E. coli* is infected with both ϕT3 and ϕT2, the ϕT2 progeny obtained have no methylated DNA, whereas they normally do. In both of the preceding cases phage

DNA fails to undergo normal host-induced modification, resulting in the incorporation of unaltered, hence conformationally abnormal, phage DNA in the virion.

Arber, W., and Linn, S. 1969. DNA modification and restriction. Ann. Rev. Biochem., 38: 467–500.

Gold, M., Gefter, M., Hausmann, R., and Hurwitz, J. 1966. Methylation of DNA. J. Gen. Physiol. (Suppl.), 49 (No. 6, Part 2): 5–28.

Hattman, S., and Fukasawa, T. 1963. Host-induced modification of T-even phages due to defective glucosylation of their DNA. Proc. Nat. Acad. Sci., U.S., 50: 297–300.

S8.9   RNA viruses, like DNA viruses, utilize host material and machinery to replicate their genetic material.

The genomes of many RNA viruses serve as their own mRNA and code the RNA-dependent RNA polymerases needed for RNA replication *in vivo*. An exception is the satellite tobacco necrosis virus (STNV), which contains information for only one protein, its coat protein, and requires the presence of TMV—which codes for an RNA polymerase—in order to replicate. (The replication of STNV RNA by TMV–RNA-dependent RNA polymerase suggests that these viruses have genetically homologous RNA replicase recognition genes.)

In the case of the vesicular stomatitus virus, whose virion contains single-stranded RNA, the virus proteins are coded in mRNA's that are complementary to virion RNA. Virus replication thus requires the presence of an RNA polymerase that uses virion RNA as template. Such an enzyme is found in the virion.

RNA viruses can also affect the RNA's of their hosts. For example, poliovirus infection inhibits the synthesis of host RNA and induces the synthesis of poliovirus RNA. Furthermore, after a cell is infected with TMV, cytoplasmic rRNA is broken down and the ribonucleosides liberated are utilized in the synthesis of TMV RNA.

Baltimore, D., Huang, A. S., and Stampfer, M. 1970. Ribonucleic acid synthesis of vesicular stomatitus virus, II. An RNA polymerase in the virion. Proc. Nat. Acad. Sci., U.S., 66: 572–576.

QUESTIONS AND PROBLEMS

1. Discuss the occurrence and function of genes that modify genes or gene products.

2. In what respects would you expect the properties of tRNA to be changed or unchanged by methylation?

3. Is it reasonable to suppose that the regions of DNA adjacent to those coding for r, m, and tRNA's may be silent in that they are transcribed but neither translated nor used to make translational machinery? Explain.

4. Discuss the variation in the organic bases which occur in DNA and RNA.

5. Supermethylation of tRNA can occur using nonhomologous tRNA methylases, that is, using enzymes from other organisms. No change occurs in absorbency at 260 nm, however. Explain.

6. Sperm cell extracts are unable to methylate undermethylated tRNA. Is this finding expected or unexpected? Explain.

7. Defend the thesis that the biological individuality of a species resides in the chemistry of its nucleic acids.

8. How would you proceed to determine the relative abundance of nonredundant and partially redundant DNA in frog sperm?

9. How are annealing rate and melting temperature related to the detection of the number of copies of redundant DNA and the accuracy of the redundancy?

10. Describe the procedure you would use to determine whether redundant DNA was transcribed?

11. How would you show that redundant DNA is not restricted to one region of the genome?

12. Total synthesis of the gene for an alanine tRNA from yeast has been accomplished *in vitro*. In what respect does this *in vitro* DNA gene differ from the native tDNA?

13. Unmethylated RNA can be translated *in vitro*, whereas methylated rRNA cannot. What possible bearing do these observations have on the functioning of rRNA *in vivo*?

14. TMV RNA is composed of approximately 6,400 ribonucleotides. How much of this RNA is not used to code for TMV coat protein (a polymer of 2,220 identical subunits, each of which consists of 158 amino acids)? What do you suppose is the function of this portion?

15. Make a list of the minimal requirements for the functioning and reproduction of the simplest-free-living organism you can imagine; estimate the minimum number of nucleotides required to perform these functions assuming that the genetic material is RNA; assuming that it is DNA. Compare your estimates with the number of nucleotides in TMV and ϕX174. What are your conclusions?

Chapter 9

Mutational Variation

In Chapter 8 we found that a cell's own genetic DNA programs quantitative and qualitative variations in the chemical composition of its progeny DNA as well as of the different classes of its RNA transcripts. Further variations in nucleic acids in cells result from (1) gain or loss of infective DNA and RNA genetic material, (2) the effects these have on the host's DNA and RNA, and (3) the RNA transcripts coded in infecting DNA genetic material. All the preceding variations are regularly occurring because they are coded or programmed in the genetic material of organisms.

Sometimes elements of the external environment of organisms are the primary cause of rare, sporadic, unusual changes in genetic nucleic acids; other times elements of the internal environment of organisms are directly or indirectly the primary cause of uncoded or unprogrammed changes in genetic nucleic acids. Caused either way, any more-or-less permanent change in the amount or primary structure of genetic material that is unusual or unnatural to the biological system we will call a *mutation*, and the product of such a change, a *mutant*. The present chapter considers the detection, molecular basis, production, repair, and prevention of mutations as well as the factors in the external and internal environments that are responsible.

9.1 Although some mutants are detected directly from chemical–physical changes in nucleic acids or the molecular effects these changes have, most are detected indirectly by their supramolecular, biological effects.

Mutants can be detected in the following direct and indirect ways:

1. By the change in chemical composition of the genetic material.
2. By a change in physical properties caused by the chemical change.
3. By the preceding changes detected indirectly at the molecular level, for example by means of (a) a modified ability of DNA or RNA polymerase to initiate or terminate nucleic acid synthesis; (b) a modified rate at which errors occur during replication (c) a modified rate at which errors occur during transcription; and (d) a modified amino acid content of a polypeptide synthesized in a ribosomal system.[1]
4. By the preceding changes detected indirectly from their effects on the supramolecular (relatively gross) characteristics of an organism—for

---

[1] The polypeptide coded by a given gene may either contain wrong amino acids or be incomplete because of nucleotide changes in (1) that gene, (2) genes coding an aminoacyl-tRNA synthetase or tRNA, or (3) genes coding for ribosomal components or various other factors needed for translation. Mutations of types 2 and 3 can, of course, also produce changes in many other proteins, too, sometimes making amino acid sense from what is normally nonsense.

example, from changes in color, size, intelligence, etc. It should be noted that, in general, mutants resistant to a drug are present before, and are not induced by, exposure to the drug (as proved in Section S11.2). Drugs are, therefore, usually useful for the detection, not the induction, of drug-resistant mutations.

Although mutants can be detected by the first three criteria listed, under especially favorable conditions, most are detected *in vivo* by the last—by their effects on gross biological traits. Some chemical changes in nucleic acids doubtless occur which are not yet detectable by any of the above criteria using our present chemical–physical–biological methods of investigation. More (but probably not all) mutants will be detected as our techniques for investigation improve. In the sections that follow we will find that a variety of ways have been used to detect mutations that involve parts of a nucleotide, single whole nucleotides, and polynucleotides.

9.2   Some mutations involve only the sugar portion of a nucleotide.

Although deoxyribose is the only sugar detected in the DNA of most organisms, an occasional ribose may be present. Arabinose is thought to be incorporated into the DNA of mammalian cells in culture, and D-mannose has been found in the DNA of a mutant of phage SP8. It is possible that some *mutagens*, physical or chemical agents which greatly increase mutation frequency, add an O at the 2′ position of deoxyribose in a DNA strand or remove the 2′ O of ribose in an RNA strand. (R)

9.3   Mutations can involve base changes in already formed nucleic acids.

Bases that are already incorporated in nucleic acid are subject to two kinds of change that have mutational consequences: (1) internal modification, and (2) removal and/or replacement. We shall discuss these in turn.

Internal modification of bases

Each of the bases of DNA and RNA can assume several different structural arrangements, or *tautomeric forms*. In previous discussions and diagrams, the most likely tautomer of each base (its keto or amino form) was assumed to occur. The tautomers of uracil and adenine, shown in Figure 9-1 differ in the positions at which one hydrogen atom is attached. In both instances this change is accompanied by a shift of electrons so that some double bonds become single bonds, and vice versa. The less likely tautomers are said to be in enol ($=C—OH$) or imino ($=NH$) form. The relative frequencies of tautomers depend upon several factors, including the pH.

Although the usual tautomer of adenine (in amino form) pairs with thymine, one of the less common imino tautomers of adenine can base-pair with cytosine by forming two hydrogen bonds, as shown in Figure 9-2. Reciprocally, a rare imino tautomer of cytosine can pair with adenine by forming two H bonds. In like manner, thymine and guanine can pair by forming three H bonds between guanine and an enol tautomer of thymine (Figure 9-3A), or between thymine and a tautomer of guanine. A tauto-

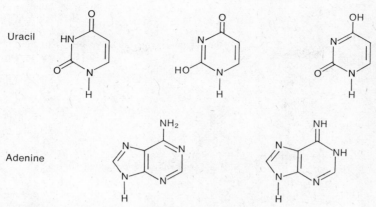

Uracil

Adenine

Figure 9-1   Tautomers of uracil and adenine.

meric shift thus makes a new and "incorrect" purine–pyrimidine base pair possible. Tautomeric shifts may play an important role in spontaneous mutation.

Chemical mutagens can modify individual bases in other ways. For example, *nitrous acid* (HNO_2) acts by removing the amino group from purines and pyrimidines of DNA and RNA and substituting a keto group. After such deamination, (1) adenine becomes hypoxanthine, (2) cytosine becomes uracil, and (3) guanine becomes xanthine (which can still pair with cytosine but only with two H bonds). *Hydroxylamine* (NH_2OH) seems to react only with the amino group of cytosine, permitting the modified base to pair with adenine but not guanine.

Let us consider a consequence of the adenine-to-hypoxanthine mutation. At the time of the first semiconservative replication, hypoxanthine base-pairs with cytosine with two H bonds (Figure 9-3B). At the second replication, cytosine base-pairs with guanine, as it ordinarily does (see Figure 9-4). A consequence of the adenine to hypoxanthine mutation is, therefore, that the original dA-containing strand gives rise to a second-generation strand with dG instead of dA at that position. Such a net change, for example in DNA, from purine to purine (dA $\rightleftharpoons$ dG) or from pyrimidine

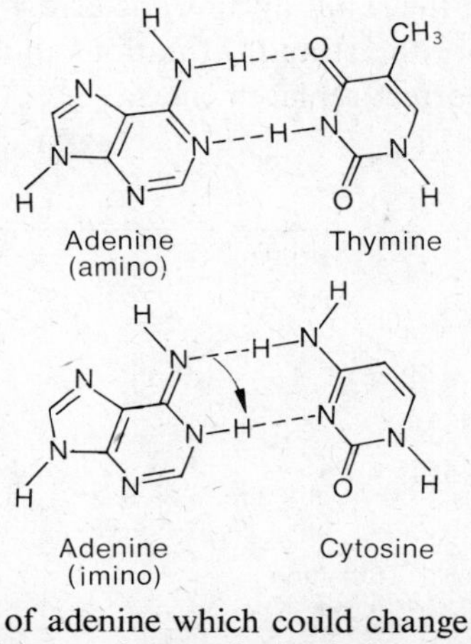

Adenine
(amino)   Thymine

Adenine
(imino)   Cytosine

Figure 9-2   Tautomeric shift of adenine which could change its complementary base from thymine to cytosine. Upper diagram shows adenine before, and lower diagram after, undergoing a tautomeric shift of one of its hydrogen atoms. (After J. D. Watson and F. H. C. Crick.)

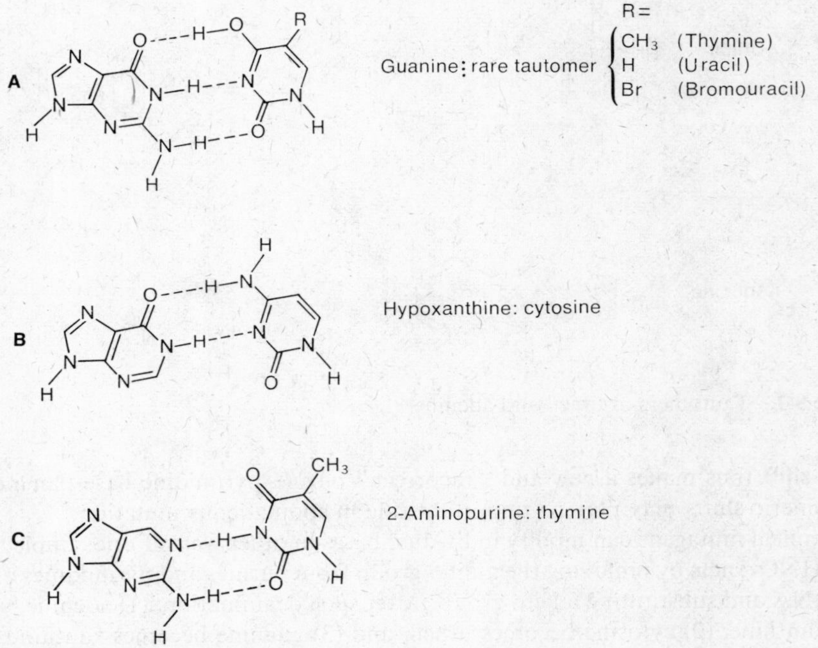

A   Guanine: rare tautomer
$$R= \begin{cases} CH_3 & (Thymine) \\ H & (Uracil) \\ Br & (Bromouracil) \end{cases}$$

B   Hypoxanthine: cytosine

C   2-Aminopurine: thymine

Figure 9-3 Some less-usual base pairs.

to pyrimidine (dC $\rightleftharpoons$ dT) is called a base *transition*. A net change between purine and pyrimidine (dA or dG $\rightleftharpoons$ dC or dT) is a base *transversion*.

Removal and/or replacement

Exposure of ϕT4 to conditions of low pH may also induce base changes. *In vitro* it brings about the *depurination* of the phage's DNA—the complete removal of all guanine and adenine. When the resulting apurinic acid is returned to higher pH, some purines are thought to rejoin the strand. Mutations thus may involve either the loss of purine bases or their incorrect replacement.

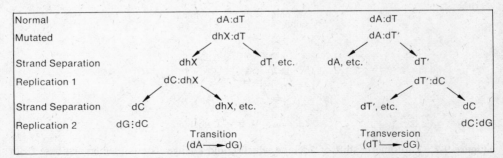

Figure 9-4 Postulated sequence of events leading to transition or transversion. dhX, deoxyinosine; T′, modified thymidine.

9.4   Newly made genes may be mutant because they contain incorrect bases resulting from mistakes in incorporation or replication.

The incorporation of *5-bromouracil* (present in the form of deoxybromouridine, *dBU*) into a strand of DNA[2] can be considered a "*mistake of incorporation*" since bromouracil is not an ordinary component. Since the usual tautomer of bromouracil is in the keto state, it is usually incorporated as the complement of adenine (Figure 9-5). The rare enol tautomer of bromouracil (like the tautomer of thymine) can pair with guanine to form dG : dBU. Over all, therefore, two different kinds of mistakes of incorporation are possible for bromouracil—formation of dA : dBU pairs and of dG : dBU pairs. As part of a DNA strand, the bromouracil of a dA : dBU pair can continue to specify adenine so that no "*mistakes in replication*" follows. If, however, the bromouracil assumes its rare enol form and accepts guanine as its complement (Figure 9-3A), a mistake in replication will occur—adenine will be replaced by guanine, a transition mutation. Since the bromouracil in dG : dBU is usually in keto form at the time of the next replication, it will accept adenine as its complement, resulting in the guanine to adenine transition. In summary, the pyrimidine bromouracil gives rise to purine transitions in both directions (dA $\rightleftharpoons$ dG).

In vitro studies of the replication of copolymers of DNA containing bromouracil[3] indicate that the base analog may also cause normal bases that are adjacent to it in the same strand to commit errors of replication. Although the mutational effect of bromouracil in DNA copolymers *in vitro* may not be identical to what it is in native

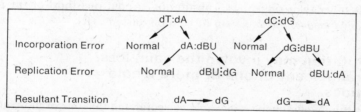

Figure 9-5   Mistakes of incorporation and replication involving 5-bromouracil. Mistakes of incorporation occur when different tautomers of bromouracil base-pair with adenine or guanine in their usual tautomeric forms. A change in the tautomeric form of incorporated bromouracil results in errors of replication that result in dA↔dG transitions.

[2] Base analogs are incorporated into DNA *in vitro* when they are present as deoxyribonucleoside 5'-triphosphates. For example, uracil, 5-bromouracil, and 5-fluorouracil can substitute for thymine (and for thymine only); 5-methyl-, 5-bromo-, and 5-fluorocytosine can substitute for cytosine only; and hypoxanthine can substitute for guanine only. *In vivo* 5-bromo-, 5-chloro-, or 5-iodouracil can replace some of the thymine in DNA of bacteria, phages, and human cell cultures.

[3] The DNA copolymer of adenine and bromouracil, poly (dA-dBU), can serve as primer-template in an extensive synthesis with the deoxyribonucleotides of dBU, dA, and dG. Since the primer-template presumably contains dBU and dA in strict alternation (Figure 9-6), two nucleotides in a synthesized strand must usually be in the dBUdA or dAdBU sequence. dG, however, is also found in the product (but not when poly [dA-dT] is the primer-template). If the presence of dG in the product were always due to a mistake of incorporation by template dBU, dG should be adjacent to dBU in the synthesized polymer, and should be in either a dBUdG or dGdBU dinucleotide sequence. dG is, in fact, incorporated not only after dBU (the dBUdG sequence) but after dG (dGdG) with about equal frequency and less often after dA (dAdG). Because dG-containing dinucleotide sequences other than dBUdG and dGdBU are found, we cannot explain the results only by mistakes in replication made by the bromouracil in the primer-template. Apparently, the presence of dBU adjacent to dA causes dA to base-pair incorrectly with dG.

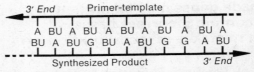

Figure 9-6 Sample base sequences of a primer-template copolymer poly(dA-dBU) and of the product synthesized *in vitro* by *E. coli* DNA polymerase using dATP, dBUTP, and dGTP as substrate. Each vertical dropline is understood to be a d = deoxyribose group.

DNA *in vivo*, evidence has been obtained *in vivo* that transitions at one base pair resulted in a 23-fold increase in mutagen-induced transitions at an adjacent base pair.

Another base analog, *2-aminopurine*, incorporated into DNA also produces base substitutions. In its normal tautomeric form, it can pair with thymine by two hydrogen bonds (Figure 9-3C) or with cytosine by one. As the less common tautomer, it can bond with cytosine by two H bonds. As a consequence, pyrimidine transitions (dT $\rightleftharpoons$ dC) are possible.

A great deal of work has been carried out to identify the particular base changes occurring in mutations *in vivo*. A useful technique in determining whether the change is a transition is to subject the mutant to a chemical mutagen (such as nitrous acid) which causes transitions in both directions (Figure 9-7). If the initial change was a transition, then the spontaneous frequency of change back to the original condition (the spontaneous *reversion* frequency) should be greatly increased by treatment of the mutant with the mutagen. The direction of a transition can be inferred from the revertability of the mutant by hydroxylamine, which only reverts GC pairs to AT pairs. Mutants that cannot be identified as transitions may result from transversions or mutations other than single base substitution. About one third of the mutations induced by *ethyl ethanesulfonate* seem to be transversions. (R)

9.5 Mutation may involve the gain, loss, or rearrangement of one or more whole nucleotides.

Mutations can involve changes in whole nucleotides in that one or more nucleotides may be added, deleted, replaced, inverted, or transposed to a new position (Figure 9-8). All these rearrangements can be produced by breaking the backbone at two or more places. All except inversion are possible for single-stranded nucleic acids. Inversion requires a double-stranded nucleic acid, since the same polarity must be maintained along a strand.

The extent and position of a deletion mutation can be visualized in the following

Mutagen	Base-Pair Changes	
	Transitions	Transversions
5-bromouracil	AT ⟷ GC	
2-aminopurine	AT ⟷ GC	
Nitrous acid	AT ⟷ GC	
Hydroxylamine	GC ⟶ AT	
Ethyl ethanesulfonate	GC ⟶ AT	GC ⟶ TA GC ⟵ CG

Figure 9-7 Types of transitional and transversional base-pair changes produced by various mutagens.

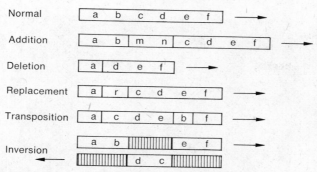

Figure 9-8   Whole nucleotide changes. Arrows show polarity.

way. Two kinds of DNA duplexes are used: One has the normal nucleotide sequence (obtained, for example, from normal phage), and the other has part of this sequence deleted (obtained, for example, from such a phage known from transcription–translation studies to have certain genes deleted.) Each duplex is heat-denatured and the single strands separated. The single strands of one duplex are then permitted to base-pair with the complementary single strands of the other duplex to form *heteroduplexes*, composed of one normal and one deficient complement. When shadowed with uranium oxide, electron micrographs of heteroduplexes show single-stranded regions, in otherwise double-stranded DNA, where the deletion is located (Figure 9-9).

Single whole-nucleotide changes which do not involve breakage of the sugar–phosphate backbone can be brought about by chemical mutagens. An *acridine* (Figure 9-10), for example, produces phase-shift or *frame-shift* mutations which involve the addition or subtraction of whole deoxyribonucleotides, and cause mRNA to be read out of phase or frame (as discussed in Section 7.5). Acridines are thought to act either by binding to the outside of a double-stranded nucleic acid or by inserting between adjacent nucleotides of a strand in a duplex. Under the latter circumstances the strand seems to be altered lengthwise so that, if used as a template, an unspecified nucleotide may be inserted in the complementary strand at the position corresponding to the acridine molecule. Other molecules, such as free nucleotides or other naturally occurring substances, may act like the acridines. Nucleosides can associate together to form stacks. These stacks may then interact with the bases in nucleic acid to cause mispairings and nucleotide insertions.

In the presence of Mn^{2+} DNA polymerase can use a DNA template *in vitro* to make a complementary strand that contains both deoxyribo- and ribonucleotides, provided of course that the appropriate ribonucleoside 5′-triphosphates are included as substrates (as previously noted in the footnote to Section 4.7). Since the DNA transcript contains uracil and ribose rather than thymine and deoxyribose, we can consider it a mutant strand. The highly mutagenic character of manganese salts in bacteria implies that such an incorporation may occur *in vivo* as well. (R)

9.6   The mutability of genetic nucleic acids depends upon their composition and conformation.

The physical–chemical composition of each of the following is unique in some respects: mononucleotides, single-stranded nucleic acid, double-stranded nucleic acid,

Figure 9-9 Electron micrograph of a deletion mutation visualized in a heteroduplex. The $b2^+$ loop is single-stranded, the remainder is double-stranded. (Courtesy of B. C. Westmoreland, W. Szybalski, and H. Ris, 1969. Science, 163: 1345. Copyright 1969 by the American Association for the Advancement of Science.)

Proflavin

Acridine orange

Figure 9-10 Two acridine dyes.

protein-encapsulated single-stranded nucleic acid, protein-encapsulated double-stranded nucleic acid. Accordingly, since each also has a unique physical–chemical conformation, each has different spectrum of mutability by various chemical mutagens.

In general, the more uncombined chemical groups these substances have, the more
mutable they are; the more groups they have combined, the more protected they are
from chemical change. Thus, for example, single-stranded nucleic acid is more mutable
than protein-encapsulated double-stranded nucleic acid. The relative reactivity and
mutability of various categories of nucleic acids and their components is described in
more detail in Section S9.6.

9.7   Ultraviolet light causes pyrimidines to link in pairs.

When exposed to *ultraviolet (UV) light*, pyrimidines commonly add a water
molecule across the C4-C5 double bond (see Figure 9-11A). Although this photoproduct reverts to its original form upon heating or acidification, it appears to persist
frequently enough *in vivo* to weaken the H bonding with its purine complement and
thus cause localized strand separation. Furthermore, two pyrimidines can be induced
by UV light to join at their 4 and 5 positions to form a pyrimidine dimer (Figure
9-11B). This *dimerization* can result in thymine thymine, cytosine cytosine, uracil
uracil, and mixed pyrimidine dimers (for example, cytosine thymine) but rarely (if at
all) in the dimer of bromouracil.

Localized strand separation (induced by UV) gives pyrimidines greater freedom of
movement and thereby increases the likelihood of dimerization involving bases in
different strands, in widely separated regions of one strand, and especially in adjacent
regions of the same strand. Interstrand dimerization, by producing cross links between nucleic acid chains, inhibits strand separation and distribution. Both hydration

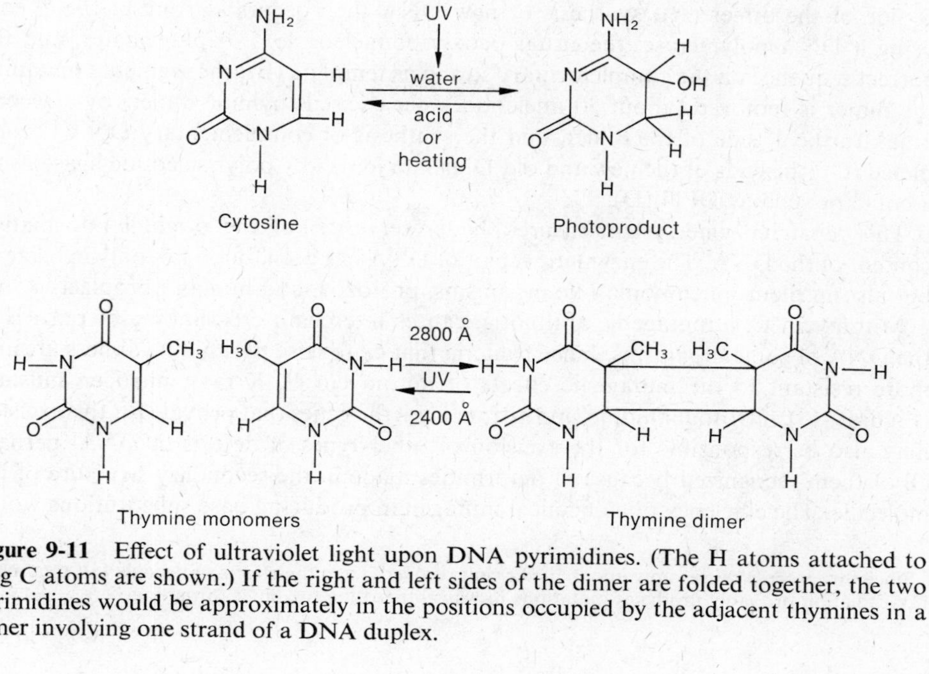

Figure 9-11   Effect of ultraviolet light upon DNA pyrimidines. (The H atoms attached to
ring C atoms are shown.) If the right and left sides of the dimer are folded together, the two
pyrimidines would be approximately in the positions occupied by the adjacent thymines in a
dimer involving one strand of a DNA duplex.

and dimerization of double-stranded DNA interfere with nucleic acid synthesis—they block DNA synthesis (probably by modifying the major groove) and, it is likely, block RNA synthesis as well (by modifying the minor groove); mRNA modified either by hydration or dimerization is mistranslated.

Dimer formation may be the reason that UV light destroys the primer-template activity of single-stranded DNA, causes mutations in ϕX174, and destroys naked infective genetic DNA. UV radiation has two opposite effects, however, depending upon the wavelengths used. At 2,800 Å, UV light promotes the formation of dimers from mononers, whereas at 2,400 Å it promotes the formation of monomers from dimers. In fact, the genetic activity of bacterial DNA inactivated by 2,800 Å UV radiation can be partially restored by light at 2,390 Å. (R)

9.8   In different enzymatic processes, dimers and other defects can be removed from a double-stranded nucleic acid and the duplex repaired.

UV-induced dimers can also be split enzymatically. In the presence of certain blue lights, an enzyme system in *E. coli* can split thymine dimers (including interstrand dimers) into monomers. In this reaction the enzyme attaches to the thymine dimer, with the blue light providing energy for the breakage.[4]

Certain strains of *E. coli* are somewhat resistant to UV-radiation; that is, they can recover from some of the damage incurred and can resume DNA synthesis. Since this recovery can take place even in the dark, the process cannot involve the splitting of dimers in a photochemical reaction. Instead, the dimers are enzymatically removed from the DNA. One possible sequence of events is diagrammed in Figure 9-12. After a dimer is produced a UV-specific endonuclease produces a single breakage on the 5′-side of the dimer (A); synthesis of new DNA then occurs starting at the 5′ end, using a DNA polymerase, the usual deoxyribonucleoside 5′-triphosphates, and the correct sequence on the complementary strand as template (B); the segment containing the dimer is removed (about 30 nucleotides per excised thymine dimer) by a second break to the 3′ side of the dimer, and the synthesis of complementary DNA is completed (C); the ends of the new and old DNA are joined by polynucleotide ligase using a cofactor such as DPN (D).

This repair enzyme system ensures the preservation of the original information content of the DNA. The enzymatic repair of DNA has been found not only in bacteria but also in pleuropneumonia-like organisms, protozoa, and human fibroblasts.

Mitomycin C, a mutagenic antibiotic, causes interchain crosslinking of purines in the DNA of some organisms. Since bacteria that can excise pyrimidine dimers are also more resistant to the mutagenic effects of mitomycin C, X rays, nitrogen mustard (Figure 9-13), nitrosoguanidine, and nitrous acid, the genes that provide for this excision may also be responsible for the excision of other types of defects in DNA, perhaps all of them recognized because of deformities made in the secondary structure of the molecule. The efficiency of a chemical mutagen in producing base substitutions would

---

[4] Since this process causes only about 50 per cent recovery from the effects of a single UV treatment, UV radiation probably produces mutations in ways other than by dimer formation.

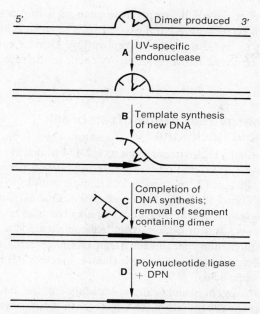

5′ —— Dimer produced —— 3′

A | UV-specific
  | endonuclease

B | Template synthesis
  | of new DNA

C | Completion of
  | DNA synthesis;
  | removal of segment
  | containing dimer

D | Polynucleotide ligase
  | + DPN

Figure 9-12   Postulated sequence of events that excises dimers and repairs DNA. (After R. B. Kelly, M. R. Atkinson, J. A. Huberman, and A. Kornberg, 1969.)

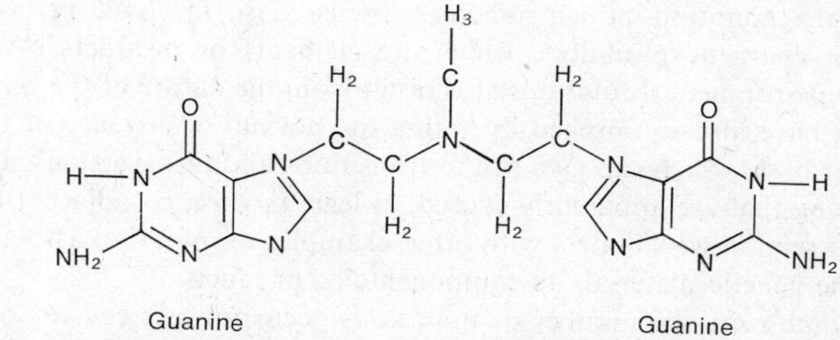

Nitrogen mustard

Guanine   Guanine

Figure 9-13   Nitrogen mustard is able to cross-link guanines. Such cross links in DNA are reparable.

be related, therefore, to its ability to produce changes within a strand which are not sufficiently drastic to be recognized and excised by a repair mechanism but which are sufficiently different to cause mistakes in replication. Dimers can lead to mutations even when they are removed, however, if errors occur in the repair process. (R)

9.9   High-energy radiations often break the nucleic acid backbone.

When single-stranded DNA viruses such as ϕX174 and ϕS13 incorporate nucleotides with radioactive ^{32}P instead of P, a single radioactive decay of ^{32}P is sufficient to inactivate them. Phage T2 and others containing double-stranded DNA, on the other hand, require about 10 decays for inactivation. One explanation for the results of such *suicide experiments* is that each decay breaks the backbone of the polynucleotide in which it occurs; and in double-stranded nucleic acids a nearby break in the backbone of a complementary strand may lead to the severing of the duplex. Thus, single-stranded nucleic acids will be severed (hence, inactivated) more frequently than double-stranded nucleic acids.

Another important agent which causes breakage of the backbone is *X rays*, a high-energy electromagnetic radiation. The decrease in sedimentation rate of denatured and native DNA after X-radiation of *E. coli* indicates that the radiation caused single- and double-strand scissions of the DNA backbone. Although double-strand scissions are not repaired when treated cells are reincubated, single-strand scissions are repaired in certain *E. coli* strains. Double-strand scissions in DNA appear to be primarily responsible for the lethality of high-energy radiations in *E. coli*.

X rays can also oxidize deoxyribose, deaminate and dehydroxylate bases, and form peroxides in DNA. These changes, which may increase the chance of strand breakage, together with strand breakage can result in stimulating the DNA repair system or in completely or partially preventing DNA replication and transcription.

9.10   A considerable portion of the spontaneous mutation rate results from mutation-causing and mutation-preventing substances normally produced during metabolism.

Most of the mutation-inducing factors discussed so far have involved chemical mutagens or energetic radiations which are elements or products of the external, nongenetic environment. Mutations also result from the nature of the genetic material itself, as we have already implied in noting the normal occurrence of the less usual tautomers of bases which can give rise to transitions and transversions, and the errors in base pairing that are apparently caused, at least *in vitro*, by adjacent bases. In this and the next section we will deal with other examples of mutation associated with the nature of the genetic material, its components or products.

The *mutation rate*, the number of mutations occurring per cell (or organism) per unit time (discussed in Section S9.10), can be studied in *E. coli* exposed to various substances added to the culture medium in concentrations that produce no appreciable killing. Many purines and purine derivatives are found to be mutagenic. The most mutagenic is caffeine; azaguanine is also mutagenic, as is adenine—to a lesser degree. In contrast, no pyrimidines or their derivatives are mutagenic under the same conditions. If purine ribonucleosides such as adenosine or guanosine are added to the medium containing any of one of several purine mutagens, the mutagenic activity is completely suppressed. Thus, for example, adenosine completely suppresses the mutagenicity of adenine or caffeine. Clearly the purine ribonucleosides are acting as *antimutagens* and are not merely acting as selective agents against induced mutants. On the other hand, pyrimidine ribonucleosides, deoxyadenosine, and deoxyguanosine either are not at all antimutagenic to purines and their derivatives, or they are much less efficient than the purine ribonucleosides.

The normally occurring, *spontaneous mutation rate* is also reduced by the addition of purine ribonucleosides (adenosine or guanosine) but not pyrimidine ribonucleosides (uridine or cytidine) to the culture medium. With adenosine added to the medium, the spontaneous rate is reduced to about one third its original value. Moreover, when adenosine is not added to the medium, the spontaneous rate is lower under anaerobic than aerobic conditions, as would be expected from the presence of significant amounts of adenosine in *E. coli* growing under anaerobic but not aerobic conditions.

Even though it is not clear how ordinary organic bases and nucleosides produce these effects on mutation rate, we can conclude that a considerable portion of the spontaneous mutation rate is the normal consequence of the cell's biochemical activity in producing mutagens and antimutagens. It should be noted, however, that the spontaneous mutation rate also depends upon the general external environment of the organism.[5] (R)

9.11 The DNA polymerases of some mutants are mutators, and of others antimutators.

Phage T4 codes for a T4 DNA polymerase essential for the ϕDNA replication. Under standard conditions, normal phage genes undergo mutation and mutant genes undergo reverse mutation (reversion) at specific spontaneous rates. Many mutants of the gene coding for T4 DNA polymerase have been obtained, some acting as mutators (since the spontaneous mutation rate is increased, sometimes tenfold) and others as antimutators (reducing the spontaneous mutation rate, sometimes tenfold). Not all types of mutation are prevented, however, since the spontaneous reversion of dG : dC base pairs in mutants is not prevented by two antimutators tested.

The mutational effects of such mutants have also been studied in two general ways:

[5] Although the mutations which occur spontaneously bear no obvious relation to the external environment, either with respect to the genes affected or the type of alternative produced, modifications in the external environment do, however, influence mutation frequency. For example, in the range of temperatures to which individuals are usually exposed, each rise of 10°C produces about a fivefold increase in mutation frequency. The magnitude of this increase is similar to, although somewhat greater than, that obtained with an increase in temperature in ordinary chemical reactions. Violent temperature changes in either direction produce an even greater effect upon mutation frequency. Actually, detrimental environmental conditions of almost any kind increase mutation rate.

(1) in *in vitro* DNA synthesis, and (2) *in vivo* with chemical mutagens.[6] The results of such studies suggest that the DNA polymerase plays a crucial role in base selection and, therefore, an important role in spontaneous mutability. It should be noted that all stages of the transcription–translation sequence can influence the mutation process indirectly by affecting any one or more of various aspects of the cell's metabolism, including the following: (1) the entrance, distribution, and persistence of environmental mutagens; (2) the production and fate of cellular mutagens and antimutagens (such as those discussed in this and the preceding sections); and (3) the conformation of genetic templates. (R)

SUMMARY AND CONCLUSIONS

Mutations, usually detected by their effects on the gross supramolecular character-istics of an organism, can be described molecularly in terms of changes involving a portion of the nucleotide or one or more whole nucleotides. Mutations that involve only part of a nucleotide include changes in the pentose sugar, the phosphate (for example, replacing P by ^{32}P), and the bases. For example, bases that are already part of genes can be (1) modified internally by tautomerism or mutagens, (2) removed, and (3) replaced, all of which can also lead to transitions and transversions; bases that are to enter new genes may be incorrect because of mistakes of incorporation (in which the correct template base-pairs with the incorrect substrate) and mistakes of replication (in which an incorrect template base-pairs with its correct substrate). *In vitro* studies indicate that base changes in one region of nucleic acid may also cause mistakes of replication to occur in adjacent regions.

Mutations that involve the gain, loss, and rearrangement of one or more nucleo-tides often involve breakage of the backbone of already formed genetic material followed by appropriate shifts of nucleotides; sometimes, however, additions or losses of one or a few nucleotides (frame-shift mutations) can be produced in newly made genetic material by deforming, not breaking, the template strand.

All these types of mutation can be produced by a variety of chemical and physical

---

[6] Some specific results obtained in such studies are presented.

1. The normal DNA polymerase coded by ϕT4 makes the transversional error of incorporating dTMP instead of dGMP, when poly dC is the template *in vitro*, with a frequency of 1 dTMP per 10^5 or 10^6 incorporated dGMP. A mutation in the gene for this DNA polymerase makes this error four times more frequently. The frequency of this error by both enzymes depends upon the dGTP and dTTP concentrations in the medium and is increased 5 to 20 times by replacing the Mg^{2+} in the medium by Mn^{2+}.

2. When a strong mutator allele of the gene for T4 DNA polymerase is studied together with chemical mutagens *in vivo*, little or no interaction or synergism is observed. For example, the relative mutation rates are 1 for the normal gene alone, 10 for the mutator alone, 18 for the normal gene plus 5-bromodeoxyuridine, and 36 for the mutant gene plus the base analog.

On the other hand, if either of two antimutator alleles is present when the phage is exposed to chemical mutagens, mutation rate is reduced as much as 1000-fold. These antimutators specifically decrease the frequency of transition mutations induced by a variety of chemical mutagens. For example, mutagenesis by thymine deprivation, which promotes transitions at dA : dT but not dG : dC sites, is strongly suppressed by antimutators. Although the antimutators do not suppress nitrous acid–induced transitions at dG : dC sites, they do suppress nitrous acid–induced transitions at dA : dT sites. Transitions induced at both types of site by 5 bromouracil are suppressed by the antimutators; such suppression means that the enzyme plays an active role in recognizing and excluding 5-bromouracil when it is presented for incorporation in either its enol tautomer (preventing the dG : dC → dA : dT base-pair transition) or its keto tautomer (preventing the reverse transition).

mutagens, the type of mutagenic effect depending upon both the composition and conformation of the genetic material (the larger the number of uncombined chemical groups it has, the more mutable it is) as well as the nature of the mutagen.

A considerable portion of the spontaneous mutation rate of an organism, that is, the number of normally occurring changes that normally persist in its genetic material per generation, is induced by external physical and chemical mutagens as well as internal mutagens—in some cases purines and their derivatives and mutator DNA polymerases. A portion of the genetic changes that are induced, such as pyrimidine dimers produced by ultraviolet light or others that crosslink DNA strands or grossly deform their conformation, do not persist because they are recognized by an enzymatic repair system which excises the damaged portion and replaced it with a normal sequence using the undamaged strand of the duplex as template. Some expected genetic changes probably never occur because of the presence of antimutagens (such as purine ribonucleosides) and antimutator DNA polymerases.

Mutations will be considered in detail later with respect to

1. Spontaneous and radiation-induced gross chromosomal changes (in Chapter 18 and its supplementary sections, respectively).
2. Localized points of chromosomes (in Sections S10.4a and 21.2, and S21.2).
3. Their effects on various traits of phages, procaryotes, and eucaryotes (in numerous chapters, especially Chapters 20 through 23).
4. The regulation of their occurrence (in Chapter 25).
5. Their role in populations and evolution (in Chapters 34 through 37).

GENERAL REFERENCES

Alexander, P. 1960. Radiation-imitating chemicals. Scient. Amer., 202 (No. 1): 99–108. Scientific American Offprints, San Francisco: W. H. Freeman and Company, Publishers.

Drake, J. W. 1969. *An introduction to the molecular basis of mutation.* San Francisco: Holden-Day, Inc.

Muller, H. J. 1922. Variation due to change in the individual gene. Amer. Nat., 56: 32–50. Reprinted in *Classic papers in genetics*, Peters, J. A., (Editor), Englewood Cliffs, N.J.: Prentice-Hall, Inc., 1959, pp. 104–116.

Setlow, R. B. 1968. The photochemistry, photobiology, and repair of polynucleotides. Progr. Nucleic Acid Res. and Mol. Biol., 8: 257–295.

SPECIFIC SECTION REFERENCES

9.2   Rosenberg, E. 1965. D-mannose as a constituent of the DNA of a mutant strain of a bacteriophage SP8. Proc. Nat. Acad. Sci., U.S., 53: 836–840.

9.4   Benzer, S., and Freese, E. 1958. Induction of specific mutations with 5-bromouracil. Proc. Nat. Acad. Sci., U.S., 44: 112–119. Reprinted in *Papers on bacterial viruses*, second edition, Stent G. S. (Editor), Boston: Little, Brown and Company, 1965, pp. 276–283.

Koch, R. E. 1971. The influence of neighboring base pairs upon base-pair substitution mutation rates. Proc. Nat. Acad. Sci., U.S., 68: 773–776.

9.5   Pitha, P. M., Huang, W. M., and Ts'o, P. O. P. 1968. Physiochemical basis of the recognition process in nucleic acid interactions, IV. Costacking as the cause of mispairing and intercalation in nucleic acid interactions. Proc. Nat. Acad. Sci., U.S., 61: 332–339.

Westmoreland, B. C., Szybalski, W., and Ris, H. 1969. Mapping of deletions and substitutions in heteroduplex DNA molecules of bacteriophage lambda by electron microscopy. Science, 163: 1343–1348.

9.7   Deering, R. A. 1962. Ultraviolet radiation and nucleic acid. Scient. Amer., 207 (No. 6):
       135–144, 192. Scientific American Offprints, San Francisco: W. H. Freeman and
       Company, Publishers.
       Ottensmeyer, F. P., and Whitmore, G. F. 1968. Coding properties of ultraviolet
       photoproducts of uracil. I. Binding studies and polypeptide synthesis. J. Mol. Biol.,
       38: 1–16.

9.8   DeLucia, P., and Cairns, J. 1969. Isolation of an *E. coli* strain with a mutation affecting
       DNA polymerase. Nature, Lond., 224: 1164–1166. (The enzyme may be primarily
       for repair of DNA.)
       Hanawalt, P. C., and Haynes, R. H. 1967. The repair of DNA. Scient. Amer., 216
       (No. 2): 36–43, 146. Scientific American Offprints, San Francisco: W. H. Freeman
       and Company, Publishers.
       Kelly, R. B., Atkinson, M. R., Huberman, J. A., and Kornberg, A. 1969. Excision of
       thymine dimers and other mismatched sequences by DNA polymerase of *Escherichia
       coli*. Nature, Lond., 224: 495–501.
       Strauss, B., Coyle, M., and Robbins, M. 1969. Alkylation damage and its repair. Cold
       Spring Harbor Sympos. Quant. Biol., 1968, 33: 277–287.

9.9   Kanazir, D. T. 1969. Radiation-induced alterations in the structure of deoxyribonucleic
       acid and their biological consequences. Progr. Nucleic Acid Res. and Mol. Biol., 9:
       117–222.
       Lett, J. T. 1970. Repair of X-ray damage to the DNA in *Micrococcus radiodurans*: the
       effect of 5-bromodeoxuridine. J. Mol. Biol., 48: 395–408.
       Muller, H. J. 1927. Artificial transmutation of the gene. Science, 66: 84–87. Reprinted
       in *Classic papers in genetics*, Peters. J. A. (Editor), Englewood Cliffs, N.J.: Prentice-
       Hall, Inc., 1959, pp. 149–155, and also in *Great experiments in biology*, Gabriel, M.
       L., and Fogel, S. (Editors), Englewood Cliffs, N.J.: Prentice-Hall, Inc., 1955, pp.
       260–266.

9.10   Novick, A. 1956. Mutagens and antimutagens. Brookhaven Symposia on Biology, 8:
       201–215. Reprinted in *Papers on bacterial genetics*, Adelberg, E. A. (Editor), Boston:
       Little, Brown and Company, 1960, pp. 74–90.

9.11   Drake, J. W., and Greening, E. O. 1970. Suppression of chemical mutagenesis in
       bacteriophage T4 by genetically modified DNA polymerases. Proc. Nat. Acad. Sci.,
       U.S., 66: 823–829.
       Hall, Z. W., and Lehman, I. R. 1968. An *in vitro* transversion by a mutationally
       altered T4-induced DNA polymerase. J. Mol. Biol., 36: 321–333.
       Rosset, R., and Gorini, L. 1969. A ribosomal ambiguity mutation. J. Mol. Biol., 39:
       95–112.

SUPPLEMENTARY SECTIONS

**S9.6   Different categories of nucleic
acids and their monomeric components
have different reactivities and mutabilities.**

1. *Monomers.* This is generally the most
   reactive category. The reactivities of the free
   bases, which lack pentose at the N-3 and
   N-9 positions, differs from those of nucleotides and nucleosides.

2. *Single-stranded nucleic acid.* Chain breakage
   is introduced in this category as a possible
   mutational reaction. The bases tend to stack
   up, increasing mutations by mutagens which
   require base stacking; for example,
   nitrosoguanidine, which readily methylates
   guanine and possibly adenine. Otherwise,
   this category is generally less reactive than
   the monomer, although it is still readily
   mutated by nitrous acid, hydroxylamine,
   methoxyamine, and bromine.

3. *Double-stranded nucleic acid.* The H-bonded
   regions are generally less reactive in this
   than in previous categories. The same is
   true for the 4, 5 double bond of pyrimidines.
   Although this category is generally resistant
   to mutagenesis (it can, however, be
   alkylated when denatured), the N-7 of
   guanine and the N-3 of adenine are equally
   and more reactive, respectively, than in
   previous categories.

4. *Protein-encapsulated single-stranded nucleic
   acid.* As exemplified by TMV, the amino
   groups of guanine and adenine are less
   reactive than in previous categories. The
   N-7 of guanine is also less reactive to
   nitrosoguanidine than above; cytosine is
   unreactive to hydroxylamine. Typical

alkylating agents and nitrous acid are, however, still mutagenic.

5. *Protein-encapsulated double-stranded nucleic acid.* As exemplified by protein-coated duplex DNA, this category is similar to category 3 in mutagenic resistance.
Mutation by powerful chemical mutagens occurs and is attributed to the presence of single-stranded regions.

The preceding would also suggest that the distribution of mutations affecting different portions of a given DNA sequence depends upon the specific agent or agents whose mutagenic action is under study. Further discussion of the effect of specific mutagens on a specific chromosomal region is postponed until Section S10.7.

Singer, B., and Fraenkel-Conrat, H. 1969. The role of conformation in chemical mutagenesis. Progr. Nucleic Acid Res. and Mol. Biol., 9: 1–29.

S9.10   Mutation rate refers to the number of mutations occurring per cell or individual per unit time.

Mutation rate involves the number of mutations occurring per unit event. In multicellular organisms, mutation rate is usually expressed in terms of mutations per cell, individual, or generation. This definition can also be applied to unicellular organisms. Thus, the mutation rate from strepto-mycin sensitivity to resistance in one particular strain of *E. coli* is 1 per 1 billion bacteria—one of the lowest mutation rates so far measured in any organism.

The following results indicate that it is sometimes desirable to express mutation rate in terms of mutations per unit time. In bacteria, one can vary considerably the length of time required to complete a generation. For generation times between 37 minutes and 2 hours, the shorter the generation time, the larger the mutation rate per hour. When generation time is lengthened from 2 to 12 hours, the rate of mutations per hour is constant—each hour of delay increasing the number of mutants by the same amount.

It becomes apparent, therefore, that mutation rate is best defined as the chance of a mutation per cell (or organism) per unit time. When, however, each of the division cycles or generations requires the same length of time (as would be true for bacteria under optimal environmental conditions), mutation rate is usually measured with one generation as the unit of time.

Novick, A., and Szilard, L. 1951. Experiments on spontaneous and chemically induced mutations of bacteria growing in the chemostat. Cold Spring Harbor Sympos. Quant. Biol.: 16: 337–343. Reprinted in *Papers on bacterial genetics*, Adelberg, E. A. (Editor), Boston, Little, Brown and Company, 1960, pp. 47–57.

QUESTIONS AND PROBLEMS

1. Compare the mutagenic efficiency of UV treatment of the same total number of nucleotides in
   a. single- and double-stranded DNA.
   b. single-stranded DNA and single-stranded RNA.
2. What specific consequences would you expect from a mutation which causes a single base substitution in the tRNA whose anticodon is AAA?
3. Name the gene whose mutation is likely to be most detrimental. Justify your choice.
4. What will be the effect of a mutation in one gene for rRNA when this rRNA is incorporated in ribosomes that can accept mRNA and tRNA but otherwise function incorrectly?
5. Mutation-causing mutations can occur in several different kinds of genes. Explain.
6. Is a human blood cell that fails to lose its nucleus a mutant? Why?
7. Under what circumstances would you expect single-strand scissions of the *E. coli* chromosome to be lethal?
8. What would be the transitional consequence of the bromouracil
   a. if a rare tautomer of adenosine caused the incorporation of a rare tautomer of bromouracil?
   b. if a rare tautomer of guanine caused the incorporation of the normal tautomer of bromouracil?
9. What are the transitional consequences when a rare tautomer of guanine
   a. is incorporated?
   b. occurs after incorporation?
10. A codon CUU is exposed to nitrous acid. What chemical and translational changes are expected? Is such chemical change mutation? Explain.
11. A heterodimer of cytosine with thymine is photoinduced, then deaminated. What is the result?
12. Knowing some of the properties of the

photoproduct of UV-treated cytosine (see Figure 9-11A), what effects would you expect the dihydrothymines formed in UV-radiated DNA to have on the secondary structure of the polymer?

13. Compare the genetic effects of UV on species having the same DNA content but different base ratios.

14. How is the duplex nature of DNA utilized in maintaining DNA integrity?

15. Two strains of *E. coli* are treated with UV and are also exposed to 5-bromouracil and daylight. One strain incorporates significantly less of the base analog than the other. Offer an explanation for this result.

16. Discuss the possibilities for dimerization of the organic bases in genetic and nongenetic RNA.

17. A number of *rII* mutants can be classified as resulting from transitions A : T → G : C or G : C → A : T according to their reversibility after treatment with various chemical mutagens. Addition of 5-fluorouracil to the nutrient medium does not produce the normal r^+ trait in any of the mutants which supposedly carry the G : C pair at the mutant DNA site. On the other hand, some r^+ trait is produced by 5-fluorouracil in 17 of the 46 mutants presumed to carry A : T at the mutant site. What conclusions can be drawn?

18. Discuss the causes of the "spontaneous" mutation rate.

19. S. Zamenhof and S. Greer found that heating *E. coli* up to 60°C is mutagenic. What molecular explanations can you suggest for this result?

20. What controls are needed for electron-microscopy visualization of deletions and substitutions in heteroduplexes?

21. How could you demonstrate UV-induced pyrimidine dimer formation in the electron microscope? (See Bujard, H. 1970. *J. Mol. Biol.*, 49: 125–137).

22. *Escherichia coli* contains a gene that confers resistance to ϕT1 irradiated with ultraviolet light. Substituting 5-bromodeoxyuridine for the thymidine in the phage, however, removes this protection. What do you suppose is the product and mechanism of action of the bacterial gene involved?

23. How can you explain the finding that although methylated acridines also intercalate in DNA, they are not mutagenic?

PART IV

Genetic Recombination

Chapter 10

In Bacteria—Between Viruses

Different parts of the genetic material can change their arrangement relative to each other. Such rearrangements can involve the primary, secondary, tertiary, and quaternary structures of genetic nucleic acids—for example, the fragmentation or rearrangement of segments of a single strand; the separation or pairing of complementary strands; a change in folding; or the grouping or separation of duplexes. Conformational changes can affect the quality, quantity, or availability of the information contained in genetic material.

Whenever rearrangement leads to a combination of genes that is new, relative to some preexisting combination, the new group is called a *genetic recombinant*, produced by a process of *genetic recombination*. In common practice, changes in secondary or tertiary structures alone are not considered genetic recombinations since the genes involved merely change their conformation while remaining the same group; whereas changes in primary or quaternary structure are considered genetic recombinations because they place genetic material in new groups (Figure 10-1). We will begin our consideration of genetic recombination by looking at certain recombinational events in viruses.

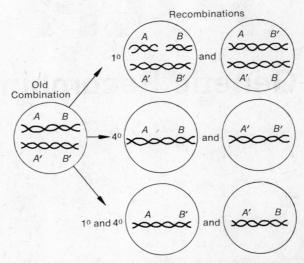

Figure 10-1 Some specific examples of genetic recombination involving only primary struc-ture (1^0), only quaternary structure (4^0), or both (1^0 and 4^0). The old combination consists of one duplex containing genes A and B and another containing mutants of these genes, A' and B'.

10.1 T-even phages inject their genetic material into bacterial hosts, where viral progeny are made and released by lysing their hosts.

Before considering recombination in viruses, we should become familiar with some details of their life cycles. A T-even phage[1] (Section 1.3; Figure 1-3) attaches itself tail first to an *E. coli* host; the sheath contracts so that the core is driven through the bacterial cell wall; and all the phage DNA, a single duplex about 200,000 nucleotides long (MW $= 1.2 \times 10^8$) located in the head, plus a small amount of protein, is injected into the bacterium. An eclipse period follows (Figure 10-2B–D) during which the phage DNA replicates to produce a pool of phage DNA. Near the end of the eclipse period (Figure 10-2D), a certain amount of DNA from the pool is surrounded

---

[1] The T-even group of phages that attack *E. coli* are tadpole-shaped, 0.1 to 0.2 μ long—roughly one tenth the bacterial diameter (Figure 1-3). The surface of the *head* has a hexagonal outline and facets like a crystal. The *head membrane* is composed of numerous subunits each having a molecular weight of about 80,000. The *tail* is cylindrical and is used to attach the phage to the host cell. Its outer *sheath*, composed of about 200 spirally arranged subunits each having a molecular weight of approximately 50,000, forms a hollow cylinder. The sheath can contract, shortening its length while increasing its diameter without changing its volume appreciably. Internal to the sheath is the *core*, a hollow cylinder with an inner diameter of about 25 Å. At the distal end of the core is a *hexagonal plate* to which six *spikes* and six *tail fibers* are attached; each tail fiber is bent in the middle and seems to contain subunits with molecular weight of not less than 100,000 each. The subunits of the head membrane, sheath, and tail fibers are composed of protein. When digested with trypsin, each of these subunits produces a unique set of peptides indicating that each is different. The core is also protein. In the interior of the phage particle is found a serologically distinct protein which makes up 4 to 6 per cent of the total phage protein; also reported in the phage interior are polyamines (putrescine and spermadine), lysozyme, and a minor polypeptide.

The volume of the DNA is approximately the same as that of the total protein. Since this DNA is about 68 μ long, it must be highly coiled inside the phage head. No RNA has been reported in DNA-containing phages.

The physical and chemical complexity of the T-even phages is not typical of all phages. For example, the single-stranded DNA ϕX174 seems to have a simple spherical structure (Figure 1-2).

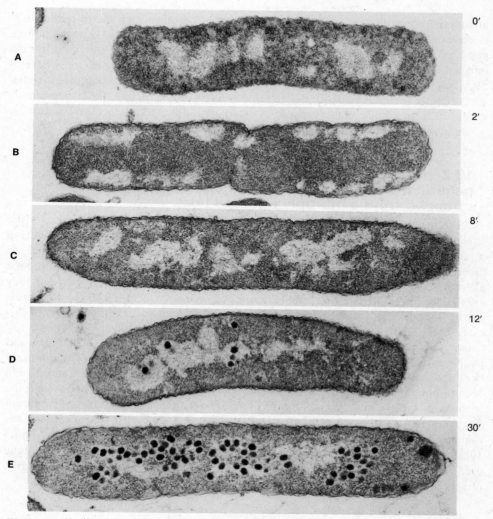

Figure 10-2 Electron micrographs of growth of T2 virus inside the *E. coli* host cell. (A) Bacillus before infection. (B) Two minutes after infection. The thin section photographed includes the protein coat of T2, which can be seen attached to the bacterial surface. (C) Eight minutes after infection. (D) Twelve minutes after infection. New virus particles are starting to condense. (E) Thirty minutes after infection. More than 50 T2 particles are completely formed and the host is about ready to lyse. Original magnification, 17,500×; present magnification, 14,000×. (Courtesy of E. Kellenberger.)

by phage head protein (coded by ϕDNA). The assembly of mature phage is completed with the addition of other protein components. About 20 to 40 minutes after infection, a phage-coded enzyme, lysozyme, ruptures or lyses the bacterial cell wall and liberates infective phage progeny. This *lytic* or *vegetative* cycle is the only possible course of existence for *intemperate*, or *virulent*, phages.

Given a suspension of mature phage virions it is possible to determine the number of infective particles by the "plaque assay" technique. After diluting the suspension (which may contain 10^{10} or 10^{11} virions per milliliter) a known amount, a few hundred phage particles are allowed to infect a much greater number of bacteria by mixing them together in a test tube. Under these conditions, each phage particle will infect a different host. The contents of the tube are then poured onto an agar-containing plate, and the plate incubated. Several hundred daughter phage are produced in each infected bacterium and, upon lysis, are released to infect neighboring bacteria. Several such cycles produce a progressively increasing zone of lysis in the continuous, somewhat opaque bacterial lawn. This is detected as a clearing, or *plaque*. Since each plaque is derived from a single phage because of the low multiplicity of infection, the number of plaques corresponds to the number of phage in the infecting sample.

10.2   Phages with new combinations of genetic material occur among the progeny obtained from a multiply infected host.

Some genetically different strains of a phage produce plaques with characteristic sizes or shapes. In T4, for example, *plaque-type mutant*, r, lyses rapidly, producing a larger plaque with sharper margins than the more common, wild-type phage, r^+. Gene r presumably codes for a modification of the polypeptide coded by its genetic alternative r^+. Strains may also vary in host range, that is, the types of bacteria they are able to infect. In T2, for example, *host-range mutant*, h, can infect *E. coli* strains B and B/2, whereas the wild-type phage, h^+, can only infect *E. coli* strain B; in this case h^+ and h are alternatives of the same gene, or *alleles*.

One strain of T-even phage carries mutant "markers" for both host range and plaque type, $h\,r$. When sensitive bacteria are infected with both the double mutant ($h\,r$) and wild-type ($h^+\,r^+$) phages, not only do the parental types ($h\,r$ and $h^+\,r^+$) occur among the progeny but also the new types $h^+\,r$ and $h\,r^+$ (Figure 10-3). Since the frequency of these new types is significantly greater than the spontaneous mutation frequency of $h\,r$ and $h^+\,r^+$ to $h^+\,r$ or $h\,r^+$, there must have been a genetic recombination between the region or *locus* in the phage chromosome occupied by h^+ or its alleles and the separate locus occupied by r^+ or its alleles. Note that the technique used to detect genetic recombination requires that a bacterium be infected with two phages having different alleles at two loci in their genetic material.

10.3   The sequence of loci in the same nucleic acid strand can be determined because the frequency of recombination is directly proportional to the distance between loci.

All genes located in the same molecule of genetic nucleic acid are physically bound or *linked* to each other. Knowing that the T-even genetic material is a single duplex of DNA in the virion and that the genetic material undergoes recombination, we know that linked genes undergo recombination. Assuming that the phage recombination under discussion results from a change in the primary structure of its nucleic acid (Figure 10-4), we can assume that the greater the distance between two loci in a given DNA segment, the greater the chance that recombination will occur between them. We can determine the frequencies of recombination after multiply infecting a bacterium with two phage strains that differ genetically at three loci. If a host carries parental phages of types $a\,b\,c$ and $a^+\,b^+\,c^+$, the genes being arranged in the sequence given, we expect the frequency of recombinant progeny or recombinant types with

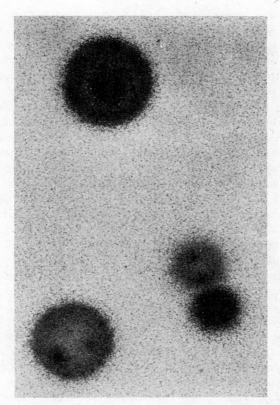

Figure 10-3 Plaques produced by parental and recombinant phage types. Progeny phage of a cross between $h\,r$ and $h^+\,r^+$ were tested on a mixture of suitable indicator bacteria. The large clear and the small turbid plaques are made by the parental types of phage progeny ($h\,r$ and $h^+\,r^+$, respectively). The small clear and the large turbid plaques are produced by the recombinant types of progeny ($h\,r^+$ and $h^+\,r$, respectively). (Courtesy of A. D. Hershey and the Cold Spring Harbor Laboratory of Quantitative Biology.)

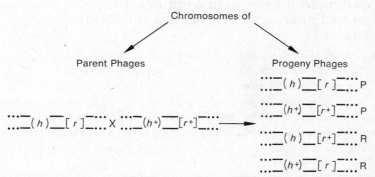

Figure 10-4 Recombination between two different loci in phage. P, parental type; R, recombinant type. Different loci are bracketed differently.

respect to the a and c loci ($a^+ c$ and $a c^+$) to be greater than the frequency of recombinants with respect to either the a and b loci ($a^+ b$ and $a b^+$) or the b and c loci
($b^+ c$ and $b c^+$). We see, therefore, that it may be possible to use the relative frequency
of recombination between linked genes, in reverse, to sequence the loci, that is, to
position them relative to each other, in a *recombinational linkage map* that reads
$a b c$ (or $c b a$) in the present case.

Just as evidence of mutation may be obtained in a variety of ways, so may we
obtain evidence of linkage in several ways.[2] Determination of the base sequence in the
single duplex DNA of the T-even virion would provide a *linkage map* of all the genes
determined chemically. At present, however, it is not feasible to make such a detailed
chemical linkage map. We can, however, substantiate the correctness of the mapping
of loci by recombination frequencies by visualizing the positions of mutations in
chromosomes. For example, one can anneal single strands of phage DNA which
differ by one or more deficiencies and observe the heteroduplexes under the electron
microscope (see Figure 9-9). If one strand has nonoverlapping deficiencies at two loci,
$a b^+ c$ and the complement has a nonoverlapping deficiency at a third, $a^+ b c^+$, the
visualized DNA linkage map of the three loci is congruent with the recombinational
linkage map of them. We conclude, therefore, that the frequency of recombination is
directly proportional to the distances between loci and can be validly used to sequence
them.

Note that linkage between genes ordinarily provides a kind of resistance that must
be overcome by the recombination process. Thus, the old, parental linkage combinations with regard to two loci tend to remain in more than 50 per cent of the progeny,
whereas the new, recombinational linkage types occur in less than 50 per cent. The
percentage of recombination is used as the number of *recombinational map units* the
two loci are located from each other. Thus, two loci producing 10 per cent recombinant
types are linked recombinationally and are 10 recombinational map units apart. If
two loci are found to produce equal numbers of recombinational and parental types
among the progeny (being 50 recombinational map units apart), we conclude that
they recombine independently of each other, that is, at random. These two loci may
recombine independently because they are located in fact either on different strands
(that is, they are physically unlinked) or on the same strand (that is, they are physically
linked) so far apart that recombination between them is not limited by the distance
between them.

10.4 A linear linkage map of phage T4 loci can be constructed from recombination frequencies.

If we determine the recombination frequencies for all known markers of ϕT4, we
find that all groups of three loci show the spatial relationship mentioned above,
especially when the loci are close to each other. The recombination linkage map is,
therefore, linear (even within one polypeptide-coding gene, or *cistron*, as described
in Sections S 10.4a and S 10.4b), and is about 2,500 map units long. It is not possible
to construct the map as a straight line, however, since genes at opposite ends of such
a line are also found to be close to each other. At the time of recombination, therefore,

---

[2] Since genes located in the same genetic molecule may be dependent on or related to each other at
the time of replication, transcription, or mutation we may also expect to be able to make *replicational
linkage maps*, *transcriptional linkage maps*, and *mutational linkage maps*.

the loci must be arranged in either a repeating linear sequence (for example, *abcdeabcdeabcde*) or a single linear sequence arranged in a circle or ring (for example,

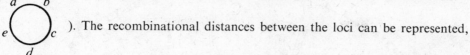

). The recombinational distances between the loci can be represented, therefore, in a circular recombinational linkage map (Figure 10-5), in which the genes located on either side of a given gene are placed on the map at distances proportional to their recombinational distances.

10.5   The genetic material in the virions of some phages contains terminally redundant loci.

After a bacterium is infected with both r and r^+ phages, about 2 per cent of the progeny tested singly produce *mottled plaques*, that is, plaques that are partly r and partly r^+. This result shows that these progeny must not have been *haploid*—containing only one r locus—but must have been *diploid*—containing two r loci, in this case r and r^+. A diploid individual which carries two different alleles of a given gene is said to be *hybrid*, or *heterozygous*, for that gene. When the alleles are the same, the individual is *pure*, or *homozygous*. In the present case 2 per cent of the progeny phage were heterozygous, $r^+ r$, and produced recombinant r^+ and r progeny in the same plaque.

The existence of phage heterozygotes that contain more than one copy of a given locus suggests, as one possibility, that virion T4 DNA routinely contains a genome's worth of DNA plus some extra, *terminally redundant*, DNA (see Section 10.9 for another explanation of mottled plaques). The following describes a test of this idea. Since electron micrographs show an open or *rod* duplex structure for the DNA of the T4 virion, let us assume that this DNA is terminally redundant and can be represented in a rod, linear form as $\frac{ab \ldots\ldots ab}{a'b'\ldots\ldots a'b'}$, where segment a is complementary to a', and b complementary to b'. A DNA exonuclease that can attack only free 3' positions will thus produce $\frac{\ldots\ldots ab}{a'b'\ldots\ldots}$. Subsequently, a double-stranded circle can form by base pairing. Such circles have been readily found with the electron microscope after but not before treatment of T4 chromosomes with such a DNase. (R)

10.6   Progeny T4 chromosomes are terminally redundant circular permutations of the parental DNA sequence because they are selected in standard, longer than one genome, lengths at random from longer DNA's composed of repeating haploid genomes.

Having learned from the previous section and other work that all, or almost all, virion T4 chromosomes are terminally redundant (true also for many other phages), and that different loci are redundant in different phage progeny, we can describe next a generalized model of T4 chromosome replication and then examine some evidence in its favor.

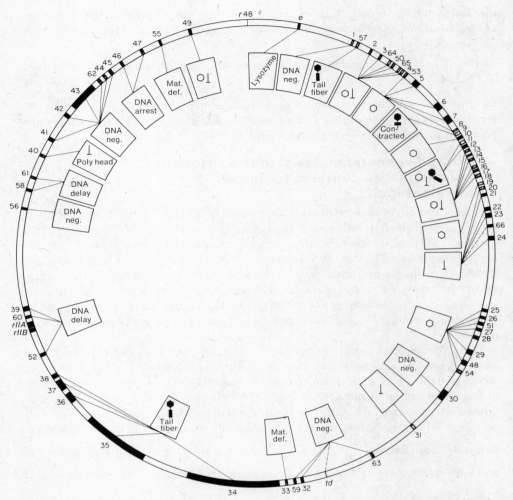

Figure 10-5 Recombination map of phage T4D. Filled-in areas represent minimal lengths for genes. The symbols for phage components represent the typical morphological products present in lysates of mutant-infected *E. coli*. (Courtesy of R. S. Edgar and W. B. Wood, 1966. Proc. Nat. Acad. Sci., U.S., 55: 498.)

A single parental φT4 chromosome, terminally redundant for the "ab" region (Figure 10-6A), produces progeny chromosomes that bear all the loci in the same relative sequence but have different loci terminally redundant in different progeny chromosomes (Figure 10-6C). In fact, the progeny DNA's comprise a terminally redundant series of *circular permutations* of the parental DNA sequence. (Note, with regard to . . . abcabcabc . . . , that abc, bca, and cab comprise nonredundant circular permutations of the sequence, and that abca, bcab, cabc comprise terminally redundant circular permutations of the same sequence.) Note in the figure that the redundancy of the ab region, for example, occurs in about one sixth of the progeny. Suppose that a phage strain that has a deletion of region cd produces significantly more than one sixth of the progeny terminally redundant for the ab region. Such a result can be understood if the parental chromosome determines the sequence of loci of the progeny

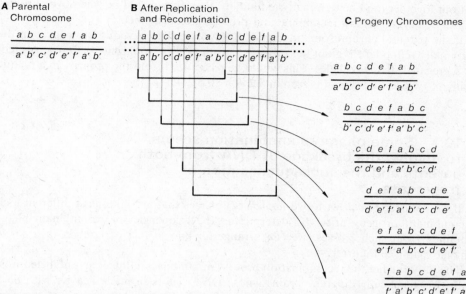

A Parental
Chromosome

B After Replication
and Recombination

C Progeny Chromosomes

Figure 10-6 Relation between parental and progeny chromosomes in ϕT4. (A) Parental phage chromosome terminally redundant for $\dfrac{a\,b}{a'\,b'}$ loci. (B) Source of progeny chromosomes are chromosomes that are a minimum of two phage equivalents long, from which a measured headful is taken at random for phage progeny chromosomes. (C) Resultant progeny chromosomes, each terminally redundant, are a circular permutation of the parental sequence of loci.

chromosomes but does not determine their length. Chromosome length is assumed to be determined by some measuring factor (a "yardstick") that selects at random a standard length of chromosome (perhaps a phage "headful" of DNA) from a longer segment containing repeating haploid genomes, called a *concatemer* (Figure 10-6B). If such a phage headful were slightly longer than a complete haploid phage chromosome, all progeny chromosomes would be terminally redundant.

The preceding model assumes that between entry of the parental DNA and the random cutting out of the progeny chromosomes there is a stage, after chromosome replication, in which the DNA present is in the form of a duplex composed of at least two linear lengths of a haploid phage chromosome (Figure 10-6B). This is supported by finding that a linear sequence of two or more chromosomes is produced during T4 reproduction (a result also consistent with the rolling-circle model of DNA replication described in Section 4.5).

The finding of *phage heterozygotes* indicates that the genomes of two entering phages can recombine and become part of the same concatemer. Accordingly, when two different *h* mutants are crossed, one can determine the occurrence of terminal redundancy by the occurrence of heterozygotes at the *h* locus. When the phages crossed are otherwise normal in chromosome length or carry only short deletions at the *r* locus, fewer cases of *h* heterozygotes are found than when the phages crossed also carry large deletions at the *r* locus. In other words, in accordance with the explanation proposed, when two phages grossly deleted in the *r* region recombine and produce a concatemer, the two different *h* loci are closer together and hence more likely to be

cut out together (and be terminally redundant) than they would be when two chromosomes of normal length recombine and produce a concatemer.

If the parental chromosome in Figure 10-6A were heterozygous for a locus in the
terminally redundant region, the progeny chromosomes would have often separated,
or segregated, the two alleles. This would be recognized from the progeny in a plaque
being of two genetic types (as seen in Section 10.5). (R)

10.7 Some phage recombination seems to involve the breakage of DNA from both parents and the subsequent union of fragments.

If we coinfect *E. coli* with two *lambda* (λ) phages that are mutant at different loci,
recombinant progeny arise. By determining the frequencies of recombinant phage
obtained from such crosses, we can arrange all known loci of lambda in a single
linkage map (see Figure 12-4).

To study further the recombination process in lambda, we infect an unlabeled host
with two genetically different strains whose DNA has been made heavier with both
^{13}C and ^{15}N. Progeny phage are ultracentrifuged in cesium chloride gradients and
the fractions of different densities are analyzed for recombinants. Since one peak (of
several present) in the recombinant curve is found very close to the density of the
heavy parental phage, it is clear that almost all the DNA of these recombinants is
original parental DNA. A simple explanation for this result is that the genetic material
of these progeny is formed by the breakage of parental DNA and the union of segments from both parents by ligase, probably preceded by a small amount of DNA
excision and repair. (R)

10.8 Molecular recombinants in ϕT4 DNA usually involve single strands containing both parental and progeny segments.

When ϕT4 is studied for the dispersion of parental radioactive heavy DNA among
its progeny, each progeny phage is found to contain about 5 to 7 per cent parental
DNA. This is expected from the relatively large number of recombinations per
chromosome in this organism. Extraction of the DNA and a study of its behavior in
centrifuges after strand separation and sonication reveal that the parental contribution
is single-stranded and in one piece which is covalently linked to progeny DNA.
Moreover, it is found that up to 5 minutes after infection neither replication nor
molecular recombination seem to occur; by 9 minutes after infection the parental
DNA has been broken into smaller segments and joined to progeny DNA.

It seems, therefore, that in ϕT4 molecular recombination ordinarily requires the
functioning of three enzymes—DNA polymerase, needed 5 minutes after infection;
an endonuclease that makes single breakages ("nickase") present 9 or so minutes
after infection; and—after repairing any excision—a ligase.

We see from the above that the primary structure recombination of T4 DNA
detected molecularly between parent and progeny sequences parallels that detected
earlier by recombination frequencies between loci. In $\phi\lambda$, a smaller amount of inter-

locus recombination is associated with a smaller amount of parent–progeny molecular recombination.[3]

10.9   A molecular model of phage recombination is presented in which various lengths of single-stranded parental and progeny fragments base pair, gaps and nicks are repaired, and a con-catemer is produced.

A linear sequence of two or more genomes, that is, a concatemer, is produced by recombination during ϕT4 replication. The pieces of the concatemer may have one chromosome as parent, when the host is singly infected, or two, when the cell is doubly infected. According to the results described in Sections 10.7 and 10.8, the concatemer is probably produced by the joining of pieces of chromosomes. The coming together of pieces from different chromosomes can best be explained by single-stranded segments base-pairing with single-stranded complements other than their original ones. The origin of the required single-stranded condition is unknown—it could have resulted from (1) strand separation, (2) single breakages and excisions, or (3) cases of two breakages, located at different but nearby positions on complementary strands, that scission the duplex. The minimum length of base pairing between recombining fragments is reported to be roughly 20 to 200 nucleotides; such pairing may be catalyzed by a protein like the product of T4 gene 32. In an intermediate stage in concatemer formation, single-stranded gaps are reported to occur between base-paired recombining fragments. The concatemer can be completed after gaps and nicks are repaired by a DNA polymerase and polynucleotide ligase, respectively.

Figure 10-7 shows a molecular model for the production of a recombinant segment of a concatemer, which is consistent with the preceding information. Note that when the base sequences of different alleles are largely, although not completely, identical, their complementary strands can base-pair sufficiently to produce a heteroduplex for the locus. Such a heteroduplex included in a progeny phage will yield different homoduplexes after semiconservative replication, and will be, therefore, another source of mottled plaques. A one-locus heterozygote is also referred to as an *internal heterozygote*. Some spontaneous mutations in T4 (especially those that occur in the "hot spots" discussed in Section S 10.7) seem to be due to single-stranded fragments, containing complementary stretches of identical bases, which mispair during recombination.[4]

---

[3] *Escherichia coli* can be coinfected with λ's containing radioactive heavy DNA and different genetic markers. When grown on nonradioactive light medium, such infections produce DNA's that are for the most part completely nonradioactive and light. This is so because, in this organism, the production of each progeny chromosome involves less than one recombination with the parent or another chromosome, on the average, so the parental DNA is not widely dispersed among its progeny. It is also found that most of the recombinants in the above-described example are all-light in composition. Since all the phage progeny are pooled we cannot tell whether such progeny are original recombinants or copies of them.

[4] For example, if a duplex containing a run of 5 A : T base pairs breaks and the following mispaired duplex region is formed,

$$\ldots \underline{\text{C A G T T T T T}} \ \ \underline{\text{G C A}} \ldots$$
$$\ldots \overline{\text{G T C}} \ \ \overline{\text{A A A A A C G T}} \ldots$$

repair will produce a run of six AT pairs, a gain of one AT pair. Other mispairings can lead to deletion of base pairs. Runs of identical bases may be responsible, at least in part, for *negative interference* with recombination, that is, for the excessive occurrence of two recombinations within a short chromosome region.

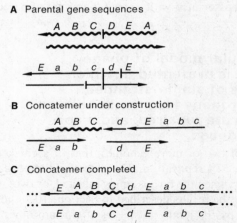

A Parental gene sequences

B Concatemer under construction

C Concatemer completed

Figure 10-7   Model for the production of a recombinant region in a concatemer. (A) The two parental phages are terminally redundant for different loci; one has the genes *A B C D*, the other has the mutant markers *a b c d*. Vertical lines indicate places of nicking or scission in parental sequences or copies of them. (B) base pairing between single-stranded fragments produces heteroduplex regions (*A b/a b*), single-strand gaps (*C/–*), and homo-duplex regions (*d E/d E*). (C) After filling in any single-stranded regions by a DNA poly-merase, polynucleotide ligase joins fragments together.

Note that since all the genes in a concatemer are linked to other genes at both ends (the very end genes can be ignored), the linkage map of the concatemer, made from the recombination frequencies among terminally redundant circularly permuted chromosomes sampled in the progeny, will necessarily be circular (Section 10.4). The circular recombination map of ϕX174 may result from the single circles of progeny DNA being circular permutations drawn from recombinational double-length circles, as described in Section S 10.9.

10.10   Interlocus genetic recombination can occur also between RNA viruses.

SWE, with markers *a* and *c*, and MEL, with markers *A* and *C*, are two haploid strains of *influenza virus*,[5] a single-stranded RNA virus. Although the usual host is the mammalian cell, it can also infect cells of the chicken egg. When SWE and MEL viruses are allowed to coinfect a chicken egg, progeny are obtained not only of the parental types (*a c* and *A C*) but also of the recombinant types (*A c* and *a C*). These and other experiments prove that genetic recombination occurs between RNA-containing viruses as well as DNA-containing viruses.

---

[5] The influenza virus consists of a helical ribonucleoprotein core surrounded by a lipoprotein mem-brane. The lipids in the virus envelope are derived mainly from preexisting lipids of the host cell, since the composition of the lipids varies with the strain of the host cell rather than the type of virus. This lipoprotein membrane is apparently derived from the cell membrane and applied to the virus when it leaves the cell. After infection by the virus, normal cellular growth continues for several hours. Therefore, most of the RNA, protein, and DNA synthesized are normal cellular products and bear little relation to the growth of the virus. Using the drug actinomycin D to inhibit normal cellular RNA synthesis, one can demonstrate a specific synthesis of viral RNA. Moreover, with the closely related Newcastle disease virus, which grows in the cytoplasm, one can show that the new (viral) RNA appears in the cytoplasm and not, as much RNA in normal cells, in the nucleus. Therefore, viral RNA and internal protein are made by synthesis and translation of viral RNA inside the host cell.

Different strains of poliomyelitis virus, another RNA virus,[6] also show genetic recombination. The resultant RNA seems to occur in one piece in these recombinants and in parainfluenza virus, whereas the RNA of recombinant influenza particles appears to be in five pieces.

We do not yet have any evidence that genetic recombination occurs between the RNA viruses that attack plants. The difficulties of multiply infecting plant cells with TMV or other viruses may account for the lack of positive results in experiments testing for genetic recombination. (R)

SUMMARY AND CONCLUSIONS

Genetic recombination involving the primary structure of the DNA's of phages that attack *E. coli* has been studied using three different techniques.

1. *Interlocus recombination.* Studies of progeny after coinfection with phages that are genetically marked by different alleles at two or more loci.

2. *Molecular recombination.* Studies of the relation between parental DNA marked by being heavy or radioactive, or both, and progeny DNA which is not.

3. *Visualized recombination.* Studies under the electron microscope of phage genetic material at different stages of the phage reproductive cycle.

The results of all three techniques used singly and in combination are mutually supportive and reveal the following general features of recombination as it occurs specifically in T4 DNA, although at least some features also apply to the DNA's of many other phages of *E. coli*:

1. All the genes of a phage are linked to each other.
2. Recombinations occur in frequencies that permit the construction of a linear recombination map for genes having known alleles.
3. The recombination process seems to involve three different rearrangements of phage DNA:
   a. Fragmentation of the parental chromosomes present, requiring the action of an endonuclease.
   b. The formation of a concatemer by
      (1) the base pairing of single-stranded fragments from different parents and from parents and their progeny.
      (2) a DNA polymerase filling in single-stranded gaps and a ligase uniting the segments.
   c. Excision from the concatemer of circularly permuted, terminally redundant, standard lengths of DNA for inclusion in virions.

Note that the repair of mutational damage (Chapter 9) and the recombinations described here have features in common, and both processes may require some of the same or similar enzymes.

Interlocus recombination also occurs in RNA viruses when host cells can be multiply infected.

---

[6] Viruses that contain no DNA and are entirely, or mainly, ribonucleoprotein in content include the small RNA-containing bacteriophages (f2, MS2, R17, and others). These phages are all extremely similar, but not identical. They are the same size, shape, and molecular weight; they cross react serologically, having similar coat proteins; all attack only male (Hfr or F⁺) *E. coli*. RNA viruses also include many viruses that attack plants (such as the tobacco mosaic and the turnip yellow mosaic viruses), and many of the smaller viruses that attack animals (causing encephalitis, for example).

GENERAL REFERENCES

Burnet, F. M., and Stanley, W. M. (Editors) 1959. *The viruses*; vol. I, *General virology*; vol. 2, *Plant and animal viruses*; vol. 3, *Animal viruses*. New York: Academic Press, Inc.

Hayes, W. 1968. *The genetics of bacteria and their viruses*, second edition. New York: John Wiley & Sons, Inc.

Meselson, M. 1967. The molecular basis of genetic recombination. In *Heritage from Mendel*, Brink, R. A. (Editor), Madison: University of Wisconsin Press, pp. 81–104.

Signer, E. 1971. General recombination. In *The bacteriophage lambda*, Hershey, A. D. (Editor), New York: Cold Spring Harbor Laboratory of Quantitative Biology, Chap. VII, pp. 139–174.

SPECIFIC SECTION REFERENCES

10.5   Hershey, A. D., and Chase, M. 1951. Genetic recombination and heterozygosis in bacteriophage. Cold Spring Harbor Sympos. Quant. Biol., 16: 471–479. Reprinted in *Papers on bacterial viruses,* second edition, Stent, G. S. (Editor), Boston: Little, Brown and Company, 1965, pp. 204–217.

Thomas, C. A., Jr. 1966. The arrangement of information in DNA molecules. J. Gen. Physiol., 49: 143–169. (Terminal redundancy in ϕT2 revealed by DNase action.)

10.6   Scotti, P. D. 1969. Events occurring during the replication of bacteriophage T4 DNA. Proc. Nat. Acad. Sci., U.S., 62: 1093–1100.

Streisinger, G., Emrich, J., and Stahl, M. M. 1967. Chromosome structure in phage T4, III. Terminal redundancy and length determination. Proc. Nat. Acad. Sci., U.S., 57: 292–295.

10.7   Kellenberger, G., Zichichi, M. L., and Weigle, J. J. 1961. Exchange of DNA in the recombination of bacteriophage λ. Proc. Nat. Acad. Sci., U.S., 47: 869–878.

Meselson, M., and Weigle, J. J. 1961. Chromosome breakage accompanying genetic recombination in bacteriophage. Proc. Nat. Acad. Sci., U.S., 47: 857–868. Reprinted in *Papers on bacterial viruses,* second edition, Stent, G. S. (Editor), Boston: Little, Brown and Company, 1965, pp. 218–229.

10.8   Kozinski, A. W. 1969. Molecular recombination in the ligase negative T4 amber mutant. Cold Spring Harbor Sympos. Quant. Biol. (1968), 33: 375–391.

Max Delbrück (1906–) in 1969. Dr. Delbrück was the recipient of a Nobel prize in 1969 for his pioneer work on the genetics of viruses.

Salvador E. Luria (1912–   ) in 1969, the year Dr. Luria was the recipient of a Nobel prize for his pioneer work on the genetics of viruses.

10.9   Alberts, B., and Frey, L. 1970. T4 bacteriophage gene 32: A structural protein in the replication and recombination of DNA. Nature, Lond., 227: 1313–1318.
       Broker, T. R., and Lehman, I. R. 1971. Branched DNA molecules: intermediates in T4 recombination. J. Mol. Biol., 60: 131–149.
10.10   Duesberg, P. H. 1968. The RNA's of influenza virus. Proc. Nat. Acad. Sci., U.S., 59: 930–937.

SUPPLEMENTARY SECTIONS

S10.4a   Even in its fine structure—within one polypeptide-coding gene—the genetic recombination map of ϕT4 is linear. It is hypothesized that recombination can occur between sites as close together as two adjacent nucleotides.

The r mutants in the rII region of the ϕT4 genetic map can produce plaques when *E. coli* strain B is their host. They cannot form plaques, however, when their host is *E. coli* strain K12(λ), although r^+ phages can. rII mutants are very useful in genetic studies of mutation and recombination. Their mutation frequency from r to r^+ can be determined readily by plating them on strain K12(λ), since only mutants to r^+ will form plaques [r^+ is "selected" on strain K12(λ)]. A large number of rII mutants that have a low mutation frequency (sometimes as low as 1 per 10^8 phages) can be obtained.

rII mutants can be divided into two classes, A and B, on the basis of their behavior after mixed infection of strain K12(λ). That is, when K12(λ) is coinfected with an r phage from each class, growth of the two different mutant phages and lysis of the host occurs. This behavior suggests that the rII region is composed of two subregions,

A and B, and the normal polypeptide products of both are required to produce lysis of strain K12(λ). Mutants defective only in the A subregion presumably can still make normal B product, and vice versa. In a bacterium of strain K12(λ) multiply infected with one phage mutant in A and another in B, the B and A products produced by the mutants can cooperate—that is, show *complementation*—to produce lysis (Figure 10-8).

If, on the other hand, the two different rII mutants coinfecting strain K12(λ) are located in

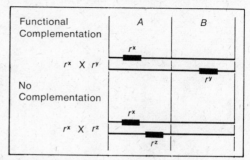

Figure 10-8 Occurrence or nonoccurrence of complementation between different rII mutants.

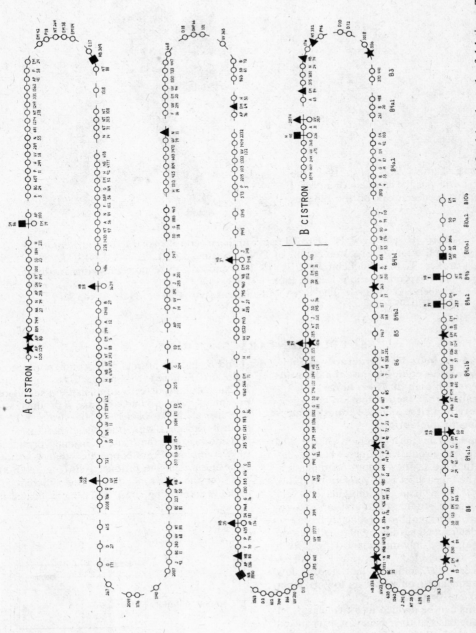

Figure 10-9 Genetic map of the *rII* region of phage T4. The breaks in the map indicate segments as defined by the ends of deletions. The order of the segments has been determined as shown. The order of mutants within any one segment has not been determined, but all give recombination with each other. The hollow circles and other filled-in symbols represent different types of effects on phage traits. (Courtesy of S. Benzer and S. P. Champe, 1961. Proc. Nat. Acad. Sci., U.S., 47: 1030–1031.)

the same subregion—region A, for example—they will be unable to grow and produce lysis via complementation since neither phage can produce normal A product.

Different mutants may involve defects in different parts of the A (or B) subregion. If two such nonoverlapping mutants r^x and r^y in, let us say, the A subregion coinfect $E.$ $coli$ strain B, both can multiply; they can, in addition, produce recombinant r^+ and double-mutant $r^x r^y$ progeny as well as the parental types. By plating the progeny phage on $E.$ $coli$ (K12(λ)), the frequency of r^+ recombinants, and hence one half of the recombination map distance between the mutational sites, can be determined.

When three independently arising mutants in the same subregion are studied, $r1$ and $r3$ may recombine with each other but not with $r2$. Such results suggest that $r2$ has a long deficiency or deletion that includes all or part of the region defective in $r1$ and $r3$. Such deletion mutants are never found to revert to r^+. Other mutations which do revert and give no evidence of being long deficiencies are considered to be mutants involving one or a few nucleotide pairs. Since these appear to affect a single point in the chromosome they are called *point mutants*. Of the more than 1,500 spontaneously occurring rII mutants which have been typed, about 500 are different; that is, each is separable from all the others by recombination (Figure 10-9). Using overlapping deficiencies and point mutants, all the mutant sites of the A and B subregions can be arranged in a single linear sequence with the recombinational distances between mutants being approximately additive. Thus, even over short regions (within one polypeptide-coding gene, or cistron—see Section S10.4b) the genetic recombination map of bacteriophage is linear.

Since the T4 DNA backbone does not seem to have any interruption in its sequence of nucleotides, it is reasonable to hypothesize that recombination can occur between any two adjacent nucleotides.

Benzer, S. 1962. The fine structure of the gene. Scient. Amer., 206 (No. 1): 70–84. Scientific American Offprints, San Francisco: W. H. Freeman and Company, Publishers.

S10.4b Cistrons can be identified by a cis-trans test.

Consider the functional characteristics of the rII region which contains about 2,000 linearly arranged nucleotides. With respect to plaque-type character, the rII region behaves as a single functional unit. The rII region, however, is composed of two subregions, A and B, which

show complementation and demonstrate that A and B are independent, separate units at the posttranscriptional level. Although the end product of some genes is tRNA or rRNA, the rII region seems to transcribe to mRNA, which is translated into protein, since r^+ function is lost by mutations that produce a terminator codon. Thus, although the translation products of A and B have not been identified, they are presumably separate, complementing polypeptides.

When $E.$ $coli$ strain K12(λ) is doubly infected with wild-type T4 (+ +) and T4 doubly mutant ($a_1 a_2$) in the A (or B) region, the r^+ trait, that is, lysis, is produced. In this case, the mutations are present in the same DNA double helix, that is, in the *cis position* (Figure 10-10). When a bacterium of the same strain is doubly infected and each virus particle carries one of these mutations ($a_1 +$, $+ a_2$), the mutations are now in the *trans position*. No complementation occurs, and no plaque is produced. When such a *cis-trans test* gives this result, two polypeptide-coding mutants failing to complement in the *trans* position are said to belong to the same functional (A or B) unit, or cistron. Polypeptide-coding mutants that do complement in the *trans* configuration belong to different cistrons; for example, mutant a_1 in the A cistron and mutant b_1 in the B cistron complement when they are in the *trans* position, $a_1 +/+ b_1$. Since the closest mutational sites between the A and B cistrons (Figure 10-7) are no more than 0.4 map unit apart, it appears that the two cistrons are not separated by a large amount of DNA and are probably adjacent.

S10.7 The rII region has different mutational "hot spots" for different mutagens.

In discussing the genetics of the rII region of the ϕT4 genetic map, it was mentioned that the more than 1,500 spontaneously occurring mutants tested involved changes in one or more of about 500 different sites in the rII region. This statement, of course, implies that some mutation sites must have been involved more than once. In fact, the number of times different sites are involved in mutation varies considerably. In terms of DNA, this variability means that certain nucleotides, singly or in small groups, are much more likely

a_1	a_2		a_1	+
+	+		+	a_2
Cis			*Trans*	

Figure 10-10 *Cis* and *trans* positions for two mutants in cistron $rIIA$.

to undergo mutation than others, so *mutational "hot spots"* must occur.

Recall that, except for the substitution of 5-hydroxymethylcytosine (glucosylated or not) for cytosine, the T-even phage genome is an otherwise typical DNA duplex. Note also that 5-bromouracil can substitute for thymine—and only thymine—in the synthesis of DNA *in vitro*. What will be the mutational consequences of incorporating 5-bromouracil into T4 DNA?

Addition of 5-bromouracil to the normal culture medium of *E. coli* before infection with T4 does not necessarily result after infection in the incorporation of this base analog in T4 DNA, since thymine can be synthesized by the bacterium and it—rather than the analog—may be used preferentially or exclusively in the synthesis of phage DNA. Sulfanilamide, itself not mutagenic, inhibits synthesis of folic acid, which in its reduced form (tetrahydrofolic acid) is required for enzymatic methyl transfer reactions, including thymine synthesis. Therefore, sulfanilamide is added to the culture medium to assure that no thymine is synthesized from uracil. The medium is supplemented with a variety of essential chemical substances already containing methyl and hydroxymethyl groups but not with the deoxyribonucleotides of thymine or of 5-hydroxymethylcytosine. (The deoxyribonucleotide of 5-hydroxymethylcytosine is omitted to prevent its possible conversion to an analog of thymine, which might be incorporated in preference to the 5-bromouracil.) In this way, the bacterium can function properly as a phage host.

Under these conditions, 5-bromouracil is highly mutagenic in the *rII* region. A comparison of 5-bromouracil-induced and spontaneously occurring *rII* mutants reveals that the induced mutations also occur in clusters on the genetic map, although the hot spots are in different positions. Moreover, contrary to the spontaneous mutants, very few of those induced are of the gross (internucleotide) type, and almost all are subsequently capable of reverse mutation to, or near, the *r*+ trait. The *mutational spectra* for 5-bromouracil, other chemical mutagens, and spontaneous mutants are all different at the nucleotide level.

Chemical mutagens (and high-energy radiations) can increase the spontaneous point mutation rate as much as 150-fold. Since the point mutation frequency probably increases in direct proportion with the dose of many different chemical mutagens, there is probably no threshold dose for chemical mutagens (and high-energy radiations), and the number of point mutations produced by a given total dose is constant, other things being equal, regardless of the rate of treatment.

For ultraviolet light—which is not a highly energetic radiation—the situation is different. Here the probability for the individual unit or quantum of energy inducing point mutation is considerably less than 100 per cent. Moreover, because several quanta can cooperate to produce mutation, ultraviolet-induced point mutation frequency increases faster than in direct proportion to the dose—at least for low doses—and an attenuated dose is less mutagenic than a concentrated one.

Freese, E. 1963. Molecular mechanism of mutations. In *Molecular genetics*, Part I. Taylor, J. H. (Editor), New York: Academic Press, Inc., Chap. 5, pp. 207–269.

Okada, Y., Streisinger, G., Owen (Emrich), J., Newton, J., Tsugita, A., and Inouye, M. 1972. Molecular basis of a mutational hot spot in the lysozyme gene of bacteriophage T4. Nature, Lond., 236: 338–341. (A high frequency of frame shift mutations is associated with the occurrence of sequences of five or more consecutive, identical base pairs.)

S10.9   A chromosomal cycle of single rings → recombinational double-length rings → single rings explains the circular nature of the φX174 recombinational linkage map.

After single infection with the + single-stranded circular DNA of φX174, a + − double-stranded circular DNA replicative form (RF) is produced. About 2 to 3 per cent of the covalently closed duplex molecules seen under the electron microscope, however, are twice the length of the φX174 genome. That these double-length rings result from recombination rather than some error in replication of a single template is proved by the following.

Phage S13 and φX174 are closely related and occur in various mutant forms. When a cell is doubly infected with phages mutant at different loci (m^1 $+^2$ φX174 × $+^1$ m^2 φS13), double-length DNA circles can be isolated and used to infect *protoplasts*, bacteria with cell walls removed. The progeny of single infections with double-length DNA circles include recombinants (wild-type $+^1$ $+^2$, and double-mutant m^1 m^2) as well as the parental types. These findings prove that the double-length circles result from recombinations involving both φX174 and φS13 genomes. This recombination may have been produced by an error of replication in which both templates are used to make a continuous double-length duplex ring DNA; or two rings, synapsed with each other in regions having similar base sequences, may have broken and rejoined to make a double-length ring. In either event, the double ring is produced as a recombination of the information in two single rings. The release of single parental and recombinant type rings may be explained as being due to the reverse of the type of process that formed the double ring.

This recombinational cycle of single circles → double circles → single circles must also occur when different mutants of ϕX174 multiply infect *E. coli*. The circular recombination map that has been obtained for ϕX174 may be explained, therefore, as the result of the single circles of progeny DNA sampled being circular permutations drawn from recombinational double-length circles that were formed in a circularly permuted manner from single rings.

We have seen above that genetic recombination occurs during transfection with double-length DNA circles. In the case of *B. subtilis* ϕSP82, if the transfecting DNA comes from genetically different strains (the host needs about four pieces of DNA, each the size of the phage genome, to be transfected), some of the virions produced appear to be genetic recombinants.

Green, D. M. 1964. Infectivity of DNA isolated from *Bacillus subtilis* bacteriophage, SP82. J. Mol. Biol., 10: 438–451.

Rush, M. G., and Warner, R. C. 1969. Molecular recombination in a circular genome— ϕX174 and S13. Cold Spring Harbor Sympos. Quant. Biol. (1968), 33: 459–466.

QUESTIONS AND PROBLEMS

1. How could you demonstrate that recombination between T phages does not occur from the time the phages are mixed until the time their DNA is injected into a host?
2. What conclusions can you draw from the percentages of recombination in the progeny from mixed infection with mutants of phage T2 given below?

CROSS	PARENTS		% RECOM- BINANTS		% RECOM- BINATION
a	*h*	*r*13	*h r*13 0.74	+ + 0.94	1.7
b	*h r*13	+ +	*h* 0.8	*r*13 0.8	1.6
c	*h*	*r*7	*h r*7 6.9	+ + 6.4	13.3
d	*h*	*r*1	*h r*1 12	+ + 12	24

3. In 1959 I. Tessman found that after nitrous acid treatment ϕT2 gave mottled plaques, whereas ϕX174 gave only nonmottled plaques. What do these results suggest about DNA structure and the molecular basis of these mutations?
4. Would you expect the mutational hot spots in the *rII* region to be different after exposing T4 to 5-bromouracil from what they would be after exposing T4 to hydroxylamine? Why?
5. Approximately one half of the genes in the ϕT4 chromosome have temperature-sensitive alleles which permit phage development at 25°C but not at 40°C. What molecular explanation can you give for such conditional lethal mutants?
6. If two phages that are temperature-sensitive mutants for different genes coinfect a host, both types of mutants can be recovered in the lysate; the mutants thus show complementation. Indicate the temperature conditions and methods you would employ to cross two temperature-sensitive mutants and determine the frequency of wild-type recombinants.
7. How would you show that the mRNA made from a ϕT2 template in *E. coli* is not as long as the T2 chromosome? (See Asano, K., J. Mol. Biol., 14: 71–84, 1965).
8. How would you detect and maintain a ϕT4 nonsense mutant that produces an incomplete head protein?
9. What portion of the total frequency of genetic recombination in ϕT4 can you attribute to the heterozygosity of terminal redundancies versus internal heterozygosities?
10. What have we learned about the linkage maps of phages by studying their DNA chemically? Mutationally? Recombinationally?
11. Differentiate between interlocus and intralocus genetic recombination.
12. Does concatemer formation require a parental sequence that is terminally redundant? Circular?
13. What evidence can you offer that ligase does not join single-stranded nucleic acids?

Chapter 11

In Bacteria—Clones; Genetic Transformation

We have already seen that genetic recombination involving the primary structure of nucleic acid takes place in bacteria. In Chapter 10 this recombination involved phage DNA's that entered the host with (or without) the assistance of the remaining portion of the virion. Since the host provides the environment, raw materials, and some of the machinery needed for recombining phage genes, it will be no surprise that primary structure recombination can occur between the bacterial DNA's of a recipient cell and of a donor cell, regardless of the means by which the donor DNA enters the recipient. This chapter and the next two will deal with genetic recombinations of bacterial genes that enter the recipient cell (1) without any outside biological assistance (Chapter 11, genetic transformation), (2) with the direct assistance of a phage (Chapter 12, genetic transduction), or (3) with the direct assistance of the donor bacterium (Chapter 13, conjugation).

The present chapter starts with a consideration of recombination involving the quaternary structure of bacterial DNA, which occurs each time a bacterial cell divides.

11.1 The machinery for bacterial cell division assures that each progeny cell contains a copy of each replicated bacterial chromosome.

Some bacteria are completely haploid only under special circumstances (for example, when in spore form). They are at various stages of diploidy when their DNA is being replicated; that is, they are diploid for replicated sections and haploid for sections not yet replicated. In some instances a second (and even a third) cycle of replication is in progress before the first cycle is completed; hence, different genes are present in single, double, and quadruple amount. When replication is not underway, some bacterial strains are stabilized as haploids and others as diploids. Regardless of the ploidy, however, when bacterial division takes place, each daughter bacterium normally receives a complete set of genes. This redistribution is an example of recombination involving DNA quaternary structure, since duplex genomes together in the parent are separate in the progeny.

The mechanism for this orderly distribution seems to involve a *mesosome* (Figure 11-1), an infolding of the bacterial cell membrane, to which the bacterial chromosome is attached. After the chromosome divides, so does the cell membrane (Figure 11-2), daughter chromosomes being attached to daughter cell membranes. Thus, each daughter cell is assured of receiving a copy of each chromosome. (R)

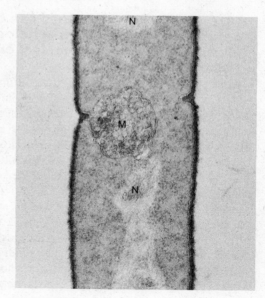

Figure 11-1 Electron micrograph of a thin section of *B. subtilis* fixed in osmium tetroxide showing a mesosome (M) and nuclear areas (N). ×50,000. (Courtesy of N. Nanninga, 1971. J. Cell Biol., 48: 219.)

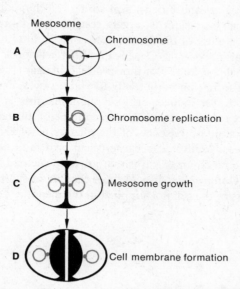

Figure 11-2 Distribution of daughter chromosomes to daughter bacterial cells. (The duplex is shown as a single line.) (A) Special point of chromosome is attached to the mesosome. (B) Chromosome replicated except at special point. (C) Mesosome growth separates now-completely-duplicated chromosome. (D) Mesosome is replicated when separate cell membrane boundaries form within it.

11.2   Bacterial genotypes can be determined from the morphological, physiological, or biochemical characteristics of clonal phenotypes.

After chromosome replication, a bacterium divides to produce daughter bacteria. This method of increasing bacterial cell number is a uniparental (asexual) process called *vegetative reproduction*. Starting with a single bacterium (or other organism), continuous vegetative reproduction results in a population of cells called a *clone*; barring mutations, all members of a clone are genetically identical. If mutation occurs during clonal growth, the mutant is transmitted to all the progeny of the mutant cell, thus producing a genetically mosaic clone whose proportion of mutant individuals varies, depending upon the time the mutation occurred and the relative reproductive potential of mutant and nonmutant cells.

Under appropriate culture conditions, *E. coli* divides about once each half hour; in 15 hours, after 30 successive generations have taken place, one cell produces a clone containing about 10 billion (10^{10}) individuals. The number of *E. coli* produced from a single cell after n generations (or t hours) can be calculated by the expression 2^n (or 2^{2t}) (Figure 11-3). Space is no problem in working with bacteria since 10^{10} individuals can readily be grown in liquid broth in an ordinary test tube.

The small size of bacteria (and other microorganisms) is a handicap, however, in determining the genetic makeup of the individual (organism or cell), that is, the *genotype*, from the *phenotype*, the traits or characteristics produced by the genotype. Mutants that change the morphological phenotype of bacteria must be detected in individuals by microscopic examination. Unfortunately, individual bacteria show relatively few clearcut morphological variations—traits such as size, shape, capsule, pigment, and the presence or absence of flagella. Moreover, since it is not feasible to make routine physiological and biochemical studies on the individual bacterium, the study of the individual bacterium is largely restricted to morphological variations. One can, however, make use of the fact that, barring mutation, clones are composed of genetically identical individuals. Genetically different clones can show phenotypic differences in the size, shape, and color they produce on agar (Figure 11-4). Genetically different clones can also respond differently to various dyes, drugs, and viruses. (The use of drugs to detect, not induce, drug-resistant mutants is described in Section S11-2.) Therefore, one can also establish the genotype of a single bacterium from the morphological or physiological aspects of the phenotype of the clone it produces.

Escherichia coli is easily cultured because it can grow and reproduce on a simple, chemically defined food medium. Strains that grow on such a basic, minimal medium are considered to be *prototrophic*, or wild type, capable of synthesizing the numerous metabolic components of the cell not supplied in the medium. One can also determine

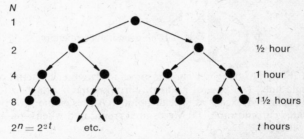

Figure 11-3   Geometric increase in the number of bacteria (N) due to vegetative reproduction.

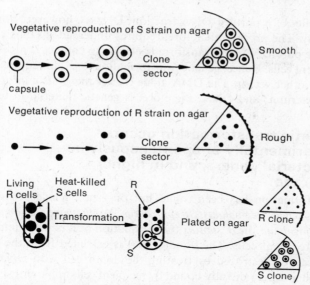

Figure 11-4 Cloning of S and R strains of *Pneumococcus* and the transformation of some R by heat-killed S.

bacterial genotypes via biochemical variations which occur in different clones, particularly those involving changes in nutritional requirements. For various mutants to grow and reproduce—whether they arise spontaneously or after treatment with physical or chemical mutagens—one or more of a variety of chemical substances must be added to the basic medium. For example, one mutant strain of *E. coli* requires the addition of threonine to the minimal medium; another mutant strain requires methionine. Nutritionally dependent strains whose growth depends on a supplement to their basic food medium are said to be *auxotrophic*.

11.3 The genetic material of a bacterium can be stably altered in specific ways by isolated DNA from a different strain. This phenomenon, genetic transformation, proves that DNA is genetic material in bacteria.

As characterized by clonal phenotypes, the bacterium *Pneumococcus* (*Diplococcus pneumoniae*) occurs in several genetically different forms. One type, S, is surrounded by a polysaccharide capsule, and forms a colony with a smooth surface. When heat-killed S cells are added to nutrient broth in which R cells are growing and the mixture is poured onto nutrient agar, numerous clones of type S appear (Figure 11-4). No matter what subtype of S is heat-killed, live bacteria of that type are obtained after mixture with R cells. Thus, we see that R cells have undergone a *genetic transformation* to S cells.

To determine the chemical nature of the transforming agent, we test the transforming ability of different fractions of heat-killed S bacteria. Those containing protein, RNA, or capsule polysaccharide are completely inactive. Only the fraction containing DNA is able to transform type R bacteria to type S. The purest DNA extracts (containing no detectable amounts of unbound lipids, polysaccharides, or proteins) retain full transforming ability. As we might expect, RNases have no effect on the transforming ability of a purified DNA fraction. DNases, however, can block trans-formation entirely. The process, therefore, requires undegraded DNA.

Note that since pure DNA can transform bacteria, no contact is necessary between donor and recipient cells. Hence, genetic transformation does not require the mediation of a virus or any other vector. The DNA alone carries the genetic information which transforms a bacterium; and DNA, therefore, is genetic material in bacteria. (R)

11.4   Genetic transformation occurs either experimentally or spontaneously in several bacterial genera, and in higher organisms, too.

Genetic transformation has been found not only in *Pneumococcus* but in other bacterial genera such as *Hemophilus*, *Streptococcus*, *Xanthomonas*, *Salmonella*, *Bacillus*, *Neisseria*, and *Rhizobium*. In *B. subtilis* transformation occurs when intact donor cells are mixed with recipient cells. The donor DNA is extruded from the surface of the living cell and can be destroyed by treating the donor cell with DNase. The DNA which is extruded and permanently bound by recipient cells apparently occurs in pieces that are longer than those extracted from bacteria.

In *Neisseria*, DNA is regularly liberated (into the slime layer) by the cells which undergo self-digestion, or autolysis, in aging cultures; such DNA is effective in transformation, as is the DNA obtained from penicillin-sensitive pneumococci dis-integrated or lysed after treatment with penicillin. Using different genetically marked pneumococci, it is found that genetic transformation—due to DNA liberated from one strain transforming members of the other strain—occurs spontaneously in the living mouse host.

Good evidence has been presented for transformation occurring in higher organisms —including the mouse, the fruit fly *Drosophila*, the flour moth *Ephestia*, the silkworm *Bombyx*, and human cells cultured *in vitro*. (R)

11.5   Genetic transformation in bacteria seems to be a type of genetic recombina-tion in which donor genetic information replaces host genetic information.

Genetic transformation in bacteria can occur in either direction ($A \rightleftharpoons A'$), and if one gene can be transformed any gene in the chromosome can be. Type A cells can be transformed to an A' type which, in turn, provides increased amounts of A'-DNA capable of transforming other A cells to A'. So, the DNA extracted from transformed bacteria provides increased amounts of the same transforming gene. Moreover, if we take the DNA from a cell of type A' (which has been transformed from a cell of type A) and use it to transform an A'' cell, we get only A' transformants. The transforming agent is thus the DNA of the *immediate* donor. Consequently, the initial A-to-A' transformation must have involved the replacement of genetic information of A by that of the donor, A'.

The result of genetic transformation in bacteria is new information for the recipient cell. We should keep in mind, though, that the host does not itself invent this informa-tion but merely incorporates information previously existing in the donor. Thus, transformation seems to be essentially the result of a recombination of donor and recipient genetic DNA. We will consider the mechanism of transformation in the next four sections.

11.6   The entry of transforming DNA into a bacterial cell involves competence, competence factors, and, possibly, mesosomes.

Studies of genetic transformation in bacteria show that the process occurs in a series of discrete steps. A necessary prerequisite to the first step is that the recipient bacteria be *competent*, that is, be able to accept DNA and be transformed by it. Although protein synthesis continues at a normal rate when a bacterium is competent, growth of the cell wall and chromosome replication occur either not at all or at a reduced rate. Competence, therefore, occurs only at a certain time in the bacterial life cycle.

Cell competence requires the presence of divalent cations. *Competence factors*, extracellular factors obtained from competent cultures that can induce competence in noncompetent cells, include a heat-unstable, low-molecular-weight protein in some cases, and a heat-stable molecule in other cases. The instability of the former type of competence factor may be due to a heat-stable, nondialyzable *inhibitor*. Perhaps some competence factors work by assisting the entry of donor DNA.[1]

Although removal of the cell wall, that is, *protoplasting*, helps *E. coli* to be transfected, transformation does not ordinarily occur in *E. coli* protoplasts (or nonprotoplasts). Transformable cells, moreover, lose their transformation capacity upon protoplasting, at which time mesosomes are expelled from the cytoplasm. Mesosomes are also implicated in transformation by the following observation. When cells are in the competent stage, not only is the host chromosome more readily seen attached to a mesosome but labeled donor DNA is also associated with mesosomes as shown by radioautography. (R)

11.7   Genetic transformation in bacteria is a genetic recombination which involves the binding and penetration, synapsis, and integration of donor DNA, so that a single-stranded segment of donor DNA is incorporated and replicated as a part of the recipient's DNA.

Binding and penetration

When bacteria are competent, DNA can bind at the cell surface at several receptor sites—two, on the average, in *Hemophilus*. Uptake sites may consist of, or be associated with, mesosomes. The binding is at first reversible and the bound DNA can be removed by several methods, including exposure to DNase or by extensive washing. This reversible stage is very short, sometimes a matter of 4 to 5 seconds. Only DNA of high molecular weight can bind to these sites; but it does not have to be transforming DNA.

---

[1] In mammalian tissue culture, DNA enters a cell in a vacuole formed by engulfment, that is, by *phagocytosis*, which occurs only when the DNA adheres to a suitably large non-DNA particle. *Pinocytosis*, similar to phagocytosis, is another process by which materials can enter eucaryotic cells. Although pure nucleic acids are not subject to pinocytosis, protein is; if pure nucleic acid is mixed with protein, pinocytosis is stimulated, and the nucleic acid is carried into the cell with the protein. Perhaps the penetration of DNA into bacteria is dependent upon the presence of sufficient contaminating material capable of stimulating pinocytosis or some other mechanism for DNA penetration. Whatever the precise method by which transforming DNA penetrates, it is found that even relatively short sequences of DNA will enter microbial cells if sufficient protein is also present.

Nontransforming DNA (for example, from unrelated sources) can also bind to the cell surface, thereby saturating the receptor sites and preventing duplex, transforming DNA from binding.[2] Using radioactive donor DNA it is found that the bacterial population as a whole permanently binds one to two bacterial genomes for each transformation of a particular genetic marker.[3]

The DNA that becomes permanently bound to such sites then penetrates the bacterium. Penetrating DNA must have a minimal molecular weight of 5×10^5. Since the time required for DNA uptake increases in direct proportion to the map distance between genetic markers (see Section 11.10), transforming DNA appears to be taken up linearly. According to one hypothesis, one end of the duplex DNA fragment enters the cell where an endonuclease (acting, let us say, from the 3' end) digests one of the strands while the other strand is pulled into the cell. This view is consistent with the finding, immediately after entry of ^{32}P-labeled donor DNA into the competent cell, that half the radioactivity is in single-stranded DNA fragments and half is present in a degraded condition.

Synapsis

Once inside the recipient cell, single-stranded donor DNA fragments are thought to pair locus for locus, that is, to *synapse*, with the corresponding segments of the recipient's DNA, which evidence indicates is single-stranded in short regions. Since synapsis can occur between DNA's from the same and, in some instances, from different species, transformation is not only possible within a species, but occasionally between species. We should not be surprised by the latter possibility, because different but related species produce many of the same polypeptides and consequently possess some very similar or identical genetic information. Transformation between species is, however, relatively infrequent.[4] The greater the difference between the species, the

---

[2] In *Pneumococcus*, denatured DNA has a small amount of transforming ability, apparently because it retains some secondary structure. On the other hand, the transforming ability of renatured DNA can be as much as 50 per cent of that shown by an equivalent concentration of native DNA. An increased concentration of DNA plus a high ionic strength increase both renaturation and transforming ability.

[3] Although transformation frequencies as high as 25 per cent have been reported, the usual maximum is about 10 per cent in *Pneumococcus*, and is 1 per cent or less in other organisms. We can accept the figure of 1 per cent as representative and 200 as a representative number of fragments into which the bacterial chromosome is broken during extraction. A study of the relation between the concentration of transforming DNA and the number of transformants reveals that a bacterium accepts no more than 10 fragments of DNA. Accordingly, the maximum possible transformation frequency should be about $\frac{10}{200}$, or 5 per cent.

[4] Alternative states of the same trait—for example, resistance and sensitivity to streptomycin, or dependence and nondependence upon a particular nutrient for growth—can be found in different species of bacteria. Although it is a reasonable assumption that the same type of gene (and its alleles) codes the same or a similar polypeptide in different species, the interspecific transformation is usually less frequent than the intraspecific one. Moreover, the transformation frequency is actually lower and not due to a delay in gene expression which occurs in interspecific (but not in intraspecific) transformation. That interspecific transformation does take place favors the idea that the transformed locus is normally part of the genetic material of both species. The relative infrequency of interspecific transformations is, therefore, not due to incompetence of the recipient cell or to a failure of the foreign DNA to bind to or penetrate the recipient. Rather it is due to the failure of pairing or synapsis between the donor and host segments in regions adjacent to those transformed; such adjacent loci are likely to be nonhomologous in interspecific transformation and, therefore, may often fail to synapse or act to prevent synapsis. The transforming capacity of already-penetrated DNA therefore probably depends not only upon the homology of the loci transformed but upon the nature of the genes adjacent to those undergoing transformation.

less the likelihood that their DNA's will synapse. The transforming ability of DNA which has penetrated a cell seems to depend primarily upon its similarity to the DNA of the recipient cell.

Integration

Experimental evidence indicates that the transforming DNA which is replacing corresponding, or *homologous*, loci of the recipient is *integrated*, that is, stably incorporated, into the recipient's DNA. For example, after bacteria have been exposed to labeled transforming DNA for a suitable period of time, labeled DNA is found to be bound by covalent linkages to the host's DNA. Moreover, the frequency with which the host cell is transformed is directly proportional to the amount of labeled DNA so incorporated. Apparently, only single-stranded DNA fragments are incorporated into a bacterium's genetic material, either strand capable of insertion as long as the fragment is at least 900 nucleotides long. The weight-average length of integration is 2×10^6 daltons. No extensive DNA synthesis seems to be involved in the integration of transforming DNA into recipient DNA. (R)

11.8   In transformation a heteroduplex is formed consisting of integrated single-stranded donor DNA and homologous, if not identical, complementary single-stranded recipient DNA.

The transformed region is a heteroduplex in that it has a segment of one complement of donor origin and its complement of recipient origin. The base sequence of the donor's DNA in the heteroduplex need not be exactly complementary to the recipient's; if it is not, the heteroduplex is heterozygous (as it was in Section 9.5 and in the *AB/ab* region in Figure 10-7C). The next semiconservative replication produces two homozygous homoduplexes, one all-donor, the other all-recipient in origin for the transformed region.

That heterozygous heteroduplexes occur in transformation is supported by the following work. Just as cells are transformed by a genetically different strain, they are treated with UV or mitomycin C which will produce dimers and cross links in the DNA. When, later, DNA synthesis is permitted and clones are formed, there is a *reduction* in the number of clones of transformants in the treated group as compared with the untreated transformation controls. This is the result expected if a repair system operates to excise a damaged single strand from the transformation heterozygous heteroduplex, repair being made by copying the undamaged complementary strand of the heterozygous heteroduplex to form a homozygous homoduplex. When the good strand copied is the donor one, a clone of transformants is still scored; when it is the recipient, the clone of transformants is lost. Moreover, fewer segregations of the two alternatives occur in the first two cells produced from treated just-transformed cells, as expected if the treated cells are repaired to homoduplex condition.

Note that the portion of penetrating donor DNA which is not integrated, obviously, is also not retained or conserved as chromosomal genetic material. This is also true for the single-stranded segment of the host chromosome, which is replaced by the transforming DNA. (R)

11.9 The single-stranded segment of transforming DNA may become integrated by a duplex-repair system of the recipient cell.

Present evidence suggests that the synapsis required for integration is due to base pairings between single-stranded donor DNA and homologous single-stranded recipient DNA (Figure 11-5B). This synapsis requires that H bonds constantly being made and broken between recipient parental strands be replaced in a segment by others between single-stranded donor DNA and a complementary single-stranded region of the recipient. Such synapsed segments of donor DNA can be integrated if it is assumed that at the ends of the synapsed segment the secondary structure of the DNA is abnormal and that a DNA-repair system operates to correct the aberrant conformation. Repair would involve an endonuclease that breaks the donor and corresponding recipient strand in two places each (Figure 11-5C), followed by insertion of donor segment into host strand by the action of polynucleotide ligase preceded, perhaps, by a small amount of DNA synthesis (Figure 11-5D). Broken pieces remaining after repair would be degraded by DNase.

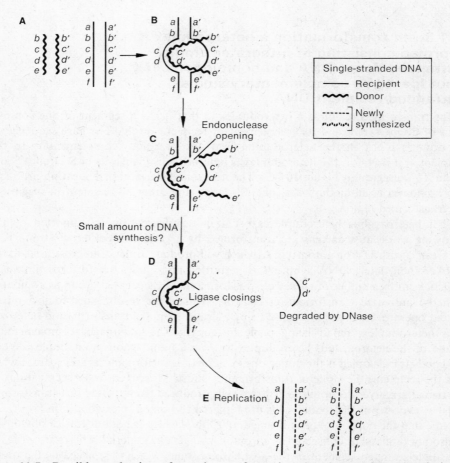

Figure 11-5 Possible mechanism of genetic transformation. See the text for a description.

11.10   Recombination maps for bacterial genes can be constructed using frequencies of double transformation.

Within a species, different loci are transformed with characteristic frequencies. Using strains that differ at two loci, we can study the frequency of *double transformations*, that is, the frequency with which recipients are transformed for both loci. When the proportion of competent cells is high and the frequency of double transformation is greater than the product of the frequencies with which the individual genes are transformed, both loci involved in the double transformation are apparently in the same transforming DNA fragment.[5] Using double transformation frequencies (which are larger as loci become closer), we can construct linkage maps for segments of the bacterial chromosome which bear suitable markers. As expected, the maps of such segments are linear.

The longer the DNA pieces available for uptake by recipients are[6] (see Section 11.4), the farther apart two loci can be yet show linkage by double transformation, and the longer the linkage segments will be. With information obtained from other recombinational processes (such as described in Chapter 12), these segments can be sequenced into a single recombinational linkage map for the entire bacterial chromosome. (R)

SUMMARY AND CONCLUSIONS

Alternative genotypes can be detected when they produce alternative phenotypes. The phenotype of the clone is especially useful in determining the genotypes of bacteria (and other microorganisms).

The genetic material of bacteria, proved to be duplex DNA, undergoes quaternary structure recombination each cell division and primary structure recombination via genetic transformation. The cell membrane (with special emphasis on its mesosomes) plays an essential role in both recombinational processes. In the latter case, donor DNA must bind to and penetrate the cell membrane of the recipient bacterium.

[5] In several cases (for example, penicillin and streptomycin resistance), the frequency of doubly transformed bacteria is approximately equal to (actually somewhat less than) the product of the frequencies for the single transformations. Such results probably mean that the transforming DNA carries the two loci either on separate particles or in widely separated positions on the same particle. On the other hand, the markers for streptomycin resistance and mannitol fermentation are transformed together with a frequency (0.1 per cent) which is about 17 times that expected from the product of the frequencies of the single transformations (0.006 per cent). This result implies that these two genetic markers are located on the same transforming particle; that is, they seem to be reasonably close together in the same bacterial chromosome.

Because of fragmentation during extraction, a given penetrating DNA particle may not always have the same composition relative to two closely linked markers; it may sometimes carry only one and, at other times, may carry both of these markers. The effect of reducing the particle size of penetrating DNA upon the frequencies of single and double transformations can be tested. When particle size is reduced by DNase or sonic treatment, the overall rate of transformation is lower, as expected. No change is found, however, in the ratio of double to single transformations, implying that the two markers are so closely linked that they are rarely separated when particles are fragmented. Accordingly, it seems that the penetrating particles must usually carry both markers, or neither, and the failure to obtain 100 per cent double transformations from the former type must be because sometimes only a portion of a penetrating, synapsing particle is integrated.

[6] Although chromosomal DNA is broken to different degrees by different extraction procedures, a common average MW for the segments is 15×10^6. If a base pair has an average weight of 660, such an average segment would contain about 23,000 base pairs and be about $\frac{1}{170}$ the length of the bacterial chromosome. If an average protein contains 150 amino acids, average segments would thus be about 50 protein-coding genes long.

Subsequently, single-stranded segments of the donor DNA synapse and integrate with the recipient chromosome, replacing a homologous, if not identical, segment of the recipient DNA. When donor and recipient differ genetically in the segment replaced, the initial transformant is an internal heterozygote which, upon replication, produces two homoduplexes, one transformed and one not. If, as is hypothesized, this replacement process requires an endonuclease, perhaps a DNA polymerase, and a ligase, it would have these features in common with the processes of repair of damaged DNA and phage recombination discussed in previous chapters.

GENERAL REFERENCES

Adelberg, E. A. (Editor) 1966. *Papers on bacterial genetics*, second edition. Boston: Little, Brown and Company.

Hayes, W. 1968. *The genetics of bacteria and their viruses*, second edition. New York: John Wiley & Sons, Inc., Chap. 20, pp. 574–619.

Schaefer, P. 1964. Transformation. In *The bacteria*, Vol. 5. Gunsalus, I. C., and Stanier, R. Y. (Editors), New York: Academic Press, pp. 87–153.

SPECIFIC SECTION REFERENCES

11.1   Tremblay, G. Y., Daniels, M. J., and Schaechter, M. 1969. Isolation of a cell membrane-DNA-nascent RNA complex from bacteria. J. Mol. Biol., 40: 65–76.

11.3   Avery, O. T., MacLeod, C. M., and McCarty, M. 1944. Studies on the chemical nature of the substance inducing transformation of pneumococcal types. J. Exp. Med., 79: 137–158. Reprinted in *Papers on bacterial genetics*, Adelberg, E. A. (Editor), Boston: Little, Brown and Company, 1960, pp. 147–168; and in *The biological perspective, introductory readings*. Laetsch, W. M. (Editor), Boston: Little, Brown and Company, 1969, pp. 105–125.

11.4   Burkholder, G. D., and Mukherjee, B. B. 1970. Uptake of isolated metaphase chromosomes by mammalian cells *in vitro*. Exp. Cell Res., 61: 413–422. (Integration of macromolecular DNA from this source may occur in the nucleus.)

Fox, A. S., Yoon, S. B., and Gelbart, W. M. 1971. DNA-induced transformation in

Oswald T. Avery (1877–1955). [From Genetics, 51: 1 (1965).]

Drosophila: genetic analysis of transformed stocks. Proc. Nat. Acad. Sci., U.S., 68: 342–346.

Nawa, S., Sakaguchi, B., Yamada, M.-A., and Tsujita, M. 1971. Hereditary change in *Bombyx* after treatment with DNA. Genetics, 67: 221–234.

Ottolenghi-Nightingale, E. 1969. Induction of melanin synthesis in albino mouse skin by DNA from pigmented mice. Proc. Nat. Acad. Sci., U.S., 64: 184–189. (Mouse cells can be transformed by homologous DNA.)

11.6   Avadhani, N.-G., Mehta, B. M., and Rege, D. V. 1969. Genetic transformation in *Escherichia coli*. J. Mol. Biol., 42: 413–423.

11.7   Gurney, T., Jr., and Fox, M. S. 1968. Physical and genetic hybrids in bacterial transformation. J. Mol. Biol., 32: 83–100.

Harris, W. J., and Barr, G. C. 1969. Some properties of DNA in competent *Bacillus subtilis*. J. Mol. Biol., 39: 245–255.

11.8   Guerrini, F., and Fox, M. S. 1968. Effects of DNA repair in transformation-heterozygotes of *Pneumococcus*. Proc. Nat. Acad. Sci., U.S., 59: 1116–1123.

11.10 Hotchkiss, R. D., and Marmur, J. 1954. Double marker transformations as evidence of linked factors in desoxyribonucleate transforming agents. Proc. Nat. Acad. Sci., U.S., 40: 55–60.

SUPPLEMENTARY SECTION

S11.2   Mutations that make bacteria resistant to a drug occur spontaneously prior to an exposure to the drug.

When a strain of *E. coli* that apparently has never been exposed to streptomycin is plated onto an agar medium containing this drug, almost all individuals are *streptomycin-sensitive*, fail to grow, and therefore, do not form colonies. About 1 bacterium in 10 million does grow on this medium, however, and forms a colony composed of *streptomycin-resistant* individuals, the basis for this resistance clearly being transmissible. Is the adaptive, resistant mutant produced in response to the streptomycin exposure, with the streptomycin acting as a directive mutation-causing agent? Or, do streptomycin-resistant mutants occur in the absence of streptomycin, spontaneously, with the streptomycin acting only as a selective agent to reveal the prior occurrence (or nonoccurrence) of resistant mutants? Or, are both explanations true? Restating the problem more generally, we ask whether mutants adapted to a treatment are *postadapted* (having arisen after treatment), *preadapted* (having already been present before treatment), or of both types.

Clearly, an ambiguous decision results as long as it is necessary to treat the individuals scored with what is being tested—streptomycin, in this example—for, under these conditions, one cannot decide whether the resistant mutant had a post- or preadaptive origin. This difficulty can, however, be resolved. If streptomycin-resistant mutants are preadaptive, they should occur in the absence of the drug and give rise to clones, all of whose members are resistant. Since the mutation to streptomycin-resistance is a very rare event, however it originates, one must grow about 10 million clones on a streptomycin-free agar medium and test each clone for streptomycin resistance by placing a sample of each on a streptomycin-containing medium. After this transfer, part or all of one clonal sample is expected to be resistant to the drug. If resistance is due to a preadapted mutant, one can return to the appropriate original clone—which has never been exposed to streptomycin—and readily obtain other samples which prove to be resistant. If, on the other hand, the mutant is postadaptive, additional samples of the original clone will have no greater chance of furnishing resistants than additional samples taken from different clones.

One method that can be used to simultaneously sample large numbers of clones involves *replica plating*. A billion or so bacteria (from a streptomycin-sensitive clone) are placed on drug-free agar. This produces small clones so closely spaced that they grow together and form a *bacterial lawn* (Figure 11-6A). This *master plate* is then pressed on the top of a sheet of velvet whose fibers pick up a sample of many of the colonies present. The velvet is then used to plant a corresponding pattern of growth on a series of *replica plates*. The first replica is made on a drug-free medium, whereas the second and later ones are made with streptomycin-containing plates on which, obviously, only streptomycin-resistant bacteria can grow into colonies. Replicas made on streptomycin-containing agar will show growth wherever drug-resistant mutants occur (Figure 11-6B–D). One can then turn to the corresponding regions on the master plate to obtain samples to be tested for resistance to the drug. If such samples are no richer in resistant mutants than samples from randomly chosen sites on the master plate

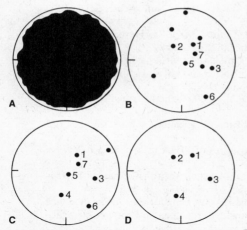

Figure 11-6 Replica-plating a bacterial lawn for the detection of mutants to streptomycin resistance. (After J. Lederberg and E. M. Lederberg.)

corresponding to those which are not mutant on any replica, the postadaptive view is proved. When the experiment is actually performed, the master plate is found to be much richer in mutants at replica sites that are mutant than at those that are nonmutant. Moreover, replicas tend to have mutant clones at corresponding positions on all replica plates (Figure 11-6B–D).

Accordingly, many mutants are clearly preadaptive. Other experiments show conclusively, in the case of streptomycin, that almost all, if not all, mutants resistant to the drug are preadaptive —that is, streptomycin does not induce a detectable number of resistant mutants. Since the same results are obtained with the drug chloramphenicol, one can extrapolate and conclude that, in general, the resistant mutants on drug plates arise spontaneously, prior to exposure to the drugs and, therefore, are preadaptive in origin.

Lederberg, J., and Lederberg, E. M. 1952. Replica plating and indirect selection of bacterial mutants. J. Bact., 63: 399–406. Reprinted in *Papers on bacterial genetics*, Adelberg, E. A. (Editor), Boston: Little, Brown and Company, 1960, pp. 24–31; and in *The biological perspective, introductory readings*, Laetsch, W. M. (Editor), Boston: Little, Brown and Company, 1969, pp. 456–464.

QUESTIONS AND PROBLEMS

1. How could you map the positions of various markers in the *B. subtilis* chromosome assuming that (1) the chromosome always replicates sequentially starting at the same point, (2) stationary-phase cultures contain nonreplicating chromosomes, and (3) exponentially growing cultures contain replicating chromosomes at various stages of completion?

2. In *Pneumococcus*, substances A, B, C, and D are required for growth. Strain 1 is prototrophic because it can synthesize these substances with genes A^+, B^+, C^+, and D^+, respectively; strain 2 is auxotrophic because it carries the mutant alleles A^-, B^-, C^-, D^-. DNA from strain 1 is used to transform strain 2 and the results tabulated are obtained:
   a. Which three of the four loci studied are close together?
   b. Give the sequence of these three loci.

3. Immediately after DNA is permanently bound there is an eclipse period during which the DNA recovered from the cell shows no transforming ability. How could you show that the eclipse was due to this DNA being genetically suitable but single-stranded? (See Ghei, O. K., and Lacks, S. A. 1967. J. Bact., 93: 816.)

4. Compare the maximum number of *A B* transformations you expect from treatment

STRAIN 2 IS PLATED ON UNSUPPLEMENTED MEDIUM PLUS	NUMBER COLONIES FORMED
ABCD	10,000
nothing	0
BCD	1,080
ACD	1,060
ABD	1,100
ABC	1,098
CD	40
BD	651
BC	973
AD	45
AC	41
AB	801
D	31
C	37
B	650
A	33

of *a b* cells with DNA obtained:
a. from closely related genetic strain *A B*.
b. from the same amount of *A B* DNA which is first heated, then cooled slowly in the presence of an excess amount of denatured DNA from the closely related *a B* strain. (See Herriot, R. M. 1963. Biochem. Z., 338: 179.)

5. What conclusions can you draw from the following result?

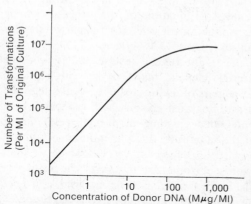

6. On what basis is transformation classified as a type of genetic recombination? Is transformation ever a mutation? Explain.
7. Interspecific transformation in bacteria is rare or absent when the relative dG + dC contents of host and donor differ. When the dG + dC contents are the same, donor–host hybrid DNA's can form even when interspecific transformation is rare. Discuss the relative values of dG + dC content, hybrid DNA formation, and interspecific transformation in taxonomic studies of bacteria.
8. The two strands of a heteroduplex may differ in parental derivation, genotype, or both. Give an example of each type.
9. Suppose 1,000 streptomycin-free test tubes are each inoculated with one bacterium from a streptomycin-sensitive clone, and growth is permitted until about 1 billion bacteria are present in each tube. When the contents of each tube are plated on streptomycin-containing agar, what kind of result would you expect if the mutations to streptomycin resistance were postadaptive in origin? Preadaptive in origin? From the expected results can you distinguish between these two alternatives? How?

Chapter 12

In Bacteria—Episomes, Plasmids, and Genetic Transduction

In Chapter 11 we saw that genetic recombination occurs when a chromosome fragment of one bacterium is incorporated into the chromosome of another bacterium. The present chapter is also concerned with such recombinations as well as others in bacteria in which, for example, entire chromosomes can join to each other or, if joined, can separate. All the recombinations described here will involve genes that enter a bacterium via a phage vector. The first four sections deal mainly with recombinations between the entering phage chromosome and the bacterial chromosome; the remaining sections deal mainly with recombinations between bacterial genes that gain entrance due to phage infection and the bacterial chromosome.

12.1   An episome is a dispensable piece of genetic material that can replicate either autonomously or as part of a chromosome.

Let us consider hypothetically a ring-shaped chromosome which includes two identical regions, as shown in Figure 12-1A. An appropriate twist will bring these redundant parts together so that single strands of one region can base-pair with their complements in the other (Figure 12-1B). Breakage of the strands as indicated in Figure 12-1B and cross unions of correct polarity will then result in the formation of two rings from one (Figure 12-1C)—a new combination of the original genetic material. The reverse recombination, the production of one ring from two smaller ones can be produced by the same mechanism (Figure 12-1, sequence C, D, A).

According to this model, a chromosome might release (excise, *deintegrate*) or incorporate (integrate) some genetic material. Genetic material that can replicate either autonomously when deintegrated or as part of a chromosome when integrated is called an *episome*. We can expect that an integrated episome will replicate along with the host chromosome. A free, or unintegrated, episome might replicate (1) faster or slower than a host chromosome, (2) at the same rate, or (3) if mutant, not at all. In the latter event, the episome will be absent from some progeny cells which we shall assume will survive nonetheless. In other words, episomes are assumed to be ordinarily optional and dispensible to their host cells. Since they are genetic material, episomes might be DNA or RNA , although to date none of the latter type have been found.

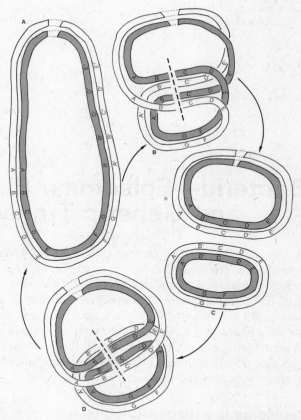

Figure 12-1 Postulated mechanism of genetic recombination in which a small ring chromosome leaves (sequence A B C) or enters (sequence C D A) a large ring chromosome. Thick interrupted lines represent places of breakage; gray lines represent one complement and white lines the other complement of DNA. Primed letters indicate duplicated loci.

12.2   The genetic material of lambda (and probably most other temperate phages as well) is an episome.

Temperate phages do not always lyse the hosts they infect. Some infected cells survive and henceforth are able to block growth of superinfecting phages. These cells are said to be *immune*. If the immunity system is inactivated (for example, by ultraviolet light), phage growth is induced and the bacterial host is lysed. Bacteria harboring such latent ability to be lysed and produce phage are, therefore, called *lysogenic bacteria* or *lysogens*.

When lambda (λ), a temperate phage, infects an *E. coli* cell, the chromosome of the phage has two possible fates. It can reproduce lytically to release approximately 100 phage progeny and kill the host. In this case the ϕDNA remains free of the host chromosome (Figure 12-2B). Or, the ϕDNA can assume a circular form which becomes integrated with the host chromosome as a *prophage*, in which case the host survives (Figure 12-2C). Since the prophage DNA is inserted into the bacterial chromosome, replication of the bacterial chromosome yields bacterial progeny which also carry the phage DNA. Under certain conditions, however, a prophage may deintegrate; that is, the phage DNA may be excised from the host chromosome and enter the lytic cycle of replication. Sometimes, the freed DNA is lost and "cured" bacteria survive. Clearly phage DNA is dispensable. We see, therefore, that the DNA of lambda behaves like an episome. In fact, it is likely that the genetic material of most temperate phages is episomal; an exception is the temperate *E. coli* phage P1, which is not integrated into the chromosome of the host in the lysogenic state. A dispensable piece of genetic material that can replicate autonomously is called a *plasmid* (for example, the chromosome of ϕP1).

Note that in a lytic cycle, lambda DNA *replicates more often* than the host DNA, and that in a lysogenic cycle, the episome replicates *synchronously* with the host DNA. Certain lambda mutants can also replicate as a plasmid, like P1, *approximately synchronously* with the bacterial chromosome; in this case the cell is cured of the lambda plasmid when it replicates *less often* than the bacterial chromosome. (R)

12.3   The bacterial chromosome has unique attachment sites for the integration of temperate phage DNA's.

The DNA's of certain temperate phages in *E. coli* integrate with the host chromosome at their own unique attachment sites (att^B sites) in the bacterial chromosome. Some of these sites are indicated in Figure 12-3. Note that att^B_λ is bordered on one side by the *galactose* loci, *gal E, gal T*, and *gal K*, and on the other side by the *biotin* (*bio*) gene cluster. Because lambda DNA must synapse with the host chromosome before being integrated into it, the site in the phage chromosome for attachment, att^ϕ_λ, and the att^B_λ site in the bacterial chromosome presumably have some nucleotide sequence in common. Integration also requires the product of the phage gene for *prophage integration*, int^+. Note that integration is a recombinational event that probably requires the action of an endonuclease and a ligase. (R)

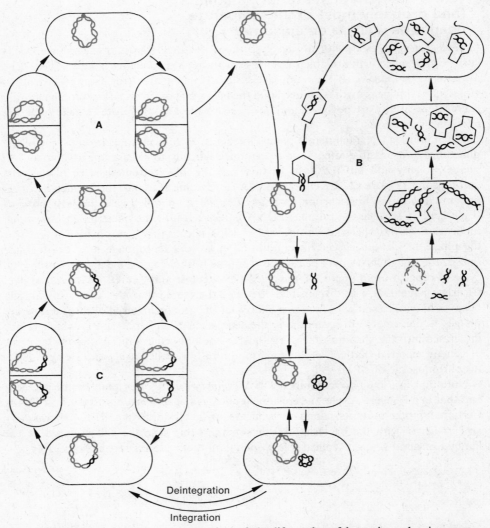

Figure 12-2 Diagrammatic representation of the life cycles of bacteria and episome-con-
taining temperate phage. (A) Cycle for nonlysogenic bacteria. (B) Lytic cycle of temperate
phage. (C) Cycle for lysogenic bacteria. Gray spot represents mesosome; gray duplex material
represents bacterial DNA; black portions, phage episomal DNA.

12.4 The linear gene sequence of vegetative lambda is converted to the different linear gene sequence of lambda prophage via an intermediate circular gene sequence.

When the DNA of the λ virion is first introduced into *E. coli* and, subsequently,
when it is ready to be included in a phage head, it is linear and said to be in the
vegetative stage. Vegetative lambda DNA has a sequence of known genes—detected

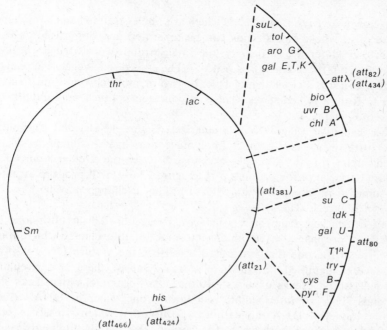

Figure 12-3 Partial genetic map of *E. coli* showing prophage attachment loci (*att*). (The extended segments show markers all of which are transduced by λ or φ80; 82 and 434 are also known to transduce *gal*.) Abbreviations: *thr*, threonine; *lac*, lactose; *su L*, suppressor L; *tol*, colicin tolerance; *aro G*, aromatic amino acids; *gal E, T, K*, galactose epimerase, transferase, kinase; *bio*, biotin; *uvr*, ultraviolet damage repair; *chl*, chlorate; *su C*, suppressor C; *tdk*, deoxythymidine kinase; *gal U*, UDPG pyrophosphorylase; $T1^R$, receptor for phage T1; *try*, tryptophan; *cys*, cysteine; *pyr*, pyrimidine; *his*, histidine; *Sm*, streptomycin. (See E. Signer, 1968.)

by recombination[1]—shown in Figure 12.4. The linear sequence of these genes is different, however, when the DNA is in the prophage state. Obviously, the former and latter gene arrangements must be interconvertible by a genetic recombination.

The interconversion of the vegetative and prophage gene sequences of λ becomes understandable from studies which show that many if not all the DNA's of temperate

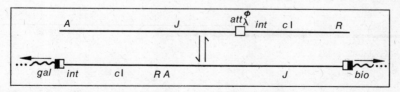

Figure 12-4 Vegetative (top) and prophage (bottom) recombinational maps of phage λ. Distances shown are genetic and not necessarily physical. *A*, phage head gene; *J*, phage tail gene; *int*, integration of λ DNA; *cI*, lambda repressor (prophage immunity); *R*, lysozyme. (See E. Signer, 1968.)

---

[1] Primary structure recombination of λ is promoted by the normal (+) alleles of *rec⁻*, a recombination-deficient mutant in the bacterial chromosome; *red⁻*, a recombination-deficient mutant in the λ chromosome; and *int⁻*, an integration-deficient mutant of λ. Studies of *red⁺*-promoted recombination in *rec⁻* hosts show that recombination between vegetative λ's is not usually reciprocal (contrary to the situation described in Section 17.1), similar to what seems to occur in recombination between T-even phages.

phages have *cohesive ends*, that is, ends which are single-stranded and complementary. In the case of λ, whose two strands can be separated and designated as light and heavy from their difference in density, the single-stranded unpaired portion extends 12 nucleotides from the 5′ ends (Figure 12-5). The ends of one vegetative phage DNA can base-pair to form a circular molecule, or two or more chromosomes may attach in tandem to form a linked series, that is, a concatemer (linear and circular dimers, trimers, . . . polymers).

Once the vegetative phage DNA circularizes (Figure 12-6B) and phosphodiester bonds are formed between ends by polynucleotide ligase (Figure 12-6C, D)—a supercoiled duplex ring is produced—exchange between the circular λ chromosome's $att_λ^Φ$ and the bacterial chromosome's $att_λ^B$ (Figure 12-6D) will produce an integrated λ chromosome, or prophage λ (Figure 12-6E). This exchange may be like that hypothesized in Figure 12-1D.

When an *E. coli* lysogenic for λ is *induced*, by agents such as ultraviolet light or certain drugs, λ prophage leaves the chromosome by an exchange which appears to be the reverse of the one that integrated it. Before the mature DNA is produced, however, several identified intermediates occur. One of these is a circular DNA without single-strand breaks or nicks; another is a linear DNA that lacks 5′-single-stranded ends. The last intermediate is a linear concatemer of DNA's (recall the rolling circle model of DNA replication in Section 4.5) which is used to cut out a headful of λ DNA. Since, contrary to the case of φT4, the headful is always cut out of the pattern at the same position in the gene sequence, all mature λ chromosomes have the same sequence. Mature λ DNA has single-stranded ends, as mentioned earlier. (R)

12.5   In genetic transduction a temperate phage mediates genetic recombination between bacteria by carrying bacterial genes from one host to another.

So far we have considered primary structure recombinations that occur within the episome of a temperate phage and between it and the chromosome of the bacterial

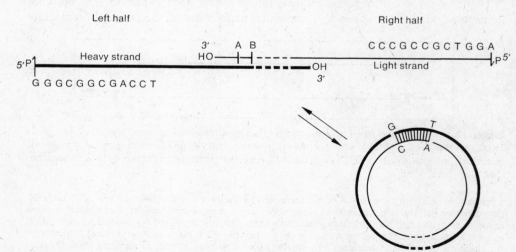

Figure 12-5   Structure of λ DNA and formation of circular molecules. G, A, T, and C are assumed to be deoxyribonucleosides. The right half is rich in adenine and thymine.

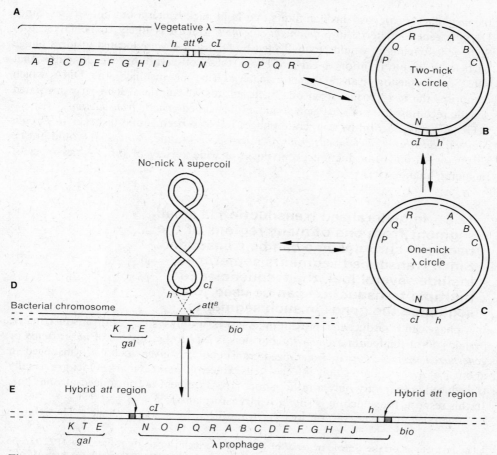

Figure 12-6   Integration of λ into the bacterial chromosome. att^ϕ and att^β are the attachment regions of φ and host, respectively. (After S. E. Luria and J. E. Darnell, Jr., 1967.)

host. Consider next evidence that temperate phages also cause recombination to occur between the chromosomes of two different bacteria. Prototrophs of *Salmonella typhimurium*, like those of its close relative *E. coli*, can synthesize most of the organic molecules they need for growth from the relatively simple nutrients supplied in a minimal medium. Among the many different mutant auxotrophic strains of *Salmonella* is one that requires methionine, and another that requires threonine. We can represent these strains as $met^-\ thr^+$ and $met^+\ thr^-$, respectively. If we centrifuge a liquid culture of the $met^+\ thr^-$ strain to remove most of the bacteria, heat the supernatant liquid for 20 to 30 minutes to kill any remaining bacteria, and then add this liquid to a culture of the $met^-\ thr^+$ strain, a great many prototrophic colonies ($met^+\ thr^+$) appear on the minimal medium. Spontaneous reversion of the met^- mutation cannot account for all these prototrophs. Moreover, since treatment of the supernatant liquid with DNase does not reduce the number of prototrophs, we can rule out genetic transformation as the mechanism for the genetic change.

Several experiments point to what this met^+ factor is. If we add a filtrate of the $met^-\ thr^+$ strain to $met^+\ thr^-$ cells (an experiment opposite to that described above), essentially to prototrophs arise. Other results show that $met^+\ thr^-$ bacteria (donors) but not $met^-\ thr^+$ (recipients) are lysogenic for the temperate phage P22, and that the met^+ factor can pass through filters that hold back bacteria but not viruses. Since DNA is genetic material in *Salmonella*, the met^+ factor is likely to be DNA, too. Such genetic material would be unaffected by DNase if it were located inside a phage particle—a result mentioned earlier. From these observations, we conclude that ϕP22 can somehow transfer genetic material (in one instance, the DNA which comprises the met^+ locus) from one bacterial host to another. Such virus-mediated genetic recombination of host genetic material is called *genetic transduction*.

Genetic transduction by temperate phages has also been found to occur in *E. coli*, *Shigella*, *Bacillus*, *Pseudomonas*, *Vibrio*, *Staphylococcus*, and *Proteus*. It would not be surprising to find transduction occurring in a wide variety of other types of cells, including human. (R)

12.6 In generalized transduction, a small segment from one of many regions of the bacterial chromosome can be transduced. Since transduced segments sometimes include several loci, the frequencies of multiple transduction can be used to sequence the genes in such segments.

A phage can transduce loci present in its last host only.[2] ϕP22 can transduce many, perhaps all of the loci in *Salmonella* and thus is said to be capable of *unrestricted* or *generalized transduction*. In generalized transduction a given locus is transduced in about 1 of every million singly infected cells. Since only single marker loci are usually transduced, apparently only a rather short DNA segment is transduced at one time. In this respect, transduction is similar to transformation.

Sometimes, however, several loci are transduced by a single phage.[3] The relative

---

[2] The restrictions on the genetic material of *Salmonella* which can be transduced by ϕP22 can be studied in the following way. The virus is grown on sensitive bacteria genetically marked $M^+ T^+ X^+ Y^- Z^-$; the crop of phage produced after this infection is harvested, and a portion tested on sensitive indicator strains (M^-, T^-, X^-, Y^-, Z^-) one at a time. The results of such tests show transduction of M^+, of T^+, and of X^+—but not of Y^+ or Z^+. Another portion of the harvested phage is grown on another genetically marked, sensitive strain—$M^+ T^- X^+ Y^+ Z^-$, for example. When the new phage crop is harvested and then tested on the indicator strains already mentioned, it is found now that the new crop of phage has lost T^+ but has gained Y^+ transducing ability. These results demonstrate that a phage filtrate has a range of transduceable markers exactly equal to that of the markers present in the bacteria on which the phage was last grown. In other words, the phage is passive with respect to the content of genes it transduces and retains no transducing memory of any hosts previous to the last.

[3] To determine whether more than one locus is ordinarily transduced at a time, P22 can be grown on $M^+ T^+ X^+$, harvested, and then grown on $M^- T^- X^-$. The latter bacteria are replica-plated (see Section S11.2) on three different media—one selecting only for M^+ recombinants (it contains T and X), another only for T^+, and the third only for X^+. When the M^+ clones are further typed, they are still $T^- X^-$. Similarly, T^+ clones are still $M^- X^-$, and X^+ clones are still $M^- T^-$. Since these results show transduction of only single bacterial markers, they indicate that a relatively short DNA segment is transduced at one time.

In *Salmonella* examples are known, however, of several genetic markers transduced together in *linked transduction* or *cotransduction*. Other work has established that the biological synthesis of tryptophan is part of a sequence of genetically determined reactions that proceed from anthranilic acid through indole to tryptophan. Different genes controlling different steps of this biosynthetic sequence are cotransduced; this finding suggests such genes are closely linked to each other. The biosynthesis of histidine in *Salmonella* is known to involve nine loci which produce 10 enzymes that control the sequence of chemical reactions involved. Linked transductions have been found between two or more of these loci. By using the relative frequencies of different cotransductions and other evidence, all nine loci are found to be continuous with each other and to be arranged linearly (see Figure 12-7).

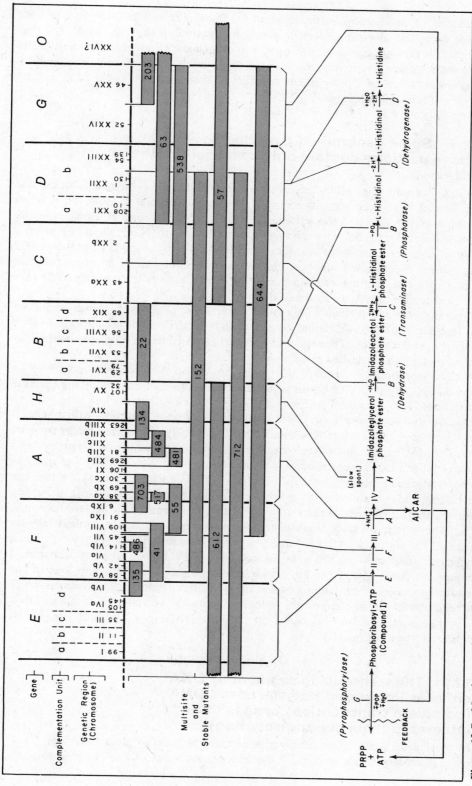

Figure 12-7 Nearly complete 1961 map of the histidine region in *Salmonella*. (Courtesy of P. E. Hartman.) Later studies revealed another gene, *I*, located between *E* and *F*. Note that gene region *B* produces two enzymes.

frequencies of these *multiple transductions* in *Salmonella* can be used to construct linkage maps for short sequences of genes. By combining short linkage maps that have marker genes in common, it is possile to sequence all known loci in *Salmonella* into a single genetic recombination map—a single circle, as in *E. coli*. The simultaneous transduction of closely linked markers is also known to occur in *E. coli* by generalized transducing phage P1.

12.7 Some generalized transducing phage particles contain only bacterial DNA.

In most transduction studies, each cell is infected with several phage particles; and the cells that have been transduced usually become lysogenic. If, however, a single temperate phage infects a bacterium, the result is usually one of three mutually exclusive events for the host: lysis, lysogeny, or transduction. (Note that in this instance lysogeny does not accompany transduction.) If infected by a single transducing P22 phage, then, *Salmonella* cannot be made lysogenic, but can be if simultaneously infected with one or more nontransducing ϕP22 particles. A transducing ϕP22 thus must be defective in its genetic material.

Since the phage is passive with regard to the kind of DNA it carries within its coat (see Section 12.6), we should consider further the nature of the packaged DNA involved in transduction. The viral and bacterial DNA content of a generalized transducing phage can be studied as follows.

A thymine-requiring strain of *E. coli* is grown on 5-bromouracil to make its chromosomes "heavy." The strain is then transferred to medium containing thymine and radioactive ^{32}P and infected with a phage P1 mutant that has lost the ability to lysogenize its host. Since host DNA synthesis stops upon infection with phage, it remains "heavy" and nonradioactive, whereas the newly synthesized phage progeny DNA is "light" and radioactive. When the progeny phage particles are separated in a density-gradient experiment, a band of them occurs in the same "heavy" position as do nontransducing phage grown in 5-bromouracil. The former "heavy" phage are transducing and contain no newly synthesized, radioactive DNA. It is clear, therefore, that these transducing phage carry only preexisting fragments of the bacterial chromosome. The origin of such transducing phage is represented diagrammatically in Figure 12-8, column A. After infection by phage, the host DNA is shown as being fragmented so that some phage heads come to carry only a segment of bacterial chromosome while others contain only phage genomes. Note that only one of the transducing phages in the diagram carries the + bacterial marker gene. Some evidence has been obtained that the process which chops up the concatemer of phage DNA during phage maturation also chops up the host DNA into "headful" pieces for generalized transduction. (R)

12.8 The transducing segment of DNA either is integrated into the host's DNA (complete transduction) or fails to be integrated (abortive transduction).

In most generalized transduction experiments the prototroph obtained by transduction of an auxotroph produces a clone identical to that of any other prototroph.

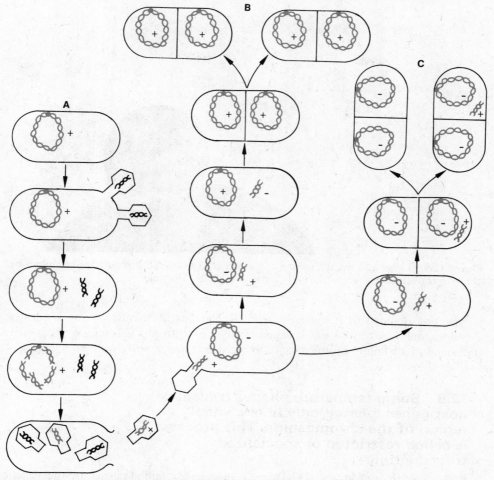

Figure 12-8   Diagrammatic representation of generalized transduction by temperate phage. Column A shows the formation of transducing phage; column B shows complete transduction; and column C, abortive transduction. Gray spot represents mesosome; gray duplex material represents bacterial DNA; black portions, phage DNA. + represents a bacterial gene for prototrophy, − represents the allele for auxotrophy.

In this process of *complete transduction* (Figure 12-8, column B), the transduced genetic material becomes stably integrated into the chromosome of the host and each member of the clone produced has a copy of the genetic information for prototrophy.

Occasionally, though, great numbers of minute colonies occur—about 10 times as many as the large, prototrophic colonies (Figure 12-9). We can account for the presence of these minute colonies in the following way. An auxotrophic cell receives by transduction a segment of DNA which contains the information to make the bacterium prototrophic (Figure 12-8, column C). This DNA, however, is not incorporated into the chromosome of the host, nor is it replicated. But it is transcribed to mRNA. Consequently, the necessary protein is produced which makes the bacterium prototrophic, so the cell can grow and divide. Only one of the first two daughter cells, however, receives the transduced chromosomal segment. This cell can grow normally and divide; the other can grow only for the period of time that the necessary mRNA or

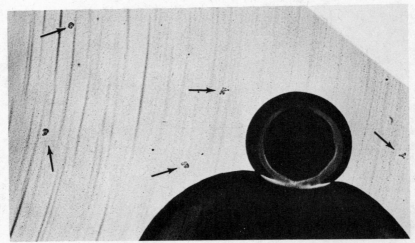

Figure 12-9 Large and minute (arrows) colonies of *Salmonella*, representing complete and abortive transductions, respectively. (Courtesy of P. E. Hartman.)

polypeptide donated to it by the parent cell remains. A minute colony is formed, therefore, only one of whose cells is genetically a prototroph. This failure of complete transduction, or failure of integration, to occur is called *abortive transduction*. (R)

12.9 Some temperate phages transduce host genes located only in one small region of the chromosome. This process is called restricted or specialized transduction.

Bacteria of *E. coli* strain K12(λ) are lysogenic for lambda; that is, the genetic material of lambda (MW 3×10^7) has become part of the host DNA (Figures 12-2C and 12-6). We can induce the prophage to deintegrate by briefly exposing a lysogenic culture to ultraviolet light. Several hours later the bacteria are lysed and great numbers of phage progeny are liberated. If these lambda are tested for their transducing ability, we find that about 1 phage in 10^6 can transduce, and that only a few different bacterial markers are transduced. These markers are all located in or adjacent to the *gal* region and the *bio* region; that is, in the chromosome regions adjacent to att_λ^B. Lambda is thus capable only of *restricted* or *specialized transduction*. (R)

12.10 Restricted transducing phage carry bacterial DNA attached to defective phage genomes.

A lambda phage that transduces bacterial loci lacks a portion of its own genetic material. In most transducing lambda, a variably sized segment of lambda DNA is replaced by a host chromosome segment containing the *gal* locus. This type of defective lambda particle, called λdg, retains certain phage properties but is unable to give rise to infective progeny even though it does lysogenize its host.

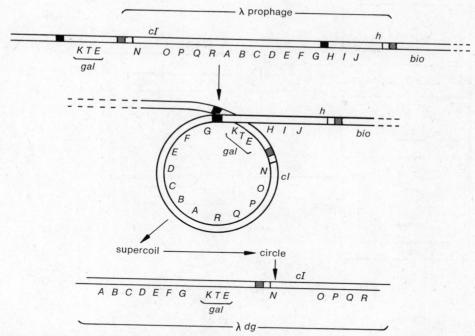

Figure 12-10   Formation of defective transducing phage λdg. The two black spots represent regions that are sufficiently homologous to undergo the deintegrating exchange. (After S. E. Luria and J. E. Darnell, Jr., 1967.)

Figure 12-10 illustrates the most commonly accepted hypothesis as to how restricted transducing phage originate. Although the deintegration required for prophage induction is usually accomplished by an exchange between *att* regions which is the reverse of the integrating exchange (diagrammed for λ in Figure 12-6), occasionally a deintegrating exchange occurs between two other sufficiently homologous regions— one within the prophage, the other without. The resultant phage, in the diagram, is *gal*-transducing but deficient in phage loci *H I J*. Other alternative regions of homology in host and λ DNA's produce different λdg (*defective gal-transducing*) or λdb (*defective bio-transducing*) phage.

12.11   The preferred chromosomal site for synapsis and integration of λdg seems to be *gal*.

When a new host is infected, the main region of homology between λdg and the bacterial chromosome seems to be the *gal* region. Accordingly, λdg usually seems to integrate by an exchange between the *gal* regions of the donor and host (Figure 12-11A, B). The order of the two alleles will depend upon whether the integrating exchange occurs to the right or left of the mutational site within the *gal⁻* allele being used as a host marker. Integration to the right of the defect gives the *gal⁻ gal⁺* sequence; integration to the left, the *gal⁺ gal⁻* sequence. A *gal⁻* bacterium that integrates *gal⁺* from a transducing phage has a *gal⁺ gal⁻* genotype and a gal⁺ phenotype.

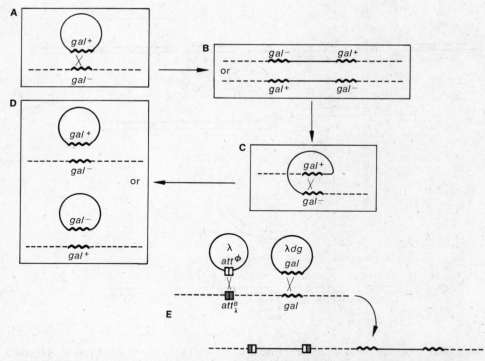

Figure 12-11 Genetic recombinations between λ and λdg DNA's and the bacterial chromosome. (A, B) Integration of *gal*⁺ λdg exogenote in a *gal*⁻ endogenote. (C, D) Deintegration of λdg. (E) Formation of a doubly lysogenic bacterium by integrating λ and λdg DNA's at *att*ᴮ and *gal* loci of the endogenote. Broken line, remainder of bacterial chromosome; solid line, remainder of phage chromosome. Wavy lines (or boxes) represent homologous loci. Single lines (or boxes) represent duplex DNA.

(Phenotypes are not italicized.) Individuals that are partially diploid for functional loci are said to be *heterogenotes*.

Sometimes a *gal*⁺ *gal*⁻ heterogenote gives rise to a *gal*⁺ *gal*⁻ clone, in which the fragment of bacterial DNA carried by the donor, the *exogenote*, remains integrated in the host DNA, or *endogenote*. Within such a heterozygous heterogenotic clone, the transduced and host alleles may or may not exchange positions at the time of deintegration (Figure 12-11C, D), depending upon the relative positions of the deintegrating exchange and the lesion in *gal*⁻. When deintegration occurs on the side of the lesion opposite to that used in integration, the exogenote will carry the endogenote allele. Occasionally a *gal*⁺ *gal*⁻ heterozygous heterogenote can yield both *gal*⁺ and *gal*⁻ types of haploid among its progeny; these bacteria have presumably been cured of deintegrated λdg's carrying *gal*⁻ and *gal*⁺, respectively.

A host cell can be coinfected with a λdg and a nontransducing λ. In this case the λdg DNA can synapse and integrate at the *gal* locus and λ DNA at the *att*$_\lambda^B$ locus of the endogenote (Figure 12-11E). Since λ DNA provides all the information needed for phage DNA and phage protein synthesis, it permits the defective phage to multiply after induction. At the time of lysis of such a *doubly lysogenic cell*, therefore, infective phages of nontransducing (λ) and transducing types (λdg) are liberated in approximately equal numbers. (R)

12.12   Cohesive ends of phage DNA may play a role in several kinds of recombination.

Since transformation does not normally occur in *E. coli*—probably because of difficulties in penetration of DNA—*gal⁻* individuals exposed to *gal⁺* DNA isolated from λdg remain auxotrophs. When, however, *gal⁻* auxotrophs are simultaneously exposed to *gal⁺* DNA of λdg and to nontransducing lambda, the phage serves as a "helper" for λdg DNA penetration, and "transformation" to *gal⁺* occurs. The DNA of λ seems to help that of λdg to enter the host by a single-stranded terminus of λdg DNA base-pairing with one of λDNA to form a concatemer, a linear dimer.

The explanation of helper phage action is supported by the following parallelisms. Phages λ, 424, 434, φ80, and 21 are all cohelpers in naked DNA penetration; all their DNA's also have similar cohesive ends since they can concatenate with themselves and each other *in vitro*. Although phages P2 and 186 are neither cohelpers nor is their DNA cohesive with the phages of the preceding group, they are cohelpers and their DNA's are cohesive with each other.[4]

We see, therefore, that the cohesive ends of phage DNA's are implicated in several kinds of recombination: (1) circularization of vegetative DNA, (2) concatenation of genetically different phage DNA's, and (3) transduction by helper phage. (R)

12.13   Restricted transducing phage are only obtained from induced lysogenic bacteria. The DNA's of most temperate phages capable of restricted transduction are episomes; those of most temperate phages capable of generalized transduction are plasmids.

In the case of generalized transduction, transducing phage occur in the lysates of infected nonlysogenic or induced lysogenic bacteria. In restricted transduction, however, transducing phage occur only in the lysates of induced lysogenic bacteria. Accordingly, generalized transduction seems usually to involve vegetative phage; restricted transduction, ordinarily prophage.

What is the basis for the difference between the temperate phages capable of generalized and those capable of restricted transduction? A restricted-transducing phage usually has a specific att^B site in the host chromosome, a generalized-transducing phage has not. Therefore, the DNA's of most phages capable of restricted transduction are episomes, whereas those of phages capable of generalized transduction seem to be plasmids. The production of restricted-transducing phages involves either a normal prophage integrated at a att^B site being defectively excised, or a defective prophage integrated at a transduced locus being excised.

Although most generalized transducing phages do not seem to have a prophage attachment site, those that do (for example, φP22) may, therefore, contain episomal DNA. Moreover, some generalized transducing phages such as P22, when induced from lysogenic bacteria, can on occasion transduce a bacterial gene attached to a

---

[4] It may be noted that all the phages in the former group are UV-inducible, those in the latter are not UV-inducible; the DNA ends within the former group are less strongly attractive to each other than those within the latter group; and the rate of cohelping is higher in the former than in the latter group.

(defective?) phage genome, just like a restricted transducing phage does. Such observations together with our previous discussion lead us to believe that generalized transducing phages transduce primarily via headfuls of host DNA, and only occasionally by primary structure recombinations between phage and bacterial DNA's which occur because of some specific homology between phage and host loci, including a phage attachment site.

SUMMARY AND CONCLUSIONS

Three types of genetic recombination in bacteria are associated with temperate phages:

1. Recombinations involving the chromosomes of one or more phages only; these occur for all temperate phages.
2. Primary structure recombinations between phage and bacterial chromosomes; these occur primarily for temperate phages whose DNA's are episomes and are usually capable only of restricted transduction.
3. Recombinations involving bacterial genes only; these occur for temperate phages whose DNA's are plasmids and are usually capable only of generalized transduction.

Recombinations involving one or more phage chromosomes

Temperate phages, just like virulent ones, undergo primary structure recombination of their DNA's when they multiply infect their bacterial host, and draw samples of progeny chromosomes from a concatemer produced during their lytic cycle. Specific recombinations which depend upon the presence of complementary single-stranded regions at the ends of the virion DNA include conversion of an open rod duplex to a circular duplex form, and the reverse change; the formation of concatemers between two or more open rod duplexes of the same or homologous types of phage chromosomes (such DNA's assist each other in entering a host), and, presumably, the reverse change.

Recombinations involving an episome and the bacterial chromosome

These recombinations include the integration of the circular form of the episome at the prophage attachment site of the bacterial chromosome; normal deintegration; defective deintegration, which produces restricted transforming phage carrying bacterial genes attached to a defective phage genome; transduction; integration of transducing phage genomes at bacterial loci allelic to those being transduced; deintegration from such loci.

Recombinations involving bacterial genes only

These recombinations include the destruction of the primary structure of host DNA by phage-coded DNase activity; abortive transduction of segments of bacterial chromosomes; complete transductions that result from exchanges which integrate donor markers with the host chromosome.

Just as in genetic transformation, genetic transduction begins with the production of partially diploid bacteria, that is, heterogenotes, and its completion may involve an integration mechanism that uses endonuclease and ligase.

GENERAL REFERENCES

Adelberg, E. A. (Editor) 1966. *Papers on bacterial genetics*, second edition. Boston: Little, Brown and Company.

Campbell, A. 1964. Transduction. In *The bacteria*, Vol. 5, Gunsalus, I. C., and Stanier, R. Y. (Editors), New York: Academic Press, Inc., pp. 49–89.

Campbell, A. 1969. *Episomes*. New York: Harper & Row, Inc.

Hayes, W. 1968. *The genetics of bacteria and their viruses*, second edition. New York: John Wiley & Sons, Inc., Chap. 21, pp. 620–649.

Hershey, A. D. (Editor) 1971. *The bacteriophage lambda*. New York: Cold Spring Harbor Laboratory.

Jacob, F., and Wollman, E. L. 1958. Episomes, added genetic elements. (In French.) C. R. Acad. Sci., Paris, 247: 154–156. Translated and reprinted in *Papers on bacterial genetics*, Adelberg, E. A. (Editor), Boston: Little, Brown and Company, 1960, pp. 398–400.

Jacob, F., and Wollman, E. L. 1961. Viruses and genes. Scient. Amer., 204 (No. 6): 92–107.

Lwoff, A. 1966. Interaction among virus, cell, and organism. Science, 152: 1216–1220. (Nobel prize lecture on the history, significance, and molecular biology of lysogeny.)

Scaife, J. 1967. Episomes. Ann. Rev. Microbiol., 21: 601–638.

SPECIFIC SECTION REFERENCES

12.2   Signer, E. R. 1969. Plasmid formation: a new mode of lysogeny by phage λ. Nature, Lond., 223: 158–160.

12.3   Signer, E. 1968. Lysogeny: the integration problem. Ann. Rev. Microbiol., 22: 451–488.

André Lwoff (1902–) in 1970. Dr. Lwoff was the recipient of a Nobel prize in 1965.

12.4   Luria, S. E., and Darnell, J. E., Jr. 1967. Lysogeny. In *General virology*. New York: John Wiley & Sons, Inc., Chap. 11, pp. 265–290.

Thomas, C. A., Jr., Kelly, T. J., Jr., and Rhoades, M. 1969. The intracellular forms of T7 and P22 DNA phages. Cold Spring Harbor Sympos. Quant. Biol. (1968), 33: 417–424.

Wu, R., and Taylor, E. 1971. Nucleotide sequence analysis of DNA, II. Complete nucleotide sequence of the cohesive ends of bacteriophage λ DNA. J. Mol. Biol., 57: 491–511.

12.5   Merril, C. R., Gier, M. R., and Petricciani, J. C. 1971. Bacterial virus gene expression in human cells. Nature, Lond., 233: 398–400. (*Gal* locus transduced by λdg is functional in human fibroblast.)

Zinder, N. D. 1958. "Transduction" in bacteria. Scient. Amer., 199: 38–43.

Zinder, N. D., and Lederberg, J. 1952. Genetic exchange in *Salmonella*. J. Bact., 64: 679–699.

12.7   Ikeda, H., and Tomizawa, J. 1965. Transducing fragments in generalized transduction by phage P1. I. Molecular origin of the fragments. III. Studies with small phage particles. J. Mol. Biol., 14: 85–109, 120–129.

12.8   Ozeki, H. 1956. Abortive transduction in purine-requiring mutants of *Salmonella typhimurium*. Carnegie Inst. Wash. Publ. 612, *Genetic studies with bacteria*, 97–106. Reprinted in *Papers on bacterial genetics*, Adelberg, E. A. (Editor), Boston: Little, Brown and Company, 1960, pp. 230–238.

12.9   Morse, M. L., Lederberg, E. M., and Lederberg, J. 1956. Transduction in *Escherichia coli* K-12. Genetics, 41: 142–156. Reprinted in *Papers on bacterial genetics*, Adelberg, E. A. (Editor), Boston: Little, Brown and Company, 1960, pp. 209–223.

12.10 Arber, W., Kellenberger, G., and Weigle, J. 1957. The defectiveness of lambda-transducing phage. (In French.) Schweiz. Zeitschr. Allgemeine Path. und Bact., 20: 659–665. Translated and reprinted in *Papers on bacterial genetics*, Adelberg, E. A. (Editor), Boston: Little, Brown and Company, 1960, pp. 224–229.

12.11 Campbell, A. M. 1962. Episomes. Adv. in Genetics, 11: 101–145.

12.12 Kaiser, A. D., and Hogness, D. S. 1960. The transformation of *Escherichia coli* with deoxyribonucleic acid isolated from bacteriophage λdg. J. Mol. Biol., 2: 392–415.

Mandel, M., and Berg, A. 1968. Cohesive sites and helper phage function of P2, lambda, and 186 DNA's. Proc. Nat. Acad. Sci., U.S., 60: 265–268.

12.13 Ozeki, H., and Ikeda, H. 1968. Transduction mechanisms. Ann. Rev. Genet., 2: 245–278.

Norton D. Zinder, in 1968.

QUESTIONS AND PROBLEMS

1. Describe the procedure and genotypes you would use in demonstrating that *E. coli* can undergo genetic transduction with respect to *gal*.

2. Are temperate phages good or bad for bacteria? Explain.

3. How would you determine whether a genetic recombination was due to phage-mediated transduction?

4. Under what circumstances is a recipient bacterium haploid with respect to a transduced locus?

5. Discuss the origin of att$^\phi$.

6. Should the transduced DNA in an abortive transduction be considered genetic material? Explain.

7. When a motile *Salmonella* is placed on the surface of nutrient agar, growth and reproduction can be traced by the branching trail that is produced through the medium. Design an experiment to detect abortive transduction of the gene for motility.

8. Design an experiment to convert abortive transductions to complete transductions using ultraviolet light. How do you suppose this conversion is accomplished?

9. Describe the primary, secondary, and tertiary structures of λ DNA.

10. $\phi\lambda$ codes for fewer enzymes that make DNA components than does T-even phage. Is this what you expect? Explain.

11. How could you prove, making use of a non-lysogenic strain, that *E. coli* strain K12(λ) is lysogenic for lambda?

12. How would you prove that only one transduced chromosome fragment exists in a microcolony of *Salmonella* produced by an abortive transduction?

13. Discuss the statement: "Temperate phage has chromosomal memory, and the chromosome has temperate phage memory."

14. Rare persons suffer a genetic defect in ability to synthesize arginase, resulting in a large excess of arginine in the body, mental retardation, and other undesirable phenotypic effects. The Shope papilloma virus, however, often reduces for a long time the level of arginase in the blood of humans exposed to or injected with the virus. How can you genetically explain this effect of the virus? Do you think it is fruitful to inject this virus into persons genetically defective for arginine? Explain. (See p. 28 of *The New York Times*, September 21, 1970.)

15. What do you suppose is the origin of the DNA found within the virion of the RNA Rous sarcoma virus?

16. What new type of gene is discussed in the present chapter which has a function other than to be transcribed?

Chapter 13

In Bacteria—Episomes, Plasmids, and Conjugation

We have seen that bacterial genes may undergo genetic recombination in a number of ways: by cell division, by genetic transformation, and by genetic transduction mediated by a temperate phage. In this chapter we shall consider another mechanism for recombination in bacteria, one requiring cell to cell contact and the presence of another type of episome or plasmid.

13.1   In certain strains of bacteria a genetic recombination occurs which cannot be satisfactorily explained as transduction or transformation.

One auxotrophic strain of *E. coli* requires three nutrients in addition to minimal medium for growth. Another strain needs a supplement of three different nutrients. If we mix these strains and then plate them on a minimal medium, which contains none of these six nutrients, we obtain a number of prototrophs—recombinants for three loci. (Details of a procedure that can be used to detect recombination in this case are given in Section S13.1.) Since it is unusual for three different loci to be transformed or transduced at the same time, we may not be able to explain this recombination as genetic transformation or transduction. Transformation can be ruled out because treatment of the bacteria with DNase does not appreciably change the number of prototrophs.

To determine whether the recombinants arise as the result of transduction, we can carry out the following experiment. The arms of a U tube are separated by a sintered glass filter, and one of the two auxotrophic strains in minimal medium is added to each arm. The sintered glass prevents the bacteria but not the culture medium, soluble substances, and small particles (including viruses) from passing back and forth. Yet, essentially no prototrophs are found in platings from either arm. Thus, virus-mediated transduction does not seem to account for the recombination. (R)

13.2   The recombination is the result of conjugation, which involves the transfer of bacterial genetic material from donor cell to recipient, and requires physical contact between them.

Further studies show that cell-to-cell contact is necessary for the production of the recombinants just described. The contact allows the transfer of bacterial genetic material from one type of cell, the donor (or male) cell to another, the recipient (or female) cell. This process, called *conjugation*, can thus be considered a sexual process. Genetic recombination by conjugation occurs in bacteria such as *Pseudomonas*, *Serratia*, *Vibrio*, and—under special conditions—in *Shigella* and *Salmonella*, as well as in *Escherichia*. Intergeneric conjugation between *Escherichia* and *Salmonella* has been observed to occur in nature, that is, in a mammalian host.

Donor and recipient parents in bacterial conjugation can be identified as follows: Two streptomycin-sensitive and auxotrophically different strains, say of *E. coli*, are obtained that can conjugate with each other and produce recombinant progeny. If both strains are exposed to streptomycin before—but not after—being mixed and plated, none of the pretreated individuals can divide. In fact, all eventually die, and no recombinant clones are formed. No recombinants are detected also when only one of the two parental strains is pretreated with streptomycin. But when only the other parental strain is pretreated, prototrophic recombinants do occur. This finding demonstrates that the parent giving no recombinants when pretreated acts as the gene-receiving cell during conjugation. When this parent is killed by streptomycin, it is impossible to obtain recombinant clones. The other type of parent must always serve as gene donor in conjugation. After acting as donor, the death of this parent has no effect on the recombination. The donor strain is also called F^+ (F for "fertility") and the recipient, F^-. In bacterial conjugation the transfer of bacterial genes is, therefore, a one-way process from F^+ to F^-.

13.3   Maleness is due to the presence of the sex factor, F, an infective, self-replicating, circular double-stranded molecule of DNA.

Male (F^+) sexuality results from the presence of the *sex factor, F,* a self-reproducing particle separate from the bacterial chromosome. F is also infective independently of the bacterial chromosome, and is efficiently transferred in conjugation from male to female (Figure 13-1). Some properties of F^+ males are

1. F^+ cells can change to F^- by losing the F particle spontaneously or after chemical treatment.[1]

2. If a single F^+ male is placed in a culture of F^- cells, soon thereafter (in a matter of hours) all cells become F^+.

3. F^- cells converted to F^+ produce F^+ progeny.[2]

4. F^+ cells produce a low frequency of recombination of bacterial genes—only about 1 cell in 10^4 F^+ cells transfers bacterial chromosomal DNA into an F^- cell.[3]

Since the F particle does not retain its ability to convert F^- to F^+ when removed from the cell, it does not appear to be a virus. Some of its chemical and physical characteristics have been determined by density-gradient centrifugation. When F is transferred by conjugation to a bacterium of a different genus, *Serratia,* a DNA band appears in the cesium chloride density gradient that is not found in *Serratia* alone. This band is due to the DNA of F, which is found to contain nearly 1.0×10^5 base pairs arranged in a circular molecule, about 2 per cent of the total number in an *E. coli* chromosome. (R)

13.4   Since an F particle is dispensible and can replicate as a separate chromosome or as an integrated part of an *E. coli* chromosome, it is an episome.

In addition to F^- and F^+, another mating type can arise from F^+ cells. Like F^+, this type is a donor of bacterial genes; unlike F^+, however, it produces a *high frequency*

[1] Exposure of F^+ individuals to the dye acridine orange inhibits the replication of F so that cured, F^- cells appear among the progeny. Acridine dyes also inhibit the synthesis of chromosomal DNA, although not as completely as they inhibit F factor replication. Thus, acridine "curing" is really a differential phenomenon.

[2] In stable F^+ cultures, F multiplication proceeds at exactly the same rate as does bacterial chromosome multiplication. This means that there is precise regulation of the number of F particles per bacterial chromosome and it is only when this regulation is inoperative—when a population of F^- cells is undergoing conversion to F^+ by a few F^+ cells, for example—that one sees the explosive multiplication of F.

[3] F, which makes a cell a potentially fertile male—that is, potentially capable of acting as bacterial chromosome donor—causes the formation of some kind of protoplasmic connection between the male and female cell through which genetic material is passed. F is known to cause the formation, on the surface of the functional male cell, of *sex fimbriae,* or *pili,* tubular filaments which act as exclusive receptors for certain RNA and DNA phages that, therefore, attack only males. Although the number of pili per donor is low and their presence is essential for conjugation, it is not certain whether the donated genes pass through a pilus or through a separate conjugation bridge.

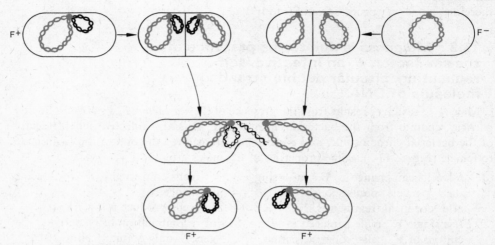

Figure 13-1 Diagrammatic representation of the conversion of an F⁻ cell to F⁺ by F transferred during conjugation. Gray spot represents mesosome; gray duplex material represents bacterial DNA. Black portions, F DNA represented as a circular duplex in the F⁺ male; dotted black strands represent newly synthesized complements.

of recombination of bacterial genes in its mates during conjugation, and hence is called *Hfr*. In a cross of Hfr with F⁻ (Figure 13-2), almost all the progeny are F⁻—the Hfr state is rarely transferred. Hence, Hfr bacteria do not seem to carry the infective F particle free, which would result in F⁺ progeny. On rare occasions, however, an Hfr cell can spontaneously revert to F⁺—the strain from which the Hfr originated. These F⁺ strains are identical to other F⁺ lines and contain highly infective F particles. Therefore, since Hfr individuals arise only from F⁺ and revert only to F⁺, even though they do not seem to contain an F particle, they must somehow retain F in a masked or bound form. The following evidence supports the hypothesis that the Hfr bacterium has an F particle integrated into its chromosome.

We can study further the properties of the Hfr factor and its role in conjugation by means of an interrupted-mating experiment. If we mix two particular strains of Hfr and F⁻ bacteria in a 1:20 proportion, we can be assured of rapid contact of all Hfr with F⁻ cells. At various intervals after mixing, we withdraw samples of the mixture and subject them to the strong shearing force of a blender. This treatment separates conjugants without affecting their viability, their ability to undergo recombination, or their ability to express the characteristics under test. The bacteria are then plated to determine what marker loci of the donor have been transferred to the recipient.

A most important finding of this experiment is that different loci of the male enter the female at different but specific times (Figure 13-3). For example, the *thr* and *leu* markers of the Hfr enter F⁻ after about $8\frac{1}{2}$ minutes of conjugation, whereas the *gal* marker requires about 25 minutes of conjugation before it is transferred. From these observations we conclude that the Hfr chromosome is always transferred in a specific manner: one particular end of the genetic material (called the *origin*, *O*) enters the F⁻

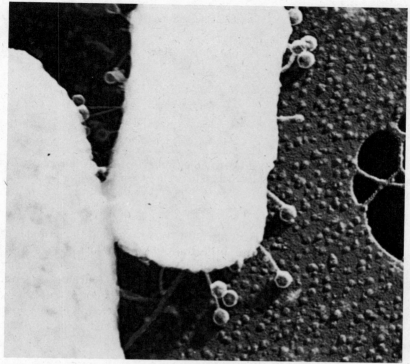

Figure 13-2 Electron micrograph showing conjugation between two strains of *E. coli*. The F⁻ female cell has been labeled with tadpole-shaped bacteriophage lambda particles which do not attach to the Hfr male cell. In the zone of contact the cell walls seem to have disappeared. When exconjugants of such visibly marked pairs of Hfr and F⁻ cells are isolated by micromanipulation and are cultured, only the colonies from the F⁻ partner yield recombinants. (Courtesy of T. F. Anderson, E. L. Wollman, and F. Jacob, Ann. Inst. Pasteur, 93: 450–455, 1957.)

cell first, and the loci that follow do so in a regular, linear process (Figures 13-3 and 13-4).[4]

Under normal conditions only a portion of the Hfr chromosome is transferred, owing to the random breakage of the Hfr chromosome during its transfer in conjugation. Consequently, different recipient cells receive pieces of different lengths; and the *zygote* of an Hfr cross, which contains the genetic material of the recipient plus whatever is donated, is (usually) only partially diploid. In the interrupted-mating

[4] The recombination frequencies observed after conjugation depend, of course, upon both the frequency of a marker's penetration and the efficiency with which it is integrated. Interrupted-mating experiments reveal the sequence of markers, regardless of the frequency (greater than zero) with which their integration occurs. Once the marker sequence is known, integration efficiency can be studied. If, for example, matings are permitted to continue long enough so that just about all F⁻ cells to be recipients have been penetrated by the marker under test, the percentage of zygotes producing recombinants for that marker will indicate the efficiency of integration. If 50 per cent of the recipient cells show integration of a transferred marker, this locus has an integration efficiency of 0.5. One can also test whether recombinants for a given locus are recombinants for markers transferred earlier. By these and other methods, the integration efficiency after penetration can be determined for various markers. On the average, the integration efficiency is about 0.5 for each marker. Therefore, because of differences in penetration, the closer a gene is to O, the greater is its overall chance for integration.

Minutes	Recombinants having Hfr markers
0	None
8	*thr*
8½	*thr, leu*
9	*thr, leu, azi*
11	*thr, leu, azi, tonA*
18	*thr, leu, azi, tonA, lac*
25	*thr, leu, azi, tonA, lac, gal*

Figure 13-3 Recombinants obtained when conjugation is artificially interrupted at various times after mixing F⁻ and Hfr strains. The Hfr strain has markers for *thr, leu, azi, ton A, lac, gal*. (After W. Hayes.)

experiment, a recipient becomes Hfr only in the rare event that the terminal bacterial marker (the one farthest from the origin) is transferred. The locus responsible for the Hfr mating type seems, therefore, to be at the end of the chromosome being transferred and is apparently the locus of an integrated F factor. Since the dispensable sex factor F can exist either autonomously (in F⁺ cells) or integrated into the bacterial chromosome (in Hfr cells), it is an episome. A further description of the two states of F and how these are related to the transfer of F and bacterial genes can be found in Section S 13.4.

13.5   The Hfr male transfers only a single strand of its duplex DNA to the F⁻ conjugant; this strand and the one retained in Hfr synthesize their complements.

As indicated by studies of incorporation of labeled DNA precursors, chromosomal transfer from Hfr to F⁻ is associated with chromosomal replication. As we noted earlier, replication of bacterial DNA begins at a single locus. Although this starting point seems to be in one special region in F⁻ strains, replication apparently starts at or adjacent to F in Hfr cells that are conjugating. After coming into contact with an F cell it is reported that one preferential strand of the duplex ring Hfr chromosome opens and the 5′ end enters the F⁻ cell through a conjugation bridge. As indicated in Figure 13-4 (and in Figure 13-1 when F is transferred), a complement of the linear transferred parental strand is apparently synthesized in the female cell, the rolling circle single-stranded template (recall Section 4.5) synthesizing its complement in the male. Since considerable evidence indicates that the cell membrane is the site of DNA synthesis in bacteria and the bacterial chromosome is attached to a mesosome, the first diagram of Figure 13-4 shows the Hfr chromosome attached to a mesosome near the future conjugation bridge, and later ones show synthesis of a complement of the single-stranded ring at that site. Although not shown in the diagram, the 5′ end of the linear transferred complement might be attached to the cell membrane of the F⁻ recipient. In any case, sequential semiconservative replication of the Hfr chromosome occurs during conjugation. (R)

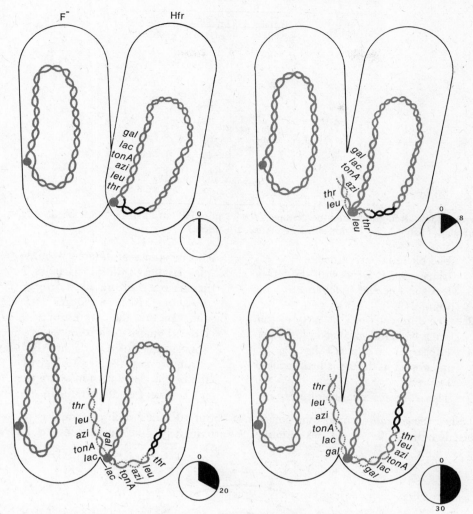

Figure 13-4   Diagrammatic representation of the sequential transfer of an open-ring replica of the Hfr ring chromosome into the F⁻ cell after conjugation has continued for the number of minutes indicated. See also Figure 13-3. Gray spot represents mesosome; gray duplex material represents bacterial DNA; black portion of duplex represents integrated F; gray dotted strands represent newly synthesized complements.

13.6   The genetic recombination linkage maps for different Hfr strains are different, linear rod maps produced by opening the circular *E. coli* chromosome at different loci.

We can determine the sequence of transfer of certain genetic markers for three different Hfr strains by interrupted-mating experiments. The markers common to all three strains are found to occur in the same order in the recombination map (Figure 13-5), but the time of entry is different for each strain. These results are expected if:

Genetic Marker	Strain		
	AB311	AB312	AB313
his +	42	2.5	—
gal +	12	4	—
pro +	—	8	—
met +	4	22	—
mtl +	3.7	25	49
xyl +	2.8	26	43
mal +	1.5	40	32
trp +	—	—	6
arg +	—	—	0.3

Figure 13-5 Recombination percentages for certain Hfr strains. ○, point of origin; — , untested. (After A. L. Taylor and E. A. Adelberg, 1960.)

1. The bacterial chromosome transferred is a rod with the Hfr locus at one end (refer to Figure 13-4).
2. The different times of entry of the same bacterial marker in different Hfr strains is due to F having integrated at different loci in these strains.
3. The reverse directions of entry by chromosomes of different strains may be due to their F particles having been integrated in reverse directions. (Note in Figures 13-5 and 13-6 that the chromosome of AB-312 enters in the direction opposite that of AB-311 or AB-313 chromosomes.) Figure 13-7 gives the origin and direction of transfer for a variety of Hfr strains in *E. coli*.

Since the *E. coli* chromosome consists of about 10^7 nucleotide pairs and is transferred entirely in about 90 minutes, approximately 10^5 nucleotides (a DNA

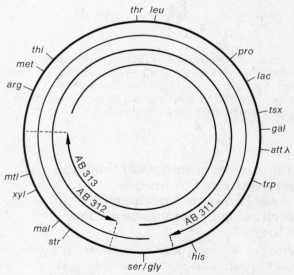

Figure 13-6 Linear chromosomes of three Hfr strains. Arrows show direction of chromosome penetration during conjugation. (After A. L. Taylor and E. A. Adelberg, 1960.)

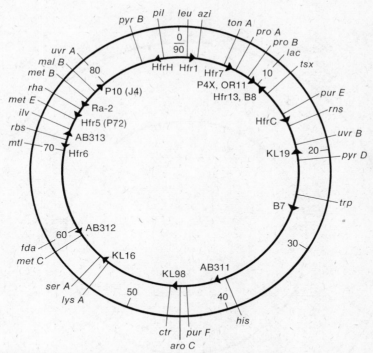

Figure 13-7 Linkage map showing the point of origin of chromosome transfer for several Hfr strains of *E. coli*. Arrowheads on the inner circle indicate the direction of transfer. The first and last markers known to be transferred by each Hfr are displayed on the outer circle. Genetic markers are shown at their approximate positions only; precise map locations are given in Figure 13-8. (From A. L. Taylor and C. D. Trotter, 1967. Bact. Rev., 31: 332–353.)

segment of close to 34 μ are transferred per minute at 37°C. Taking into account variations in the rate of transfer and the efficiency with which a transferred marker is integrated (see the footnote to Section 13.4), we can construct a general genetic recombination linkage map for all Hfr donors. This circular map, with relative distances expressed in minutes, is given in Figure 13-8 and Table 13-1. (R)

13.7   In deintegrating from the *E. coli* chromosome, an F particle can take with it genes of its host. The process of bringing these bacterial genes into an F⁻ cell is called F-mediated transduction.

An Hfr strain reverts to F⁺ when the F particle deintegrates from the Hfr chromosome. The particle is then able to replicate autonomously and infect other cells. An experiment involving deintegrated F factors gives a somewhat surprising result. Using *lac⁻* F⁻ cells and a strain of Hfr with F integrated very close to the *lac⁺* locus, we obtain a small number of recombinants which receive *lac⁺* much earlier than in other interrupted-mating experiments. These recombinants have the following properties:

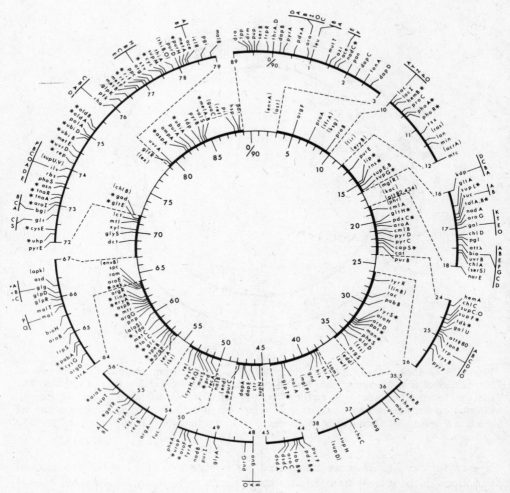

Figure 13-8 Scale drawing of the linkage map of *E. coli*. The inner circle, which bears the time scale from 0 through 90 minutes, depicts the intact circular linkage map. The map is graduated in 1-minute intervals beginning arbitrarily with zero at the *thr A* locus. Selected portions of the map (for example the 10- to 12-minute segment) are displayed on arcs of the outer circle with a 4.5-times expanded time scale to accommodate all the markers in crowded regions. Gene symbols are explained in Table 13-1. Markers in parentheses are only approximately mapped at the positions shown. A gene identified by an asterisk has been mapped more precisely than the markers in parentheses, but its orientation relative to adjacent markers is not yet known. (From A. L. Taylor, 1970, Fig. 1.)

1. They receive only F and *lac*⁺.
2. They are unstable and occasionally give rise to *lac*⁻ F⁻ individuals. Hence, the original recombinant apparently carried both *lac*⁺ and *lac*⁻ alleles.)
3. When mated with *lac*⁻ F⁻ cells, they transfer both F and *lac*⁺ with a frequency of 50 per cent or higher.

(This transfer starts soon after conjugation begins, just like transfer of free F.)

4. Both F and *lac*⁺ can also be transmitted in a series of successive conjugations, each recipient possessing the properties of the original recombinant.

Thus F and *lac*⁺ behave during

transmission as a single element, F-*lac*[+].

5. The F-*lac*[+] element also causes the transfer of the host chromosome in the same sequence as the original Hfr line but with one tenth the frequency.

Table 13-1   List of genetic markers of *E. coli*

GENE SYMBOL	NAME OR TRAIT AFFECTED	MAP POSITION (MIN)[a]	GENE SYMBOL	NAME OR TRAIT AFFECTED	MAP POSITION (MIN)[a]
aceA	acetate	78	*att*[82]	attachment	(17)
aceB	acetate	78	*att*[434]	attachment	(17)
aceE	acetate	2	*azi*	azide	2
aceF	acetate	2	*bglA*	β-glucoside	73
acrA	acridine	(11)	*bglB*	β-glucoside	73
alaS	alanine	(60)	*bglC*	β-glucoside	73
ampA	ampicillin	82	*bioA*	biotin	17
apk	lysine-sensitive aspartokinase	(66)	*bioB*	biotin	17
			bioC	biotin	17
araA	arabinose	1	*bioD*	biotin	17
araB	arabinose	1	*bioE*	biotin	17
araC	arabinose	1	*bioF,G*	biotin	17
araD	arabinose	1	*bioH*	biotin	66
araE	arabinose	56	*capS*	capsule	22
araI	arabinose	1	*cat*	catabolite repression	23
araO	arabinose	1	*cheA*	chemotaxis	36
argA	arginine	54	*cheB*	chemotaxis	36
argB	arginine	77	*cheC*	chemotaxis	37
argC	arginine	77	*chlA*	chlorate	18
argD	arginine	64	*chlB*	chlorate	(71)
argE	arginine	77	*chlC*	chlorate	25
argF	arginine	5	*chlD*	chlorate	17
argG	arginine	61	*cmlA*	chloramphenicol	19
argH	arginine	77	*cmlB*	chloramphenicol	21
argP	arginine	57	*ctr*	mutations affecting the uptake of diverse carbohydrates	46
argR	arginine	62			
argS	arginine	35			
aroA	aromatic	21	*cyc*	cycloserine	78
aroB	aromatic	65	*cysB*	cysteine	25
aroC	aromatic	44	*cysC*	cysteine	53
aroD	aromatic	32	*cysE*	cysteine	72
aroE	aromatic	64	*cysG*	cysteine	65
aroF	aromatic	50	*cysH*	cysteine	(53)
aroG	aromatic	17	*cysP*	cysteine	(53)
aroH	aromatic	32	*cysQ*	cysteine	(53)
aroI	aromatic	73	*dapA*	diaminopimelate	47
asd	aspartic semialdehyde dehydrogenase	66	*dapB*	diaminopimelate	0
			dapC	diaminopimelate	2
asn	asparagine synthetase	73	*dapD*	diaminopimelate	3
aspA	aspartase	82	*dapE*	diaminopimelate	47
aspB	aspartate	62	*darA*	See *uvrD*	—
ast	astasia	(4)	*dct*	uptake of C_4-dicarboxylic acids	69
*att*λ	attachment	17			
*att*φ[80]	attachment	25	*deo*	deoxythymidine	—

[a] Numbers refer to the time scale shown in Figure 13-8. Parentheses indicate approximate map locations.

Table 13-1   *Continued*

GENE SYMBOL	NAME OR TRAIT AFFECTED	MAP POSITION (MIN)[a]	GENE SYMBOL	NAME OR TRAIT AFFECTED	MAP POSITION (MIN)[a]
dra	deoxyriboaldolase	89	*guaC*	guanine	(88)
drm	deoxyribomutase	89	*guaO*	guanine	48
dsdA	D-serine	45	*hag*	H antigen	37
dsdC	D-serine	45	*hemA*	hemin	24
edd	Entner-Doudoroff dehydrase (gluconate-6-phosphate dehydrase)	(35)	*hemB*	hemin	10
			his	histidine	39
			hsp	host specificity	89
			icl	*See aceA*	—
end	endonuclease I	(50)	*iclR*	regulation of the glyoxylate cycle	78
envA	envelope	(3)			
envB	envelope	(65)	*ilvA*	isoleucine-valine	74
eryA	erythromycin	62	*ilvB*	isoleucine-valine	74
eryB	erythromycin	(11)	*ilvC*	isoleucine-valine	74
exr	*See lex*	—	*ilvD*	isoleucine-valine	74
fabB	fatty acid biosynthesis	44	*ilvE*	isoleucine-valine	74
fda	fructose-1, 6-diphosphate aldolase	60	*ilvO*	isoleucine-valine	74
			ilvP	isoleucine-valine	74
fdp	fructose diphosphatase	84	*kac*	K-accumulation	17
ftsA	*See azi*	—	*kdpA-D*	K-dependent	16
fts	filamentous growth and inhibition of nucleic acid synthesis at 42°C	(35)	*ksg*	kasugamycin	(8)
			lacA	lactose	10
			lacI	lactose	10
fuc	fucose	54	*lacO*	lactose	10
gad	glutamic acid decarboxylase	72	*lacP*	lactose	10
			lacY	lactose	10
galE	galactose	17	*lacZ*	lactose	10
galK	galactose	17	*lct*	lactate	71
galO	galactose	17	*leuA*	leucine	1
galT	galactose	17	*leuB*	leucine	1
galR	galactose	55	*lex*	resistance or sensitivity to X rays and UV light	(79)
galU	galactose	25			
glc	glycolate	58			
glgA	glycogen	66	*linA*	lincomycin	62
glgB	glycogen	66	*linB*	lincomycin	(28)
glgC	glycogen	66	*lip*	lipoic acid	15
glpD	glycerol phosphate	66	*lir*	increased sensitivity to lincomycin or erythromycin, or both	(11)
glpK	glycerol phosphate	76			
glpT	glycerol phosphate	43			
glpR	glycerol phosphate	66	*lon*	long form	11
gltA	glutamate	16	*lysA*	lysine	55
gltC	glutamate	73	*lysB*	lysine	55
gltE	glutamate	72	*malB*	maltose	79
gltH	glutamate	20	*malQ*	maltose	66
gltR	glutamate	79	*malT*	maltose	66
gltS	glutamate	73	*man*	mannose	33
glyA	glycine	49	*melA*	melibiose	84
glyS	glycine	70	*melB*	melibiose	84
gnd	gluconate-6-phosphate dehydrogenase	39	*metA*	methionine	78
			metB	methionine	77
guaA	guanine	48	*metC*	methionine	59
guaB	guanine	48	*metE*	methionine	75

[a] Numbers refer to the time scale shown in Figure 13-8. Parentheses indicate approximate map locations.

Table 13-1   *Continued*

GENE SYMBOL	NAME OR TRAIT AFFECTED	MAP POSITION (MIN)[a]	GENE SYMBOL	NAME OR TRAIT AFFECTED	MAP POSITION (MIN)[a]
metF	methionine	77	*ppc*	phosphoenolpyruvate carboxylase	77
mglP	methyl galactoside	(40)	*pps*	phosphopyruvate synthetase	33
mglR	methyl galactoside	(17)			
min	minicell	11	*prd*	propanediol	53
mot	motility	36	*proA*	proline	7
mtc	mitomycin C	12	*proB*	proline	9
mtl	mannitol	71	*proC*	proline	10
mtr	methyl tryptophan	61	*pup*	purine nucleoside phosphorylase	89
mutS	mutator	53			
mutT	mutator	1	*purA*	purine	82
nadA	nicotinamide adenine dinucleotide	17	*purB*	purine	23
			purC	purine	48
nadB	nicotinamide adenine dinucleotide	49	*purD*	purine	78
			purE	purine	13
nadC	nicotinamide adenine dinucleotide	2	*purF*	purine	44
			purG	purine	48
nalA	nalidixic acid	42	*purH*	purine	78
nalB	nalidixic acid	51	*purI*	purine	49
nar	nitrate reductase	—	*pyrA*	pyrimidine	0
narE	nitrate reductase	18	*pyrB*	pyrimidine	84
nek	resistance to neomycin and kanamycin (30*S* ribosomal protein)	63	*pyrC*	pyrimidine	22
			pyrD	pyrimidine	21
			pyrE	pyrimidine	72
nic	*See nad*	—	*pyrF*	pyrimidine	25
oldA	oleate degradation	75	*rac*	recombination activation	29
oldB	oleate degradation	75			
oldD	oleate degradation	34	*ram*	ribosomal ambiguity	64
pabA	*p*-aminobenzoate	65	*ras*	radiation sensitivity	(11)
pabB	*p*-aminobenzoate	30	*rbs*	ribose	74
pan	pantothenic acid	2	*recA*	recombination	52
pdxA	pyridoxine	1	*recB*	recombination	55
pdxB	pyridoxine	44	*recC*	recombination	55
pdxC	pyridoxine	20	*ref*	refractory	(88)
pfk	structural or regulatory gene for fructose 6-phosphate kinase	76	*rel*	relaxed	54
			rep	replication	74
			rhaA	rhamnose	76
pgi	phosphoglucoisomerase	79	*rhaB*	rhamnose	76
pgl	6-phosphoglucono-lactonase	17	*rhaC*	rhamnose	76
			rhaD	rhamnose	76
pheA	phenylalanine	50	*rif*	rifampicin	77
pheS	phenylalanine	33	*rns*	ribonuclease	15
phoA	phosphatase	11	*rts*	altered electrophoretic mobility of 50*S* ribosomal subunit	77
phoR	phosphatase	11			
phoS	phosphatase	74			
phr	photoreactivation	(17)			
pil	pili	88	*serA*	serine	57
pnp	polynucleotide phosphorylase	61	*serB*	serine	89
			serS	serine	(18)
polA	polymerase, DNA	75	*shiA*	shikimic acid	38
por	P1 restriction	89	*som*	somatic	(37)
			spc	spectinomycin	64

[a] Numbers refer to the time scale shown in Figure 13-8. Parentheses indicate approximate map locations.

Table 13-1   Continued

GENE SYMBOL	NAME OR TRAIT AFFECTED	MAP POSITION (MIN)[a]	GENE SYMBOL	NAME OR TRAIT AFFECTED	MAP POSITION (MIN)[a]
speB	spermidine	57	tolB	tolerance	17
strA	streptomycin	64	tolC	tolerance	58
stv	streptovaricin	77	tonA	T-one	2
sucA	succinate	17	tonB	T-one	25
sucB	succinate	17	tpp	thymidine phosphory-lase	89
supB	suppressor	16			
supC	suppressor	25	trpA	tryptophan	25
supD	suppressor	(38)	trpB	tryptophan	25
supE	suppressor	16	trpC	tryptophan	25
supF	suppressor	25	trpD	tryptophan	25
supG	suppressor	16	trpE	tryptophan	25
supH	suppressor	38	trpO	tryptophan	25
supL	suppressor	17	trpR	tryptophan	90
supM	suppressor	78	trpS	tryptophan	65
supN	suppressor	45	tsx	T-six	11
supO	suppressor	25	tyrA	tyrosine	50
supT	suppressor	55	tyrR	tyrosine	27
supU	suppressor	74	tyrS	tyrosine	32
supV	suppressor	74	ubiA	ubiquinone	83
tdk	deoxythymidine kinase	25	ubiB	ubiquinone	75
tfrA	T-four	(8)	ubiD	ubiquinone	75
thiA	thiamine	78	uhp	uptake of hexose phos-phates	72
thiB	thiamine	(78)			
thiO	thiamine	(78)	uraP	uracil	50
thrA	threonine	0	uvrA	ultraviolet	80
thrD	threonine	0	uvrB	ultraviolet	18
thyA	thymine	55	uvrC	ultraviolet	37
tkt	transketolase	(55)	uvrD	ultraviolet	74
tnaA	tryptophanase	73	valS	valine	84
tnaR	regulatory gene	73	xyl	xylose	70
tolA	tolerance	17	zwf	zwischenferment	(35)

[a] Numbers refer to the time scale shown in Figure 13-8. Parentheses indicate approximate map locations.

We can explain these results most simply by saying that an F particle can take with it, when it deintegrates, a neighboring piece of the bacterial chromosome, lac^+ (Figure 13-9). Usually, only the F-lac^+ particle is transferred in conjugation. When, however, the F-lac^+ particle integrates within or near lac, the entire bacterial chromosome can be transferred during conjugation. If we have an Hfr bacterium with two integrated F factors, the chromosome transferred during conjugation will be in two pieces, each with an F at the end; both segments are transferred to the F⁻ cell. We see, therefore, that host genes attached to F are mobilized whether they are in an entire chromosome or a small segment.

F-lac^- particles, which consist of F and a mutant lac locus, can also be selected. Moreover, since F can become integrated at a variety of loci, different loci can become part of a deintegrated F particle. A deintegrated F particle that carries any genes of its host is called F', which is a *substituted sex factor*. A *sex factor* can now be defined as genetic material that can initiate conjugation and mobilize bacterial whole chromo-

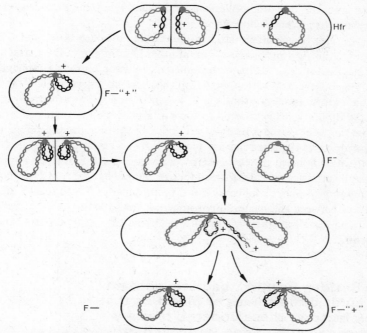

Figure 13-9 Diagrammatic representation of the formation of a substituted sex factor, F-"+", and of the occurrence of F-mediated transduction. The gray spot represents meso-some; gray duplex material represents bacterial DNA; black portions, F DNA. + represents a bacterial gene for prototrophy, − represents the allele for auxotrophy. Gray dotted strands represent newly synthesized complements.

somes or chromosome segments. Like F, F′ is circular duplex DNA. The process in which substituted sex factors bring bacterial genes from one cell to another is called *F-mediated transduction*, *sexduction*, or *F-duction*. (Notice the parallel between F′ and F, on the one hand, and λdg and λ, on the other.)

The functioning of a sex factor depends upon both its genotype and its host's. For example, after ultraviolet treatment of F-*lac* males, some individuals are found no longer able to transfer *lac* or chromosomal markers. Apparently a mutation in the F portion of the F′ resulted in a loss of one or more sex-factor functions. When *Salmo-nella* or *Shigella* act as recipients in crosses with F⁺ or Hfr *E. coli*, F is transferred but sometimes is unable to act as a sex factor until it is sent back into F⁻ *E. coli*. Such results show that F functions can be temporarily inhibited or unexpressed, depending upon the host genotype. (R)

13.8   Primary structure genetic recombination seems to occur reciprocally, sometimes at least, between a bacterial chromosome and a substituted sex factor.

F′-linked bacterial loci make a recipient cell partially diploid. In such cells pri-mary structure recombination may occur between homologous loci of the bacterial chromosome and the episome.[5] We can study such recombination between homologous prophage loci in the following way.

An F⁻ bacterium lysogenic for lambda (containing markers *A*, *B*, and *C*) is mated with an F′ male that has prophage λ (containing markers *a*, *b*, and *c*) attached to the substituted sex factor. The recipient becomes diploid for lambda prophage, and we can study genetic recombination between the lambda prophage in the bacterial chromosome and the lambda prophage in F′ since these differ at three loci. Each of these partially diploid cells is allowed to form a large clone, and one cell from each is selected. The lambdas of these bacteria are induced to form mature phage which are scored with respect to the three marker loci.

Among the recombinant progeny, reciprocal classes are found to be approximately equal in frequency; for example, the number of phage that carry *A b c* recombinants equals the number of phage that carry *a B C* recombinants. These results indicate that recombination between the bacterial chromosome and a substituted sex factor—and, by inference, between the chromosome of the Hfr and F⁻ individuals—is, sometimes at least, reciprocal. (R)

13.9 Besides F and F′, bacteria contain other kinds of episomes or plasmids that are sex factors; these undergo primary structure recombination with each other and with phage episomes.

Quaternary and primary structure recombinations of F and F′ depend not only upon the number of them present, but also upon the presence of other kinds of sex factors in a bacterium or its partner in conjugation. These sex factors, also episomes or episome-like plasmids, include *colicinogenic factors*, or *col factors* (discussed in Section S13.9a) that code for bactericidal substances called colicins and *drug-resistance factors* (discussed in Section S13.9b) which render the bacterial host resistant to certain antibiotic drugs. Quaternary structure recombinations of sex factors occur because certain sex factors affect the replication and transfer of other types of sex factors. Primary structure recombinations occur not only between certain sex factors and the bacterial chromosome, and between two sex factors of the same type, but between sex factors of different types, as well as between sex factors and the episomes of phages (as discussed in Section S 13.9c).

SUMMARY AND CONCLUSIONS

Bacteria may harbor another class of episomes and plasmids, different from that in temperate phages, most or all of whose members are also composed of circular DNA duplexes during their existence as autonomous chromosomes. The presence of a member of this class in either the free or integrated state promotes conjugation which

---

[5] Bacteria with *rec⁻* mutants do not undergo primary structure recombination of bacterial genes; such bacteria cannot integrate into their genetic material segments of chromosomes transduced by episomes. These bacteria are also sensitive to ultraviolet light and cannot excise thymine dimers. Recombination following conjugation normally seems to involve a small amount of DNA synthesis (and probably breakdown), since there is evidence for incorporation of labeled DNA precursors at this time. Such evidence indicates that primary structure genetic recombinations in bacteria and the excision and repair of dimers involve similar enzymatic steps.

can lead to the transfer of genetic material from one conjugant to the other. Accordingly, such episomes as F and such episome-like particles and plasmids as *col* factors and drug-resistance factors are called sex factors.

The most well understood sex factor is the episome F. When F is a free chromosome it is mobile, being transferred from F^+ males (which contain them) to F^- females (which do not) a few minutes after conjugation starts. With F integrated into the circular bacterial chromosome (at one of a number of possible loci), the chromosome is opened at the time of conjugation—the presence of integrated F rendering one of the DNA strands of the bacterial chromosome mobile. F^- cells mated to males of this, Hfr, type usually become partial diploids before the bacterial DNA strand being donated breaks spontaneously. Donated bacterial loci can integrate by replacing host markers in a primary structure recombination that seems, at least sometimes, to be reciprocal.

Integrated F can deintegrate either normally, producing an F^+ male from an Hfr, or abnormally. In the latter case the product, a substituted sex factor, F', may retain, in addition to the genetic material that codes for the conjugational properties of the cell and the mobile properties of F, some bacterial loci that were adjacent to F in the integrated state. Therefore, matings between F'-containing males and F^- females will also transfer bacterial genes, in a process called F-mediated transduction. F is always located at the end of the bacterial markers being transmitted, whether the entire chromosome (as in Hfr) or only a portion of it (as in F') is mobilized. Hence, F^- females must receive linearly arriving bacterial genes for a suitably long interval before they will receive F and can become males.

Sex factors affect the replication and distribution of other sex factors—thereby effecting quaternary structure recombinations. Moreover, sex factors may undergo primary structure recombination not only with the bacterial chromosome, but with other sex factors as well as phage episomes.

GENERAL REFERENCES

Campbell, A. 1969. *Episomes.* New York: Harper & Row, Inc.

Hayes, W. 1968. *The genetics of bacteria and their viruses,* second edition. New York: John Wiley & Sons, Inc.

Jacob, F., and Wollman, E. L. 1961. *Sexuality and the genetics of bacteria.* New York: Academic Press, Inc.

Jones, D., and Sneath, P. H. A. 1970. Genetic transfer and bacterial taxonomy. Bact. Rev., 34: 40–81. (Transfer by all known mechanisms.)

SPECIFIC SECTION REFERENCES

13.1   Lederberg, J., and Tatum, E. L. 1946. Gene recombination in *Escherichia coli.* Nature, Lond., 158: 558. Reprinted in *Classic papers in genetics,* Peters, J. A. (Editor), Englewood Cliffs, N.J.: Prentice-Hall, Inc., 1959, pp. 192–194.

13.3   Hickson, F. T., Roth, T. F., and Helinski, D. R. 1967. Circular DNA forms of a bacterial sex factor. Proc. Nat. Acad. Sci., U.S., 58: 1731–1738.

Vapnek, D., and Rupp, W. D. 1971. Identification of individual sex-factor DNA strands and their replication during conjugation in thermosensitive DNA mutants of *Escherichia coli.* J. Mol. Biol., 60: 413–424. (The sex-factor strand synthesized in the donor has the same polarity as the strand transferred to the recipient.)

13.5   Altenburg, B. C., Suit, J. C., and Brinkley, B. R. 1970. Ultrastructure of deoxyribonucleic acid-membrane associations in *Escherichia coli.* J. Bact., 104: 549–555. (Evidence that the replication fork is mesosome-bound.)

François Jacob (1920–   ) in 1968. Dr. Jacob was the recipient of a Nobel prize in 1965.

Joshua Lederberg (1925–   ) in 1969. Dr. Lederberg was the recipient of a Nobel prize in 1958. (Photograph by Stanford University.)

Gross, J. D., and Caro, L. G. 1966. DNA transfer in bacterial conjugation. J. Mol. Biol. 16: 269–284.

Vapnek, D., and Rupp, W. D. 1970. Asymmetric segregation of the complementary sex-factor DNA strands during conjugation in *Escherichia coli*. J. Mol. Biol., 53: 287–303.

Vielmetter, W., Bonhoeffer, F., and Schütte, A. 1968. Genetic evidence for transfer of a single DNA strand during bacterial conjugation. J. Mol. Biol., 37: 81–86.

13.6   Taylor, A. L. 1970. Current linkage map of *Escherichia coli*. Bact. Rev., 34: 155–175.

Taylor, A. L., and Adelberg, E. A. 1960. Linkage analysis with very high frequency males of *Escherichia coli*. Genetics, 45: 1233–1243.

Edward Lawrie Tatum (1908–   ) in 1968. Dr. Tatum was the recipient of a Nobel prize in 1958.

13.7   Adelberg, E. A., and Burns, S. N. 1960. Genetic variation in the sex factor of *Escherichia coli*. J. Bact., 79: 321–330. Reprinted in *Papers on bacterial genetics*, Adelberg, E. A. (Editor), Boston: Little, Brown and Company, 1960, pp. 353–362.

Freifelder, D. 1968. Studies on *Escherichia coli* sex factors. IV. Molecular weights of the DNA of several F′ elements. J. Mol. Biol., 35: 95–102.

13.8   Berg, D. E., and Gallant, J. A. 1971. Tests of reciprocality in crossingover in partially diploid F′ strains of *Escherichia coli*. Genetics, 68: 457–472. (Reciprocality is found to be the exception rather than the rule.)

Meselson, M. 1967. Reciprocal recombination in prophage λ. J. Cell Physiol., 70 (Suppl. 1): 113–118.

Weil, J. 1969. Reciprocal and non-reciprocal recombination in bacteriophage λ. J. Mol. Biol., 43: 351–355.

SUPPLEMENTARY SECTIONS

S13.1   The replica-plating technique can be used to detect the production of prototrophic bacteria by genetic recombination between auxotrophic bacteria.

Two strains of *E. coli* are used that contain six nutritional mutants, all of these having arisen independently. One mutant strain is auxotrophic for threonine (thr^-), leucine (leu^-), and thiamine (thi^-); the other mutant strain is auxotrophic for biotin (bio^-), phenylalanine (phe^-), and cysteine (cys^-). The genotypes of these two lines can be given, respectively, as $thr^-\ leu^-\ thi^-\ bio^+\ phe^+\ cys^+$ and $thr^+\ leu^+\ thi^+\ bio^-\ phe^-\ cys^-$. Of course, the given gene sequence may be different in the linkage map.

The two pure lines are grown separately on complete liquid culture medium, that is, one that contains all nutrients required for growth and reproduction. To form a bacterial lawn, about 10^8 bacteria from one line are plated onto agar containing complete medium. These bacteria, for example the $thr^-\ leu^-\ thi^-$ strain, are replica-plated (Figure 13-10; this technique is described in Section S11.2) onto three plates containing a complete medium deficient in a different single nutrient (thr, leu, and thi, respectively). In general, only approximately 1 in 10^6 bacteria placed on replicas form clones because a pre-adaptive reverse mutant (*revertant*) produces prototrophy for the nutrient missing from the medium. Such clonal growth is not found, however, in the corresponding position on all three replicas (or even on two) with greater than chance frequency. The same results are obtained when an equal number of bacteria of the $bio^-\ phe^-\ cys^-$

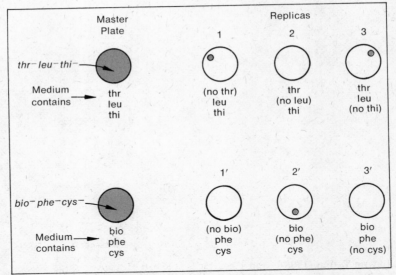

Figure 13-10 Use of replica plating (shown diagrammatically) to detect spontaneous mutations in *E. coli*. Replica 1 detects one mutant to *thr*⁺, replica 3 detects one mutant to *thi*⁺, and replica 2′ detects one mutant to *phe*⁺.

line are plated on complete medium and tested on appropriate replicas. We may conclude, therefore, that on relatively rare occasions mutants to prototrophy for one nutrient do occur singly, but double or triple mutants do not occur with detectable frequency.

In another test, the preceding experiment is repeated exactly, with the exception that the same numbers of the two triply mutant strains are mixed in the liquid medium before being plated on agar containing complete medium. In this case (Figure 13-11), six replicas are made with medium which is complete except that three lack bio, phe, and cys in addition to lacking thr, leu, or thi; the other three lack thr, leu, and thi and also bio, phe, or cys Individuals of the *thr⁻ leu⁻ thi⁻* strain cannot grow on the first three replicas mentioned because a single required nutrient is missing; they cannot grow in the last three because all three required nutrients are missing. Individuals of the *bio⁻ phe⁻ cys⁻* strain cannot grow on the first three replicas because all three required nutrients are missing; they cannot grow on the last three because one of the three is absent. If the master plate contains a revertant to nutritional independence for one of the nutritionally dependent loci, in only one of the six replicas will the mutant form a colony. For example, if a *thr⁺* revertant occurs among the individuals of *thr⁻ leu⁻ thi⁻* strain on the master plate, a colony will grow only on the replica lacking bio, phe, cys, and thr. Actually, about 100 different positions on the master plate show

growth on the replicas. This number is very much larger than that found in the two groups of three replicas made after plating the two lines separately. In the present case, some positions show growth only on one of the six replicas. Many positions, however, show growth on two replicas, suggesting that these clones must have gained nutritional independence at two loci. Finally, at many positions growth occurs on all six replicas, each position of growth representing the occurrence of a complete prototroph (*thr⁺ leu⁺ thi⁺ bio⁺ phe⁺ cys⁺*). A study of these clones on the replicas and on the master plate shows that the changes involved are transmissible and preadaptive. When tested, such clones prove to be pure; that is, the nutritional independence gained is not attributable to any type of physical association between two or more different auxotrophs. Since the findings that large numbers of clones grow on the replicas and many are either complete prototrophs or auxotrophs for only one nutrient cannot be due to spontaneous mutation, they must be attributed to some type of genetic recombination.

S13.4   Cells in an F⁺ clone that transfer bacterial markers have probably changed to an Hfr condition.

As mentioned previously, free F is transferred from F⁺ to F⁻ with high efficiency when bacterial markers are not. When an interrupted-mating experiment is performed to determine the time when the F particle in F⁺ males is trans-

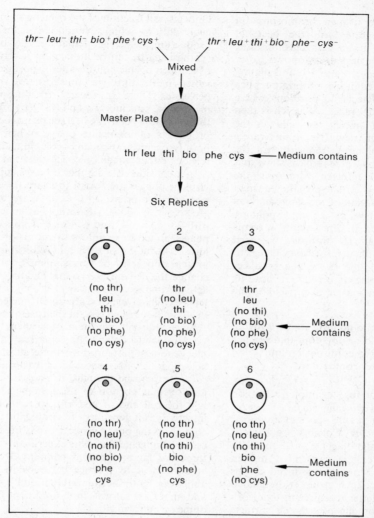

Figure 13-11   Replica plating (shown diagrammatically) to detect genetic recombination in *E. coli*. A completely prototrophic recombinant is found at 12 o'clock in all replicas. A recombinant for both *phe* and *cys* is found at 3 o'clock on replicas 5 and 6. Replica 1 has a clone growing at 9 o'clock which may be due either to recombination or to mutation to *thr*⁺.

ferred, it is found that F is transferred about 5 minutes after mixing F⁺ and F⁻, or several minutes earlier than any known marker in the chromosome is transferred in an Hfr × F⁻ cross. We, therefore, have additional evidence that F is a free chromosome in the F⁺ male.

As already mentioned, Hfr strains are always derived from F⁺ strains. It was also noted that Hfr strains can revert to F⁺, indicating that Hfr harbors a latent F particle. Since the fertility of Hfr is unaffected by exposure to acridine orange, the latent F particle is probably not a free chromosome. This contention is supported by the

fact that maleness is not infective; that is, maleness is not transmitted to F⁻ cells after short mating intervals with Hfr males. Consequently, the latent F particle in Hfr must be located chromosomally, and the chromosomal locus assigned to the Hfr must be that of chromosomal F. Once F enters the bacterial chromosome, replication of any remaining cytoplasmic F particles normally is prevented or repressed.

What happens in those few cells of an F⁺ clone which transfer bacterial markers, causing the F⁺ clone as a whole to give a low frequency of recombination of bacterial genes? Suppose that for an F$^+$ cell to transfer its own chromosome, an F particle must integrate with the bacterial chromosome, making it an Hfr chromosome. This hypothesis can be tested as follows. After mixing suitably marked F$^+$ and F$^-$ and plating them on a complete medium, appropriate replica plates are made to detect the positions where recombination has taken place. A search is then made for Hfr strains among the cells on the master plate. Although new Hfr strains rarely occur, they are found most frequently on the master plate at positions where replicas show that recombination has taken place. Moreover, the Hfr strains discovered often produce a high frequency of recombination of the same markers that show recombination in the corresponding positions in the replicas. In other words, it seems valid to believe that to transfer bacterial markers, an F$^+$ individual must first change to an Hfr condition. It is the Hfr which produces the recombination detected on the replica, its clonal members on the master plate yielding the same type of Hfr.

S13.9a Some of the genetic factors for colicins are plasmid or episome-like sex factors; they initiate conjugation and mobilize bacterial chromosomes.

Many strains of enteric bacteria (*Escherichia, Salmonella, Shigella,* for example), contain genetic elements called *colicinogenic factors,* or *col factors,* that code for highly specific, antibiotic substances called *colicins.* Colicins are bactericidal but not bacteriolytic agents; a thousandth of a microgram of colicin can kill 1 million sensitive *E. coli* cells. More than a dozen groups of colicins are known; each group is designated by a different capital letter; each seems to adsorb to a different receptor site at the cell surface. Different colicins belonging to the same group can be distinguished by other characteristics. Colicins have a high molecular weight; colicin K and colicin V are lipopolysaccharide proteins that seem to be the same as the O antigen of the bacteria; the antigen molecule can be separated into a lipopolysaccharide and a protein fraction, the latter having all the bactericidal activity.

A bacterium that harbors a *col* factor is *colicinogenic* and is immune to the corresponding colicin. The bacterium can possess, however, receptor sites that make it susceptible to colicins of other groups. Certain other genes confer resistance to whole groups of colicins by causing the loss of receptors.

Colicinogeny is stable and can be transmitted through thousands of cell generations. Although it can be lost spontaneously, spontaneous acquisition of colicinogeny has never been observed.

Only a small fraction of the bacteria in a colicinogenic culture actually produce colicins. Colicin production, which is lethal to the bacterium synthesizing it, can be induced in nearly all cells of a colicinogenic culture after exposure to ultraviolet light, nitrogen mustard, or hydrogen peroxide. Thus, in several of the properties mentioned, colicinogeny and lysogeny are similar, the *col* factors behaving in these properties like the prophages of temperate phage. When a cell is both lysogenic and colicinogenic, induction often releases either phage or colicin but not both.

In a considerable number of cases colicins and virulent phages are found to share the same cell surface receptor sites; for example, receptor sites are shared by colicin K and ϕT6; colicin E and ϕBF-23; colicin C and ϕT1 or ϕT5. Since virulent phages attach to receptors by means of a protein located at the tip of their tails, colicin and tailtip protein appear to be very similar. Some colicins change the cell surface so that endonucleases are activated—DNase in the case of colicin E2; RNase, which cleaves about 50 nucleotides off the 3' end of 16s rRNA, in the case of colicin E3.

Since the tailtip protein of virulent phages is very similar to colicin, it seems reasonable that the genomes that produce these substances are homologous with respect to at least one gene. A *col* factor can be thought of as a virulent phage missing that portion of the genome required to lyse the cell and to give rise to particles whose infectivity is independent of conjugation, yet with enough of the phage genome persisting to make a cell colicinogenic. Labeling experiments show that three *col* factors studied contain DNA in the amount of 4 to 7 times 10^4 nucleotide pairs— about one tenth the amount in F or T-even phage, and about the same as in λ. *Col* factor DNA is in duplex ring form.

Not only are *col* factors transmitted to progeny via cell division, but new strains can become colicinogenic through phage-mediated transduction and bacterial conjugation. Although *col K* is not transmissible by conjugation, other *col* factors can arrive in the recipient cell as early as $2\frac{1}{2}$ minutes after conjugation is initiated. In *Salmonella,* moreover, *col I* is transferable in the absence of F, via conjugation that involves I pili (which differ from the F pili caused by F). On the other hand, *col E1* cannot initiate conjugation. Since cells that contain *col E1* and *col I* transfer both factors, *col I* promotes the transfer of *col E1.* When *Salmonella* harbors only *col I,* transfer of the bacterial chromosome in conjugation occurs but is rare. But when such cells also contain *col E1,* however, chromosome transfer increases one hundredfold. Accordingly, in *Salmonella col I* promotes the transfer of *col E1,* and *col E1* promotes the transfer of the bacterial chromosome. *Col I* is, therefore, a sex factor.

The transfer of *col* factors is subject to the presence of other types of sex factors. For example, in the cross F⁻ *col El* × F⁻ *col⁻*, no transfer of *col El* occurs; whereas *col El* is transferred when the *col El* parent also contains F⁺, for example F⁺ *col El* × F⁻ *col⁻* (recall that *col I* also promotes this transfer). In another example, in the cross F⁺ *col⁻* × F⁻ *col I*, F is transferred to the F⁻ *col I* conjugant, and *col I* is transmitted to the F⁺ *col⁻* conjugant with high efficiency; in the cross F⁺ *col I* × F⁻ *col⁻*, however, *col I* is transferred at a low rate, so that F interferes with transfer of *col I* from the same parent. (Acridine dyes also inhibit the transfer of *col* factors.) *Col V2* and *col V3* cannot coexist in the cell with F or F'.

No direct proof has been obtained for a *col* factor being integrated into a bacterial chromosome. Since *col V, col I*, or *col E2* present in Hfr *E. coli* are not linked to any bacterial genes when the Hfr's are mated, the *col* factors may exist autonomously in the cell as plasmids. Thus, even though *col* factors are episome-like in nature, they are not yet proved to be episomes.

Bowman, C. M., Dahlberg, J. E., Ikemura, T., Konisky, J., and Nomura, M. 1971. Specific inactivation of 16s ribosomal RNA induced by colicin E3 *in vivo*. Proc. Nat. Acad. Sci., U.S., 68: 964–968.

Fredericq, P. 1963. On the nature of colicinogenic factors: a review. J. Theoret. Biol., 4: 159–165.

Roth, T. F., and Helinski, D. R. 1967. Evidence for circular DNA forms of a bacterial plasmid. Proc. Nat. Acad. Sci., U.S., 58: 650–657.

S13.9b   Drug-resistance factors are also plasmid or episome-like sex factors.

Drug-resistance factors, R factors, discovered in *Shigella*, have since been found in *Salmonella, Vibrio, Pasteurella, Pseudomonas, Escherichia, Klebsiella, Citrobacter*, and *Proteus*—all of these Gram-negative bacteria. The R factor is a sex factor composed of a *resistance transfer factor, RTF* (an episome-like element comparable to F) that is responsible for replication and transferability, plus several genes that simultaneously provide the bacterium with resistance to as many as seven or eight antibiotic drugs. The drug resistance genes include those for sulfonamide, streptomycin, chloramphenicol, tetracycline, kanamycin (and neomycin), penicillin (ampicillin), furazolidone, gentamycin, and spectinomycin. R factors are DNA with about 5×10^4 base pairs probably arranged in a circle. The RTF portion of the R factor has been found without drug-resistance genes and probably originated from the chromosome of some unknown bacterium.

The R factor is transferred by conjugation from F⁻ R⁺ to F⁻ R⁻ cells usually independently of the host chromosome. Transfer starts within 1 minute of mixing the parents. Since the R factor can be eliminated by acridine dyes, it seems, like F, usually to exist autonomously. In the autonomous state it replicates sufficiently faster than the chromosome and is transferred frequently enough so that in about 24 hours an entire culture can be changed from R⁻ to R⁺ starting with a single R⁺ donor cell.

R factors are of two types, *fi⁺* and *fi⁻*. In a low percentage of cells, *fi⁺* (fertility inhibition positive) R factors form F-type pili (like those formed by F-containing cells) and a unique surface substance, possibly polysaccharide in nature (different from that formed by F-containing cells). Cells containing *fi⁻* R factor form I-type pili (like those formed by *col I*-containing cells) and a unique surface substance. (The presence of *fi⁺* R factor inhibits the fertility of F in *E. coli* K12, whereas *fi⁻* R factor does not. The DNA injected by certain virulent and temperate phages is broken down if the cell contains an *fi⁻* R, but not *fi⁺* R, factor.) The RTF portions of *fi⁺* R and *fi⁻* R probably differ.

Just as F and *col I*, R factors can cause the conjugational transfer of *col El*. Although transfer of the host chromosome is promoted with low frequency by *fi⁺* as well as by *fi⁻* R factors, there is insufficient evidence that R can integrate into the bacterial chromosome. Accordingly, although R factors are not proved episomes, they can be considered to be episome-like plasmids.

Consider the effect R factors have on the replication and distribution of other R factors. A recipient cell that contains *fi⁺* R (or *fi⁻* R) shows immunity to superinfection by a donor cell of the same type but not to the alternative *fi⁻* R (or *fi⁺* R) type. If a cell contains two R factors of the same *fi⁺* (or *fi⁻*) type, segregation tends to occur so that the progeny contains only one representative. A cell can support two R factors if one is *fi⁺* and the other is *fi⁻*. Although an *fi⁺* R-containing cell will accept an *fi⁺* R factor by transduction, segregation of the two occurs in the progeny.

R factors and other sex factors interact to affect each other's replication and distribution. F and *fi⁺* or *fi⁻* R factors can coexist in the same cell. Although R remains transferable in an F⁺ or Hfr cell, conjugational transfer of R is reduced by one-third to one-fifth if the recipient carries F, and vice versa. The inhibition of fertility (transfer) of F, F', and Hfr chromosomes in cells containing *fi⁺* R is attributed at least partly to the reduced frequency of formation of F-type pili. *Col K* and *col X* are eliminated by superinfection with R factors. (*Col I* is transferred normally, however, from *fi*[+] R cells.) All the examples of exclusion (immunity to superinfection via conjugation and the tendency for segregation) mentioned here and in Sections S13.4 and S13.9a may be the result of competition by plasmids and episomes for the same replication site (mesosome?) on the bacterial surface.

Cohen, S. N., and Miller, C. A. 1969. Multiple molecular species of circular R-factor DNA isolated from *Escherichia coli*. Nature, Lond., 224: 1273–1277.

Watanabe, T. 1963. Infectious heredity of multiple drug resistance in bacteria. Bact. Rev., 27: 87–115.

Watanabe, T. 1967. Infectious drug resistance. Scient. Amer., 217 (No. 6): 19–27, 158.

S13.9c Plasmids and episomes undergo a variety of recombinations involving changes in DNA primary structure.

The recombinations involving episomes and plasmids in the last two supplementary sections dealt with the gain and loss of whole genetic particles when bacterial cells divide or undergo conjugation or transduction. As previously described, recombinations that involve changes in the primary structure of episomal DNA occur in integration, in restricted transduction by phages, in sexduction, and between two integrated episomes (Section 13.8). Other examples of primary structure recombination are listed below:

1. *F′* × *F′*. Simultaneous infection of *E. coli* with F-*lac*[+] and F-*gal*[+] yields rare F′

particles carrying both marker genes.

2. *col* × *col*. *Col V* and *col I* can exist on the same particle, which is presumed to arise as a recombinant of the two separate *col* factors.

3. *R* × *R*. Simultaneous infection with two R factors differing in their range of drug resistance produces single particles containing genes conferring resistance to both groups of drugs.

4. *F* × *col*. F-*col V*, F-*col B*, and F-*col V-col I* particles have been identified.

5. *R* × *phage*. Some drug-resistance genes are acquired by phage P1 from R so that every bacterium infected and lysogenized is resistant to these drugs.

6. *R* × (*phage*) × *chromosome*. ɸP22 transduces some drug-resistance genes which integrate at the P22 prophage attachment site in *Salmonella*.

7. *R* × (*phage*) × *F*. A defective RTF introduced into an F[+] cell by transduction recombines with F to make a hybrid particle.

The physiological interactions among temperate and virulent phages, F, R, and *col* factors discussed in Sections S13.9a and 13.9b plus the evidence of primary structure recombinations among these plasmids and episomes points to a genetic similarity which must be based on a close evolutionary relationship.

Nagel de Zwaig, R. 1966. Association between colicinogenic and fertility factors. Genetics, 54: 381–390.

Watanabe, T. 1967. Evolutionary relationships of R factors with other episomes and plasmids. Federation Proc., 26: 23–28.

QUESTIONS AND PROBLEMS

1. Replication of unintegrated F, but not integrated F, is inhibited by exposing *E. coli* to acridine orange. Make use of this finding
   a. to obtain F[−] from F[+] cells,
   b. to identify clones as F[+], Hfr, or F[−].

2. When Hfr males conjugate with F[−] cells lysogenic for lambda, zygotes normally survive. When, however, Hfr males lysogenic for lambda conjugate with F[−] nonlysogenic for lambda, zygotes produced from matings that have lasted for almost 90 minutes lyse due to the *zygotic induction* of lambda.
   a. How can you explain zygotic induction?
   b. How can you determine the position of the *att*[B] locus in the bacterial chromosome?

3. Discuss the base sequences common both to F and the *E. coli* chromosome. Note that F contains one region (making up 10 per cent of the particle) with a 44 per cent dG + dC content and another region (making up the bulk of the particle) with a 50 per cent dG + dC content.

4. In what way should Figure 13.9 be modified in the light of evidence that the deintegration which produces a substituted sex factor in an Hfr male parallels one which produces λdg in a bacterium lysogenic for λ?

5. What events do you suppose occur from the time donor DNA enters a female conjugant to the appearance of a segregant haploid for a segment of the donor DNA?

6. What properties are attributable to F when integrated at a chromosomal locus?

7. Does the occurrence of spontaneous ruptures of the donor bacterial chromosome interfere with mapping the linear order of genes via artificial interruptions of mating? Explain.

8. Assume (correctly) that the decay of ^{32}P incorporated into DNA can break the *E. coli* chromosome, and that this decay is temperature-independent. Devise an experiment to determine the gene order in this bacterium.

9. Do all matings transfer F particles of one genotype or another? Explain.

10. Discuss the relationship between the transmission of free F particles and a segment of the male chromosome.

11. From which particular Hfr strain of *E. coli* could you obtain an F-*pro* (proline) particle? How?

12. How do you suppose episomes originate?

13. It has been found that $\phi P2$, a temperate phage that normally integrates at a particular locus, position I, loses the extreme preference for position I when liberated from a strain carrying it in position II. How can you explain this finding?

14. The *lac* gene can either be chromosomal (when integrated into the chromosome), or "extrachromosomal" (when attached to free F). Should such a gene be considered an episome? Why?

15. How would you locate the position of the UV-inducible prophage of $\phi 434$ in the *E. coli* linkage map?

16. How would you locate the prophage site of a noninducible (by UV light or zygote formation) phage?

17. What are the general rules for compatibility and incompatibility for the coexistence of plasmids and episomes?

18. Populations of donors, grown to saturation density in aerated broth or cultured on agar overnight, can lose their donor phenotype temporarily and behave as genetic recipients. Since they retain their sex factor yet behave as F⁻ cells, they are known as F⁻ *phenocopies*.

    a. If a *lac⁻* F⁻ phenocopy carrying F is mated with an F⁺ male carrying F-*lac⁺*, exconjugants can be obtained that carry both types of F. Soon, however, in some experiments, one or the other F particle persists in the progeny.

    b. Hfr that are F⁻ phenocopies do not tolerate the presence of an introduced autonomous F sex factor.

    What conclusions can you draw from these results?

19. The F⁻ phenocopy is not attacked by certain RNA phages, although the normal phenotype is. Suggest an explanation for this observation.

20. What specific techniques are available for mapping gene sequence in the chromosome of *E. coli? Salmonella?*

21. Can a bacterium become immune to DNA that is not integrated? Defend your decision.

Chapter 14

In Nucleated Cells—Chromosomal Organization and Mitosis

We have noted that chromosomal replication is followed by an orderly distribution of genetic material to progeny in bacteria (and blue-green algae). In nucleated cells also special mechanisms of DNA distribution have evolved. After a brief discussion of some additional aspects of chromosomal organization and distribution in phages and bacteria, we will consider these matters in nucleated cells.

14.1   The chromosomes of phages and of bacteria are organized structures.

The chromosome in a T-even virion or a bacterium is not simply duplex DNA whose parts lie at random within the confines of the phage head or the bacterial cell membrane. Various lines of evidence indicate these chromosomes have tertiary structure.

Although other conformations are possible, the chromosome in the T-even virion seems to be folded longitudinally in the head in firehose fashion (see Figure 1-2B), and passes single file through the core when it is injected into the host. Once in the host the DNA is reported to swell because of hydration and is then replicated. When mature phage progeny are to be formed the vegetative pool of progeny DNA apparently dehydrates to produce compact DNA bodies of phage-headful size which are only one fifteenth of their hydrated volume. Although the condensation of phage chromosomes is known to require protein synthesis, little more is known about the biochemical basis for the swelling and shrinking of phage chromosomes.

The DNA of the bacterial chromosome is also reported to be highly hydrated. It shows some tertiary structure since it appears to be folded back and forth on itself, also in firehose fashion, to make a localized bundle of duplex DNA attached to a mesosome.

14.2   After being separated by chromosome replication, the two single strands of DNA in a bacterial chromosome are distributed at random to future nuclear areas.

If the DNA of the E. coli chromosome is labeled with ^{32}P and replication is permitted to occur in nonradioactive medium, the distribution of the radioactivity in subsequent generations will reveal whether the separated single strands of the parental duplex are distributed to future nuclear areas at random or in some preferential arrangement. Figure 14-1 illustrates the consequences of a random distribution. The radioactive chromosome of the parent (top cell) replicates semiconservatively once to produce two duplexes, each composed of a radioactive and a nonradioactive strand, each in its own nuclear area. If, after division, the two daughter cells do not separate (see Figure 1-5) and each chromosome replicates, one obtains four nuclear areas arranged linearly. If the separated parental single strands of DNA are distributed to descendent nuclear areas at random, one expects the four possible types of distribution of radioactivity (×) and no radioactivity (○) in the four linearly arranged nuclear areas (× ○○×, ○× ×○, ×○×○, and ○×○×) to be equally frequent in radioautographs. Since this expectation is realized experimentally, at least in some strains of bacteria, the hypothesis of random distribution is supported. (R)

14.3   The distribution to progeny of replicating bacterial chromosomal DNA and nonreplicating episomal DNA is dependent in the case of F and independent in the case of ϕλ.

Escherichia coli can carry two kinds of chromosomes—one bacterial, one episomal in origin. In such cases, how are these two kinds of chromosomes distributed relative

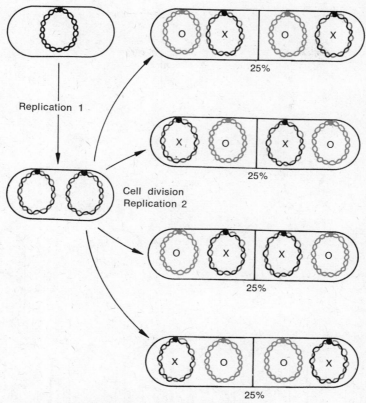

Figure 14-1   Random distribution of single strands of a replicating chromosome to different nuclear areas. Black line, ^{32}P-labeled single-stranded DNA; gray line, unlabeled single-stranded DNA; spot, mesosomal attachment; $\times$, $\bigcirc$, radioactive, nonradioactive nuclear area.

to each other in cell division? This question can be answered at least partly by determining how nonreplicating episomal DNA is distributed relative to the DNA of a dividing bacterial chromosome over several to many generations. We will consider results obtained specifically with an F′ factor and a phage λ mutant.

A lac^- bacterium carrying a particular F-lac^+ factor is grown at low temperature on medium containing ^{32}P. The F-lac^+ also carries a temperature-sensitive mutant which prevents replication of the factor at high temperature. After the DNA's of the bacterial chromosome and episome have become labeled (Figure 14-2, generation 1), the bacteria are grown on nonradioactive medium at a high temperature. At this temperature the bacterial chromosome replicates, but the F-lac^+ cannot. After two successive replications, for example, the bacterial chromosome is nonradioactive in two progeny and "half"-radioactive in the other two; the F-lac^+ particle is present in only one of the four progeny (Figure 14-2, generation 3).

Since the F-lac^+ particle contains so little ^{32}P of the total amount incorporated that it could rarely cause death due to radioactive decay, a study of the radiosensitivity of lac^+ progeny in successive generations indicates how the F-lac^+ particle is distributed relative to the half-radioactive bacterial chromosomes. If the nonreplicating F-lac^+ chromosome segregates independently of the bacterial chromosome, it should be detected more and more frequently with a nonradioactive bacterial chromosome in

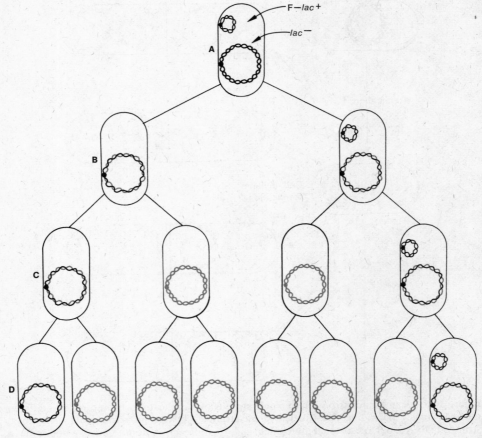

Figure 14-2 Preferential segregation of an F-*lac*⁺ nonreplicating chromosome relative to a replicating *lac*⁻ chromosome in *E. coli*. Black line, ³²P-containing single-stranded DNA; gray line, unlabeled single-stranded DNA; spot, mesosomal attachment. Note from generation 2 (B) onward the constant chance of ³²P-decay-induced death in *lac*⁺ progeny.

successive generations—the radiosensitivity of *lac*⁺ bacteria decreasing in successive generations. It is found, however, that the radiosensitivity of *lac*⁺ bacteria does not change after the first generation. This result indicates that the sex factor segregates preferentially—staying with one of the half-radioactive chromosomes. The preferential distribution of two chromosomes in this case might be explained by the F-*lac*⁺ and bacterial chromosomes sharing the same mesosomal attachment site (as shown in Figure 13-9).

A study of the nonreplicating DNA of φλb2 indicates that in this case the episomal DNA is distributed to subsequent generations independently of the bacterial DNA; that is, the two kinds of DNA separate or segregate independently. (R)

14.4   The DNA content of a nucleus doubles before nuclear division.

Unlike the bacterial cell, a cell of a eucaryotic organism has its (nuclear) DNA bounded by a double-layered *nuclear membrane* during most of its life cycle. During this time, called *interphase* (Figure 14-3A), the cell passes through three successive stages: a period of growth (G1), a period in which the DNA content of the nucleus doubles (S), and a period of more growth (G2). After interphase the nucleus is ready for division to produce two daughter nuclei, each containing one half the presently doubled amount of DNA.

Nuclear division is usually followed by cytoplasmic division in the formation of two complete daughter cells. The cytoplasmic components of a parent cell are often distributed unequally between daughter cells, but only rarely are the nuclear contents so distributed. For the nucleus does not simply separate into two parts; it typically undergoes a highly ordered series of activities in order to divide—the process of *mitosis*.

14.5   Mitosis is a spindle-using process in which both of the two daughter nuclei receive a copy of their parent's chromosomes.

During interphase the nuclear DNA-containing "chromosomes" (see the next section) are partly unwound and, hence, are not seen as discrete bodies under the ordinary light microscope. Among the first indications that the nucleus is preparing to divide is the appearance of a mass of thin, separate chromosomes (Figure 14-3B), some of which are associated with nucleoli. Each such chromosome seems to be composed of two visible threads, or *chromatids*, each containing, besides DNA, basic protein and RNA. The appearance of these chromosomes marks the start of *prophase*, the first stage of mitosis. As prophase continues, the chromatids of each chromosome become shorter and thicker and untwist from one another (Figure 14-3C); the nucleoli become smaller. By the end of prophase (Figure 14-3D), the nucleoli and nuclear membrane have disappeared, and the chromatids are seen as thick rods which move actively for the first time. Motility is not the property of the entire chromosome, however, but is restricted to a particular region called the *centromere*.

The centromeres become joined to fibers of the *spindle*, which has been forming throughout prophase. The completed spindle has a shape similar to that formed when corresponding fingertips are touched together and the hands are separately slightly. The wrists represent the poles of the spindle, and the fingers represent spindle fibers. Chromosomes migrate from whatever their position in the spindle region until each centromere comes to lie in a single plane perpendicular to the midpoint of the axis between the poles (corresponding to the plane determined by the points at which fingertips touch). This is the *equatorial plane* or *equator* of the spindle. The rest of each chromosome can assume essentially any position when all the centromeres have arrived at the equatorial plane. At this point mitosis has reached its middle phase, or *metaphase* (Figure 14-3E).

At metaphase and earlier stages, chromatids of a chromosome are attached to each other at or near the centromere, although elsewhere they are largely free. After metaphase they separate at the centromere and the two daughter centromeres suddenly move apart, one going toward one pole of the spindle, the other toward the other pole. Once separated, the chromatids are called chromosomes. This stage in which the chromatids separate and move to opposite poles as chromosomes is called *anaphase* (Figure 14-3F).

When the chromosomes reach the poles, the last stage, *telophase*, begins (Figure

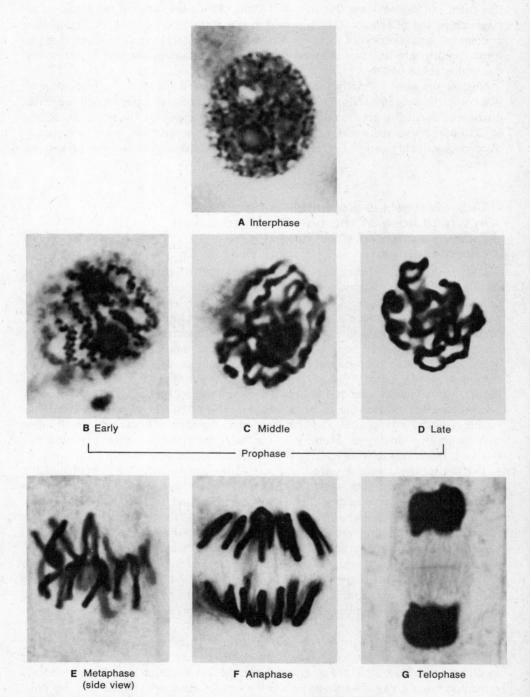

Figure 14-3   Mitosis in the onion root tip. (Courtesy of R. E. Cleland.)

14-3G). The subsequent events appear to be the reverse of those during prophase: the spindle disintegrates, a new nuclear membrane is formed around the chromosomes, and nucleoli reappear. The chromosomes once more become thinner and longer and can be seen to consist of two slender threads wound about each other. Finally, as the chromosomes again become invisible under the light microscope, the nucleus enters *interphase* (Figure 14-3A).

From this description we see that mitosis is a mechanism for the exact distribution of previously replicated chromosomal material, a means of rearranging this material so that daughter cells have the same chromosomal constitution as their parents at an identical stage. (R)

14.6   Since a nuclear "chromosome" retains a morphological and DNA identity which is replicated, its DNA is genetic material.

The DNA-containing "chromosomes" in the nucleus of cells of different species are characteristic in number and morphology. Chromosomes vary in size, stainability with various dyes, and position of the centromere. Most have a single centromere which is located subterminally, that is, not at an end, and which therefore separates the chromosome into two *arms*.

Although the chromosomes usually become invisible under the light microscope in interphase, this does not mean that the chromosomes either lose their identity or are distributed in a nucleus in a random manner. Retention and replication of chromosomal identity is supported by the following:

1. Some cells have nuclei, permanently in interphase, that contain many-threaded giant chromosomes (discussed in Section 18.9) which, although relatively uncoiled, are clearly morphologically equivalent to the more contracted chromosomes as seen in mitosis.

2. The chromosomes in a nucleus are found in the same relative positions in prophase that they had in the preceding late anaphase–early telophase, as expected had they maintained their integrity during the intervening interphase. This is also the conclusion from finding that the chromosomes in sister nuclei which are entering the next mitosis at the same time often have a mirror-image arrangement.

3. Mutagen-induced visible modifications of chromosome morphology are observed to persist in progeny chromosomes mitosis after mitosis.

The preceding morphological evidence for the retention and replication of nuclear chromosomal identity in eucaryotes is paralleled by similar evidence for the DNA which these chromosomes contain.

1. Many cellular components are replaced continuously during metabolism, showing "atomic turnover," without the total amount of cellular material being increased. Nuclear DNA is unusual because it shows little, if any, turnover; in other words, this DNA maintains its integrity at the molecular level.

2. Doubling the number of nuclear chromosomes is always—but not necessarily immediately—preceded by a doubling in nuclear DNA (but not RNA) content.

3. A nucleus that contains an additional nucleolus organizer region of a chromosome also contains an additional set of the DNA base sequences (usually rich in dC and dG) that are characteristic of this region.

Since the above results and others show that nuclear chromosomes contain DNA which has an integrity that is replicated in progeny chromosomes, we conclude that such DNA is genetic material. Mitosis, therefore, is a mechanism for a quaternary structure recombination of genetic DNA which produces daughter nuclei with the same genetic information as the parent nucleus at the identical stage. (R)

14.7   The chromosomes in a nucleus have an orderly arrangement relative to each other and to the nuclear membrane.

We mentioned in Section 14.6 that the genetic material in a nucleus is organized into chromosomes of particular size and morphology. The nucleus shows further organization of its genetic material in that its chromosomes and their parts assume special arrangements relative to each other and to the nuclear membrane, as indicated by the following evidence:

1. In interphase nuclei that contain many-threaded chromosomes, some chromosome regions are usually paired or synapsed with the corresponding region of one other chromosome, and other chromosome regions are synapsed with the corresponding regions of several other chromosomes (see Section 18.9 for details).

2. In some dividing cells the smaller chromosomes are arranged in the center of the metaphase equatorial plate, the larger ones lying at the periphery. After these chromosomes are pulled to the poles, they must be incorporated into nuclei in a nonrandom arrangement, which, according to evidence in the preceding section, must be retained in interphase.

3. Nucleoli in the giant cells of Drosophila tend to touch the nuclear membrane rather than lie at random in the nucleus. Accordingly, the nucleolus organizer region has a preferential nuclear location.

4. Cells with certain chromosomal constitutions have a clump of chromatin touching the nuclear membrane (or a dumbbell protrusion from the nucleus) that is absent from other cells of the same species with different chromosomal constitutions.

5. When cells are labeled with tritiated deoxythymidine at the start of the S period, autoradiographs show radioactivity only near the nuclear membrane. This means that DNA replication is initiated only by chromatin located near the nuclear membrane. Other evidence indicates that chromosomes are attached to the nuclear membrane (in maize, for example, knobs, centromeres, and ends all occupy positions on the nuclear membrane), and that the rate of nuclear DNA synthesis is controlled by the nuclear membrane.[1] (R)

---

[1] These findings remind us of the situation in bacteria where chromosome replication seems to take place at the mesosome, an invagination of the cell membrane. The nuclear membrane can be considered a specialized invagination of the cell membrane, connected to the latter by means of the specialized membranes comprising the endoplasmic reticulum (see Figure 1-4).

14.8   The nuclei of multinuclear cells are distributed in particular ways.

In mononucleated cells, where nuclear division alternates with cell division, the nucleus usually occupies a position in the center of cytoplasmic metabolic activity and sometimes assumes the shape dictated by the shape of the body of the cytoplasm. This is also true in multinucleated cells, whose nuclei, moreover, are spaced apart in a nonrandom manner. For example, in striated muscle the nuclei are elongated in the long axis of the fiber; they lie in the peripheral sarcoplasm, and, except toward the end of the muscle in the region of tendon attachment, are distributed fairly regularly.

When certain yolk-filled eggs of insects start development, the nucleus divides mitotically repeatedly to produce a large number of nuclei unseparated by cell membranes, distributed more or less evenly throughout the yolk. These nuclei then migrate to the surface of the egg where they are spaced apart so that each becomes incorporated into a separate cell by cell membranes forming between them. These examples show that multiple nuclei within a cell are positioned relative to each other, that is, are recombined, in specific ways.

14.9   A chromatid is hypothesized to contain one DNA duplex before (and two DNA duplexes after) DNA replication.

Although some chromosomes are visibly multithreaded, containing many side-by-side repeats of a chromatid, careful cytological observation reveals that many anaphase chromosomes contain two chromatids (the situation assumed to be true in Section 14.5). On rare occasions, anaphase chromosomes have been seen to contain four threads, or four "subchromatids." It is likely that some anaphase chromosomes have two chromatids which appear as one due to poor resolution.

Since each visible thread contains DNA, it is hypothesized that each chromatid contains one DNA duplex before DNA replication (for example, at anaphase) and two DNA duplexes after (for example, at the G2 stage of interphase or at prophase).[2] In those cases where a chromosome has two chromatids, there would be two duplexes before, and four duplexes after, DNA replication.

The distribution of parental chromosomal material marked by mutants or by radioactive elements has been studied among progeny chromosomes to determine whether, prior to replication, a chromosome usually contains one DNA duplex (hence only one chromatid) or two DNA duplexes (each presumed to be located in a different chromatid, rather than two duplexes being in a single chromatid).

Evidence from mutation

When mature sperm of the fruit fly *Drosophila* are treated with physical or chemical mutagens and used for reproduction, phenotypically abnormal offspring usually carry a mutant chromosome in every body cell. Such individuals, called "whole mutants," can be explained as being the result of a defect produced in corresponding loci in all strands of all DNA duplexes present in a chromosome in the sperm.

---

[2] In the case of the amphibian oocyte in (meiotic) prophase, however, the rate at which the loops of the lampbrush chromosome are scissioned by DNase suggests that they contain only one DNA duplex.

Less frequent are "partial mutants," whose bodies are phenotypically half-abnormal and half-normal, and still less frequent are those that are one-fourth abnormal and three-fourths normal. The phenotypic mosaicism in these individuals is believed to have a corresponding genotypic basis in mutation; that is, it results from *genotypic mosaicism*. Although half-and-half genotypic mosaics can be explained as being due to the mutation of one strand of a duplex (Figure 14-4, left side), one-fourth to three-fourths mosaics are most simply explained as due to the mutation of one strand of two duplexes present in each sperm chromosome (Figure 14-4, right side).[3] (Mosaics having one eighth or smaller mutant fractions are very rare.)

Evidence from radioisotopes

Since the cell has only a small pool of deoxythymidine, the addition of tritiated deoxythymidine to the medium of actively growing root tips of the broad bean *Vicia faba* at the beginning of the S stage makes all chromatids uniformly radioactive, or "hot," by the time of the next metaphase (Figure 14-4B). If the radioactive deoxythymidine is no longer made available after the one replication, radioautographs of the chromosomes at the second metaphase after treatment (Figure 14-4D) reveal some chromosomes with one chromatid hot and the other cold. This finding is consistent with the one duplex hypothesis (Figure 14-4DI) as well as with the two duplex hypothesis (Figure 14-4DII c' and d'). The occurrence of other chromosomes at the second metaphase, however, both of whose chromatids are hot (Figure 14-4DII a' and b'), can be readily explained only on the two duplex hypothesis.[4]

We shall assume henceforth (as in Figure 15-2), unless stated to the contrary, that nuclear chromosomes have two cytologically visible chromatids, each containing one DNA duplex prior to replication. It should be emphasized, however, that the evidence that favors this assumption is not conclusive or universally applicable.(R)

14.10   Exchanges sometimes occur between parental and offspring DNA complements in nuclear chromosomes.

Suppose within a chromatid two DNA complements of the same polarity exchange exactly equivalent segments, abcd and a'b'c'd' becoming abc'd' and a'b'cd; since such an exchange will be between identical base sequences, it will not produce any

[3] The two duplexes per chromosome explanation requires the formation of a chromosome containing two mutant duplexes (Figure 14-4EIIe). This is made possible on those occasions when a replicated chromosome containing a mutant and a normal duplex in one of the chromatids (Figure 14-4BII) segregates duplexes so that the mutant duplex goes to one daughter chromatid and the normal duplex to the other (Figure 14-4CIIa). On other occasions, however, when the segregation occurs not between duplexes (as above) but within each duplex, a resultant daughter chromosome (Figure 14-4CIIc) can have one normal and one mutant complement in each chromatid. If this chromosome reproduces and segregates between duplexes, half of its descendant chromosomes will eventually be of pure mutant type. Therefore, provided that segregation is usually between rather than within duplexes, we can explain $\frac{1}{4}$ mutant : $\frac{3}{4}$ normal mosaics as due to mutation in one DNA strand of a chromosome that normally contains two DNA duplexes in its unreplicated condition.

[4] According to the two duplex hypothesis, the newly made DNA in different duplexes in a chromatid is normally segregated into different chromosomes at the second anaphase or later following its synthesis. In *Drosophila* it is assumed that segregation ordinarily occurs between duplexes, and in *Vicia* within duplexes. This is possible since even in different *Vicia* the percentages of the two segregation types vary considerably.

transcriptional–translational change. If a change in genetic information in the a-d region is the only criterion used, the exchange would be undetected. We can, however, detect such an exchange at the molecular level if one of the complements is radioactive and the other is not, provided the two strands segregate in subsequent mitotic divisions.

The experiment described in the second part of Section 14.9, in which radioactive deoxythymidine is incorporated into nuclear DNA for one generation, permits us to identify a single exchange that occurs between a nonradioactive, parental complement and a radioactive, progeny complement of the same polarity (Figure 14-5B). Separation of duplexes produces chromosome a (or a′), which has one chromatid labeled throughout its length and the other chromatid labeled only partly.[5] Such a distribution of label has been observed experimentally.

Various other combinations of labeled and unlabeled portions of the chromatids can result, and have also been observed experimentally, if more than one exchange occurs within a chromatid. Although the precise time and mechanism of exchanges within chromatids are unknown, they apparently require breakage, at least of the parental strand involved in exchange. We expect such exchanges will also be possible between homologous chromatids of the same or different chromosomes if these are appropriately juxtaposed.

SUMMARY AND CONCLUSIONS

The DNA genetic material of phages, procaryotes, and eucaryotes is highly organized and undergoes specific, highly organized, rearrangements. Although the organization and recombination of phage and bacterial chromosomes have been discussed in earlier chapters, note is made here of the tertiary structure of their DNA's as well as hydrational condition of their chromosomes under different conditions. When replicated bacterial DNA undergoes quaternary rearrangement of its duplexes, the strands of a parental duplex are distributed at random to future nuclear areas. When present in the same cell, the duplexes of bacterial and lambda DNA's are also distributed at random to future nuclear areas, although bacterial and F DNA's, which may attach to the same mesosome, are not.

The quaternary structural rearrangement of replicated nuclear DNA (which is shown to be genetic material) is visualized microscopically by mitosis, in which spindle mechanism is used to produce two daughter nuclei that are chromosomally (and genetically) identical to the parent nucleus at the same stage. The highly organized nature of quaternary structural arrangements of DNA in eucaryotes is also evidenced by the special positions taken by chromosomes and their parts relative to each other and the nuclear membrane during interphase and mitosis, and by different whole nuclei in multinucleate cells.

The hypothesis that a nuclear chromosome ordinarily is composed of two visible threads, or chromatids, each of which contains one DNA duplex before replication serves to connect the cytology of chromosomes with the biochemistry of DNA. Although this hypothesis has some cytological and biochemical support, and will be accepted subsequently, it has not been rigidly proved and may not have universal application.

---

[5] In this case segregation is between duplexes. Note that this distribution of label cannot be explained simply on the basis of one duplex per chromosome. The same distribution is obtained as one result of segregation within duplexes (chromosomes b and b′); another result of segregation within duplexes can be a chromosome (d and d′) whose chromatids are complementarily partly labeled.

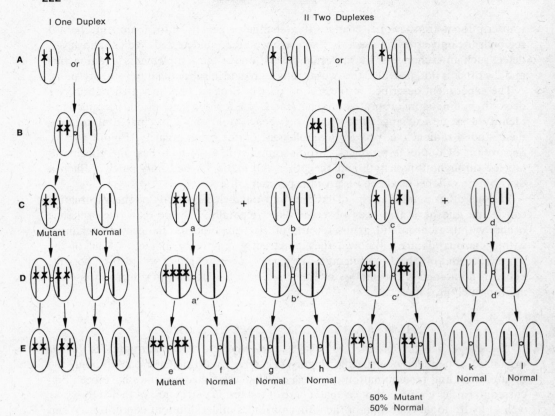

Figure 14-4 Comparison of expectations from one versus two DNA duplexes per non-replicated chromatid in studies of the distribution of a mutant DNA complement (X) or of radioactivity (—) incorporated at B.

Mutation
(A) Sperm chromosome mutated in an old complement (attached to border) or its newly made complement (unattached). Ovals are chromosomes; or, if connected by a circle (= centromere), they are chromatids.
(B) The first metaphase (after fertilization and DNA replication has occurred).
(C) The first anaphase. (The chromatids of B have separated into daughter chromosomes.)
    I. Each daughter chromosome has one chromatid; one is purely mutant, one purely normal.
   II. Each daughter chromosome (a and b or c and d) has segregated its two duplexes into separate chromatids, each containing one duplex. The complements of a duplex in B enter the same chromatid in a and b; hence segregation occurs between duplexes. This is assumed to be the usual way segregation occurs in *Drosophila*. Sometimes the complements in a chromatid (as in the chromatids of chromosomes c and d) may come from different duplexes in B; here segregation occurs within duplexes.
(D) The second metaphase (after the duplexes of C have replicated).
(E) The second anaphase. (In II, chromatids receive their duplexes by segregation occurring between duplexes. Chromosomes CII a and b produce one pure mutant daughter (e) and three pure normal (f, g, h) daughter chromosomes. Chromosome CII c and d produce four "normal" chromosomes; the daughters of i and j, however, will be 2 pure normal and 2 pure mutant. Thus, for every chromosome of type BII that becomes type CIIa or CIIc eventually $\frac{1}{2}$ of all its daughter chromosomes will be pure mutant; or $\frac{1}{4}$ of all cells will be mutant, $\frac{3}{4}$ normal.

Radioactive deoxythymidine
(A) Unreplicated chromosome.
(B) The first metaphase (after tritiated deoxythymidine is incorporated during the S stage). Both chromatids are "hot."

(C) The first anaphase [segregation as described in (C) above; the type of segregation within duplexes that leads to c and d is assumed to be the usual type in *Vicia*].

(D) The second metaphase (after the duplexes of C have replicated in the absence of tritiated thymidine in the medium).

  I. Each chromosome has one chromatid hot, one cold.

  II. Chromosomes c′ and d′ have one chromatid hot, one cold; chromosomes a′ and b′, however, have both chromatids hot—a result readily explainable only by the two duplex hypothesis.

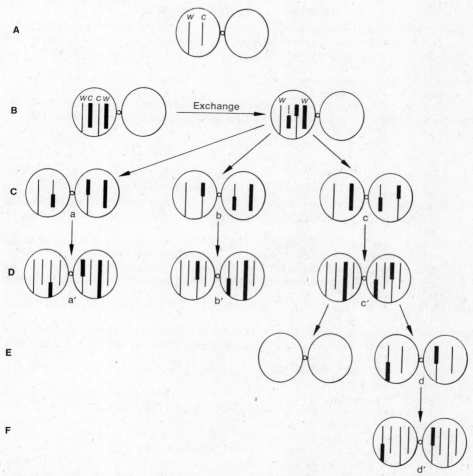

Figure 14-5 Consequences of a single exchange between parental and offspring DNA complements in a chromatid of a nuclear chromosome. Old parental complements are attached to border of ellipse (= chromatid); new offspring complements are shown unattached. Chromosome = two chromatids connected by a circle (= centromere). ▬▬, radioactive; ——, nonradioactive.

(A) Unreplicated chromosome. W and C are complementary.

(B) First metaphase after replication in tritiated deoxythymidine one generation only. Exchange occurs between parental and offspring C strands.

(C) First anaphase–interphase. Duplexes in left chromatid segregate. a, segregation between duplexes; b, c, segregation within duplexes.

(D) Second metaphase. a′ and b′ have a partly labeled left chromatid and a completely labeled right chromatid; c′ has both chromatids completely labeled.

(E) Second anaphase; (F) third metaphase. d and d′ have chromatids that are complementarily partly labeled.

The distribution in chromatids of nonradioactive parental and radioactive progeny DNA shows that primary structural recombinations occur between parental and progeny DNA's in eucaryotes, just as in procaryotes (although the mechanism may not, necessarily, be the same).

GENERAL REFERENCES

Luykx, P. 1971. *Cellular mechanisms of chromosome distribution.* New York: Academic Press.
Mazia, D. 1961. Mitosis and the physiology of cell division, in *The cell,* Vol. 3, *Meiosis and mitosis,* Brachet, J., and Mirsky, A. E. (Editors), New York: Academic Press, Inc., pp. 77–112.
Schrader, F. 1953. *Mitosis: the movement of chromosomes in cell division.* New York: Columbia University Press.
Swanson, C. P. 1957. *Cytology and cytogenetics.* Englewood Cliffs, N.J.: Prentice-Hall, Inc.
Swanson, C. P. 1969. *The cell,* third edition. Englewood Cliffs, N.J.: Prentice-Hall, Inc.

SPECIFIC SECTION REFERENCES

14.2   Ryter, A., Hirota, Y., and Jacob, F. 1969. DNA-membrane complex and nuclear segregation in bacteria. Cold Spring Harbor Sympos. Quant. Biol., (1968), 33: 669–676.
14.3   Cuzin, F., and Jacob, F. 1967. Existence chez *Escherichia coli* K12 d'une unité génétique de transmission formée de différents réplicons. Ann. Inst. Pasteur, 112: 529–545.
       Yarmolinsky, M., and Korn, D. 1968. Evidence for independent segregation of the *Escherichia coli* chromosome and non-replicating bacteriophage λb2. J. Mol. Biol., 32: 475–479.
14.5   McIntosh, J. R., Hepler, P. K., and VanWie, D. G. 1969. Model for mitosis. Nature, Lond., 224: 659–663.
14.6   Maio, J. J., and Schildkraut, C. L. 1969. Isolated mammalian metaphase chromosomes. II. Fractionated chromosomes of mouse and Chinese hamster cells. J. Mol. Biol., 40: 203–216.
       Ruddle, F. H. 1962. Nuclear bleb: a stable interphase marker in established lines of cells *in vitro.* J. Nat. Cancer Inst., 28: 1247–1251.
14.7   Mizuno, N. S., Stoops, C. E., and Peiffer, R. L., Jr. 1971. Nature of the DNA associated with the nuclear envelope of regenerating liver. J. Mol. Biol., 59: 517–525.
       Raicu, P., Vladescu, B., and Kirilova, M. 1970. Distribution of chromosomes in metaphase plates of *Mesocritetus newtoni.* Genet. Res., Camb., 15: 1–6.
14.9   Gay, H., Das, C. C., Forward, K., and Kaufmann, B. P. 1970. DNA content of mitotically-active condensed chromosomes of *Drosophila melanogaster.* Chromosoma, 32: 213–223.
       McGavin, S. 1971. Models of specifically paired like (homologous) nucleic acid structures. J. Mol. Biol., 55: 293–298. (When two double helices are identical, they fit together particularly well. This finding has possible bearing on synapsis and the normal number of duplexes per chromatid.)
       Peacock, W. J. 1963. Chromosome duplication and structure as determined by autoradiography. Proc. Nat. Acad. Sci., U.S., 49: 793–801.
       Sorsa, V., and Sorsa, M. 1968. Ideas on the lateral organization of chromosomes revived by an observation of four-stranded mitotic prophase chromosome in Hyacinthus. Ann. Acad. Scient. Fenn., Series A, IV. Biol., 133: 11 pp. (Visual evidence of four parallel half-chromatids in a mitotic prophase chromosome.)

QUESTIONS AND PROBLEMS

1. By using a microscope, how can you distinguish mitotic prophase from mitotic telophase?
2. What recombinational consequences would you expect if a chromosome
   a. lost its centromere?
   b. had two centromeres?
   c. had one extremely long arm?
3. Design an experiment that shows chromosomal DNA replicates in interphase, not in prophase.
4. Since the mechanism of chromosome distribution to progeny works efficiently in the absence of a spindle in bacteria, of what advantage is a spindle to other organisms?
5. What evidence can you cite that the chromosomes are not degraded during interphase?
6. Does each cell of the body derived by mitosis have the same genotype? Explain.
7. What are the advantages or disadvantages of chromosome coiling?
8. Can you imagine a spindle that is too small for normal cell division? Explain.
9. Suppose certain nuclei normally do not divide with the aid of a spindle. How would this affect your ideas about genetic material?
10. Discuss the statement that all nucleated cell divisions are normally mitotic.
11. What evidence can you cite for the occurrence of primary structure recombination in nuclear chromosomes?
12. Discuss the importance of membranes in gene replication.

Chapter 15

In Nucleated Cells—Meiosis and Chromosomal Cycles

In sexually reproducing higher organisms, nuclear chromosomes occur in pairs. The members of a pair are morphologically (and genetically) similar and are called *homologous chromosomes*, or *homologs*. (Despite their similarity, homologs assume their positions at mitotic metaphase independently of one another.) The paired, diploid, or 2N number of chromosomes in a typical mitotic cell of the garden pea is 14, or seven pairs. Maize has 10 pairs of homologs, the domesticated silkworm 28, and human beings 23 (Figure 15-1). Each species has a characteristic (though not different) number of nuclear chromosomes. Whatever this number is in the *fertilized egg*, or *zygote*, the same number is usually found in every cell descended from the zygote by mitotic cell divisions.

If all nuclei divided by mitosis, a sex cell or *gamete* would contain the same number of chromosomes as every other cell of a multicellular organism, all of them derived from the same zygote. Consequently, the number of chromosomes per zygote would increase in successive generations, since the zygote is a combination of two gametes. Chromosome number does not increase from one generation to the next, however. This stability is possible because gametes contain only one member of each pair of chromosomes. For example, human gametes normally contain not the diploid chromosome number—23 pairs—but 23 chromosomes (*nonhomologs*) in the unpaired,

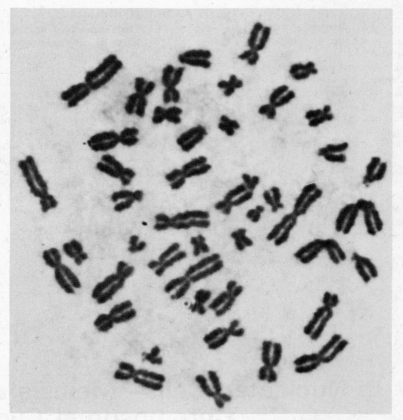

Figure 15-1 Nuclear chromosomal complement of a normal human female. Cell was in mitotic metaphase (hence chromosomes appear double except at the centromere) when squashed and photographed. Chromosomes can be cut out and paired morphologically, as can be seen in Figure 18-6, which pairs the chromosomes in a cell of an abnormal female. (Courtesy of K. Hirschhorn.)

haploid, or N condition. Fertilization consequently restores the diploid chromosome constitution, since each gamete (sperm from the father and egg from the mother) provides a haploid set of chromosomes. Clearly, then, all cell divisions cannot be mitotic; certain cells must have a way of reducing the number of chromosomes from diploid to haploid. This reduction process is *meiosis*.

15.1   Meiosis begins in a diploid nucleus each of whose chromosomes contains the replicated, or doubled, amount of DNA. After two successive spindle-using divisions and no further DNA replication, four haploid nuclei are produced, each of whose chromosomes contains the prereplication amount of DNA.

In prophase of the first meiotic division, or *prophase I*, as in the prophase of mitosis, each chromosome contains the doubled amount of DNA (Figure 15-2). Near the

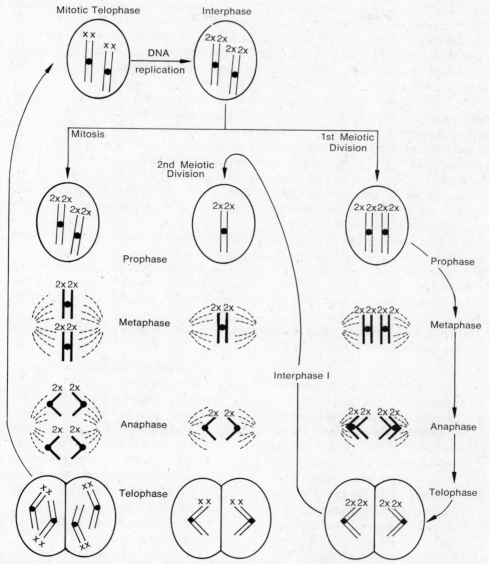

Figure 15-2 Diagrammatic representation of mitosis and meiosis showing the chromatids (cytologically visible threads within a chromosome) ordinarily detectable. The fate of one pair of chromosomes and its DNA content are traced. Each mitotic telophase chromatid (which presumably contains one DNA duplex) has a DNA content represented as x. Mitosis and the second meiotic division produce daughter nuclei with the same number of chromosomes as their parent nucleus, each chromatid containing the normal (x) amount of DNA. The first meiotic division produces telophase I nuclei with the haploid (single, or unpaired) number of chromosomes, each chromatid still containing the doubled amount of DNA. No DNA replication occurs in interphase I.

beginning of prophase I, however, the members of each pair of homologous chromosomes synapse, that is, pair lengthwise at corresponding points, to form chromosome pairs. The chromosomes proceed as pairs to the equator of the spindle for the first meiotic metaphase, or *metaphase I,* At *anaphase I* the members of each pair of homologs separate and go to opposite poles, each member still containing its doubled amount of DNA. At *telophase I,* therefore, each daughter nucleus has the haploid number of chromosomes, each containing the doubled amount of DNA. In the *interphase I* that follows, no DNA synthesis takes place.

The *second meiotic division* begins (in both daughter nuclei) at various times for different organisms, and is essentially an ordinary mitotic division. In *prophase II* each chromosome, composed of two chromatids, proceeds independently to the equator for *metaphase II.* At *anaphase II* the two chromatids separate and go to opposite poles of the spindle and are now called chromosomes, each containing half the DNA. In *telophase II* each chromosome unwinds and can be seen to consist of two chromatids. At the completion of meiosis, therefore, four haploid nuclei are produced, each of whose chromosomes (and its chromatids) contain the amount of DNA normally present before replication.

In comparison, mitosis involves an alternation of chromosome duplication and separation, whereas meiosis involves one duplication followed by two separations. As a result, the diploid chromosome number is maintained in mitosis, but is reduced to haploid in meiosis. Because meiosis is such a widespread and fundamental process in sexually reproducing eucaryotes, we shall now consider it in greater detail (Figure 15-3).

Prophase I is of long duration as compared to mitotic prophase and can be divided into the following five stages:

1. *Leptonema* (thin thread). Soon after interphase, the chromosomes appear long and thin, more so than in the earliest prophase of mitosis.

2. *Zygonema* (joined thread, not shown in Figure 15-3). The thin threads of homologous chromosomes pair lengthwise with each other. This pairing or synapsis can start at one or several places from which it spreads zipperwise until the two homologs are closely apposed.

3. *Pachynema* (thick thread). The apposition of homologs becomes so tight that it is difficult to identify two separate chromosomes.[1]

4. *Diplonema* (double thread). The tight pairing of pachynema is relaxed, each pair of synapsed chromosomes begins to uncoil and can be seen to contain four chromatids, two per chromosome. A pair of synapsed chromosomes is called a *bivalent* (composed of two *univalents*) if we are referring to chromosomes. But it is called a *tetrad* (composed of two *dyads* or four *monads*) if we refer to chromatids.

---

[1] Even in organisms that have a leptonema stage, the chromosome cannot unwind enough to enable every DNA sequence in one of its chromatids to base-pair with a corresponding sequence in a chromatid of its homolog. Therefore, synapsis due to base pairing must occur discontinuously or intermittently, and only where corresponding regions in the two chromatids have sufficiently unwound. Fungi such as *Neurospora* have no leptonema stage, and synapsis occurs and is maintained during prophase I between what appear to be condensed, coiled-up, homologs. Even such "condensed" homologs may intermittently have very short homologous segments which are uncoiled and form long, thin synapsing fibers that serve to hold the homologs together. The morphological structure, the *synaptinemal complex,* seen *between* paired chromosomes at pachynema in higher organisms may be a cytological manifestation of such thin synapsing regions between condensed chromosomes.

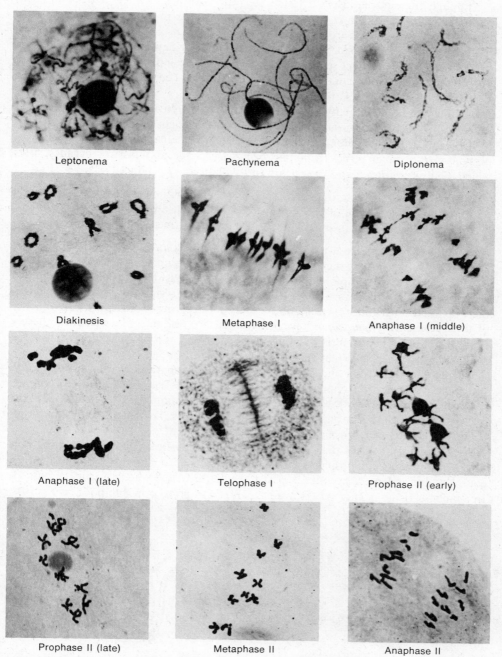

Leptonema   Pachynema   Diplonema

Diakinesis   Metaphase I   Anaphase I (middle)

Anaphase I (late)   Telophase I   Prophase II (early)

Prophase II (late)   Metaphase II   Anaphase II

Figure 15-3 Meiosis in maize (Indian corn). Anaphase I (middle) shows one bivalent whose univalents are delayed in separation because they are still held together by a chiasma. Prophase II and later stages show the events taking place in one of the two nuclei produced by the first meiotic division. (Courtesy of M. M. Rhoades, 1961. *The Cell*, Vol. 3. New York: Academic Press.)

Although the chromatids in a tetrad separate from each other in pairs in some places, they are all still in close contact with each other in other places. Each place where the four chromatids are still held together is called a *chiasma* (plural, *chiasmata*) (Figure 15-4A). In a chiasma the two chromatids that synapse to make a pair on one side of the point of contact separate at that point and synapse with different partners on the other side of the contact point (Figure 15-4B). The occurrence of a chiasma assures that the univalents are held together.[2]

In some animals, especially during the formation of female gametes, diplonema is followed by a *diffuse* (or *growth*) stage, in which the nucleus and chromosomes revert to their appearance in a nondividing cell. During this stage a great amount of cytoplasmic growth takes place. In human beings this stage may last for decades, after which meiosis continues and eggs ready for ovulation are produced.

5. *Diakinesis* is characterized by the maximal contraction of chromosomes.[3] By the end of diakinesis, nucleoli and the nuclear membrane have disappeared and the spindle has formed. Thus ends prophase I.

Metaphase I results from movement of the chromosomes to the equatorial plane as in mitosis, except that they move as bivalents whose univalents are held together by chiasmata. Between diplonema and metaphase I repulsion occurs between the two centromeres of synapsed univalents so that the chiasmata slide away from the centromere region toward and sometimes off the ends of the chromosomes. As a consequence of this *chiasma terminalization*, fewer chiasmata are ordinarily seen at metaphase I than at diplonema, and, during diakinesis the members of a bivalent often seem to be synapsed only near their ends, forming a circle.

During anaphase I the univalents of each bivalent separate from each other completely and proceed to opposite poles of the spindle. This movement, of course, completely terminalizes all chiasmata remaining at metaphase I. In telophase I the two daughter nuclei are formed; and interphase I follows. This interphase is of various lengths in different organisms.

Each daughter nucleus then undergoes the second meiotic division, which is very much like mitosis. In prophase II each chromosome, containing two chromatids, contracts and independently lines up at the equator of the spindle for metaphase II. In anaphase II the members of a dyad separate and go to opposite poles as monads,

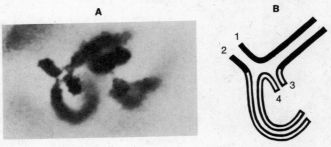

Figure 15-4   (A) Lily diplonema showing chromatids (1–4) with different synaptic partners on different sides of a chiasma. (Courtesy of R. E. Cleland.) (B) Filled-in segments have one parental origin; hollow segments, the other.

[2] Chiasma-like configurations are relatively rare during mitosis.

[3] The chromosomes become shorter and thicker, that is, more compact, during diakinesis than at any time in mitosis.

each now a single chromosome which after unwinding is seen to consist of two chromatids. Because two nuclei undergo this second division, four nuclei are formed by the end of telophase II. (R)

15.2   During meiosis primary structure recombination can occur reciprocally between nonsister chromatids in a tetrad.

The two chromatids in a chromosome are called *sister chromatids*, or *sister strands*; chromatids belonging to different members of a pair of homologs are called *nonsister chromatids* or *nonsister strands*. At some time between the beginning of meiosis and diplonema, a reciprocal exchange of genetic material can occur between nonsister chromatids in a tetrad (as expected from Section 14.10). Evidence for such exchanges will be presented in Sections 17.3 and 17.4. Because the two homologs undergoing exchange originated in different parents, the result of such primary structure rearrangement is two nonsister chromatids that are " hybrid "; that is, one recombinant chromatid is paternal–maternal in derivation, whereas the other is reciprocally maternal–paternal. We should note in Figure 15-4B that when such an exchange has occurred, a chiasma will be seen at diplonema if corresponding paternally derived (as well as maternally derived) sections of chromatids remain synapsed. Although some of these exchanges may fail to produce a visible chiasma later, we can in general take every chiasma to be cytological evidence of a prior exchange within a tetrad. By assuming henceforth that chiasma terminalization has not yet occurred, the position of a chiasma can be equated with a point of exchange, and a tetrad with one chiasma would contain chromatids with the constitutions shown in Figure 15-5. We see that, after a single exchange, one chromatid remains entirely maternal and one entirely paternal in origin; but the other two nonsister strands are reciprocally recombinant. Although only two of the four chromatids are involved in any given chiasma, a tetrad usually contains several chiasmata. Thus, it is likely that each of the four chromatids of a tetrad undergoes reciprocal exchange with a nonsister strand at some point and is, therefore, a recombinant strand.

15.3   Meiosis results in chromosome segregation (hence the segregation of homologous segments of a chromosome pair), and the independent segregation of segments of different chromosome pairs.

Since a postmeiotic nucleus normally contains only one homolog of a given pair of chromosomes in the premeiotic nucleus, segregation of the members of a pair of

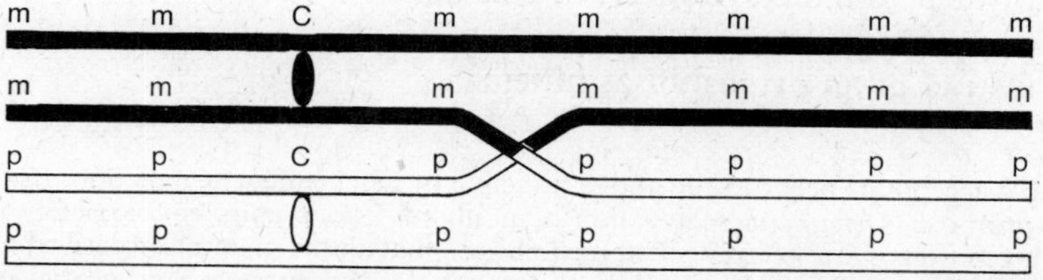

Figure 15-5 Chiasma showing paternal (p) and maternal (m) composition of strands. Compare with Figure 15-4B. C represents a centromere.

chromosomes, or *chromosome segregation*, has occurred. Homologous segments in a chromosome pair, therefore, must have also segregated.

The particular poles to which homologous segments of a single chromosome pair migrate are determined by the orientations of the centromeres of the bivalent at metaphase I and of the univalents at metaphase II. Since the orientation of centromeres is uninfluenced by the number and location of chiasmata and each bivalent or univalent is equally likely to become oriented (relative to the poles) in one of two possible ways, the segregation of homologous segments of one chromosome pair will take place independently of the segregation of homologous segments of another chromosome pair; that is, *segments on nonhomologs will segregate independently*. For example, if homologous maternal and paternal segments of one bivalent are labeled A and A′ and those of another bivalent B and B′, at the completion of meiosis the four different haploid combinations of these segments—A B, A B′, A′ B, A′ B′—will be equally frequent. Note that 50 per cent of these combinations of unpaired segments are parental combinations (A B, A′ B′) and 50 per cent are nonparental combinations, or recombinations (A B′, A′ B).[4]

15.4   The diploid–haploid–diploid chromosome cycle which occurs during the life cycle of three sexually reproducing multicellular organisms is described.

Since the diploid number of chromosomes is maintained generation after generation in sexually reproducing organisms, we expect that meiosis will result in the formation of haploid gametes at some time in the life cycle of such individuals. In most animals, mature haploid gametes are produced directly from the products of meiosis, without intervening nuclear divisions; in plants, however, haploid meiotic products usually undergo mitotic divisions before mature gametes are produced. Nevertheless, the meiotic process itself is essentially the same in plants and animals. Let us consider next the life and chromosome number cycles of three multicellular organisms which have been especially useful in genetic investigations.

Drosophila melanogaster

The adult stage of *D. melanogaster*, commonly called the fruit fly, is shown in Figure 15-6. Although its size depends upon nutritional and other environmental factors, an adult is usually 2 to 3 mm long, with females slightly larger than males. The wild-type fly has a gray body color and dull-red compound eyes. Males are readily distinguished by dark sex combs on their anterior pair of legs, absent in females; by an abdomen which terminates dorsally in a single broad black band, instead of a series of bands as in females; and by a penis and claspers at the ventral end of the abdomen, instead of an ovipositor as in females.

---

[4] Some notable exceptions occur to the above principle of independent segregation. For example, in the evening primrose, *Oenothera*, segregation of nonhomologous pairs is completely dependent— that is, the chromosomes are so arranged at metaphase I that all the maternally derived nonhomologs go toward one pole at anaphase I and all the paternally derived nonhomologs go toward the other. Therefore, this dependent segregation (described more fully in Section S35.3b) prevents the quaternary structure recombinations produced by independent segregation.

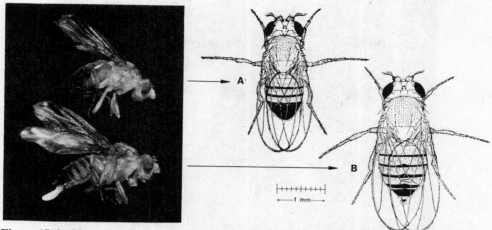

Figure 15-6   Normal (wild-type) *Drosophila melanogaster* male (A) and female (B). (Drawn by E. M. Wallace; photographs courtesy of L. Ehrman.)

The adult male is diploid and has a pair of testes in which *spermatogonia* are produced by mitosis. A spermatogonial cell which enters meiosis is called a *primary spermatocyte*. The first meiotic division produces two *secondary spermatocytes*; the second meiotic division, four haploid *spermatids*. Each spermatid differentiates without further division into a *spermatozoon*, or sperm cell. Thus, for each (diploid) primary spermatocyte entering meiosis, four haploid sperm are produced at the completion of *spermatogenesis*. Sperm are stored in the *Drosophila* male until they are ejaculated into the vagina of the female, from which they swim into the female's sperm storage organs.[5]

The adult female (also diploid) has a pair of ovaries containing diploid *oogonia*.[6] By four successive mitotic divisions each oogonium produces a cluster of 16 cells, one of which enters meiosis as a *primary oocyte* while the others serve as *nurse cells* for the maturing oocyte. As the oocyte grows it passes out of the ovary, into the oviduct, and then into the uterus. When it reaches the uterus, the egg is usually no further advanced than metaphase I. Sperm stored in the female are released to penetrate the egg, after which the first meiotic division continues. The two *secondary oocyte* nuclei produce four haploid nuclei. Three of these become *polar nuclei* and degenerate; the remaining one becomes the haploid *egg nucleus*, completing the process of oogenesis, which then unites with the haploid sperm nucleus to form the diploid zygote nucleus. Since the female fruit fly stores hundreds of sperm and uses them a few at a time, a single mating can yield hundreds of progeny.

After fertilization embryonic development proceeds for about 1 day (at 25°C), until the *larva* hatches from the *egg* (Figure 15-7). Four more days and 2 moults later, the mature larva becomes a *pupa*; and about 4 days later the young adult, or imago, ecloses (hatches) from the pupa case. Although mating usually occurs after the first 12 hours of adult life, the female usually does not begin to lay eggs until some time during the second day. Overall, the generation time is about 10 days. Adults can, however, live up to 10 weeks, during which a female can lay several thousand eggs.

[5] These are a pair of ring-shaped spermathecae and a single coiled ventral receptacle.
[6] An ovary contains a series of egg tubes, or ovarioles, each having oogonia at one end.

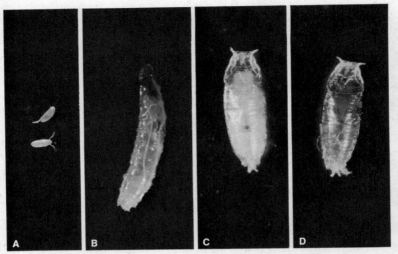

Figure 15-7   Egg (A), mature larva (B), early and late pupae (C, D) of *D. melanogaster*, all at the same magnification. (Courtesy of L. Ehrman.)

Zea mays

Like the bean and the garden pea, maize or Indian corn (*Zea mays*) usually has both male and female sex organs on the same plant. Since the diploid maize plant produces male and female spores, *microspores* and *megaspores*, respectively, it constitutes the *sporophyte* stage of the life cycle (Figure 15-8). Microspores are produced in tassels at the end of the stem. Here diploid microspore mother cells, or *microsporocytes*, undergo meiosis to produce four haploid microspores (A).

The haploid microspore, which marks the beginning of the male *gametophyte* stage, develops into a *pollen grain* (B). The pollen grain nucleus divides mitotically to produce two haploid nuclei. One of these does not divide again and becomes the *pollen tube*, or *vegetative*, *nucleus*. The other nucleus divides mitotically once more, so the gametophyte contains three haploid nuclei (C). The two nuclei that are formed last function as *sperm nuclei* (D, K).

Near the base of the upper leaves of the maize plant are clusters of pistils, each containing one diploid megaspore mother cell, or *megasporocyte*. (The styles of the pistils later become the silks.) The megasporocyte undergoes meiosis to produce four haploid nuclei (E), three of which degenerate (F). The remaining megaspore nucleus, whose appearance marks the beginning of the female gametophyte stage, divides mitotically (G), as do its daughter and granddaughter nuclei, so eight haploid nuclei result (I). In the *embryo sac* (J) three of the eight nuclei aggregate at the apex and divide to form *antipodal nuclei*. Two of the eight move to the center to become *polar nuclei*, and three move to the base of the embryo sac to form two *synergid nuclei* and one *egg nucleus*. The pollen tube grows down the style to the embryo sac, where one sperm nucleus fertilizes the egg nucleus (K, L) to produce a diploid (2N) nucleus; the other sperm nucleus fuses with the two polar nuclei to produce a triploid (3N) nucleus. With the occurrence of this *double fertilization* the sporophyte generation is initiated. Mitotic division of the diploid nucleus (L) produces the *embryo*, while the triploid nucleus develops into the *endosperm*. The endosperm is later used to nourish the embryo and seedling. The outer surface of the kernel is the *pericarp*, diploid tissue derived from the maternal sporophyte. In other words, the pericarp of a maize kernel

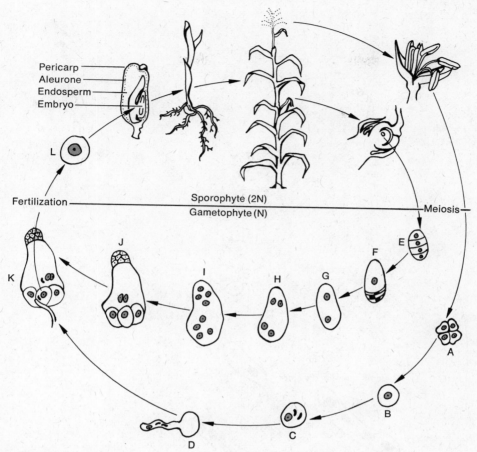

Figure 15-8   Life cycle of maize, *Zea mays*. See the text for a description.

is produced by the sporophyte of one generation and the remaining tissue of a kernel by the sporophyte of the next generation. Development from embryo sac to mature kernel takes about 8 weeks, whereas development from kernel to mature sporophyte requires nearly 4 months.

Neurospora crassa

Neurospora (" nerve spore ") is a bread mold which, in its haploid vegetative stage is composed of threads, or *hyphae*, which branch, fuse, and intertwine to form a mat, the *mycelium*. The cell walls of a hypha are incomplete so that the cytoplasm of the filament is continuous, and each hyphal cell is multinucleate.

Cultures can be propagated asexually either by spores (*conidia*) which contain one or several haploid nuclei, or by transplantation of pieces of mycelium. Sexual reproduction (Figure 15-9) requires the participation of different mating types. Two conidia or hyphae of different mating type fuse to form a *dikaryotic* cell (A), in which both types of haploid nucleus coexist in a common cytoplasm and divide more or less synchronously (B). After two haploid nuclei of different mating type fuse to produce a diploid zygotic nucleus (C), two meiotic divisions occur, resulting in four haploid

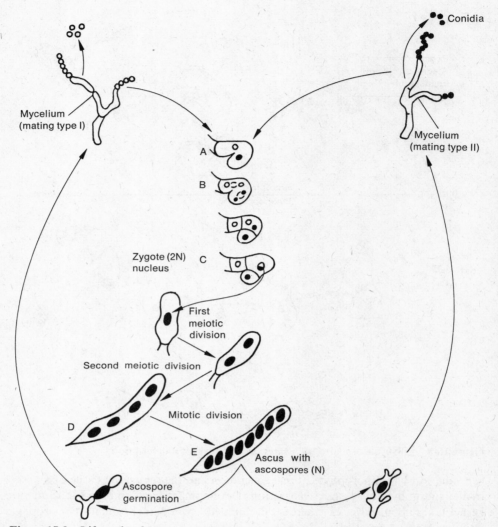

Figure 15-9 Life cycle of *Neurospora*. See the text for a description.

nuclei (D); each haploid nucleus divides once mitotically to form a total of eight haploid nuclei (E). Next, the cytoplasm and nuclei are partitioned into eight haploid, ovoid bodies, *ascospores*, which are contained in a thin-walled sac, the *ascus*. When the ascus ruptures, the ascospores are ejected into the air. Upon germination the ascospore nucleus divides mitotically, as do its descendant nuclei, to produce the mycelium. (R)

SUMMARY AND CONCLUSIONS

The problem of maintaining a constant amount of nuclear genetic material generation after generation in organisms that reproduce sexually is solved by meiosis. This process changes the chromosomes from the diploid number of the zygote to the haploid number of the gamete by the following means: replicated homologs, which synapse and are held together by chiasmata until metaphase I, undergo two successive spindle-using divisions without replicating again.

The result of these two meiotic divisions is chromosome segregation—only one member of each pair of homologs is present in a gametic nucleus. Reducing the chromosome number from diploid to haploid by meiosis, and restoring the diploid number by fusion of haploid nuclei, as in fertilization, are quaternary structure recombinations of genetic material.

Primary structure recombination also occurs routinely during meiosis. As will be supported later, a chiasma indicates that a reciprocal exchange has occurred between nonsister chromatids in a tetrad. Because each tetrad has several chiasmata, all, or almost all, segregated chromosomes have undergone such recombination and are, therefore, a mixture of parts that are paternal and maternal in derivation. Since segregation involves centromeric regions which line up at the equator and proceed to the poles uninfluenced by chiasmata, homologous segments of a chromosome pair segregate, and segments of different chromosome pairs segregate independently whether or not exchanges have occurred between nonsister chromatids.

The diploid–haploid–diploid chromosome cycles that occur during the life cycles of *Drosophila*, *Zea*, and *Neurospora* are described.

GENERAL REFERENCES

Brachet, J., and Mirsky, A. E. (Editors) 1961. *The cell,* Vol. 3, *Meiosis and mitosis.* New York: Academic Press, Inc.

Darlington, C. D., and Janaki-Ammal, E. K. 1945. *Chromosome atlas of cultivated plants.* London: Allen & Unwin Ltd.

Hsu, T. C., and Benirschke, K. 1967. *An atlas of mammalian chromosomes.* Vol .1. New York: Springer-Verlag.

John, B., and Lewis, K. R. 1965. *The meiotic system.* New York: Springer-Verlag.

Makino, S. 1951. *An atlas of chromosome numbers in animals.* Ames, Iowa: Iowa State College Press.

Spector, W. S. (Editor), 1956. Chromosome numbers. In *Handbook of biological data.* Philadelphia: W. B. Saunders Company, pp. 92–96.

George Wells Beadle (1903–). Dr. Beadle was the recipient of a Nobel prize in 1958 for his pioneer work in biochemical genetics using *Drosophila* and (especially) *Neurospora*.

SPECIFIC SECTION REFERENCES

15.1   Grell, R. F. 1962. A new hypothesis on the nature and sequence of meiotic events in the female of *Drosophila melanogaster*. Proc. Nat. Acad. Sci., U.S., 48: 165–172. (Exchange pairing—leading to exchange between nonsister chromatids—precedes distributive pairing—leading to movement as tetrads.)

Moens, P. B. 1970. The fine structure of meiotic chromosome pairing in natural and artificial *Lilium* polyploids. J. Cell Sci., 7: 55–63.

Moens, P. B. 1970. Premeiotic DNA synthesis and the time of chromosome pairing in *Locusta migratoria*. Proc. Nat. Acad. Sci., U.S., 66: 94–98. (Synthesis is completed before pairing.)

Moses, M. J. 1956. Chromosomal structures in crayfish spermatocytes. J. Biophys. Biochem. Cytol., 2: 215–218. (Synaptinemal complexes described.)

von Wettstein, D. 1971. The synaptinemal complex and four-strand crossing over. Proc. Nat. Acad. Sci., U.S., 68: 851–855. (Two sister chromatids generate a lateral component; two lateral components combine to make up the synaptinemal complex.)

Drosophila

Bibliographies on most, if not all, investigations with all species of *Drosophila* through 1967 are found in source 1 (which includes subject indexes), and on more recent work in 4. The life cycle, culture, cytological and genetic experiments for the classroom are given in 2, 3, 5, and 8. All aspects of *Drosophila* biology are treated in detail in 2. Mutants found before 1968 are described in 7; some found since then are described in 4. Stock lists of various *Drosophila* species maintained in different laboratories, addresses of *Drosophila* workers, and research and teaching notes are also available in the international, at least annual, bulletin of 4.

1. *Bibliography on the genetics of Drosophila: Part I* by H. J. Muller (Edinburgh: Oliver & Boyd Ltd., 1939, 132 pp.). *Parts II, III, IV*, and *V* by I. H. Herskowitz (Oxford: Alden Press Ltd., 1953, 212 pp.; Bloomington: Indiana University Press, 1958, 296 pp.; New York: McGraw-Hill Book Company, 1963, 344 pp.; and New York: The Macmillan Company, 1969, 376 pp., respectively).
2. Demerec, M. (Editor), *The biology of Drosophila*. New York: John Wiley & Sons Inc., 632 pp., 1950. Xerographed by University Microfilms, Inc., Ann Arbor, Michigan.
3. Demerec, M., and Kaufmann, B, P. 1961. *Drosophila guide*, seventh edition. Washington, D.C.: Carnegie Institution of Washington, 47 pp.
4. *Drosophila Information Service*. (E. Novitski, Editor, Department of Biology, University of Oregon, Eugene, Oregon.)
5. Haskell, G. 1961. *Practical heredity with Drosophila*. Edinburgh: Oliver & Boyd Ltd., 124 pp.
6. King, R. C. 1970. *Ovarian development in* Drosophila melanogaster. New York: Academic Press, Inc.
7. Lindsley, D. L., and Grell, E. H. 1968. *Genetic variations of* Drosophila melanogaster. Washington, D. C.: Carnegie Institution of Washington. Publ. No. 627.
8. Strickberger, M. W. 1962. *Experiments in genetics with* Drosophila. New York: John Wiley & Sons, Inc., 144 pp.

Zea

Kiesselbach, T. A. 1949. The structure and reproduction of corn. Univ. Nebraska Coll. Agric., Agric. Exp. Sta. Res. Bull., No. 161.

Maize News Letter (M. M. Rhoades, Editor, Dept. of Botany, Indiana University, Bloomington, Ind.).

Sprague, G. F. 1955. *Corn and corn improvement*. New York: Academic Press, Inc.

Weijer, J. 1952. A catalogue of genetic maize types together with a maize bibliography. Bibliographica Genetica, 14: 189–425.

Neurospora

Bachmann, B., and Strickland, W. N. 1965. *Neurospora bibliography and index*. New Haven: Yale University Press.

Fincham, J. R. S., and Day, P. R. 1963. *Fungal genetics*. Oxford: Blackwell Scientific Publications Ltd.

Ryan, F. J. 1950. Selected methods of *Neurospora* genetics. Methods in Medical Research, 3: 51–75.

Wagner, R. P., and Mitchell, H. K. 1964. *Genetics and metabolism*, second edition. New York: John Wiley & Sons, Inc.

QUESTIONS AND PROBLEMS

1. List the similarities and differences between mitosis and meiosis.
2. Draw a single chiasma between two homologs, if they are
   a. both rods.
   b. one rod and one ring.
   c. both rings.
   Indicate the four meiotic products for each case.
3. In light of your answer to problem 2, what can you conclude about the size and shape of a chromosome and its survival in organisms that undergo meiosis?
4. How many bivalents are present at metaphase I in man? Maize? The silkworm? The garden pea?
5. The *D. melanogaster* female has a diploid chromosome number of eight. What proportion of its gametes receive centromeres that are all paternally derived? All maternally derived? Are all the gametes chromosomal recombinants? Explain.
6. Name three mechanisms of chromosomal recombination involving nucleated cells. State what the genetic recombination is in each case.
7. Suppose the meiotic process had never evolved. What do you think would have been the consequence?
8. Discuss the statement: During meiosis, a segment of a chromosome segregates independently of its homologous segment and of all other chromosome segments.
9. What do you suppose happens during meiosis in individuals possessing an odd number of chromosomes?
10. How do the homologs that separate at anaphase I differ from those that synapsed in zygonema?
11. What do you suppose is meant by the expression "first-division segregation"? "Second-division segregation"? If exchanges giving rise to chiasmata can occur at a variety of positions along the chromosome, under what circumstances can a given chromosomal segment undergo first-division segregation? Second-division segregation?
12. If you saw a single cell at metaphase, how could you tell whether the cell was undergoing mitosis, metaphase I, or metaphase II at the time it was fixed and stained?
13. What advantages do the following organisms offer for the study of cytology and/or of the genetic material? *Drosophila*? Maize? *Neurosospora*?
14. What are the major differences between spermatogenesis and oogenesis in *Drosophila*?
15. Is the female sex cell of *Drosophila* ever haploid? Explain.
16. How does a monad at diplonema differ from the same monad at telophase II?
17. Can you suggest any functions which the polar nuclei in *Drosophila* oogenesis may serve?
18. Is mitosis in triploid endosperm expected to be normal? Why?

Chapter 16

Of Nuclear Genes—Gene Segregation and Sex Linkage

In Chapters 14 and 15 we considered the recombination of nuclear chromosomes and chromosomes segments resulting from mitosis, meiosis, and fertilization. We shall now study the consequences of these chromosomal recombinations with regard to the genes which the chromosomes and segments contain.

16.1 The members of a gene pair segregate during meiosis.

Barring mutation, all the DNA duplexes in a pre- or postmeiotic chromosome are identical and, therefore, code for the same allele at a given locus. Accordingly, a single gene symbol, say A or a, suffices to specify the genotype of the whole chromosome with regard to a locus. It is conventional (convenient and usually adequate), moreover, to represent such chromosomes as having, prior to replication, only one gene at each chromosomal locus.

Because nuclear chromosomes of sexually reproducing eucaryotes occur in pairs, so do the genes they contain; because homologous chromosome segments segregate during meiosis, so do the members of each pair of genes they contain. Thus, if homologous chromosome segments carry different alleles at a particular locus, a single haploid meiotic product ordinarily will carry either one allele or the other.

For example, when a diploid parent of $A\,a$ genotype undergoes meiosis, the chance is 50 per cent that a gamete will contain A and 50 per cent that it will contain a. Consequently, we will obtain approximately equal numbers of both gametes if the sample of gametes is sufficiently large. If the heterozygous parent, $A\,a$, is mated with a homozygous parent, $a\,a$, half the resulting zygotes will be $A\,a$ and half will be $a\,a$, since the homozygous parent produces only a gametes. If, however, the other parent is also heterozygous for the same gene pair, that is, if it is an identical *monohybrid* (Figure 16-1), random fertilizations between the A and a gametes of each parent will result in zygotes of three different genotypes: $A\,A$, $A\,a$, and $a\,a$ in the relative proportion of $1:2:1$.

A large number of human traits have been shown to be due to the action of single pairs of segregating genes. Such traits include *albinism, woolly hair, thalassemia,* and

Parents	$A\,a \times A\,a$	
Gametes	½ A, ½ a	½ A, ½ a
Zygotes	¼ $A\,A$, ½ $A\,a$, ¼ $a\,a$	

Figure 16-1 Zygotes produced from a monohybrid cross, that is, a cross between identical monohybrids.

240

MN and Rhesus *blood types* (all of these are discussed in Section S16.1a). Just like genes in procaryotes, a nuclear gene may have *multiple alleles*, each one recognized because it produces unique phenotypic changes (as proved and exemplified in Section S16.1b with ABO blood type in man, wing and eye-color traits in *Drosophila*, and self-sterility in *Nicotiana*). (R)

16.2   The members of gene pairs located in different chromosome pairs segregate independently of each other during meiosis.

An individual, having in addition to a pair of homologs that contain the alleles *A* and *a* a second pair of homologs that contains the alleles *B* and *b* (Figure 16-2), is a heterozygote for two gene pairs, or a *dihybrid*. As noted previously, different pairs of homologs arrive at metaphase I independently of each other. If, as in case A, no chiasma (hence no exchange) occurs either between the centromere and gene pair *A a* or between the centromere and gene pair *B b*, four genetically different meiotic products will occur with equal frequency, since alignments I and II are equally likely. Identical results are obtained either when a chiasma occurs in one tetrad but not the other (case B), or when a chiasma occurs in both tetrads (case C). In cases CI and CII the dyads can become oriented with respect to the poles in four equally likely arrangements at metaphase II with the same net result: four equally frequent types of gametes. Regardless of chiasma formation, therefore, the independent segregation of homologous segments of different chromosome pairs guarantees the independent segregation of the different gene pairs they contain.

Accordingly, the diploid dihybrid *A a B b* parent produces haploid gametes of four types with the following frequencies: $\frac{1}{4}$ *A B*: $\frac{1}{4}$ *A b*: $\frac{1}{4}$ *a B*: $\frac{1}{4}$ *a b*. Noting in the figure that chromosome segments of the same shade have the same parental derivation, we see that gametes having nonalleles of the same parental derivation (*A B* and *a b*; nonrecombinant, parental types) and gametes having nonalleles of different parental derivation (*A b* and *a B*; recombinant types) are equally frequent. When, alternatively, the *A a B b* parent was derived from a union of *A b* and *a B* gametes, it produces the same four equally frequent types of gametes, in which parentals (*A b* and *a B*) and recombinants (*A B* and *a b*) are equally frequent. Thus, regardless of the original parental derivations, parental and recombinant combinations occur in the gametes with equal frequency when gene pairs segregate independently.

16.3   The phenotypic ratio confirms the expected genotypic ratio when identical dihybrids for independently segregating gene pairs are crossed.

If two parents are identical dihybrids, *A a B b*, for gene pairs segregating independently, random fertilization between gametes should produce diploid zygotes with *nine* possible genotypes. These genotypes and their relative frequencies are given in Figures 16-3 and 16-4.

We can test whether the expected genotypic ratio is actually produced by observing the phenotypic ratio. In snapdragons, for example—where red flowers are due to *R R*, white to *r r*, and pink to *R r*; and narrow leaves are due to *N N*, broad leaves to *n n*,

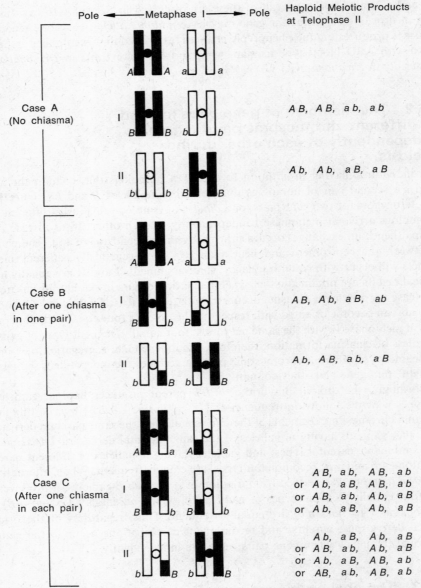

Pole ◄──Metaphase I──► Pole   Haploid Meiotic Products
                                at Telophase II

Case A
(No chiasma)

I   AB, AB, ab, ab

II   Ab, Ab, aB, aB

Case B
(After one chiasma
in one pair)

I   AB, Ab, aB, ab

II   Ab, AB, ab, aB

Case C
(After one chiasma
in each pair)

I   AB, ab, AB, ab
                             or Ab, aB, AB, ab
                             or AB, ab, Ab, aB
                             or Ab, aB, Ab, aB

II   Ab, aB, Ab, aB
                             or AB, ab, Ab, aB
                             or Ab, aB, AB, ab
                             or AB, ab, AB, ab

Figure 16-2   Meiotic fate of gene pairs located in different pairs of homologous chromosomes. The parental derivation (black vs. white) and the genotype of corresponding segments of chromatids (A or a, B or b) are shown at metaphase I. Note that when all alternatives in case CI (or CII) are considered, $AB = ab = Ab = aB$ with respect to frequency. Black chromosomes have one parental derivation, white chromosomes the other.

and medium-width leaves to Nn—independent segregation in a cross of two pink mediums ($Rr\,Nn \times Rr\,Nn$) produces a phenotypic ratio in the progeny which is identical to the expected genotypic ratio. Thus, when the sample of progeny is sufficiently large, nine phenotypes are observed to occur in a ratio that approximates the following:

	PHENOTYPE	GENOTYPE
1	red narrow	$R R\ N N$
2	red medium	$R R\ N n$
1	red broad	$R R\ n n$
2	pink narrow	$R r\ N N$
4	pink medium	$R r\ N n$
2	pink broad	$R r\ n n$
1	white narrow	$r r\ N N$
2	white medium	$r r\ N n$
1	white broad	$r r\ n n$

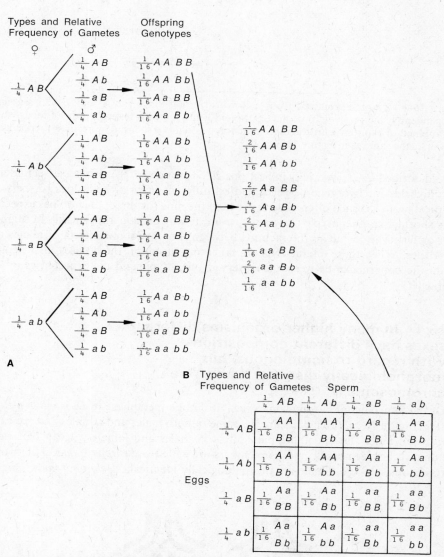

Figure 16-3 Zygotes produced by combining at random gametes formed by identical dihybrids ($A a\ B b$) whose two gene pairs segregate independently. Two methods (A, B) are shown: (A) top shows the branching track; (B) bottom, the checkerboard method. See also Figure 16-4, which obtains the same results another way.

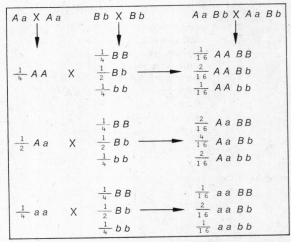

Figure 16-4 Zygotes produced from a dihybrid cross. Since the *A* and *B* loci segregate independently, the progeny must have a diploid genotype with respect to the *A* locus which is combined at random with the diploid genotype of the *B* locus. The results obtained are, of course, the same as in Figure 16-3.

As described later (especially in Sections 20.5 through 20.7), crosses between identical dihybrids for two gene pairs located on different pairs of homologs (or between identical monohybrids) often yield fewer than the nine (or three) phenotypes expected. This shortage in phenotypic classes is due not to any genetic abnormality in segregation or fertilization but to interactions between the phenotypic effects of alleles and nonalleles. When these interactions are taken into account, these cases also demonstrate the congruence between the observed phenotypic and the expected genotypic ratios. (R)

16.4   In many higher organisms different sexes have different compositions with regard to homologous, but morphologically distinct, X and Y sex chromosomes.

Of the four pairs of chromosomes seen at mitotic metaphase in *Drosophila melanogaster* (Figure 16-5), three pairs are the same in both males and females and are called *autosomes*. Since the remaining pair differs in males and females, it can be used to distinguish between sexes, and its members are called *sex chromosomes*. The two sex chromosomes of the female are morphologically identical, *X chromosomes*. One sex

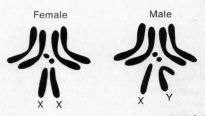

Figure 16-5   Silhouettes of condensed mitotic chromosomes of *D. melanogaster*.

chromosome in the male is also an X chromosome; the other is morphologically unique and is called the *Y chromosome*. The Y is not present, therefore, in the female. Morphologically distinct X and Y sex chromosomes are also found in man and all other mammals, the male being XY and the female, XX.

In certain organisms, the sex chromosome situation is reversed. For example, in birds, moths, butterflies, and some amphibians and reptiles, the male is XX and the female, XY. Regardless of the sex involved, all the gametes of XX individuals carry an X, whereas half the gametes of an XY individual carry an X and half carry a Y. Random fertilization of such gametes produces equal numbers of XX and XY zygotes, which have the genetic potential to develop into equal numbers of males and females. The preceding indicates the chromosomal basis for sex determination in many higher organisms; the genetic basis for sex determination in eucaryotes will be discussed in Chapter 23.

16.5   Some genes in the X chromosome have no loci in the Y chromosome

Let us consider the results of two crosses involving the wild-type, dull-red (w^+) and mutant, white (w) eye-color alleles in *D. melanogaster*. If for the *first parents* (P_1) we cross two different lines that are genetically uniform, that is, pure, dull-red ♀ (female) by white ♂ (male) (Figure 16-6A) gives rise to *first generation* (F_1) progeny that are dull-red females and dull-red males only. On the other hand, the reciprocal cross (Figure 16-6B), white ♀ by dull-red ♂, produces dull-red daughters and white sons only. Although the first cross gave rise to sons that are of the same eye color as daughters, the reciprocal cross yielded different-looking sons and daughters. If the locus for the eye-color gene were in an autosome, we would expect no difference in eye color among the F_1 progeny of the reciprocal cross, since the paired autosomal loci would have segregated independently of the sex chromosomes, and sons and daughters would have had the same eye color. Because autosomal genes always give the same results for sons as for daughters, the w locus cannot be in an autosome. Hence, the locus for white eye color is very likely to be in the sex chromosomes; that is, it seems to be *sex-linked*.[1]

Since females are XX and males XY, we can represent the first cross above as $X^{w^+} X^{w^+}$ ♀ $\times X^w Y^w$ ♂ with F_1 progeny expected to be $X^{w^+} X^w$ (dull-red daughters) and $X^{w^+} Y^w$ (dull-red sons) (Figure 16-7A-1). Reciprocally, $X^w X^w$ ♀ $\times X^{w^+} Y^{w^+}$ ♂ should produce $X^{w^+} X^w$ (dull-red daughters) and $X^w Y^{w^+}$ (dull-red sons) (Figure

	A		B	
P_1	dull-red ♀ X white ♂		P_1	white ♀ X dull-red ♂
F_1	dull-red ♂♂		F_1	white ♂♂
	dull-red ♀♀			dull-red ♀♀

Figure 16-6   Phenotypic results of reciprocal matings involving pure lines for eye color. ♂♂, males, ♀♀, females.

[1] At this point in our knowledge the locus could conceivably be in an episome, a plasmid, or in normally present extranuclear genetic material.

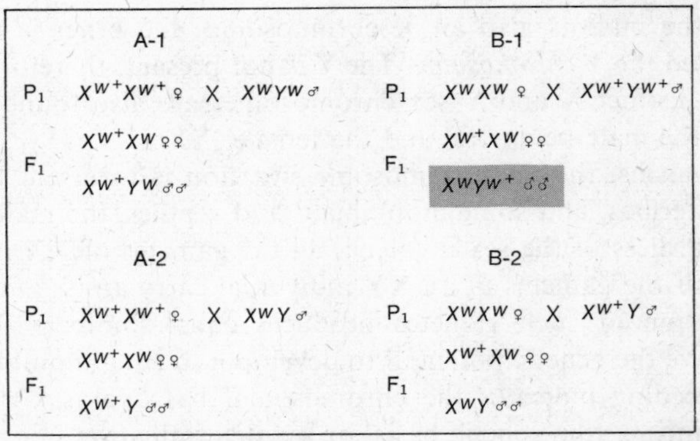

Figure 16-7 Two ways (A-1 and B-1, A-2 and B-2) to represent genotypically matings A and B in Figure 16-6. Shaded genotype must be incorrect.

16-7B-1). But under experimental conditions the reciprocal cross yields sons with white eyes, not dull red as expected from the present explanation.

We can account for the experimental results, however, by assuming that the Y chromosome carries no locus for w. Therefore, the first cross—$X^{w^+} X^{w^+}$ ♀ × X^w Y ♂—should give $X^{w^+} X^w$ (dull-red daughters) and X^{w^+} Y (dull-red sons) (Figure 16-13 A-2); and the reciprocal cross—$X^w X^w$ ♀ × X^{w^+} Y ♂—should give $X^{w^+} X^w$ (dull-red daughters) and X^w Y (white sons) (Figure 16-7B-2), as is found experimentally.

Further studies with *Drosophila* indicate that many other traits also depend upon genes that have loci in the X but not the Y chromosome. Such X-linked loci are said to be *X-limited*. Note that X-limited loci need not affect traits related to sex. In man, for example, one type of red–green colorblindness is due to an X-limited gene. Color-blind women ($X^c X^c$) who marry normal men (X^C Y) usually have normal daughters ($X^C X^c$) and colorblind sons (X^c Y). Another X-limited gene is responsible for bleeder's disease, hemophilia (type A). (R)

16.6 On rare occasions, homologous chromosomes, and hence the genes they carry fail to segregate during meiosis.

Other results with the X-limited locus for white eye in *Drosophila* are surprising. When white females ($X^w X^w$) are crossed with dull-red males (X^{w^+} Y), nearly all F_1 progeny are dull-red daughters ($X^{w^+} X^w$) or white sons (X^w Y). One or two flies per thousand progeny, however, are white daughters or dull-red sons (Figure 16-8).

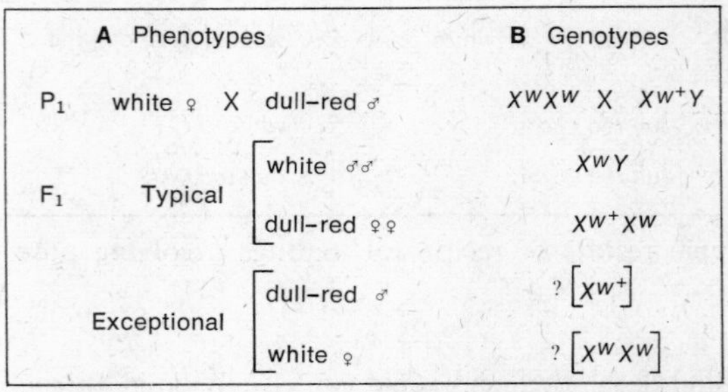

Figure 16-8 Progeny obtained in crosses involving eye-color genes in *Drosophila*.

Neither contamination nor errors in tallying the phenotypes can account for these exceptional flies. Nor can mutation, since the frequency of mutation from w^+ to w (or the reverse) is several orders of magnitude less than the observed frequency of exceptional flies.

Since the exceptional F_1 females are white-eyed, each must carry $X^w X^w$ (Figure 16-8B). The only source of X^w is the mother, which carried two such chromosomes. Each dull-red son must carry X^{w^+}, which could be contributed only by the father. Let us consider how these genotypes might arise.

In a normal meiosis of the *Drosophila* female, the two X's synapse to form a tetrad. After segregation four nuclei are produced by the end of meiosis, each of which contains one X (Figure 16-9A). One of these nuclei will become the egg nucleus. Sometimes, however, the segregation of the strands of the X chromosome tetrad is aberrant, as follows:

1. At anaphase I both dyads may occasionally go to the same pole (Figure 16-9B); hence, none go to the other pole. The latter nucleus, containing no sex chromosomes, then undergoes the second meiotic division to produce two nuclei, neither one having an X. The other nucleus, with two dyads, undergoes the second division to produce a pair of daughter nuclei that contain two X's apiece, one from each dyad. The failure of dyads to disjoin at anaphase I thus results in an occasional gamete having a 50 per cent chance of carrying two X chromosomes and a 50 per cent chance of carrying none.

2. The first meiotic division may be normal, producing two daughter nuclei with one X dyad each. The second meiotic division, however, may occasionally proceed abnormally in one of these nuclei (Figure 16-9C), so the strands of one X dyad fail to separate at anaphase II, both going to the same pole. Consequently, one daughter nucleus will contain two X's and the other will have none. Overall, meiosis in which the monads of one dyad fail to disjoin at anaphase II will result in an occasional gamete having a 25 per cent chance of carrying two X's, a 25 per cent chance it will carry none, and a 50 per cent chance it will carry one.

By either mechanism, *nondisjunction* of chromosomes results in some gametes having two X's, and some having none. Since the X chromosome carries a locus for w, chromosomal nondisjunction can account for the failure of w loci to segregate.

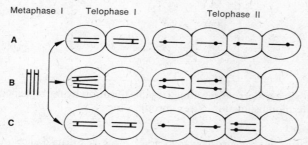

Metaphase I   Telophase I   Telophase II

A

B

C

Figure 16-9 Consequences of normal segregation of X chromosomes (row A) and of its failure to occur (rows B and C).

If nondisjunction occurs during meiosis in a white female ($X^w X^w$), the exceptional gamete will be either $X^w X^w$ or 0, where zero indicates the absence of a sex chromosome. Normal sperm produced by a dull-red male ($X^{w^+} Y$) will carry either X^{w^+} or Y. Figure 16-10 shows the different exceptional zygotes which can result from random fertilization of these exceptional eggs by the normal sperm. Type 1 is expected to be dull red; type 2, white; type 3, dull red; and type 4, of undetermined eye color. Experimentally, type 1 (which rarely survives) is dull red; type 2 is white female; type 3 is dull-red male; and type 4 is lethal. Cytological evidence that each exception white female contains two X's and one Y, being type 2, and that each exceptional dull-red male contains one X but no Y, being type 3, confirms the occurrence of nondisjunction. Autosomes can also undergo nondisjunction during meiosis. (R)

16.7   Some Y-linked genes have no loci in the X chromosome. Some sex-linked loci occur both in X and Y chromosomes.

Although XY *Drosophila* are fertile males, X0 individuals (such as type 3 in Figure 16-10) are sterile males. The Y chromosome thus seems to be necessary for male fertility, but not viability, and is found to contain several male-fertility genes that have no loci in the X. Consequently, these male-fertility genes are said to be *Y-limited*. An otherwise diploid individual carrying one or more unpaired loci is said to be *hemizygous* in this respect. For example, Y-limited and X-limited loci are hemizygous in the *Drosophila* male—only half of the zygotes he produces receive his Y-limited loci; similarly, only half (the other half) receive his X-limited loci.

Since X and Y chromosomes synapse during meiosis and are thus (by definition) homologs, we expect them to have one or more loci in common. Several such sex-linked loci probably code for the centromere. In *Drosophila* both the X and Y have a special region near the centromere, the *collochore*, where the homologs synapse, and remain so even in the absence of chiasmata.[2] Also in *Drosophila*, X and Y chromosomes each carry the locus of the gene for bobbed bristles, apparently one of the loci in the nucleolus organizer region whose wild-type alleles are transcribed to rRNA.

Exceptional Eggs	Normal Sperm	Exceptional Offspring
$X^w X^w$	X^{w^+}	(1) $X^{w^+} X^w X^w$
$X^w X^w$	Y	(2) $X^w X^w Y$
0	X^{w^+}	(3) $X^{w^+} 0$
0	Y	(4) Y 0

Figure 16-10   Possible genotypes resulting from fertilization by normal sperm of exceptional eggs produced after nondisjunction of sex chromosomes.

[2] In *Drosophila* all pairs of homologs have collochores. Since chiasmata do not occur during meiosis in the *Drosophila* male, the collochores function to hold homologs together so that they can segregate properly at anaphase I.

SUMMARY AND CONCLUSIONS

From the phenotypic effects of genes in parents and the phenotypic ratios in progeny produced by random fertilization of gametes, it is expected (and can be demonstrated) that (1) the segregation of the members of a pair of genes parallels exactly the segregation of homologous segments of a pair of chromosomes during meiosis; and (2) the independent segregation of different pairs of genes parallels exactly the independent segregation of paired segments located in different pairs of chromosomes during meiosis.

In many higher organisms, in addition to nonsex chromosomes, that is, autosomes, one sex has XX and the other XY sex chromosomes. Loci occur in pairs, of course, in paired autosomes and in paired X chromosomes. Although some sex-linked loci are paired in XY individuals (these make X and Y homologous), others are restricted to one type of sex chromosome and are, therefore, X-limited or Y-limited. Thus, the morphological differences between the X and Y homologs are paralleled by differences in the loci they carry.

When the members of a pair of normally segregating genes fail to segregate, that is, when they undergo nondisjunction, so does the entire chromosome pair in which they are located. This was detected in the present chapter because the male and female parents carried different alleles at an X-limited locus.

GENERAL REFERENCES

Mendel, G. 1866. Experiments in plant hybridization. Translated in *Principles of genetics*, fifth edition, Sinnott, E. W., Dunn, L. C., and Dobzhansky, Th. New York: McGraw-Hill Book Company, 1958, pp. 419–443; in *Genetics, the modern science of heredity*, Dodson, E. O. Philadelphia: W. B. Saunders Company, 1956, pp. 285–311; also in *Classic papers in genetics*, Peters, J. A. (Editor), Englewood Cliffs, N.J.: Prentice-Hall, Inc., 1959, pp. 1–20. (Original proofs of segregation and independent segregation of gene pairs.)

Gregor Mendel (1822–1884). (Courtesy of the Moravian Museum in Brno, Czechoslovakia.)

Mendel, G. 1867. Part of a letter to C. Nägeli. Supplement I in *Genetics*, second edition, Herskowitz, I. H., Boston: Little, Brown and Company, 1965. (A summary of his discovery of segregation and independent segregation.)

Ohno, S. 1967. *Sex chromosomes and sex-linked genes: monographs on endocrinology*, Vol. 1. New York: Springer-Verlag.

SPECIFIC SECTION REFERENCES

16.4   Morgan, T. H. 1910. Sex limited inheritance in *Drosophila*. Science, 32: 120–122. Reprinted in *Classic papers in genetics*, Peters, J. A. (Editor), Englewood Cliffs, N.J.: Prentice-Hall, Inc., 1959, pp. 63–66.

16.6   Bridges, C. B. 1916. Non-disjunction as proof of the chromosome theory of heredity. Genetics, 1: 1–52, 107–163.

16.7   Cooper, K. W. 1964. Meiotic conjugative elements not involving chiasmata. Proc. Nat. Acad. Sci., U.S., 52: 1248–1255. (Discusses collochores.)

SUPPLEMENTARY SECTIONS

S16.1a   Many human traits are due to single pairs of segregating genes.

The study of human genetics is complicated by the fact that, unlike other species of plants and animals, our species is not bred experimentally. Because of this scientific difficulty special methods of investigation have to be employed. These include the *pedigree*, *family*, *population*, and *twin* methods.

The pedigree method uses phenotypic records of familes (family trees or genealogies) extending over several generations. In recording pedigrees particular symbols are used by convention (Figure 16-11). In a pedigree chart a square or ♂ represents a male, a circle or ♀ represents a female; filled-in symbols represent persons affected by the anomaly under discussion. In contrast, the family method utilizes the pheno-

Calvin Blackman Bridges (1889–1938). [From Genetics, 25: 1 (1940).]

types only of parents and their offspring; that is, it uses data that span only one generation.

Let us consider a few of the many human traits that can be shown to be based upon the action of a single pair of segregating genes.

Albinism. Albinism, or lack of melanin pigment, is a rare disease that occurs approximately once per 20,000 births. Studies of families and of pedigrees like the one in Figure 16-12 reveal that albinism occurs in *a a* homozygotes, whereas persons with *A a* and *A A* genotypes are normally pigmented, that is, nonalbino. This hypothesis is substantiated by the following:

1. Both parents of albinos may be nonalbino. This may be explained by both parents being heterozygotes (*A a* × *A a*) and producing *a a* progeny.

2. Albinism appears most frequently in progeny sharing a common ancestor. For example, in Sweden and Japan, the percentage of marriages that are between cousins is 20 to 50 per cent among the parents of albino children, but is less than 5 per cent in the general population. Since albinos are rare, so is the *a* gene. Accordingly, the chance of obtaining the *a a* individual is lessened if the parents are unrelated; when the first parent is *A a* or *a a*, the unrelated parent will most likely be *A A*. On the other hand, if the first parent is *A a* or *a a*, marriage to a related individual increases the chance that the second parent will carry the *a* allele received from their common ancestor.

3. The relative frequencies of nonalbino and

albino children can be predicted for nonalbino parents that have two children, one or both of whom are albino. In such marriages, which must be *A a* × *A a*, the chance that the first or any subsequent child will be nonalbino is $\frac{3}{4}$ and that it will be albino $\frac{1}{4}$. Accordingly, of all two-child families whose parents are *A a*, $\frac{3}{4}$ will have the first child nonalbino, and of these $\frac{3}{4}$ will also have the second child nonalbino. Thus, we expect $\frac{9}{16}$ ($\frac{3}{4}$ of $\frac{3}{4}$) of all two-child families from heterozygous parents will have two nonalbino children, and be excluded from our sample. Our sample will include the following, however: families whose first child is normal ($\frac{3}{4}$) and second child is albino ($\frac{1}{4}$)—these will make up $\frac{3}{16}$ ($\frac{1}{4}$ of $\frac{3}{4}$) of all two-child families; families where the reverse is true ($\frac{3}{4}$ of $\frac{1}{4}$)—these will make up another $\frac{3}{16}$ of all two-child families; and families in which both children are albino ($\frac{1}{4}$ of $\frac{1}{4}$)—these will make up $\frac{1}{16}$ of all two-child families. On the average, then, every seven albino-containing families scored should contain six normal children (three from each of the two kinds of families containing one albino) and eight albinos (three from each of the two kinds of families containing one albino, and two from each family containing two albinos), so that the ratio expected is 3:4 as nonalbino:albino. The ratio actually observed closely approximates the expected one.

The observed proportions of nonalbino and albino children in families of three,

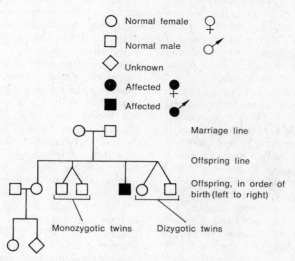

Figure 16-11   Symbols used in human pedigrees.

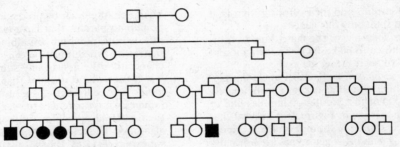

Figure 16-12   Pedigree of albinism in man.

four, or more children from normal parents also fit the expected proportions calculated in a similar manner.

4. Marriage between two albinos produces only albino children, as expected genetically from $a\,a \times a\,a$.

5. Twins arising from the same zygote (*monozygotic* or *identical twins*) are both either albino or nonalbino. Since ordinarily such twins are genetically identical, both are expected to be normal, $A\,A$ or $A\,a$, or albino, $a\,a$. Twins arising from different zygotes (*dizygotic, nonidentical,* or *fraternal twins*), however, are no more likely to be the same with respect to albinism than any two children of the same parents.

Woolly Hair. The anomaly of *woolly hair* is a rare trait in Norwegians. Pedigree studies have shown that woolly hair can be attributed to the presence of a gene, W, persons with normal hair being $w\,w$. The $W\,W$ genotype probably does not occur because, barring mutation, the mating required to produce it would have to be between two W-containing, rare, woolly-haired individuals. Accordingly, an affected person is considered to be a heterozygote. Therefore, when woolly-haired individuals ($W\,w$) marry normal-haired individuals ($w\,w$), it is expected and found that approximately 50 per cent of children have woolly hair and 50 per cent have normal hair.

Thalassemia. Certain kinds of anemia have a genetic basis. Two special kinds occur among native or emigrated Italians. One type, usually fatal in childhood, is called *thalassemia major* or *Cooley's anemia*; the other type, a more moderate anemia, is called *thalassemia minor* or *micro-cytemia*. Pedigree and family studies show that both parents of t. major children have t. minor, and all the data support the hypothesis that individuals with t. major are homozygotes, $t\,t$; persons with t. minor are heterozygotes, $T\,t$; and normal persons, $T\,T$. More than 100,000 people in Italy have been classified as $t\,t$, $T\,t$, or $T\,T$.

MN Blood Type. Numerous family studies of blood type provide us with data we can use to test whether particular blood types are due to segregating alleles. Before discussing these studies, however, it is necessary to describe what is meant by a *blood type* or *blood group*.

Human blood contains red blood corpuscles (RBC) carried in a fluid medium, the plasma. The corpuscles carry on their surfaces substances called *antigens*, whereas the plasma contains substances called *antibodies*. An antibody is a very specific kind of molecule capable of reacting with and binding a specific antigen. This reaction may be visualized as a lock (antibody) which holds or binds a particular key (antigen). If a rabbit is injected with a suitable antigenic material —say foreign red blood corpuscles—certain antibody-producing cells of the rabbit will manufacture specific antibodies that will combine with the foreign RBC. The antigen–antibody complex then formed often causes the blood to clump, or agglutinate.

When injected into rabbits, red blood corpuscles from different persons result in the formation of a number of different RBC-specific antibodies. When rabbit's blood is centrifuged carefully, one obtains a pellet fraction which contains the RBC and other large inclusions and a clear solution called the *serum*. The specific antibodies are found in the serum, which for that reason is called the *antiserum*. Two very distinct antisera which are formed in rabbits using human RBC are an antiserum for an M antigen, called anti-M, and another for an antigen, called anti-N. Since the red blood corpuscles from any person are agglutinated or clumped either in one or in both of these antisera, all persons can be classified by their RBC antigens as belonging to either M, or N, or MN blood group, respectively.

Parents and their offspring can be tested for MN blood type. The results of such family studies are summarized in Figure 16-13. Parents of type 6 produce offspring in the proportion of 1:2:1 for M : MN : N blood types. This result suggests that these blood types are due to the action of a single pair of segregating genes. If we

Parents	Children		
	M	M N	N
1. M x M	All	—	—
2. N x N	—	—	All
3. M x N	—	All	—
4. M N x N	—	½	½
5. M N x M	½	½	—
6. M N x M N	¼	½	¼

Figure 16-13 Distribution of MN blood-group phenotypes in different human families.

let M represent the gene for blood antigen M, and N, the allele that produces blood antigen N, mating 6 must be, genetically, $M N \times M N$ and the offspring 1 $M M$: 2 $M N$: 1 $N N$. Note that $M N$ individuals have both M and N blood antigens. All the other family results also are consistent with the genetic explanation proposed.

Rhesus factor. Another antiserum that can be prepared determines the presence or absence of what is called the *Rhesus* or *Rh factor.* If RBC from Rhesus monkeys are injected into rabbits, a second injection of Rhesus blood given sometime later will be clumped. This can be explained by the presence of an antigen carried on the Rhesus RBC. The antigen involved is called Rh; the antibodies induced are anti-Rh.

When testing human RBC by injecting them into rabbits having anti-Rh antibodies in their serum, it was found that 85 per cent of all white people have blood which will clump—that is, these people have the Rh antigen on their RBC, and are thus considered Rhesus-positive, or Rh-positive. The remaining 15 per cent have blood which does not clump—these people are Rhesus-negative, or Rh-negative. Accordingly, 85 per cent of the white population have the same Rh antigen as have Rhesus monkeys, and 15 per cent do not. A combination of family and pedigree studies shows that presence of Rh antigen in man is due to the presence of a gene we can represent by R, and its absence by the allele r in homozygous condition.

Gates, R. R. 1946. *Human genetics,* 2 vols., New York: The Macmillan Company.

Stern, C. 1960. *Principles of human genetics,* second edition. San Francisco: W. H. Freeman and Company, Publishers.

Whittinghill, M. 1965. *Human genetics and its foundations.* New York: Van Nostrand Reinhold Publ. Corp.

S16.1b   Genes of eucaryotic organisms have multiple alleles that are detected by their phenotypic effects.

Each different chemical modification of the A (or B) gene in the rII region of the $\phi T4$ chromosome (see Sections 7.6 and S10.4a and Figure 10-7) is a different allele which was detected because it produced a phenotypic change from r^+ to r. Although different alleles do not necessarily change the chemical nature of a translation product (Section 9.1), we can investigate whether, as expected, genes of eucaryotic organisms have multiple alleles that can be detected by the phenotypic changes they produce.

ABO Blood Type. Two antisera, called anti-A and anti-B, different from those discussed in the preceding supplement, can be prepared against human RBC. When tested with these antisera, the RBC from different persons are found to behave in one of four ways: they are clumped in anti-A (these persons have blood type A), clumped in anti-B (representing blood type B), clumped in both antisera (blood type AB), and clumped in neither antiserum (type O).

Family studies of these *ABO blood types* give the phenotypic results shown in Figure 16-14. Note that two kinds of results are obtained from $A \times O$ and also from $B \times O$ parents. In each case one kind of result (marriage types 9 and 11) can be explained if one assumes that the non-O parent is a heterozygote for the gene for O. Let i be the gene for O blood type and I^A the allele for A blood type. Then the parents are thus: in marriages type 9, $I^A i \times i i$; in type 10, $I^A I^A \times i i$; and in 13, $i i \times i i$. In order to explain 11 and 12 we shall have to assume the presence of a gene I^B for B blood type, which is also an allele of i and from which it segregates. Then mating 11 is $I^B i \times i i$ and 12 is $I^B I^B \times i i$. We are supposing that in the former case the alternative allelic form of i is I^A, whereas in the latter case it is I^B,

Parents	Children			
	A	A B	B	O
7. A B x A B	¼	½	¼	—
8. A B x O	½	—	½	—
9.* A x O	½	—	—	½
10.* A x O	All	—	—	—
11.* B x O	—	—	½	½
12.* B x O	—	—	All	—
13. O x O	—	—	—	All

Figure 16-14 Distribution of ABO blood-group phenotypes in different human families.
*In some families.

so that I^A and I^B are also alleles. The results of marriage types 7 and 8 confirm this hypothesis, the heterozygote $I^A I^B$ appearing as AB blood type. All the results indicated in the table are now explained genetically.

Blood-Type Isoalleles. Persons with A blood type really have one of three different subtypes, resulting from slightly different allelic forms of I^A—I^{A1}, I^{A2}, and I^{A3}. Three slightly different allelic alternatives are known also for I^B, producing three subtypes within the B blood group. Thus, alleles which at first seem identical may prove to be different when tested further. Such alleles are said to be *isoalleles*. Other examples of isoalleles have been detected because different alleles show varied responses to the presence of nonallelic genes, to environmental changes such as temperature and humidity, or to agents that modify mutation rates. Of course, the number of isoalleles detected will depend upon how many different phenotypic criteria are employed to compare alleles, and how small a phenotypic difference is perceptible.

In the case of ABO blood type, it is usually adequate in medicine to classify individuals on the basis of alleles that produce type A and type B antigens. When one studies the genetic relationships among individuals in detail, however, it is often necessary to deal with all seven alleles.

Isoalleles in Drosophila. In different wild *Drosophila* populations, designated as 1, 2, and 3, the venation of the wings is complete and identical. In the hybrids produced by all possible crosses between these populations, the venation is unchanged. This result suggests that all three populations are genotypically identical in this respect. The venation in a mutant strain is incomplete, however, the cubitus vein being interrupted (*ci, cubitus interruptus*) in homozy-

gotes (Figure 16-15). Hybrids formed by crosses between *ci ci* and wild populations 1 or 2 have complete venation. But the hybrid between *ci ci* and wild flies from population 3, $ci^{+3} ci$, shows the cubitus vein interrupted. Furthermore, the relationship between ci^{+3} and ci can be shown to be an effect of this gene pair rather than a modifying effect of some other gene pair. Apparently, then, the ci^+ allele in population 3 is different from that in populations 1 and 2. We are dealing, therefore, with two isoalleles in a multiple allelic series.

Eye color in Drosophila. Another series of multiple alleles in Drosophila involves eye color. In this case the different alleles can be arranged in a series that shows different grades of effect on eye color, ranging from dull red to white: dull red (w^+), coral (w^{co}), wine (w^w), eosin (w^e), blood (w^{bl}), apricot (w^a), buff (w^{bf}), and white (w). The w^+ allele is the allele commonly found in wild-type flies. Proceeding in the series from w^+ to w, one can think of the different alleles as being less and less efficient in producing the same kind of biochemical product.

We have already described isoalleles for genes normally expressed in individuals living in the wild (wild-type isoalleles). Isoalleles for mutant genes (mutant isoalleles) also occur. For instance, it has been shown that the gene producing white eye color in different strains of *Drosophila* is actually composed of a series of multiple isoalleles (w^1, w^2, w^3, etc.).

Self-sterility in Nicotiana. Among sexually reproducing plants it is not uncommon to find that self-fertilization does not occur even though the male and female gametes are produced at the same time on a given plant. The reason for this has been studied in the tobacco plant, *Nicotiana*. It was found that if pollen grains fall on the stigma of the same plant they fail to grow down the style to the ovary. When this happens self-fertilization is impossible. A clue to an explanation for this phenomenon comes from the observation that different percentages of pollen from a completely self-sterile plant may grow down the style of other plants.

The results of certain crosses are shown in Figure 16-16. Genetically identical pistils are exposed to pollen from the same plant (A), from a second one (B), and from a third (C). No pollen, approximately half, and approximately all, respectively, are able to grow down the style of the host. Note, in B, that although all the pollen used came from one diploid individual, only half of it will grow on its host. Recall that the stigma and style are diploid tissues, whereas pollen grains are haploid. These results suggest that most important in determining whether or not a pollen grain can grow down a style is not the

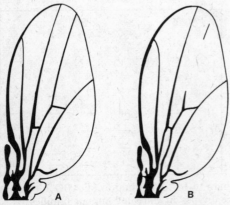

Figure 16-15 Normal (A) and cubitus interruptus (B) wings of *D. melanogaster*.

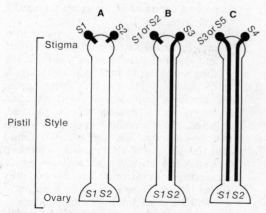

Figure 16-16   Multiple alleles for cross- or self-sterility.

but since these fail to grow, we must assume that any pollen grain carrying an *s* allele also present in the host pistil will fail to grow. Excluding the possibility of a mutation, the other allele in the host pistil cannot also be *s1*, since one *s1* would have had to be received from a paternal pollen grain growing down a maternal style that carried *s1* as one of its two alleles. Since the second allele in the pistils illustrated cannot be either *s1* or *s3*, let us call it *s2*. The other half of pollen from the pistil parent thus will contain *s2*, and also fail to grow in self-pollination (case A). In B the pollen grains that fail to grow are either *s1* or *s2* (adhering to the law of parsimony); their precise identity cannot be determined, however, without additional tests. In C, since all the pollen grew, one pollen allele must be a different one—call it *s4*. The other pollen allele may be *s3* or a still different one, *s5*. Here again more tests are needed to determine the precise identity.

In these cases the phenotypic alternatives for pollen are to grow or not to grow. Whenever the pollen grains from any one plant are placed on a given stigma and both alternatives occur, the phenotypes are in a 1:1 ratio. These results and others are consistent with the assumptions made, that self- and cross-sterility is regulated by a single pair of genes which form a multiple allelic series. Some species prove to have 50 or more multiple alleles forming a series responsible for self-sterility, group sterility, or group incompatibility.

diploid genotype of its parent but the haploid genotype of the pollen.

Let us assume that self- or cross-sterility is due to a single pair of genes. Call *s3* the allele contained in the pollen which permits pollen to grow in case B. The pollen grains from the host plant furnishing the pistil cannot contain *s3*, or the pollen would be able to grow on their own parent; and they cannot (case A). So, the host pistil tissue in this experiment cannot contain *s3*, and one of its alleles can be called *s1*. Then, half of the pollen from the host individual will carry *s1* (case A);

Bateman, A. J. 1947. Number of s-alleles in a population. Nature, Lond., 160: 337.

Nolte, D. J. 1959. The eye-pigmentary system of *Drosophila*. Heredity, 13: 219–281.

Race, R. R., and Sanger, R. 1962. *Blood groups in man*, fourth edition. Philadelphia: F. A. Davis Company.

Wiener, A. S., and Wexler, I. B. 1958. *Heredity of the blood groups*. New York: Grune & Stratton, Inc.

QUESTIONS AND PROBLEMS

1. Distinguish between segregation and independent segregation.

2. In Andalusian fowl, black feathers × white feathers produces only blue feathers in F₁. F₁ × F₁ produces in F₂ ¼ black, ½ blue, and ¼ white. Define gene symbols and give the genotypes of parents and offspring.

3. In chickens, nonbarred feather ♀ × barred feather ♂ produces only barred F₁. Barred ♀ × nonbarred ♂ produces in F₁ all sons barred, all daughters nonbarred. Define gene symbols and give the genotypes of parents and offspring.

4. Assume that you have radioactive rRNA and *Drosophila* of the following sex chromo-some compositions: XO, XY, XYY, XXY, XXYY. How would you show that rRNA is transcribed both from X and Y templates?

5. What types of gametes are formed by the following genotypes if all gene pairs segregate independently? Give gametic frequencies.
   a. *A a B B C c*
   b. *D d E E f f G g*
   c. *M m N n O o*
   d. *A a B b C c D d*

6. What proportion of the offspring of the following crosses will be completely heterozygous if all gene pairs segregate independently?

a. $Aa\ Bb \times Aa\ BB$
b. $AA\ BB\ cc \times Aa\ Bb\ Cc$
c. $Aa\ Bb\ Cc \times AA\ Bb\ cc$
d. $AA' \times A''\ A'''$

The six questions that follow involve eye color in *Drosophila melanogaster*. Let bw = gene producing brown eyes (bw^+ = normal allele), st = gene producing scarlet eyes (st^+ = normal allele), and v = gene producing vermilion eyes (v^+ = normal allele).

7. If pure stocks are used, reciprocal matings of brown-eyed by dull-red-eyed flies produce only dull-red-eyed F_1 progeny. What can you decide about the genetic basis for brown eye color from this result? Crossing F_1 individuals produces dull-red and brown flies in the proportion 3:1 in the F_2. What is your answer now to the preceding question?

8. With reference to question 7, what phenotypic results would you expect from mating a pure stock brown female with
   a. an F_1 dull-red male?
   b. an F_2 brown male?

9. A single mating produced 68 dull-red and 21 scarlet *Drosophila*; the reciprocal mating produced 73 dull red and 23 scarlet. Give the genotypes of parents and offspring. Are the genes involved X-limited? Explain.

10. A mating of a brown-eyed fly and a scarlet (or red)-eyed fly produces only dull-red F_1 progeny. $F_1 \times F_1$ gives the following phenotypic results: 375 dull red, 116 brown, 115 scarlet, 33 white.
    a. With respect to the eye pigment, in what way are brown flies and scarlet flies defective?
    b. How many gene pairs are involved?
    c. Where are these genes located?
    d. Give the genotypes of F_1 and F_2 individuals.

11. Vermilion (also red)-eyed $\male \times$ dull-red-eyed $\female$ produces only dull-red progeny. The reciprocal cross, dull-red $\male \times$ vermilion $\female$ produces dull-red daughters and vermilion sons in the F_1.
    a. Where is the locus for the gene for vermilion?
    b. Give the genotypes of all parents and offspring mentioned.
    c. What phenotypic and genotypic results do you expect from a mating of an F_1 dull-red daughter and a vermilion male?

12. Females homozygous for the genes producing brown and vermilion eye color are white-eyed.
    a. What can you conclude about the poly-

peptide products of the genes for scarlet and vermilion?
   b. A female homozygous for v mated to a male homozygous for st produces red sons and dull-red daughters in the F_1. Give the genotypes of parents and offspring.

13. In *Drosophila*, mutations in X-limited genes that are lethal in males but are viable when heterozygous in females can be induced, detected, and maintained in cultures grown at room temperature. Suppose it is found that 100 per cent of such mutations induced by mutagen Y are still lethal to males grown at a certain lower temperature, but that only 80 per cent of those induced by mutagen Z are still lethal at the lower temperature.
    a. Discuss the possible molecular basis of mutagenic action by Y and Z.
    b. Name one mutagen expected to produce an effect like Y, and one expected to produce an effect like Z.

14. A lack of neuromuscular coordination, *ataxia*, occurs in the pedigrees of certain families in Sweden. How can you explain that one form of this rare anomaly occurs in certain families where the parents are apparently unrelated, and another form occurs in other families where the parents are first cousins?

15. A baby has blood type AB. What can you tell about the genotypes of its parents? What would you predict about the blood types of children it will later produce?

16. If one parent is A blood type and the other is B, give their respective genotypes if they produced a large number of children whose blood types were
    a. all AB.
    b. half AB, half B.
    c. half AB, half A.
    d. $\frac{1}{4}$ AB, $\frac{1}{4}$ A, $\frac{1}{4}$ B, $\frac{1}{4}$ O.

17. A father with blood-group types M and O has a child with MN and B blood types. What genotypes are possible for the mother?

18. A woman belonging to blood group B has a child with blood group O. Give their genotypes and those which, barring mutation, the father could not have.

19. How many different genotypes are possible when there are four different alleles of a single gene?

20. Describe how you would test whether the genes for white eye color in two different populations of *Drosophila* were alleles, isoalleles, or nonalleles.

21. For each of the following matings involving *Nicotiana* give the percentage of aborted pollen tubes and the genotypes of the offspring.

a. *s1 s2* ♂ × *s1 s3* ♀
b. *s1 s3* ♂ × *s2 s4* ♀
c. *s1 s4* ♂ × *s1 s4* ♀
d. *s3 s4* ♂ × *s2 s3* ♀

22. Could you prove the existence of multiple allelism in an organism that only reproduces asexually? Explain.

23. How many different diploid genotypes are possible in offspring from crosses in which both parents are undergoing independent segregation for the following numbers of pairs of heterozygous genes—1, 2, 3, 4, *n*?

24. Suppose an albino child also suffers from thalassemia minor. Give the most likely genotypes of the parents.

25. Under what circumstances would sons fail to receive a Y chromosome from their father?

26. A husband and wife both have normal vision, although both their fathers are red–green colorblind. What is the chance that their first child will be
a. a normal son?
b. a normal daughter?

c. a red–green colorblind son?
d. a red–green colorblind daughter?

27. A hemophilic father has a hemophilic son. Give the most probable genotypes of the parents and child.

28. What proportion of all genes causing hemophilia type A is found in human males? Justify your answer.

29. A normal man of blood type AB marries a normal woman of O blood type whose father was hemophilic. What phenotypes should this couple expect in their children and in what relative frequencies?

30. The accompanying diagram is a partial pedigree of the descendants of Queen Victoria of England (I 1) which contains information regarding hemophilia only for generation IV. In this generation, the entire symbol is filled in if the person has hemophilia. A heterozygote for hemophilia would have been represented by a half-filled-in symbol. Fill in the symbols of previous generations using this system.

II 1 = Princess Alice
II 2 = Leopold, Duke of Albany
III 1 = Irene
III 2 = Alexandra
III 3 = Alice
III 5 = Victoria Eugenie

IV 1 = Prince Waldemar of Prussia
IV 3 = Prince Henry of Prussia
IV 8 = Tsarevitch Alexis of Russia
IV 10 = Viscount Trematon
IV 12 = Alfonso
IV 17 = Gonzalo

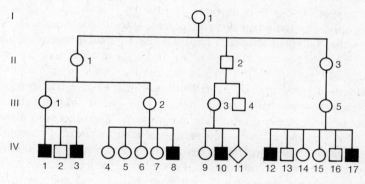

(After J. B. S. Haldane.)

Chapter 17

Of Nuclear Genes—Meiotic and Mitotic Exchanges

In Chapter 15 we assumed that the chiasma which holds the univalents of a bivalent together is cytological evidence that reciprocal recombination has taken place between nonsister chromatids of the tetrad earlier in meiosis. In this chapter we will look at genetic and cytological evidences for such exchanges in meiotic and mitotic divisions, use the relative frequencies of exchanges between nuclear genes to construct recombination linkage maps, and conclude with a brief consideration of nonreciprocal exchanges involving nuclear genes.

17.1 A reciprocal exchange of genetic material takes place between homologous chromosomes in a process called crossing over.

In *Drosophila* the loci for white eyes (*w*) and cut wings (*ct*) are both X-limited and thus are linked to one another. Using pure parents, a white-eyed female with long wings ($w\ ct^+/w\ ct^+$) is crossed to a dull-red-eyed male with cut wings ($w^+\ ct/Y$). Subsequently, F_1 females, $w\ ct^+/w^+\ ct$, and any males are used for the P_2 and the phenotypes of sons only are scored in the F_2 (Figure 17-1). (Because we are scoring sons only, any male can serve as parent, since it contributes its Y, which does not carry the X-limited *w* and *ct* loci). Of the F_2 male progeny 40 per cent are white[1] ($w\ ct^+/Y$), 40 per cent cut ($w^+\ ct/Y$), 10 per cent white and cut ($w\ ct/Y$), and 10 per cent wild type ($w^+\ ct^+/Y$). We expect the F_1 female, $w\ ct^+/w^+\ ct$, to produce equal numbers of $w\ ct^+$ and $w^+\ ct$ gametes and thus to give rise to equal numbers of the two types of sons: half $w\ ct^+/Y$, half $w^+\ ct/Y$. We do obtain equal numbers, but they make up only 80 per cent of the male progeny. The other sons arose from the female gametes $w\ ct$ and $w^+\ ct^+$—new reciprocal combinations of parental genetic material. These gametes were apparently produced by a reciprocal exchange of genetic material between the two X homologs; the exchange process, called *crossing over*, yields equally frequent, reciprocal recombinant, *crossover* chromosomes.

If $w\ ct/w^+\ ct^+$ females are mated with males of unspecified genotype as before, we get results similar to those above. About 80 per cent of the sons carry parental combinations of the two genes, 40 per cent $w\ ct$ and 40 per cent $w^+\ ct^+$; and 20 per cent carry nonparental combinations, 10 per cent $w\ ct^+$ and 10 per cent $w^+\ ct$. Since the frequency of recombinant sons is the same for either type of female parent, the distance between the loci for *w* and *ct* on the X chromosome seems to be the same for all *Drosophila* females. We expect crossing over (hence, recombinant progeny) to be more frequent when two loci are farther apart, and less frequent when closer together. (R)

---

[1] By convention, the progeny are referred to by their mutant traits only.

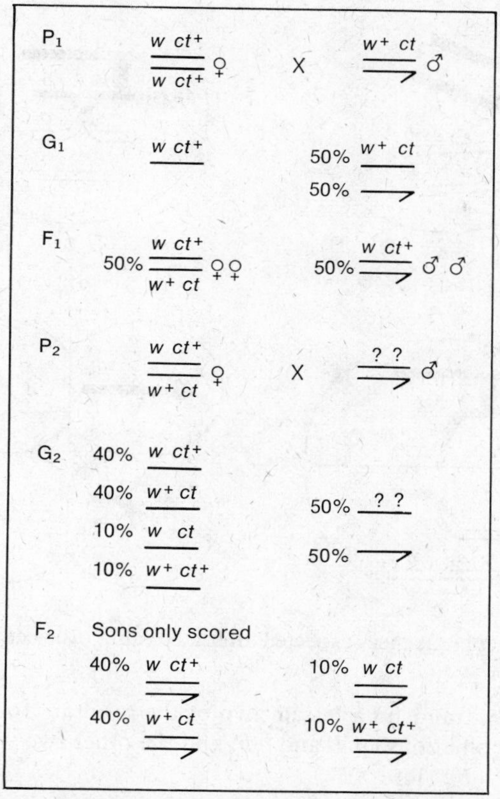

P₁ — $\dfrac{w\ ct^+}{w\ ct^+}$ ♀   X $w^+\ ct$ ♂

G₁ — $w\ ct^+$ 50% $w^+\ ct$
                     50% ⟶

F₁ — 50% $\dfrac{w\ ct^+}{w^+\ ct}$ ♀♀   50% $w\ ct^+$ ♂♂

P₂ — $\dfrac{w\ ct^+}{w^+\ ct}$ ♀   X   ? ? ♂

G₂ — 40% $w\ ct^+$
     40% $w^+\ ct$ 50% ? ?
     10% $w\ ct$ 50% ⟶
     10% $w^+\ ct^+$

F₂ — Sons only scored
     40% $w\ ct^+$ 10% $w\ ct$
     40% $w^+\ ct$ 10% $w^+\ ct^+$

Figure 17-1 Crossover frequency between two X-limited loci in *Drosophila*. ——, X; ⟶, Y; G₁, G₂, gametes of P₁, P₂.

17.2 Crossing over may occur between two nonsister strands at a four-stranded stage before diplonema.

A possible sequence of events involved in crossing over is shown in Figure 17-2. In diagram A we see a pair of homologous chromosomes; one carries the mutant genes *a* and *b*, and the other their normal, or wild-type, alleles, *A* and *B*. Meiosis begins, the homologs synapse to form a tetrad, and two nonsister strands exchange equal segments by a crossing over between the loci of *a* and *b*. The precise biochemical mechanism of crossing over (and other types of primary structure recombination between homologs of eucaryotes) is still unknown. A *small* amount of DNA synthesis has been found to occur at the late leptonema–pachynema stage of meiosis, and crossing over has been hypothesized to involve synapsis of DNA's, strand breakage, degradation, and repair synthesis—events that also seem to occur in primary structure recombinations between chromosomes of phages and of bacteria.

As the result of the crossing over, the tetrad later seen at diplonema appears as in diagram B with a chiasma between the *a* and *b* loci. Diagram C shows the recombinant dyads present after completion of the first meiotic division. In diagram D we see the four haploid nuclei of different genotypes produced at the end of the second meiotic division. In summary, if one crossing over event occurs anywhere between the *a* and *b*

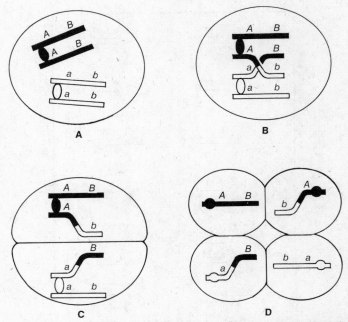

Figure 17-2   Genetic consequences expected after a crossing over between linked genes.

loci of two nonsister strands in a tetrad, two of the resultant four nuclei will contain parental genetic combinations (*A B* and *a b*) and the other two will contain reciprocal crossovers (*a B* and *A b*). (R)

17.3   Studies of recombination between linked genes in *Neurospora* prove that a single crossing over occurs between two strands at a four-stranded stage.

We can use *Neurospora* to test the idea that crossing over occurs at a four-stranded stage. As already mentioned, two haploid nuclei, each from a different mating type, can occur in the same cell of *Neurospora* (Figures 15-9A and 17-3). These two nuclei fuse to form a diploid nucleus with seven pairs of chromosomes. The cell then elongates to form a sac, or ascus. Soon after its formation, the diploid nucleus undergoes meiosis, as diagrammed in Figure 17-3, to produce four haploid nuclei arranged in tandem; the two uppermost nuclei come from one first-division nucleus, the bottom two from the other first-division nucleus. Each haploid nucleus subsequently divides mitotically once, so each meiotic product is present in duplicate within the ascus. We can remove each haploid ascospore from the ascus, grow it by itself, and determine its genotype. Thus, all of the meiotic products derived from a single diploid nucleus can be identified.

Figure 17-4 shows the hypothesized genetic consequences of a single crossing over between two linked loci, *a* and *b* in *Neurospora*. (Of the seven chromosome pairs present, only one need be represented.) As shown, a single crossing over between two nonsister strands at a four-stranded stage would result in two crossover and two noncrossover meiotic products. After dissecting and analyzing many asci of a particu-

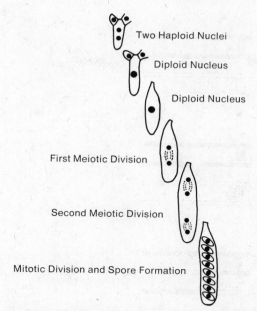

Two Haploid Nuclei

Diploid Nucleus

Diploid Nucleus

First Meiotic Division

Second Meiotic Division

Mitotic Division and Spore Formation

Figure 17-3   Meiosis and mitosis in the formation of a mature ascus in *Neurospora*.

lar dihybrid for linked genes, 90 per cent of the asci were found to have all eight spores noncrossovers for the two loci; in the remaining 10 per cent, four of the eight spores were crossovers. Never were all eight spores from a single sac crossovers. Had a single crossing over involved exchange between all the strands in two homologs, all eight spores from an ascus would have been found to be crossovers. It appears, therefore, that crossing over occurs only between two nonsister strands at a four-stranded stage, as depicted in Figures 17-4 and 17-5.[2]

Further evidence that a crossing over involves two of four strands is supplied by cytological observations of chiasmata.

17.4   Genetically detected crossovers are in a one-to-one correspondence with cytologically detected recombinant chromosomes.

What is the cytological evidence for the occurrence of crossing over? As expected, the frequency of chiasmata seen during meiosis has been found to be positively corre-lated with the frequency of crossing over during meiosis, as determined from crossover

[2] Genetic evidence that a crossing over occurs between two of four strands can be obtained also from gametes that retain not one but two or more strands of a tetrad. This explanation would be supported by finding a gamete that carries two homologous strands, one a crossover and the other a noncrossover. A suitable system for this test is found in *Drosophila* females having *attached-X's*, that is, whose two X's are not free to segregate because they are joined at their centromere regions by a common centromere. During meiosis such an attached-X replicates once, and the four arms synapse to form a tetrad; this yields two meiotic products, each carrying an attached-X, and two products devoid of X chromosomes. Using females whose attached-X's are dihybrid and scoring their female progeny, one finds attached-X's having one arm a crossover and one a noncrossover (Figure 17-6). Although this evidence also supports the idea that crossing over is between two of four strands, it does not eliminate the possibility (whereas the *Neurospora* evidence does) that a single crossing over sometimes makes all strands of two homologs crossovers.

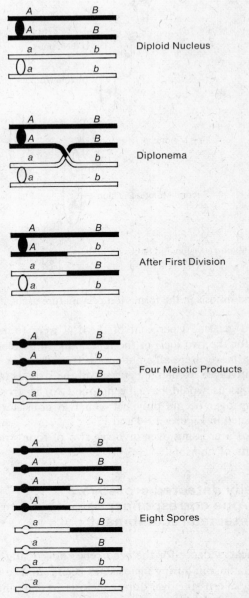

Figure 17-4 Crossing over at a four-stranded stage of meiosis in *Neurospora* and the occurrence of both crossovers and noncrossovers in the mature ascus.

frequency. Note that we detect crossing over by genetic analysis of progeny, that is, by growing progeny, observing their phenotypes, and scoring them as crossovers and noncrossovers. Since crossing over ordinarily involves two homologous chromosomes essentially identical in appearance under the microscope, crossover strands generally have the same appearance as parental strands. We can, however, detect crossover strands by cytological means, and can also correlate crossovers genetically and cyto-

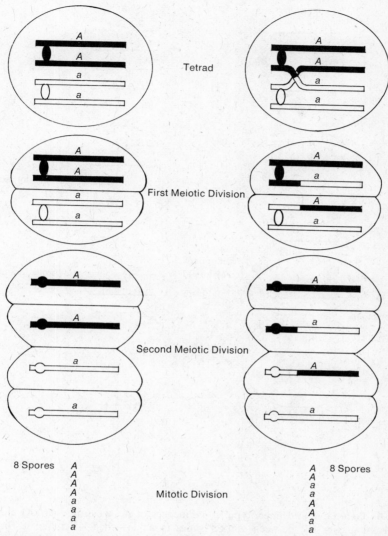

Figure 17-5 Arrangement of spores in the *Neurospora* ascus when segregation occurs at the first meiotic division (left) and at the second meiotic division (right), as determined by the absence and presence, respectively, of a chiasma between the segregating genes and the centromere. (Note that in Figure 17-4 the alleles at the *a* locus segregated in the first meiotic division, whereas those at the *b* locus segregated in the second.)

logically, by using a dihybrid for linked genes in which one homolog differs physically from its partner on both sides of the loci being tested—for example, one homolog only may have knobs close to each of the marker genes, as indicated in Figure 17-7. Under these circumstances, cytological examination of progeny shows that non-crossovers always retain the original parental chromosomal morphology (having both knobs or neither), and that crossovers always have a recombinational chromosome morphology (having one knob), as predicted from the type of special homologs used. (R)

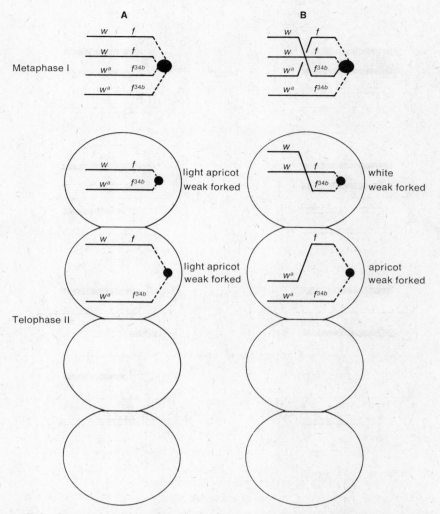

Figure 17-6 Genotypic and phenotypic consequences of no crossing over (A) and of one type of crossing over (B) between marker genes in an attached-X female of *Drosophila*. f^{34b}/f^{34b}, normal bristles; f^{34b}/f, weakly forked bristles; f/f, strongly forked bristles.

17.5 Crossover frequencies can be used to measure the relative distances between linked loci.

In accordance with our previous expectation (Sections 10.3 and 17.1) the greater the distance between two loci, the greater should be the chance for a crossing over to occur between them and the greater the frequency of crossover strands. Therefore, we shall use relative frequencies of crossovers to indicate relative distances between linked loci. By definition, a *crossover unit* is that distance between linked genes which results in 1 crossover per 100 postmeiotic products. If 10 per cent of the tetrads in *Neurospora* undergo a single crossing over between the linked loci *a* and *b*, 5 per cent of all spores will contain crossover strands. (Note that 5 per cent of the spores—not 10 per cent—contained crossover strands because only half the strands in a tetrad are crossovers.)

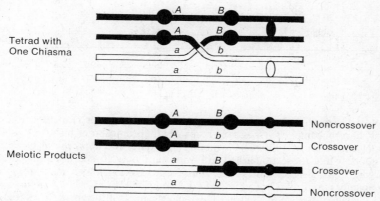

Figure 17-7 Correlation between genetic and cytological crossovers.

Thus, the distance between *a* and *b* loci is five crossover units.[3] In general, when loci are sufficiently close together (as in the preceding example), the crossover percentage, hence the distance between genes in crossover units, is expected to be one half the frequency of crossing over.

17.6 Crossover frequencies can be used to construct a linear genetic map.

In *Drosophila* the arrangement of three X-limited loci—*y* (yellow body color), *w* (white eyes), and *spl* (split bristles)—can be determined from crossover data, equating crossover units with map units. Dihybrid females $y w/y^+ w^+$, $y spl/y^+ spl^+$, and $w spl/w^+ spl^+$ are crossed to appropriate double-mutant males, and the following crossover map distances are obtained: *y* to *w*, 1.5; *y* to *spl*, 3.0; and *w* to *spl*, 1.5. Since the crossover distance between *y* and *spl* equals the sum of the crossover distances from *y* to *w* and from *w* to *spl*, the genetic map thus defined is linear, *y w spl* or *spl w y*. When the positions of other X-linked genes are mapped relative to the three studied above, with *y* arbitrarily assigned the position zero, all are found to be arranged in a linear order (Figure 17-8).

Since a linkage map for the X chromosome of *Drosophila* shows the genes *y*, *w*, *spl*, and *ct* (cut wings) taking their respective positions at 0, 1.5, 3.0, and 20 map units, *ct* and *spl* are 17 map units apart. The $spl\ ct^+/spl^+\ ct$ dihybrid thus should produce 17 per cent recombinant, or crossover, progeny (8.5 per cent $spl^+\ ct^+$ and 8.5 per

---

[3] Crossover frequency can be measured in several ways in *Neurospora*:

a. Spores are tested from each sac (two to five per sac are sufficient) to determine whether or not the sac carries a crossover in the region under investigation. In the *a-b* example above, 10 per cent of the sacs would have crossovers, 90 per cent would not. Since each sac in the 10 per cent group contains four spores that are crossovers and four that are not, crossover frequency would be 5 per cent.

b. All the spores from many sacs are mixed, then a random sample of spores is taken and tested. This method would also give 5 per cent recombination with *a-b* and is similar to the sampling procedure involved in determining crossover frequency in animal sperm.

c. One randomly chosen spore from each sac is tested; the others are discarded. Again, 5 per cent crossovers are obtained. This procedure resembles the situation in many females (including *Drosophila* and human beings) in which one random product of meiosis normally enters the egg and the others are lost.

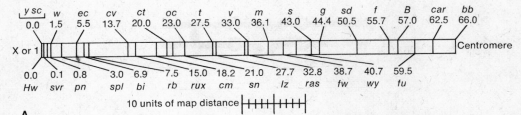

A

Figure 17-8 Crossover maps of *D. melanogaster*. (A) Crossover map of commonly used loci in the X chromosome. (B) Crossover maps of all chromosomes but the Y, showing the principal loci known as of 1925. The symbol ! designates the most useful types; +, those nearly as good; while those unmarked are important only in special connections. (After T. H. Morgan, C. B. Bridges, and A. H. Sturtevant.) Recent, much more complete, maps of all chromosomes are found in Lindsley, D. L., and Grell, E. H. 1968. *Genetic variations in* Drosophila melanogaster. Washington, D.C.: Carnegie Institution of Washington. Publ. No. 627.

KEY TO SYMBOLS

SYMBOL	NAME	SYMBOL	NAME
y	yellow body color	*sn*	singed—bristles and hairs curled and twisted
Hw	Hairy-wing—extra bristles on wing veins, head, and thorax	*oc*	ocelliless—ocelli absent; female sterile
sc	scute—absence of certain bristles, especially scutellars	*t*	tan body color
svr	silver body color	*lz*	lozenge—eyes narrow and glossy
pn	prune eye color	*ras*	raspberry eye color
w	white compound eyes and ocelli	*v*	vermilion eye color
spl	split bristles	*m*	miniature wings
ec	echinus—large and rough textured eyes	*fw*	furrowed eyes
bi	bifid—proximal fusion of longitudinal wing veins	*wy*	wavy wings
		s	sable body color
rb	ruby eye color	*g*	garnet eye color
cv	crossveinless—crossveins of wings absent	*sd*	scalloped wing margins
		f	forked—bristles curled and twisted
rux	roughex—eyes small and rough	*B*	Bar—narrow eyes
cm	carmine eye color	*fu*	fused longitudinal wing veins; female sterile
ct	cut—scalloped wing edges	*car*	carnation eye color
		bb	bobbed—short bristles

cent *spl ct*). Such a result is obtained, but only under special conditions. Observed crossover frequencies fluctuate considerably because of variations in sample size and in genetic and environmental factors which act during or after crossing over.[4] (R)

---

[4] Consider, in more detail, the basis for variability in observed crossover frequencies between particular loci. In small samples it is very likely that, by chance, the observed values will deviate considerably in both directions from the standard map distance. As the size of the sample increases, the observed value will more closely approach the standard one. Standard distances, therefore, are determined only after large numbers of progeny have been scored.

The relative viability of different phenotypic classes is another factor influencing observed crossover frequency. The phenotypic expression of a + allele is usually more viable than that of its mutant forms. For example, the phenotypically white, cut sons in Section 17.1 are not as viable as the normal (wild-type) sons; although both types are equally frequent as zygotes, the former fail to complete their development more often than the latter, and therefore, are relatively less frequent when the adults are scored. Zygotes destined to become either white or cut males are also less viable than zygotes destined to produce wild-type males. Whenever phenotypes are scored after some long developmental period, much of the error due to differential viability may be avoided by providing optimal culture conditions.

Variability in crossover frequency may be due also to factors—such as temperature, nutrition, age of the female, and presence of specific genes—which influence the process of crossing over.

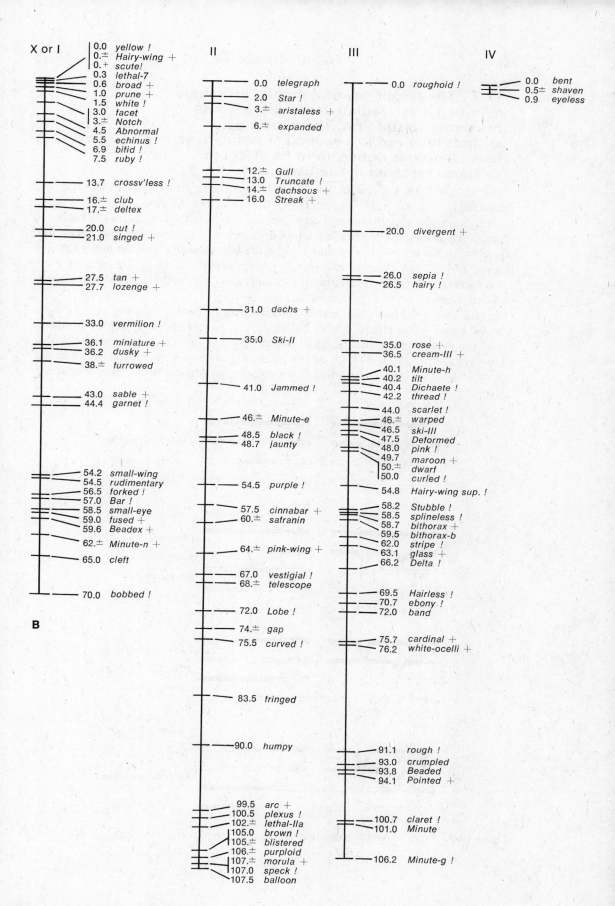

X or I

0.0	yellow !
0.±	Hairy-wing +
0.+	scute!
0.3	lethal-7
0.6	broad +
1.0	prune +
1.5	white !
3.0	facet
3.±	Notch
4.5	Abnormal
5.5	echinus !
6.9	bifid !
7.5	ruby !
13.7	crossv'less !
16.±	club
17.±	deltex
20.0	cut !
21.0	singed +
27.5	tan +
27.7	lozenge +
33.0	vermilion !
36.1	miniature +
36.2	dusky +
38.±	furrowed
43.0	sable +
44.4	garnet !
54.2	small-wing
54.5	rudimentary
56.5	forked !
57.0	Bar !
58.5	small-eye
59.0	fused +
59.6	Beadex +
62.±	Minute-n +
65.0	cleft
70.0	bobbed !

B

II

0.0	telegraph
2.0	Star !
3.±	aristaless +
6.±	expanded
12.±	Gull
13.0	Truncate !
14.±	dachsous +
16.0	Streak +
31.0	dachs +
35.0	Ski-II
41.0	Jammed !
46.±	Minute-e
48.5	black !
48.7	jaunty
54.5	purple !
57.5	cinnabar +
60.±	safranin
64.±	pink-wing +
67.0	vestigial !
68.±	telescope
72.0	Lobe !
74.±	gap
75.5	curved !
83.5	fringed
90.0	humpy
99.5	arc +
100.5	plexus !
102.±	lethal-IIa
105.0	brown !
105.±	blistered
106.±	purploid
107.±	morula +
107.0	speck !
107.5	balloon

III

0.0	roughoid !
20.0	divergent +
26.0	sepia !
26.5	hairy !
35.0	rose +
36.5	cream-III +
40.1	Minute-h
40.2	tilt
40.4	Dichaete !
42.2	thread !
44.0	scarlet !
46.±	warped
46.5	ski-III
47.5	Deformed
48.0	pink !
49.7	maroon +
50.±	dwarf
50.0	curled !
54.8	Hairy-wing sup. !
58.2	Stubble !
58.5	splineless !
58.7	bithorax +
59.5	bithorax-b
62.0	stripe !
63.1	glass +
66.2	Delta !
69.5	Hairless !
70.7	ebony !
72.0	band
75.7	cardinal +
76.2	white-ocelli +
91.1	rough !
93.0	crumpled
93.8	Beaded
94.1	Pointed +
100.7	claret !
101.0	Minute
106.2	Minute-g !

IV

0.0	bent
0.5±	shaven
0.9	eyeless

17.7 The frequency of a second crossing over in a given region decreases with its proximity to the first. The choice of strands involved in a second crossing over, however, does not seem to be affected by those involved in the first.

We have seen that a chiasma is good evidence that a crossing over has occurred. Accordingly, since several chiasmata usually hold together the univalents of a bivalent, two (or more) crossing overs may occur between two loci. To distinguish the resultant types of crossovers, the strands in a tetrad are labeled 1, 2, 3, and 4; 1 and 2 are sister strands with the normal alleles, and 3 and 4 are sister strands with the mutant alleles (Figure 17-9). Three types of two crossing overs per tetrad, or *double crossing over*, are possible: two-strand, three-strand, and four-strand. Note that three-strand double crossing over can occur in two ways.

Figure 17-9 also shows the genetic consequences of double crossing over in these tetrads. From a two-strand double crossing over, two of the four meiotic products are of the parental type, that is, noncrossovers (*A B C* and *a b c*), and two are *double crossovers* (*A b C* and *a B c*). (A double crossover is characterized by a switch in the position of the middle gene relative to the end genes.) A three-strand double crossing

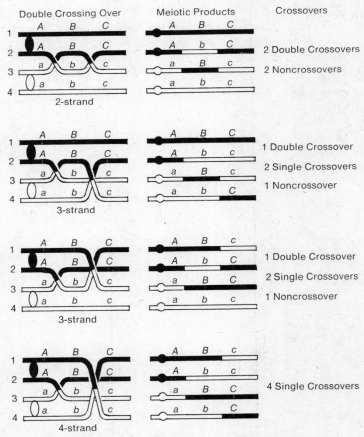

Figure 17-9 Types of double crossing over and their genetic consequences.

over produces one double crossover, two *single crossovers*, and one noncrossover. (A single crossover is characterized by a switch in the position of one end gene relative to the other two markers.) A four-strand double crossing over yields four single crossover strands. Thus, each type of double crossing over gives rise to a characteristic set of crossover and noncrossover strands. Furthermore, each set differs from the set of products resulting from a single crossing over: two single crossovers and two noncrossovers.

A crossing over in one region of the tetrad can sometimes interfere with the occurrence of another in the same tetrad; that is, sometimes the frequency of double crossing over is less than might be expected. For example, if the frequency of a single crossing over in one region is 0.10, and in an adjacent region is 0.10, then the frequency of both single crossing overs occurring simultaneously, that is, double crossing over, should be 0.10 × 0.10, or 0.01—if one crossing over does not affect the other. If the frequency of double crossing over were actually less than 0.01, we would say that *crossing-over interference* had occurred. Since, in practice, we score crossovers, not the crossing overs that produce them, the occurrence of crossing-over interference is determined by comparing the observed with the expected frequency of double crossovers. The expected frequency of double crossovers (say between *a* and *c* in the gene sequence *a b c*) is calculated by multiplying the frequency of observed single crossovers in one region (*a-b*) by the frequency of observed single crossovers in an adjacent region (*b-c*). Crossing-over interference between two loci increases as the distance between them decreases. For example, in *Drosophila* crossing-over interference is 100 per cent for distances up to 10 to 15 map units; in other words, no double crossovers occur within about 15 map units. As the distance between linked loci increases above 15 map units, however, crossing-over interference decreases and eventually disappears. In the last event, even though several to many crossing overs may normally occur between them, two loci can only undergo a maximum of 50 per cent recombination relative to each other (as explained in Section S17.7), at which time they are segregating independently.

In some experiments with *Neurospora*, all four types of double crossing over occur with equal frequency. From this result we can see that the strands undergoing one crossing over are not affected by those undergoing another. In other words, there seems to be no *chromatid interference* in cases of double (or multiple) crossing over.

17.8 The order of three linked genes can be determined from their double crossover frequencies.

Consider a cross in *Drosophila* in which a female heterozygous for three X-limited loci, *A B C/a b c*, is mated with any male. The frequencies of the various phenotypes in male progeny are shown at the left in Figure 17-10. These values correspond to frequencies of the different genotypes in the gametes of the trihybrid parent. By merely scanning this table, we can tell which is the middle gene in the sequence; it is the one that switches least often from the original gene combinations (*A B C* and *a b c*), since only the middle gene requires double crossing over for a switch. Consequently, *c* is the middle gene; and the sequence is *a c b* or *b c a*. At the right in Figure 17-10, the data are presented with the genes listed in their correct order so that the conclusion may be more apparent.

A B C	0.31	A C B	0.31
a b c	0.31	a c b	0.31
A b c	0.14	A c b	0.14
a B C	0.14	a C B	0.14
A B c	0.01	A c B	0.01
a b C	0.01	a C b	0.01
A b C	0.04	A C b	0.04
a B c	0.04	a c B	0.04
	1.00		1.00

Figure 17-10   Phenotypic results in sons from a cross of a dihybrid for X-limited genes in *Drosophila*.

17.9   Incomplete linkage maps are available for genes in man, mouse, maize, and *Neurospora*.

Whenever the number of segregating gene pairs under study is considerably larger than the number of chromosome pairs, the number of groups of recombinationally linked genes approaches (and sometimes equals) the number of chromosome pairs. Hence, the maximum number of *recombinational linkage groups* equals the haploid chromosome number (N). Utilizing crossover frequency, genetic recombinational *linkage maps* of chromosomes have been made for many multicellular organisms. Figures 17-11 through 17-14 give such linkage maps for a considerable number of genes in man, mouse, maize, and *Neurospora*.

Some comments are in order with regard to the making of linkage maps from crossover data. Recall that double crossovers occur when the distance between two loci is large. When the region between these two loci is insufficiently marked, some double crossovers will escape detection, being scored as noncrossovers. Accordingly, the detected map distance will be shorter than it would be had the distance been determined, using markers between the two loci, as the sum of shorter distances within which no double crossovers could have occurred. The longest linkage maps (and, whenever possible, standard linkage maps) are made, therefore, from distances obtained from single crossovers between closely linked genes.

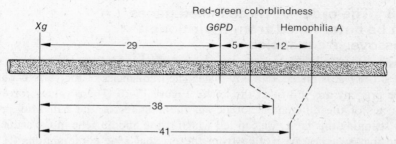

Figure 17-11   Tentative genetic recombinational linkage map of a segment of the human X chromosome. The numbers given are the values for the crossover map distance found in five separate studies. The loci mapped are the *Xg* (blood group) locus, the *G6PD* (glucose-6-phosphate dehydrogenase) deficiency locus, the red–green colorblindness locus, and the hemophilia locus.

17.10   In rare instances, crossing over occurs in nuclei entering mitosis.

Drosophila females, $y\ sn^+/y^+\ sn$, carry the mutant gene for yellow body color (y) in one X chromosome and the mutant gene for singed bristles (sn) in the other; they normally are wild type; that is, they have a gray body color and straight bristles. On rare occasions, however, a pair of adjacent spots of tissue in a wild-type background will be yellow with straight bristles, and gray with singed bristles. Such twin spots prove to be the result of *mitotic crossing over* in a somatic cell. Figure 17-15 illustrates the mitotic consequences of an exchange between nonsister chromatids of a pair of synapsed homologs. If the chromatids separate at anaphase as in A, subsequent mitoses will give rise to spots of different appearance. If separation occurs as in B, though, no such difference will result.

Mitotic crossing over is not restricted to sex chromosomes. Mitotic crossing over can also occur in germ-line nuclei, such as in gonial cells, that undergo mitosis. It also occurs in maize, yeast, and fungi such as *Aspergillus*, which undergoes meiosis and has a definite sexual cycle. Mitotic crossing over also occurs in fungi that are not known to undergo meiosis; it is detected, for example, in the mold *Penicillium notatum* in the diploid nucleus produced by the fusion of two genetically different haploid nuclei present in the same cell because of hyphal fusion. The frequency of recombinants produced by mitotic crossing over can sometimes be used to map the chromosomes of organisms without meiosis. We should keep in mind, though, that the rarity of such crossing over indicates that it is an abnormal genetic event, perhaps a type of mutation.

17.11   Postmeiotic segregation sometimes occurs in fungi.

After meiosis occurs in the *Neurospora* heterozygote $A\ a$, each of the four meiotic products usually gives rise to identical daughter nuclei by mitosis. Consequently, the spores in the mature ascus are in the relative order $A\ A\ A\ A\ a\ a\ a\ a$ when segregation occurs in the first meiotic division (as occurs, for instance, when there is no crossing over between the centromere and the A locus); or $A\ A\ a\ a\ A\ A\ a\ a$, $A\ A\ a\ a\ a\ a\ A\ A$, or $a\ a\ A\ A\ A\ A\ a\ a$ when segregation occurs in the second meiotic division (as when, for instance, a single crossing over occurs between the A locus and the centromere) (see Figure 17-5).

Sometimes asci are found to have an ascospore sequence of $A\ A\ a\ A\ a\ A\ a\ a$. Such an ordering indicates that the two middle meiotic products of the four were genetically hybrid; and each segregated in the next mitotic division to produce A and a daughter nuclei. Such postmeiotic segregation is also found to occur in other fungi.

17.12   Nonreciprocal recombinant chromosomes sometimes arise in cells that undergo meiosis or mitosis.

In *Neurospora* the exchange of genetic material between chromatids is nearly always a reciprocal exchange. Relatively rarely, however, nonreciprocal recombinant chromosomes are found. To find out how this comes about, let us examine recombination in the diploid $a\ \overline{x+}\ b/A\ \overline{+y}\ B$, where $\overline{x+}$ and $\overline{+y}$ are different mutant alleles at a locus bordered by the closely linked loci a and b. Since $\overline{x+}/\overline{+y}$ heterozygotes

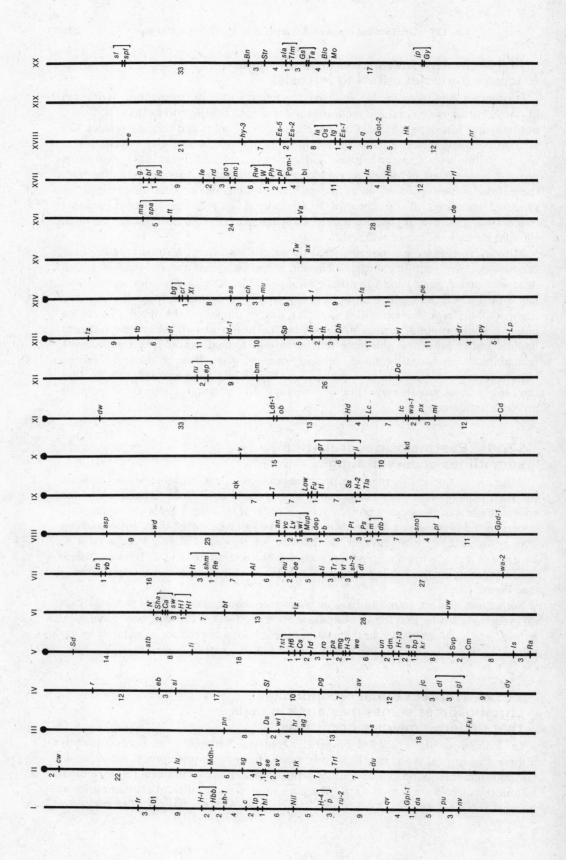

Figure 17-12   Genetic recombinational linkage groups of the mouse, *Mus musculus*. (Courtesy of Margaret C. Green, The Jackson Laboratory.) Symbols for dominant genes are capitalized, those for recessive genes are in lower case letters. Loci whose order is uncertain are not italicized in the figure, and brackets indicate that the order within the bracketed group has not been established. The knobs indicate the location of the centromere (where it is known).

SYMBOL	NAME	SYMBOL	NAME
a	nonagouti	*ft*	flaky-tail
ag	agitans	*Fu*	Fused
Al	Alopecia	*fz*	fuzzy
an	anemia	*g*	low glucuronidase
asp	audiogenic seizure prone	*gl*	grey-lethal
av	Ames waltzer	*go*	angora
ax	ataxia	*Got-2*	Glutamate oxalate transaminase-2
b	brown	*Gpd-1*	Glucose-6-phosphate dehydrogenase
bf	buff		
bg	biege	*Gpi-1*	Glucosephosphate isomerase
bl	blebbed	*gr*	grizzled
Blo	Blotchy	*Gs*	Greasy
bm	brachymorphic	*Gy*	Gyro
Bn	Bent-tail	*H-1*	Histocompatibility-1
bp	brachypodism	*H-2*	Histocompatibility-2
bt	belted	*H-3*	Histocompatibility-3
c	albino	*H-4*	Histocompatibility-4
Ca	Caracul	*H-6*	Histocompatibility-6
Cd	Crooked	*H-13*	Histocompatibility-13
ch	congenital hydrocephalus	*Hbb*	Hemoglobin β-chain
Cm	Coloboma	*Hd*	Hypodactyly
cr	crinkled	*hf*	hepatic fusion
Cs	Catalase	*Hk*	Hook
cw	curly whiskers	*hl*	hair-loss
d	dilute	*Hm*	Hammer-toe
da	dark	*hr*	hairless
db	diabetes	*Ht*	Hightail
Dc	Dancer	*hy-3*	hydrocephalus-3
de	droopy-ear	*Id-1*	Isocitrate dehydrogenase
dep	depilated	*jc*	Jackson circler
Dh	Dominant hemimelia	*jg*	jagged tail
di	Ames dwarf	*ji*	jittery
dl	downless	*jp*	jimpy
dm	diminutive	*kd*	kidney disease
dr	dreher	*kr*	kreisler
Ds	Disorganization	*la*	leaner
dt	dystonia musculorum	*Lc*	Lurcher
du	ducky	*ld*	limb deformity
dw	dwarf	*Ldr-1*	Lactate dehydrogenase regulator
dy	dystrophia muscularis	*le*	light ear
e	extension	*ln*	leaden
eb	eye blebs	*Low*	Low ratio
ep	pale ear	*Lp*	Loop tail
Es-1	Esterase-1	*ls*	lethal spotting
Es-2	Esterase-2	*lst*	Strong's luxoid
Es-5	Esterase-5	*lt*	lustrous
f	flexed tail	*lu*	luxoid
fi	fidget	*Lv*	δ-aminolevulinate dehydratase
Fkl	Freckled	*lx*	luxate
fr	frizzy	*lz*	lizard
fs	furless	*m*	misty

SYMBOL	NAME	SYMBOL	NAME
ma	matted	*sh-2*	shaker-2
mc	marcel	*Sha*	Shaven
Mdh-1	Malate dehydrogenase	*shm*	shambling
mg	mahogany	*si*	silver
mi	micropthalmia	*Sl*	Steel
Mo	Mottled	*sla*	sex-linked anemia
mu	muted	*sno*	snubnose
Mup	Major urinary protein	*Sp*	Splotch
N	Naked	*spa*	spastic
Nil	Neonatal intestinal lipidosis	*spf*	sparse fur
nr	nervous	*Ss*	Serum serological
nu	nude	*stb*	stubby
nv	Nijmegen waltzer	*Str*	Striated
ob	obese	*sv*	Snell's waltzer
oe	open eyelids	*Svp*	Seminal vesicle protein
ol	oligodactyly	*sw*	swaying
Os	Oligosyndactylism	*T*	Brachury
p	pink-eyed dilution	*Ta*	Tabby
pa	pallid	*tb*	tumbler
pe	pearl	*tc*	truncate
pf	pupoid fetus	*tf*	tufted
pg	pigmy	*Tfm*	Testicular feminization
Pgm-1	Phosphoglucomutase-1	*tg*	tottering
Ph	Patch	*th*	tilted head
pi	pirouette	*ti*	tipsy
pn	pugnose	*tk*	tail-kinks
Ps	Polysyndactyly	*Tla*	Thymus leukemia antigen
Pt	Pintail	*tn*	teetering
pu	pudgy	*To*	Tortoise
px	postaxial hemimelia	*tp*	taupe
py	polydactyly	*Tr*	Trembler
Q	Quinky	*Trf*	Transferrin
qk	quaking	*Tw*	Twirler
qv	quivering	*un*	undulated
r	rodless retina	*uw*	underwhite
Ra	Ragged	*v*	waltzer
rd	retinal degeneration	*Va*	Varitint-waddler
Re	Rex	*vb*	vibrator
rl	reeler	*vc*	vacillans
ro	rough	*vl*	vacuolated lens
ru	ruby eye	*vt*	vestigial
ru-2	ruby-eye-2	*W*	Dominant spotting
Rw	Rump-white	*wa-1*	waved-1
s	piebald	*wa-2*	waved-2
sa	satin	*wd*	waddler
Sd	Danforth's short tail	*we*	wellhaarig
se	short ear	*wi*	whirler
sf	scurfy	*wl*	wabbler-lethal
sg	staggerer	*Xt*	Extra toes
sh-1	shaker-1		

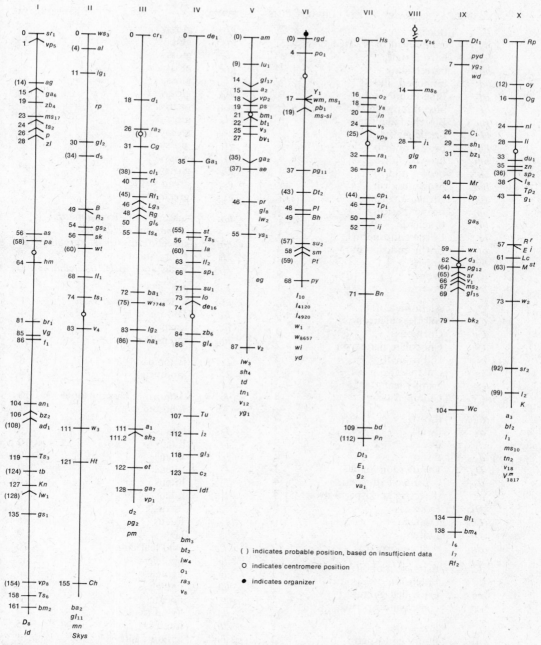

Figure 17-13   Genetic recombinational linkage groups of maize. (Courtesy of M. G. Neuffer, L. Jones, and M. S. Zuber. 1968. *The mutants of maize.* Madison, Wis.: Crop Science Society of America.)

SYMBOL	NAME	CHROMOSOME	SYMBOL	NAME	CHROMOSOME
a_1	anthocyaninless	3	ag	grasshopper resistant	1
α	component of A_1 (see β)	3	al	albescent	2
a_2	anthocyaninless	5	am	ameiotic	5
a_3	anthocyanin	10	an_1	anther ear	1
ad_1	adherent	1	ar	argentia	9
ae	amylose extender	5	as	asynaptic	1

SYMBOL	NAME	CHROMOSOME	SYMBOL	NAME	CHROMOSOME
B	Booster	2	gl_1	glossy	7
β	component of A_1 (see α)	3	gl_2	glossy	2
ba_1	barren stalk	3	gl_3	glossy	4
ba_2	barren stalk	2	gl_4	glossy	4
bd	branched silkless	7	gl_5	glossy	5
Bf_1	Blue fluorescent	9	gl_6	glossy	3
bf_2	blue fluorescent	10	gl_8	glossy	5
Bh	Blotched aleurone	6	gl_9	glossy	10
bk_2	brittle stalk	9	gl_{11}	glossy	2
bm_1	brown midrib	5	gl_{15}	glossy	9
bm_2	brown midrib	1	gl_{17}	glossy	5
bm_3	brown midrib	4	gl_a	glossy	8
bm_4	brown midrib	9	gs_1	green stripe	1
Bn	Brown aleurone	7	gs_2	green stripe	2
bp	brown pericarp	9			
br_1	brachytic	1	hm_1	susceptibility to *Helmintho-sporium carbonum*	1
bt_1	brittle endosperm	5	hm_2	susceptibility to *H. carbonum*	9
bt_2	brittle endosperm	4	Hs	Hairy sheath	7
bv_1	brevis	5	Ht	Resistance to *H. turcicum*	2
bz_1	bronze	9			
bz_2	bronze	1	I	(see C_1)	9
			id	indeterminate growth	1
C_1	Aleurone color	9	Idf	Diffuse	4
c_2	colorless aleurone	4	ij	iojap	7
Cg	Corngrass	3	in	intensifier	7
Ch	Chocolate pericarp	2			
cl_1	chlorophyll	3	j_1	japonica	8
cp_1	collapsed	7	j_2	japonica	4
cr_1	crinkly leaf	3			
Ct	Clumped tassel	8	K	Abnormal chromosome 10	10
			Kn	Knotted	1
d_1	dwarf	3	l_1	luteus	10
d_2	dwarf	3	l_2	luteus	10
d_3	dwarf	9	l_6	luteus	9
d_5	dwarf	2	l_7	luteus	9
D_8	Dwarf (dominant)	1	l_8	luteus	10
de_1	defective endosperm	4	l_{10}	luteus	6
de_{16}	defective endosperm-dwarf	4	l_{4120}	luteus	6
Dt_1	Dotted	9	l_{4920}	luteus	6
Dt_2	Dotted	6	la	lazy	4
Dt_3	Dotted	7	Lc	Red leaf color	10
du_1	dull endosperm	10	lg_1	liguleless	2
			lg_2	liguleless	3
E_1	Esterase mobility	7	lg_3	liguleless	3
E^j	Extension of japonica	10	li	lineate	10
eg	expanded glumes	5	lo	lethal ovule	4
et	etched endosperm	3	lu_1	lutescent	5
			lw_1	lemon white	1
f_1	fine stripe	1	lw_2	lemon white	5
fl_1	floury endosperm	2	lw_3	lemon white	5
fl_2	floury endosperm	4	lw_4	lemon white	4
g_1	golden	10	M^{st}	Modifier of R^{st}	10
g_2	golden	7	mn	miniature seed	2
Ga_1	Gametophyte factor	4	Mr	Mutator of R^m	9
ga_2	gametophyte factor	5	ms_1	male sterile	6
ga_6	gametophyte factor	1	ms_2	male sterile	9
ga_7	gametophyte factor	3	ms_8	male sterile	8
ga_8	gametophyte factor	9			
ga_9	gametophyte factor	4			

SYMBOL	NAME	CHROMOSOME
ms_{10}	male sterile	10
ms_{17}	male sterile	1
$ms\text{-}si$	male sterile-silky (= si_1)	6
na_1	nana	3
nl	narrow leaf	10
o_1	opaque endosperm	4
o_2	opaque endosperm	7
Og	Old-gold stripe	10
oy	oil yellow	10
P	Pericarp and cob color	1
pa	pollen abortion	1
pb_1	piebald	6
pg_2	pale green	3
pg_{11}	pale green	6
pg_{12}	pale green	9
Pl	Purple	6
pm	pale midrib	3
Pn	Papyrescent glume	7
po_1	polymitotic	6
pr	red aleurone	5
ps	pink scutellum (= vp_7)	5
Pt	Polytypic	6
py	pigmy	6
pyd	pale yellow deficiency	9
R_1	Colored aleurone and plant	10
R_2	Colored aleurone	2
ra_1	ramosa	7
ra_2	ramosa	3
ra_3	ramosa	4
Rf_1	Restorer of fertility	3
Rf_2	Restorer of fertility	9
Rg	Ragged	3
rgd	ragged	6
Rp	Resistance to *Puccinia sorghi*	10
rp	susceptibility to *P. sorghi*	2
rt	rootless	3
S^{Kys}	Suppressor of sterility	2
sh_1	shrunken endosperm	9
sh_2	shrunken endosperm	3
sh_4	shrunken endosperm (=$sh\text{-}fl$)	5
si_1	silky (=$ms\text{-}si$)	6
sk	silkless	2
sl	slashed leaf	7
sm	salmon silk	6
sn	sienna	8
sp_1	small pollen	4
sp_2	small pollen	10
spl	small plant	6
sr_1	striate	1
sr_2	striate	10
st	sticky chromosome	4
su_1	sugary endosperm	4
su_2	sugary endosperm	6

SYMBOL	NAME	CHROMOSOME
tb	teosinte branched	1
td	thick tassel dwarf	5
tn_1	tinged	5
tn_2	tinged	10
Tp_1	Teopod	7
Tp_2	Teopod	10
ts_1	tassel seed	2
ts_2	tassel seed	1
Ts_3	Tassel seed	1
ts_4	tassel seed	3
Ts_5	Tassel seed	4
Ts_6	Tassel seed	1
Tu	Tunicate	4
v_1	virescent	9
v_2	virescent	5
v_3	virescent	5
v_4	virescent	2
v_5	virescent	7
v_8	virescent	4
v_{12}	virescent	5
v_{16}	virescent	8
v_{18}	virescent	10
V^m_{1817}	Virescent mutable	10
va_1	variable sterile	7
Vg	Vestigial glumes	1
vp_1	viviparous	3
vp_2	viviparous	5
vp_5	viviparous	1
vp_7	viviparous (= ps)	5
vp_8	viviparous	1
vp_9	viviparous	7
w_1	white seedling	6
w_2	white seedling	10
w_3	white seedling	2
w_{7748}	white seedling	3
w_{8657}	white seedling	6
w^m	white mutable	6
Wc	White cap	9
wd	white deficiency	9
wi	wilted	6
ws_3	white sheath	2
wt	white tip	2
wx	waxy endosperm	9
Y_1	Yellow endosperm	6
Y_8	Lemon yellow endosperm	7
yd	yellow dwarf	6
yg_1	yellow green	5
yg_2	yellow green	9
ys_1	yellow stripe	5
zb_4	zebra striped	1
zb_6	zebra striped	4
zl	zygotic lethal	1
zn	zebra necrotic	10

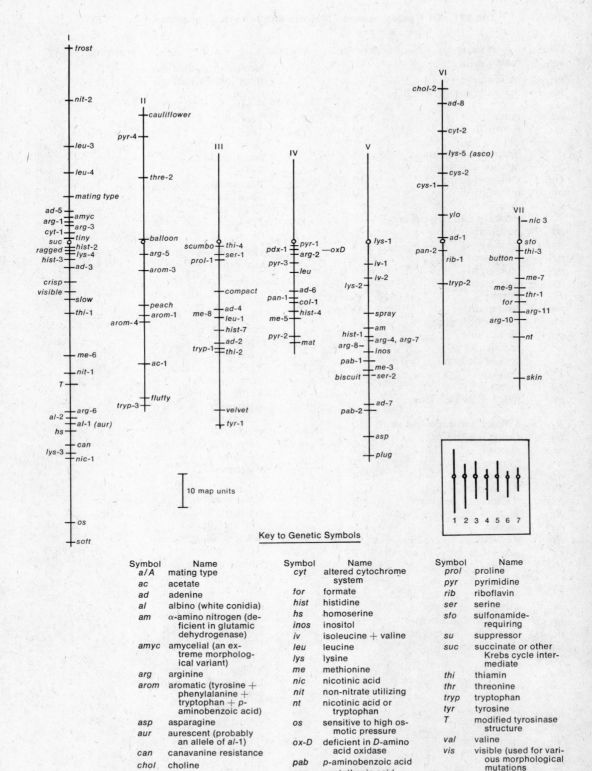

10 map units

Key to Genetic Symbols

Symbol	Name	Symbol	Name	Symbol	Name
a/A	mating type	cyt	altered cytochrome system	prol	proline
ac	acetate			pyr	pyrimidine
ad	adenine	for	formate	rib	riboflavin
al	albino (white conidia)	hist	histidine	ser	serine
am	α-amino nitrogen (deficient in glutamic dehydrogenase)	hs	homoserine	sfo	sulfonamide-requiring
		inos	inositol	su	suppressor
amyc	amycelial (an extreme morphological variant)	iv	isoleucine + valine	suc	succinate or other Krebs cycle intermediate
		leu	leucine		
arg	arginine	lys	lysine		
arom	aromatic (tyrosine + phenylalanine + tryptophan + p-aminobenzoic acid)	me	methionine	thi	thiamin
		nic	nicotinic acid	thr	threonine
		nit	non-nitrate utilizing	tryp	tryptophan
		nt	nicotinic acid or tryptophan	tyr	tyrosine
asp	asparagine	os	sensitive to high osmotic pressure	T	modified tyrosinase structure
aur	aurescent (probably an allele of al-1)	ox-D	deficient in D-amino acid oxidase	val	valine
can	canavanine resistance	pab	p-aminobenzoic acid	vis	visible (used for various morphological mutations)
chol	choline	pan	pantothenic acid		
col	colonial morphology	pdx	pyridoxine	ylo	yellow conidia
cys	cysteine				

Most descriptions refer to nutritional requirements of the corresponding mutants.

occasionally give rise to normal ($\overline{+\ +}$) progeny, whereas $\overline{x+}/\overline{x+}$ or $\overline{+y}/\overline{+y}$ individuals do not, it appears that x and y are mutant sites in the same gene between which recombination can occur to produce the normal allele. Occasionally, asci that contain recombinants in the a-b region are of the type shown in Figure 17-16. This tetrad contains two noncrossover strands ($a \overline{x+} b$ and $A \overline{+y} B$) and two double-crossover strands ($a \overline{+y} b$ and $A \overline{+\ +} B$). Note that since the a-b distance is very short, more double crossing over occurred than expected, hence *negative interference to crossing over* is said to have occurred. The two double-crossover strands here are nonreciprocal. Other exceptional asci that contain nonreciprocal crossovers have one double crossover and three noncrossover strands. Formation of these nonreciprocal recombinant strands appears to involve multiple crossing over. The closer together the two mutant sites, the more frequent are the nonreciprocal recombinants.

In yeast a study of closely linked mutants shows that as much as 1 to 2 per cent of all segregations produce a nonreciprocal exchange, indicating that this may be not a mutational event but perhaps a normal mechanism for recombination of short linked regions. Nonreciprocal exchanges occur in yeast nuclei undergoing mitotic as well as meiotic divisions.

SUMMARY AND CONCLUSIONS

The nonallelic genes in a given chromosome are linked to each other and tend to be transmitted together during nuclear division. Crossing over prevents such linkage from being permanent or complete, however. During meiosis, crossing over often occurs between two nonsister strands in a tetrad and usually produces crossover strands that are reciprocal for the marker genes studied. For closely linked genes the crossover frequency is one half the frequency with which a crossing over (or, as expected, a chiasma) occurs between their loci.

Crossover frequency is expected to be directly related to the distance between genes in a chromosome, one unit of crossover distance being defined as one crossover per hundred postmeiotic cells (spores or gametes). Using the crossover distances between them, it is possible to arrange linked loci in a linear recombination map.

Two loci on the same chromosome may be recombinationally independent during meiosis. This will be true if they are located so far apart that, on the average, one or more crossing overs occurs between them in every tetrad—so that they are recombined 50 per cent of the time, and are, therefore, segregating independently. Such loci can be placed in the same crossover map, however, if, on the average, less than one crossing over per tetrad occurs between each of them and a marker that lies between them.

As the distance between two loci decreases, so does the chance that double crossing over can occur between them in a tetrad—demonstrating crossing-over interference.

Figure 17-14 Genetic recombinational linkage groups of *Neurospora crassa*. The relative sizes and centromere positions (open circles) of the chromosomes are shown at the lower right. The chromosomes and linkage groups are numbered independently. Map distances are only approximate. (Courtesy of Blackwell Scientific Publications Ltd., Oxford, from *Fungal Genetics*, by J. R. S. Fincham and P. R. Day, 1963.) See R. W. Barratt and A. Radford, 1970, *Handbook of biochemistry, selected data for molecular biology*, second edition, H. A. Sober (Editor), Sec. I, pp. 68–78, Cleveland, Ohio: The Chemical Rubber Co., for recent, more complete, linkage groups.

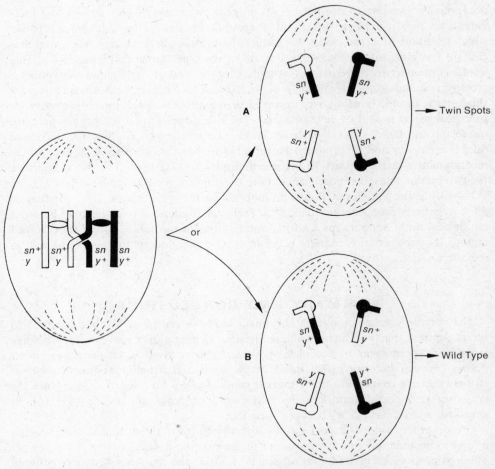

Figure 17-15 Consequences of a mitotic crossing over between the centromere and the locus of *sn* in a somatic cell of the *Drosophila* dihybrid *y sn⁺/y⁺ sn*.

Crossing-over interference is complete within 10 to 15 map units, so that only one crossing over can occur per tetrad within such short distances.

The number of recombinationally linked groups of genes—linkage groups—approaches or equals the N number of nuclear chromosomes. Meiotic crossover maps for *Drosophila*, man, mouse, maize, and *Neurospora* are presented. To avoid the possibility of missing double crossovers due to insufficient markers, standard cross-

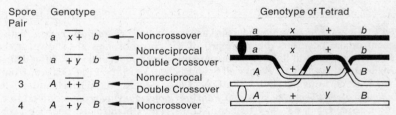

Figure 17-16 Tetrad showing nonreciprocal double crossovers.

over maps are made, whenever possible, using the distances obtained from single crossovers between closely linked genes.

Less often than in meiosis, nuclei that enter mitosis undergo crossing over, producing crossovers that are usually reciprocal. Within short chromosome regions, however, both in mitotic and meiotic cells, nonreciprocal crossovers also occur and, more often than expected, so do double crossovers—exhibiting negative interference. Another exception, in *Neurospora* for example, is that alleles will occasionally segregate during the first mitotic division of a meiotic product.

GENERAL REFERENCES

Fincham, J. R. S., and Day, P. R. 1963. *Fungal genetics*. Oxford: Blackwell Scientific Publications Ltd.

Lewis, K. R., and John, B. 1963. *Chromosome marker*. London: J. & A. Churchill Ltd.

Whitehouse, H. L. K., 1969. *Towards an understanding of the mechanism of heredity*, second edition. London: Edward Arnold (Publishers) Ltd. (Includes a detailed discussion of crossing over.)

SPECIFIC SECTION REFERENCES

17.1   Morgan, T. H. 1911. Random segregation versus coupling in Mendelian inheritance. Science, 34: 384. Reprinted in *Great experiments in biology*. Gabriel, M. L., and Fogel, S. (Editors), Englewood Cliffs, N. J.: Prentice-Hall, Inc. 1955, pp. 257–259.

17.2   Hotta, Y., and Stern, H. 1971. Analysis of DNA synthesis during meiotic prophase in Lilium. J. Mol. Biol., 55: 337–355.

Rhoades, M. M. 1968. Studies on the cytological basis of crossing over. In *Replication and recombination of genetic material*, Peacock, W. J., and Brock, R. D. (Editors), Canberra: Australian Academy of Science, pp. 229–241.

Westergaard, M. 1964. Studies on the mechanism of crossing over. I. Theoretical considerations. Compt. Rend. Trav. Lab. Carlsberg, 34: 359–405.

Thomas Hunt Morgan (1866–1945) was the recipient of a Nobel prize in 1934. (By permission of The American Genetic Association, J. Hered., frontispiece, Vol. 24, No. 416, 1933.)

Whitehouse, H. L. K., and Hastings, P. J. 1965. The analysis of genetic recombination on the polaron hybrid DNA model. Genet. Res., Camb., 6: 27–92. (Molecular explanation of recombination between partner chromosomes in eucaryotic cells.)

17.4   Creighton, H. S., and McClintock, B. 1931. A correlation of cytological and genetical crossing-over in *Zea mays*. Proc. Nat. Acad. Sci., U.S., 17: 492–497. Reprinted in *Classic papers in genetics,* Peters, J. A. (Editor), Englewood Cliffs, N.J.: Prentice-Hall, Inc., 1959, pp. 155–160; also in *Great experiments in biology*, Gabriel, M. L., and Fogel, S. (Editors), Englewood Cliffs, N.J.: Prentice-Hall, Inc., 1955, pp. 267–272.

Stern, C. 1931. Zytologisch-genetische Untersuchungen als Beweise für die Morgansche Theorie des Faktorenaustauschs. Biol. Zbl., 51: 547–587. (Correlates genetic and cytological crossovers.)

17.6   Sturtevant, A. H. 1913. The linear arrangement of six sex-linked factors in *Drosophila*, as shown by their mode of association. J. Exp. Zool., 14: 43–59. Reprinted in *Classic papers in genetics*, Peters, J. A. (Editor), Englewood Cliffs, N.J.: Prentice-Hall, Inc., 1959, pp. 67–78.

17.9   Barratt, R. W., Newmeyer, D., Perkins, D. D., and Garnjobst, L. 1954. Map construction in *Neurospora crassa*. Adv. Genet., 6: 1–93.

Emerson, R. A., Beadle, G. W., and Fraser, A. C. 1935. A summary of linkage studies in maize. Mem. Cornell Univ. Agr. Sta., No. 180.

17.12 Ballantyne, G. H., and Chovnick, A. 1971. Gene conversion in higher organisms: Non-reciprocal recombination events at the rosy cistron in *Drosophila melanogaster*. Genet. Res., Camb., 17: 139–149. (The occurrence of nonreciprocal recombination events, as well as reciprocal events, within the *rosy* region.)

Emerson, S. 1969. Linkage and recombination at the chromosomal level. Pp. 267–360. In *Genetic organization*, Caspari, E. W., and Ravin, A. W. (Editors). New York: Academic Press. (Molecular basis of nonreciprocal exchanges.)

Hurst, D. D., Fogel, S., and Mortimer, R. K. 1972. Conversion-associated recombination in yeast. Proc. Nat. Acad. Sci., U.S., 69: 101–105.

Paszewski, A. 1970. Gene conversion: observations on the DNA hybrid models. Genet. Res., Camb., 15: 55–64. (Molecular model that includes asymmetrical exchanges.)

Curt Stern, about 1950.

Alfred Henry Sturtevant (1891–1970).

SUPPLEMENTARY SECTIONS

S17.7   Recombination between two linked genes is 50 per cent maximally, no matter how many crossing overs occur in the tetrad.

If each tetrad of a given pair of homologs has only a single crossing over, the maximum frequency with which the end genes recombine relative to each other is 0.5. If each of these tetrads has two crossing overs, one might think that the end genes would form new combinations with a frequency greater than 0.5. Examination of Figure 17-9 reveals, however (each type of double crossing over being equally probable), that on the average eight products (single crossovers) will carry a new combination with respect to the end genes, and eight products will not. Of the latter, four will be noncrossovers and four, double crossovers in which the middle gene has changed position relative to the end genes. Therefore, even if every tetrad has two crossing overs, the maximum frequency of recombination for the end genes is 0.5.

When four loci are studied and three crossing overs occur in each tetrad—one in each region—one finds that for every 64 meiotic products, 32 are recombinational for the end genes and 32 are not. For cases where four or more crossing overs occur between end genes, the frequency of meiotic products bearing odd numbers of crossover regions is calculated to be 0.5. In each of these cases the gene at one end is shifted relative to that at the other. However, the remaining strands contain either even numbers of crossover regions (which do not cause the genes at the two ends to shift relative to each other) or are noncrossovers. Accordingly, the maximum frequency of recombination of 0.5 holds for the endmost genes (and, therefore, of course, for any genes between them).

Although two loci can show at most 50 per cent recombination, the length of the crossover map may exceed 50 units. For example, if a given pair of homologs contains an average of two crossing overs in each tetrad (see Figure 17-9), a total of 100 crossovers will occur among 100 meiotic products, and the map length will be 100 units even though the end genes will have recombined 50 per cent of the time. In fact, it can be predicted that the length of the standard map is equal to 50 times the mean number of crossing overs per tetrad.

QUESTIONS AND PROBLEMS

1. What frequencies of gametes do you expect from a dihybrid for two linked loci 50 map units apart? How can you prove these loci are linked?

2. How would you prove genetically that the last division in a spore sac of *Neurospora* is a mitotic one?

3. What are the advantages of *Neurospora* over *Drosophila* as material for genetic studies?

4. In mapping the *y-spl* region of the *Drosophila* X chromosome in this chapter, two marker loci were studied in each of three crosses. Was it possible to detect double crossovers had they occurred? Explain. Had any double crossovers occurred? Explain.

5. A wild-type *Drosophila* female whose father had cut wings and whose mother had split bristles is mated to a male with cut wings. Give the relative frequencies of genotypes and phenotypes expected in the F_1 sons.

6. A female *Drosophila* mated to a wild-type male produced 400 progeny in the F_1. Of the F_1 progeny, only three had white eyes and split bristles. Of what sex were these three flies? Give the genotype of the mother and the genotypes and frequencies of her gametes. What is the map distance involved?

7. What evidence do you have the crossing over does not involve the unilateral movement of one gene from its position in one chromosome to a position in the homologous chromosome?

8. A cross proves that one of the parents produced gametes of the following genotypes: 42.4 per cent *P Z*; 6.9 per cent *P z*; 7.0 per cent *p Z*; and 43.7 per cent *p z*. List all the genetic conclusions you can derive from these data.

9. What is the relationship in *Neurospora* between crossing over and first- and second-meiotic-division segregation?

10. How can you determine the position of a centromere in a linkage group of *Neurospora*?

11. Under what conditions are all eight ascospores from a single sac detectable crossovers?

12. What effect do undetected multiple crossover strands have upon gene sequence of marked loci? Observed map distance for marked loci?

13. Explain the following statement: The frequency of first-division segregation of a gene pair in *Neurospora* is inversely related to its distance from the centromere.

14. A trihybrid *A a B b C c* is crossed. The F_1 show that the trihybrid produced the following gametes:

28	*A B C*	22	*a b c*
230	*A B c*	220	*a b C*
206	*A b c*	244	*a B C*
23	*A b C*	27	*a B c*

a. Which loci are linked and which segregate independently?
b. Write the genotypes of both parents in light of your answer to part a.
c. Give the map distances between the three loci wherever applicable.

15. Suppose a pair of homologs in a diploid nucleus of *Neurospora* have the genotype *A B/a b*. Draw an eight-spore ascus derived from a diploid nucleus that had
a. no crossing over between these loci.
b. one crossing over between the centromere and the nearest marked locus.
c. one crossing over between the two marker loci.
d. one two-strand double crossing over between the marked loci.

16. How many gene pairs must be heterozygous to detect a single crossover in *Drosophila* and in *Neurospora*? Explain.

17. Map mutant *x* relative to its centromere when a heterozygous *Neurospora* produces asci with the following spore orders:

% ASCI	SPORE PAIR			
	1	2	3	4
92	*x*	*x*	+	+
4	*x*	+	*x*	+
1	+	*x*	*x*	+
3	*x*	+	+	*x*

18. How many linked loci must be hybrid in a *Drosophila* individual and a *Neurospora* individual to determine from crossover data whether these loci are arranged linearly? Explain.

19. In *Neurospora*, *arg* individuals are auxotrophs for arginine; *thi* individuals are auxotrophs for thiamine. Dihybrid nuclei for these mutants produce asci with the following spore orders:

% ASCI	SPORE PAIR			
	1	2	3	4
51	*arg thi*	*arg thi*	*arg$^+$ thi$^+$*	*arg$^+$ thi$^+$*
49	*arg thi$^+$*	*arg thi$^+$*	*arg$^+$ thi*	*arg$^+$ thi*

Discuss the positions of these loci with respect to each other and their centromere(s).

How would you determine the genotypes of these spores?

20. Suppose a given *Neurospora* cross produced asci with the following spore orders:

% ASCI	SPORE PAIR			
	1	2	3	4
88	a b	a b	A B	A B
3	a b	A B	a b	A B
3	a b	A B	A B	a b
1.5	a b	a B	A b	A B
1.5	a b	a B	A B	A b
1.5	a B	a b	A b	A B
1.5	a B	a b	A B	A b

a. Are *a* and *b* linked?

b. If they are not linked, give the crossover distance of *a* and *b* from their centromeres. If they are linked, give the cross-over distances between *a*, *b*, and the centromere.

21. In *Drosophila*, *y* and *spl* are X-limited. A female genotypically $y^+ spl^+/y spl$ produces sons. If 3 per cent carry either $y spl^+$ or $y^+ spl$ what are the genotypes and relative frequencies of gametes produced by the mother? Is the father's genotype important? Explain.

22. In light of your present knowledge how would you proceed to state a "law of independent segregation"?

23. How can you convert the percentage of asci showing second-division segregation into map distance from the centromere?

24. A *Drosophila* female with yellow body color, vermilion eye color, and cut wings is crossed with a wild-type male. In F_1 all females are wild-type and males are yellow, vermilion, cut. When the F_1 are mated to each other the F_2 are phenotypically as follows:

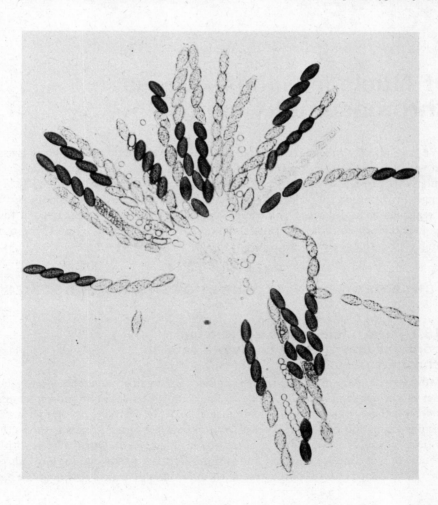

1781	wild-type
442	yellow
296	vermilion
53	cut
1712	yellow, vermilion, cut
470	vermilion, cut
265	yellow, cut
48	yellow, vermilion

Construct a crossover map for *y*, *v*, and *ct* from these data, giving the map distances between loci.

25. Draw an attached-X chromosome of *Drosophila* heterozygous both for *y* and for *m*. Show the kinds of gametes that could be obtained after
    a. no crossing over,
    b. one crossing over between the nonallelic genes,
    c. one crossing over not between the genes mentioned.

26. The photograph on page 285 (courtesy of D. R. Stadler) shows asci of *Neurospora* in various stages of maturity, the most mature containing dark ascospores. What genetic conclusions can you draw knowing that all the asci shown are products of the same parental genotype?

Chapter 18

Of Nuclear Genes—Gross Chromosomal Changes

We have already considered cytologically detectable genetic recombinations associated with mitosis, meiosis, and fertilization. Nuclear chromosomes can undergo other regularly—or irregularly—occurring changes that are detectable cytologically. These changes involve the gain or loss of entire chromosomes or chromosome sets as well as the rearrangement of large chromosome segments produced by breakage and fusion. This chapter will consider the causes and consequences of such gross chromosomal changes.

CHANGES INVOLVING UNBROKEN CHROMOSOMES

18.1 The nucleus of a euploid cell contains one or more complete sets of chromosomes.

Most sexually reproducing species are diploid. Each gamete contributes one genome, or set of chromosomes, to the zygote to maintain the diploid chromosome number. *Oenothera*, the evening primrose, is one such sexually reproducing organism. Cytological examination of a giant type of *Oenothera* called *gigas*, however, shows that it has three sets of chromosomes; in other words, it is *triploid*. Other plants, with four chromosome sets, are *tetraploids*; and still others have six or eight sets of chromosomes. The occurrence of extra sets of chromosomes is called *polyploidy*. Changes in ploidy are *euploid* (rightfold) since normal gene and chromosome ratios are maintained.

18.2   The number of chromosome sets can increase by allopolyploidy.

Ploidy can increase when two species are crossed and each contributes two or more chromosome sets to form a third species, which is said to be *allopolyploid* (Figure 18-1). Cultivated wheat is an allopolyploid organism. As we might expect, allopolyploids often show characteristics of both parent species. Allopolyploidy is discussed again in Section 36.12.

18.3   The number of chromosome sets can increase by autopolyploidy.

The ploidy of a nucleus can also increase by the addition of genomes of the same kind as those already present—resulting in *autopolyploidy*. Autopolyploidy can arise in several different ways.

1. If anaphase of mitosis is abnormal, the doubled number of chromosomes may be included in a single nucleus. Subsequent normal divisions thus will give rise to polyploid daughter nuclei. Autopolyploidy can be artificially induced in a number of plants and animals by colchicine or its synthetic analog, colcemide, drugs that destroy the spindle fibers attached to the centromeres of the chromosomes, thereby preventing chromosome movement during anaphase. Mechanical injury, irradiation, and environmental stresses like starvation and extremes of temperature can also cause autopolyploidy.

2. Sometimes two of the haploid nuclei produced by meiosis fuse to form a diploid gamete. After union with a haploid gamete, it forms a triploid zygote.

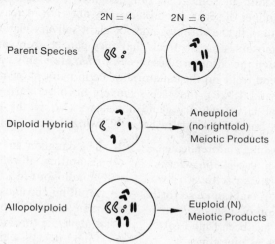

Figure 18-1 Hybridization of two species leading to new species formation by means of allopolyploidy. (This figure is discussed in Section 36.10.)

3. Some haploid organisms undergo meiosis. Although the gametes formed usually contain only part of a genome, some contain a complete genome. Fertilization between two haploid gametes produces a diploid zygote.

4. Females of certain moths produce haploid eggs; others produce diploid eggs. Both types start development *parthenogenetically*, that is, without fertilization. During development, however, nuclei fuse in pairs to establish the diploid and tetraploid conditions. In such organisms, normal parthenogenesis leads to normal diploidy and tetraploidy.

The Jimson weed, *Datura*, shows autopolyploidy; some forms are haploid; others diploid, triploid, or tetraploid. Autopolyploidy also occurs in animals. For example, the water shrimp (*Artemia*), the sea urchin (*Echinus*), the roundworm (*Ascaris*), and the moth (*Solenobia*) have autotetraploid species. Triploid and tetraploid embryos are found in a variety of mammals. Polyploid larvae of salamanders and of frogs also have been found. Triploid and tetraploid females occur in *Drosophila* (normally diploid); haploid somatic parts have been found in some fruit flies. In man, although complete triploidy is lethal, individuals that are diploid in some cells and triploid in others are viable but defective. The triploid cells of such individuals contain either XXX or XXY besides three sets of autosomes.

As we saw in earlier chapters, changes in ploidy usually occur during gameto-genesis and fertilization. Autopolyploidy is a normal process in certain somatic tissues of man (liver cells, for instance). This kind of autopolyploidy is accomplished by means of *endoreplication*, in which the products of chromosome replication remain in one nucleus. Autopolyploidy is discussed again in Section 36.11. (R)

18.4 The salivary gland cells of dipteran larvae contain giant chromosomes resulting from endoreplication and the synapsis of homologous strands.

After endoreplication in some cells, all daughter chromosome strands remain synapsed, so the number of separate chromosomes does not increase. An example of this condition is found in the chromosomes of giant salivary gland cells of dipteran larvae; these chromosomes are so thick that they can be seen easily under a light microscope. Although the chromosomes of *Drosophila* are highly coiled at metaphase (where homologs tend to lie on the equatorial plate in pairs, showing *somatic pairing*, see Figures 16-15 and 18-2B), they are relatively uncoiled during interphase. The chromosomes in the larval salivary gland nuclei are also in the relatively uncoiled state of interphase, but differ in at least the following three ways (Figure 18-2).

1. Each chromosome endoreplicates several times in succession: One chromosome gives rise to two, two to four, four to eight, and so forth. Endoreplication of a single chromosome has been found to occur as much as nine times, thereby producing 512 daughters.

2. The daughter strands, instead of separating, all remain together with homologous loci side by side. The resulting chromosome looks like a many-threaded (polynemic) cable. Polynemic chromosomes are usually found in cells which never divide again.

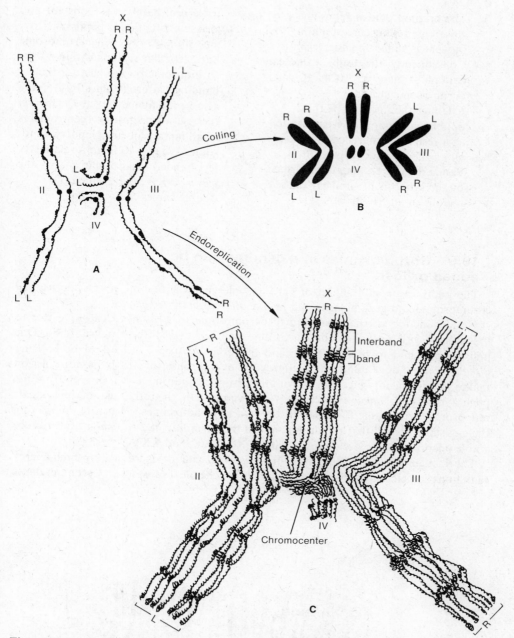

Figure 18-2 Correspondence between chromosomes in different cells of *Drosophila*. (A) Mitotic interphase in which chromosomes are relatively uncoiled and presumed to undergo some degree of somatic synapsis between homologs. (B) Metaphase with coiled chromosomes, at the equator of the spindle, exhibiting somatic pairing between homologs. (C) Interphase in which relatively uncoiled chromosomes that have endoreplicated and become polynemic exhibit tight somatic synapsis not only between homologs but between nonhomologs in the regions adjacent to the centromeres. The tight synapsis and the smallness of chromosome IV lead to the appearance of a chromocenter from which five long arms radiate.

3. The original pair of homologs are closely paired at corresponding loci in what is called *somatic synapsis*. Consequently, the double cable can contain as many as 1,024 chromosome strands.

   Under the microscope these double cables appear cross-banded as a result of differences in density along their length (Figure 18-3). Bands (and interbands) are formed by the synapsis of similarly dense regions in all the strands. The pattern of bands is so constant and characteristic that it is possible to identify not only each chromosome but particular regions within a chromosome on the basis of the banding pattern (Figure 18-4). Note also in the figure that in *Drosophila* the regions nearest the centromeres of all larval salivary gland chromosomes synapse to form a relatively less-banded mass of chromatin, the *chromocenter*, from which the double cables radiate. (R)

18.5 Chromosomes in a genome can be added or lost.

The addition or subtraction of chromosomes from a genome upsets the normal chromosomal and gene balance and results, therefore, in *aneuploidy*.

Nondisjunction of the small fourth chromosome in *Drosophila* can give rise to individuals with only one fourth chromosome or with three (Figure 18-5). One individual is said to be *monosomic* and the other, *trisomic*, instead of both being *disomic*. Even though addition or subtraction of a chromosome IV by nondisjunction makes visible phenotypic changes from the disomic condition as can be seen from the phenotypes, both *aneusomic* changes are viable. On the other hand, individuals monosomic or trisomic for either of the two large autosomes die before completing the egg stage. Recall that nondisjunction in the germ line of *Drosophila* can produce viable offspring, otherwise diploid, that are X0, XXX, and XXY.

The incidence of nondisjunction in *Drosophila* can be increased by high-energy radiations as well as by carbon dioxide and other chemical substances. Certain mutants

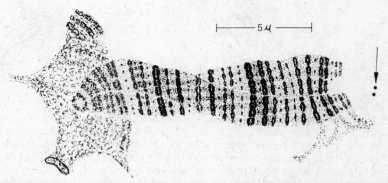

Figure 18-3 Pair of fourth chromosomes as seen in salivary gland nuclei (each homolog is highly polynemic) and at mitotic metaphase (arrow), drawn to the same scale. (By permission of The American Genetic Association, from C. B. Bridges, 1935. J. Hered., 26: 62.)

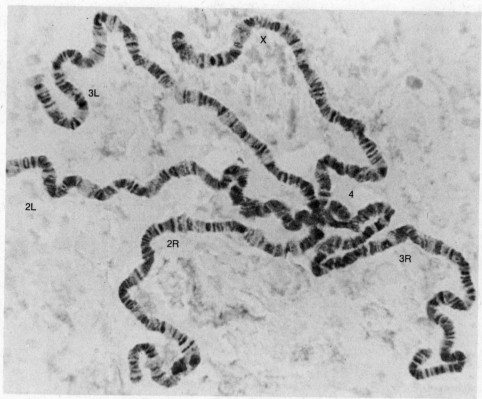

Figure 18-4 Salivary gland chromosomes of a female larva of *D. melanogaster*. Note the chromocenter, from which the giant chromosomes radiate. (Courtesy of B. P. Kaufmann; by permission of The American Genetic Association, J. Hered., frontispiece, Vol. 30, No. 5, May 1939.)

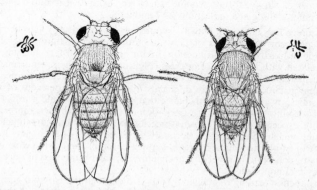

Figure 18-5 *Monosomic-IV* (left) and *trisomic-IV* (right) females of *D. melanogaster*. The *monosomic-IV* is smaller than the wild-type female shown in Figure 15-6. (Drawn by E. M. Wallace.)

have an increased frequency of nondisjunction. The gametes of autopolyploid individuals are especially likely to contain one or more extra chromosomes.[1]

In human beings the largest autosome is numbered 1, the smallest, 22; the sex chromosomes are not numbered, the Y being the smallest of all the chromosomes, the X being middle-sized (Figures 15-1 and 18-6). Each of these chromosomes can undergo nondisjunction. The nondisjunction that occurs during gametogenesis in men and women results, therefore, in the production of a variety of monosomics and trisomics.[2] Evidence that older women are more likely to have trisomic children indicates that a metabolic defect associated with increased age increases the chance for nondisjunction.[3]

As we will see later in this chapter, chromosomes can also be lost after breakage. (R)

---

[1] When triploid *Drosophila* females—with all chromosomes trisomic—undergo meiosis, bundles of three homologous chromosomes (*trivalents*) may be formed at synapsis. This is because at one place along the length of a chromosome synapsis is between two homologs, and at another place it is between one of these two and the third homolog. In this way, although meiotic synapsis is two by two at all levels, all three homologs are held together as a trivalent. At the first meiotic division the two homologs that are synapsed at their centromeric regions separate and go to opposite poles, while the third homolog goes to either one of the poles. At the end of the second meiotic division, two nuclei each have one homolog of the trivalent, and two nuclei each have two homologs. The same result is obtained when synapsis is entirely between two homologs and excludes the third. Since each of the four trisomics present at metaphase I segregates independently, eggs are produced which have one of the following:

a. Each chromosome type singly, and therefore, contain one complete genome (being haploid).
b. Two chromosomes of each type, and therefore, contain two genomes (being diploid).
c. Any combination in which some chromosomes are represented once and others twice (being aneusomic).

Meiosis produces many aneusomic gametes when the number of homologs is odd, as it is in triploids, pentaploids, etc. In tetraploids, since each chromosome can have a partner at meiosis, the four homologs often segregate two and two. Sometimes, however, the four homologs form a trivalent and segregate three and one, so that some aneusomic gametes are produced by polyploids with even numbers of homologs.

[2] *Down's syndrome* (*mongolism*) in man is sometimes the result of a trisomic diploid chromosomal constitution, the trisomic being number 21 (Figure 18-6). Trisomics for several other of the smaller autosomes are also known, each producing its own characteristic set of congenital abnormalities. Trisomy for the largest autosomes is apparently lethal before birth, probably because of the imbalance of too many genes. The very severe phenotypic defects observed among the least affected autosomally trisomic individuals makes it a reasonable expectation that the monosomic condition of any autosome is lethal before birth—in accordance with the view (see the next section) that chromosome subtraction is even more detrimental than chromosome addition. (On rare occasions monosomics for chromosome 21 or 22 survive for a few months to years, exhibiting multiple defects). Aneusomy of the sex chromosomes is discussed in Sections 23.7 and 23.8.

[3] The frequency among live births of Down's syndrome due to trisomy has been determined as approximately 0.2 per cent. Most cases of Down's syndrome occur among the children of older mothers and are due primarily to nondisjunction during oogenesis. In fact, in man, almost all nondisjunction is associated with the aging of oocytes (Figure 18-7). If all chromosomes have a similar frequency of nondisjunction, there might be a minimum of 4.4 per cent (22×0.2 per cent) of zygotes autosomally trisomic at conception. There might also be another 4.4 per cent of zygotes that are autosomal monosomics, owing to the equal chance that the haploid meiotic product complementary to the one which is disomic—the *nullosomic* one—becomes the egg. In fact, more nullosomic than disomic gametes are expected, since a chromosome left out of one daughter nucleus need not be included in the sister nucleus. Supporting a normally high frequency of aneusomy is the observation that about one fourth of aborted human fetuses show a chromosomal derangement. It is expected, moreover, that many conceptions involving aneusomy, especially monosomy, are lost so early in pregnancy that they go unnoticed.

Although nondisjunction leading to aneusomy can also occur in the paternal germ line of man, as already indicated, this does not seem to contribute very significantly to the total observed frequency. The contrary is true in the mouse, however, even though mouse females—like human females—are born with all their germ cells in the oocyte stage. Thus, in the mouse, marked chromosomes show that spontaneous aneusomy of sex chromosomes almost always has a paternal origin. In the mouse, as in man, trisomy for certain small autosomes is viable.

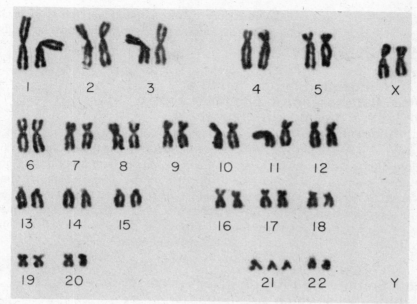

Figure 18-6 Chromosomal constitution found in a female showing Down's syndrome. (Courtesy of K. Hirschhorn.) After photographing a squash preparation like that in Figure 15-1, the chromosomes are cut out and "paired" as shown here.

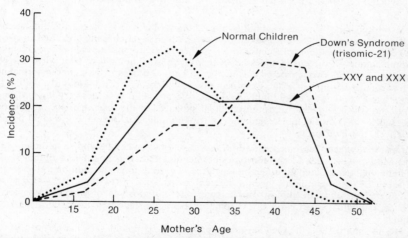

Figure 18-7 Relationship between maternal age and the incidence of normal and of certain aneusomic offspring. (Modified from L. S. Penrose, 1964. Ann. Human Genet., 28: 199–200.)

18.6   The loss of a chromosome is usually more detrimental to a diploid organism than the gain of one.

A diploid individual contains in its whole sets of chromosomes a balance of genes which is responsible for the proper functioning of that organism. The gain or loss of a chromosome will affect this balance; but the loss of a chromosome is likely to be of greater consequence to the individual since it brings about more of an imbalance.[4] As we might expect, autopolyploids usually survive whole chromosome additions and subtractions better than diploids.[5] (R)

18.7 A mutation in one cell of a multicellular organism can make that individual a mosaic with respect to chromosome number.

As mentioned in Section 18.3, persons are known who are diploid in some tissues and triploid in others (normally diploid). Such *mosaicism* for ploidy occurs both in plants and in animals, and can involve tissues of both the germ and somatic lines. If nondisjunction occurs in later development, monosomic and trisomic patches can occur in a diploid background. Such patches are often detrimental and sometimes lethal to the organism. Mosaicism for sex chromosomes is discussed in Section 23.5 (involving *Drosophila*) and in Section 23.8 (involving human beings).

18.8 Somatic cell fusion gives rise to polyploid cells which subsequently undergo chromosome losses.

Several mouse-tissue culture lines are unique in that each has a number of morphologically distinct chromosomes. After certain pairs of such cell lines are mixed and grown together, hybrid cells with a single nucleus are produced in which the chromo-

[4] That a lesser imbalance is brought about by the addition of chromosomes to the diploid condition than by the subtraction of chromosomes from it can be seen by comparing how far from normality (diploidy) each of the two abnormal conditions is. When one chromosome is in excess, the abnormal chromosome number of three is $1\frac{1}{2}$ times larger than the normal number of two; when one chromosome is missing, the abnormal chromosome number of one is 2 times smaller than the normal number. Thus, if a particular trisomic is lethal, we expect that its monosomic condition is also lethal. It is not surprising, therefore, that a haploid individual mated to a diploid produces very few progeny, since after fertilization most zygotes are chromosomally unbalanced by the absence of one or more chromosomes needed to make two complete genomes; a triploid individual mated to a diploid usually produces relatively more offspring.

[5] The comparative effect of chromosome addition and subtraction can be studied in diploid and auto-tetraploid *Datura*, which has 12 chromosomes per genome (N). It is possible to obtain 12 different kinds of individuals, each having a different one of the 12 chromosomes in addition to the 2N number. Each of these 2N + 1 trisomics is given a different name, such as "Globe." It is also possible to obtain viable plants that are diploid but missing one chromosome of a pair; these are 2N − 1 monosomics. Individuals with two extra chromosomes of the same type (2N + 2, *tetrasomics*) are also found.
    Compare, in Figure 18-8, the seed capsules of the normal diploid (2N) with those of diploids having either one extra chromosome (2N + 1) of the type producing Globe or two of these (2N + 2). The latter two *polysomics* can be called trisomic diploid and tetrasomic diploid, respectively. Although the tetrasomic is more stable chromosomally (each chromosome can have a partner at meiosis) than is the trisomic, the tetrasomic phenotype is too abnormal to establish a race, since it has a still greater genetic imbalance than the trisomic and produces a still greater deviation from the normal diploid phenotype.
    In comparison, the autotetraploid (4N) individual is phenotypically almost like the diploid, since chromosomal balance is undisturbed. The tetraploid which has one extra Globe chromosome (4N + 1, making it a pentasomic tetraploid) deviates from the tetraploid in the same direction as the 2N + 1 deviates from 2N, but it does so less extremely. Hexasomic tetraploids (4N + 2) deviate from 4N just about as much as 2N + 1 deviates from 2N. It is clear, therefore, that adding a single chromosome to a tetraploid has less phenotypic effect than its addition to a diploid, since the shift in balance between chromosomes is relatively smaller in the former than in the latter.

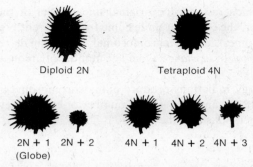

Diploid 2N   Tetraploid 4N

2N + 1   2N + 2   4N + 1   4N + 2   4N + 3
(Globe)

Figure 18-8   Effect upon the capsule of *Datura* of the presence of one or more extra "Globe" chromosomes.

some number is approximately equal to the sum of those of the two parent lines and in which chromosomes morphologically characteristic of each line are found. Over a period of several months, colonies of these hybrid cells show a reduction in chromosome number—probably due to nondisjunction. Similar results have been obtained with hybrid nuclei produced after the fusion of human cells with mouse cells. Although the *in vivo* frequency of such *somatic cell fusion* is unknown, examples have been reported in cattle[6] and frogs.

Somatic cell fusion also occurs in filamentous fungi such as *Aspergillus* and *Penicillium* (see Section 17.10). This process leads to the formation of diploid nuclei by rare (probably accidental) nuclear fusions in a multinucleate mycelium containing haploid nuclei. The diploid nuclei that are formed multiply side by side with the haploid nuclei, and undergo chromosome loss by nondisjunction. (Recombination can also occur by means of mitotic crossing over.) (R)

CHANGES INVOLVING BROKEN CHROMOSOMES

18.9   Pieces of fragmented chromosomes can join with pieces from the same or from different chromosomes. Most single breaks rejoin as before, since the proximity of ends at a point of breakage favors their union.

A chromosome broken into two or more pieces has "sticky" ends at the points of breakage, each of which can rejoin with another "sticky" end but not with a normal end. Ordinarily, terminal genes called *telomeres* seal off the ends of a normal chromosome so that they cannot join with others. The two ends produced by a single break usually rejoin as before even when other sticky chromosome ends occur in the same nucleus. It appears that the proximity of sticky ends favors their rejoining in a

[6] Both members of a pair of twins were mosaic: each had the same two genetically different types of erythrocytes. At 3 years of age twin A had blood of which 10 per cent was of his own genotype and 90 per cent of his twin's genotype. At 8 years of age, however, twin A had blood corpuscles of three types: the two "parental" types (each making up 2 per cent) and a "hybrid" type (constituting 96 per cent of the erythrocyte population).

restitutional union, which restores the original linear order of the chromosome segments. When, however, the ends that unite come from different breaks (from the same or different chromosomes), a new chromosomal arrangement results. Such unions are of the *nonrestitutional*, or *exchange*, type. The number of unions is related, of course, to the number of breaks.

Although high-energy radiations produce many chromosome breaks (as discussed in Sections S18.9a, S18.9b, and S18.9c), the number of breaks they cause in a nucleus is influenced by the metabolism of the cell.[7]

18.10 A single chromosome break can result in chromosome segments without a centromere, and can lead to the formation of chromosomes with two centromeres. The acentric segments are usually lost, but the dicentric chromosomes can block nuclear division or enter a special chromosomal cycle.

Let us consider the consequences of a single *chromosome break*, that is, a break through both chromatids (Figure 18-9). Diagram 1 shows a normal chromosome (its chromatids are not shown) whose centromere is indicated by a black dot. In diagram 2 the chromosome is broken; and in diagram 3, the broken chromosome has replicated to form an identical daughter chromosome. The union of a and b, a′ and b′, a′ and b, or a and b′ would be restitutional. In diagram 4 we see the results of nonrestitutional unions: one *acentric chromosome* (without a centromere) and one *dicentric chromosome*

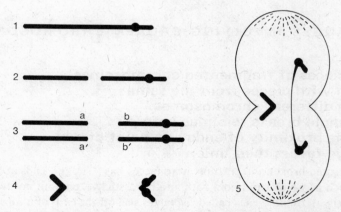

Figure 18-9 Consequences of a single nonrestituting chromosome break. Diagram 4 shows the chromosomes as they are contracted prior to metaphase.

[7] Thus, the number of nuclear breaks (1) increases when, during irradiation, the cell's oxygen supply is increased or its reducing substances are destroyed; and (2) decreases when, during irradiation, nitrogen replaces air. The joining of two sticky ends is a metabolic reaction that apparently involves adenosine triphosphate and appropriate enzymes. Replacing air by pure or an increased percentage of oxygen after irradiation enhances joining; replacing air by nitrogen after irradiation inhibits joining. Consequently, restitution is less likely if nitrogen replaces air after irradiation, since ends from the same break stay open for a longer time. Oxygen thus has opposite effects on rearrangement frequency—it increases the number of breaks during irradiation, but afterwards promotes restitution.

(with two centromeres). Diagram 5 shows the acentric chromosome being pulled toward neither pole in anaphase while the dicentric one is pulled toward both poles at once. Consequently, the acentric chromosome is not included in either daughter nucleus, and is lost to both. The dicentric chromosome (Figure 18-10B) forms a *bridge* which by hindering migration to the poles can prevent both daughter nuclei from receiving any of its chromosomal material. Thus, the dicentric chromosome, too, may be lost. Sometimes, however, the bridge snaps (usually into unequal pieces) so that a piece with one centromere goes to each pole; after replication a new dicentric chromosome can form in one or both daughter nuclei, and once again make a bridge at the next anaphase. In this manner, a *bridge–breakage–fusion–bridge cycle* can occur in successive nuclear generations. (Under similar conditions, shorter dicentrics break more often than longer ones.) A bridge that fails to break can tie the two daughter nuclei together and interfere with subsequent nuclear division. Such interference may have a much greater effect than the unequal distribution of the genes located in the bridge.

Detriment or death to daughter cells can result from the loss of genetic material when an acentric or dicentric fragment is left out of a daughter nucleus. Furthermore, a succession of bridge–breakage–fusion–bridge cycles may be harmful to future cell generations because of abnormal quantities of chromosomal regions received.

Such chromosome breaks as those above can occur in either the somatic or the germ line. Consequently, genetically aneuploid gametes, that is, those with some genes of incorrect ploidy, may arise. Since all, or almost all, genes are physiologically inactive in the gametes of animals, an aneuploid gamete can ordinarily function in fertilization with a normal gamete. (Harmful or lethal effects may occur, however, in the zygote or subsequent development.) In many plants, on the other hand, the meiotic products form a gametophyte generation during which numerous genes are active, so the detrimental effects of aneuploidy are usually seen before fertilization.

18.11   Most unions occur during interphase. After replication, a nonrestituted chromatid becomes a nonrestituted chromosome.

Sometimes a break involves only one chromatid of a chromosome. For such *chromatid breaks*[8] restitution is more likely than for chromosome breaks, since the unbroken chromatid serves as a splint to hold the newly produced ends close to each other. We should note, however, that what appears under the microscope as a break involving only one chromatid may be a chromosome break which at that time has restituted one chromatid.

When restitution of chromatid fragments does not take place, nonrestituted chromosome fragments result if the fragments last long enough to replicate. To be detected cytologically, a chromatid or chromosome fragment produced during

---

[8] In view of the probability that a chromatid contains two (or more) DNA duplexes, at least after replication, the problem of breaking a chromatid or chromosome ultimately becomes a problem of learning how all its duplexes are broken. Union between (probably uneven) ends of duplexes produced by breakage also needs to be elucidated at the molecular level, to explain, for example, how the ends of all strands of the same polarity find each other for enzymatic ligation after any necessary excisions and repair synthesis. That nonrestitutional unions occur and the chromosome survives subsequent replications suggests, but does not prove, that the pieces joining together have the same number of duplexes at the breakpoints.

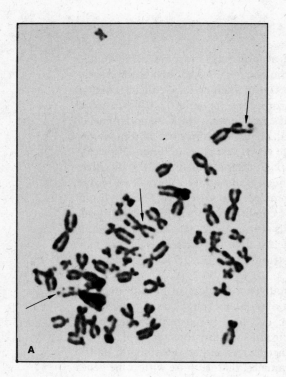

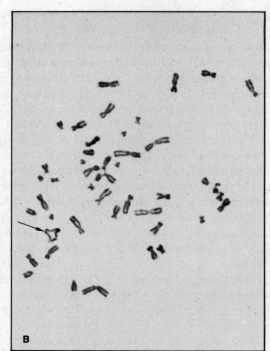

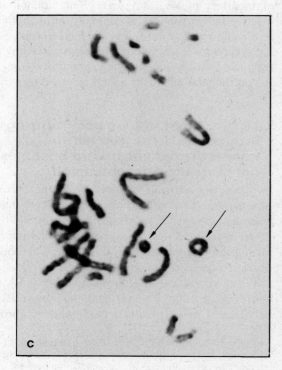

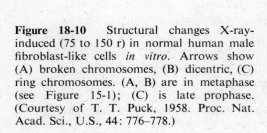

Figure 18-10 Structural changes X-ray-induced (75 to 150 r) in normal human male fibroblast-like cells *in vitro*. Arrows show (A) broken chromosomes, (B) dicentric, (C) ring chromosomes. (A, B) are in metaphase (see Figure 15-1); (C) is late prophase. (Courtesy of T. T. Puck, 1958. Proc. Nat. Acad. Sci., U.S., 44: 776–778.)

interphase usually has to persist without restitution until nuclear division occurs. Some breaks induced in metaphase chromosomes may not be visible, because fragments can be held together by the nongenetic material in a chromosome. Since nearly all ends resulting from breaks are not sticky when the chromosome is contracted (as it is during nuclear division), union is less likely at this time than between late telophase and early prophase. Since most unions occur during interphase, broken ends produced from early prophase to late telophase have the maximum time for restitutional union and probably also the greatest chance for cross union, that is, nonrestitutional union.

As indicated above, the consequences of single nonrestituted chromatid breaks are similar to those of single nonrestituted chromosome breaks. Hence, the following discussion will be restricted to chromosome breaks that fail to restitute. We should not think, however, that chromatid breaks are less frequent or less mportant than chromosome breaks.

18.12   Two nonrestituted breaks in one chromosome can lead to deficiency, inversion, or duplication.

In a nuclear chromosome with two breaks, the two points of breakage may be *paracentric* (to one side of the centromere) or *pericentric* (with the centromere between them), as shown in Figure 18-11.

Deficiency

Consider a chromosome with segments in the order ABCDEFG.HIJ, where the centromere is represented by the period between G and H (Figure 18-11). Paracentric breaks (say, between A and B, and between F and G) give rise to a centric chromosome, AG.HIJ, deficient for the piece BCDEF after the sticky ends at A and G join.

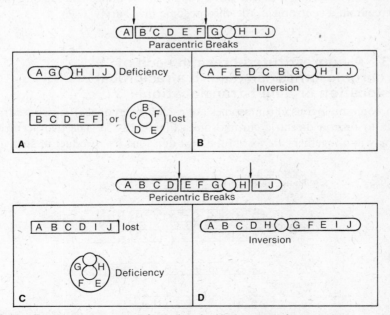

Figure 18-11   Some consequences of two breaks in the same chromosome.

The ends of the acentric fragment can join to form a ring chromosome. The acentric piece is usually lost, however, before the next nuclear division. When the breaks are pericentric (for instance, between D and E, H and I) the acentric end pieces are lost even if they join together (Figure 18-11C). The centric piece can survive if its ends join to form a ring (Figure 18-10C) and if the deficient sections are not essential. Such a ring is at a disadvantage because a single crossing over with another chromosome (in rod or ring form) results in a dicentric chromosome.

A nondividing nucleus in which breakage or another structural change occurs is still euploid (that is, its genes remain in the normal ratio) since it neither gains nor loses any genetic material. The daughter nuclei formed by such a nucleus, however, will likely be aneuploid: *hyperploid* if one or more chromosomes or chromosome parts are in excess; *hypoploid* if one or more of these are missing.

Inversion

Two breaks in the same chromosome can lead to the inversion of a chromosomal segment (Figure 18-11B, D). We can see in the figure that a middle piece of chromosome ABCDEFG.HIJ becomes inverted with respect to the end pieces—the paracentric breaks producing AFEDCBG.HIJ, and the pericentric breaks producing ABCDH.GFEIJ. In this manner, paracentric or pericentric inversions (both euploid rearrangements) result.

Duplication

If the joining of ends made by two breaks is delayed until after the chromosome is replicated, the pieces can join to form a chromosome with an internal region repeated, or duplicated (Figure 18-12); neither, either, or both of the regions involved in the duplication may be inverted with respect to the original arrangement. The remaining pieces may join to form a deficient chromosome. If the duplicated region is small and does not contain a centromere, the chromosome may survive. (R)

18.13   A nonrestituted break in each of two chromosomes can lead to a reciprocal translocation or a half-translocation.

If two nonhomologous chromosomes are each broken once, the two centric pieces can unite to form a dicentric chromosome (Figure 18-13). The two acentric pieces (which may join together) are lost in the next division. The product of such a mutual

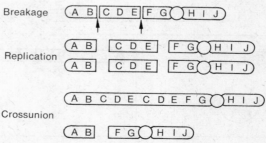

Figure 18-12 Duplication.

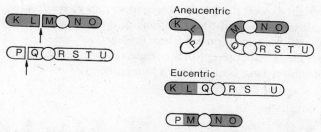

Figure 18-13   Reciprocal translocation between nonhomologous chromosomes.

exchange of chromosomal segments is called a *reciprocal translocation*; the *aneucentric type* is often lethal. Reciprocal translocations of *eucentric type* are equally likely to occur and are less frequently lethal. In individuals heterozygous for this kind of exchange (Figure 18-14), that is, with one eucentric reciprocal translocation between two pairs of chromosomes, gametes are formed with deficiencies and duplications if they receive one but not both members of the reciprocal translocation.

When chromosomes are located in a relatively small nuclear volume, no broken end is far from any other. Hence, if one of the two unions needed for reciprocal translocation occurs, the other usually does also. (Such is the case in the nucleus of *Drosophila* sperm just after fertilization.) In cells that have a relatively large nuclear volume (like oocytes), however, the distance between the broken ends of nonhomologs is so great that reciprocal translocation is a rare event. Even if one cross union occurs, the two other broken ends usually fail to join to each other, and a *half-translocation*

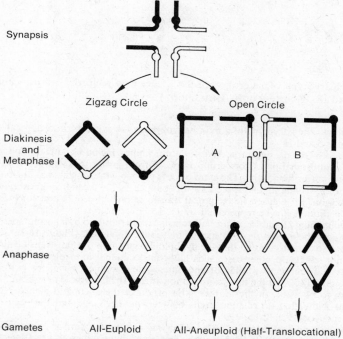

Figure 18-14   Diagrammatic representation of segregation in eucentric reciprocal translocation heterozygotes. (Chromatids not shown; the spindles—also not shown—have their poles oriented vertically.)

results. As we might expect, the unjoined fragments can cause descendant cells to die or to develop abnormally. Half-translocations also occur when heterozygotes for a eucentric reciprocal translocation undergo segregation and only one of the two rearranged chromosomes is present in a gamete (Figure 18-14). Eucentric reciprocal and half-translocations have been found in human beings.[9]

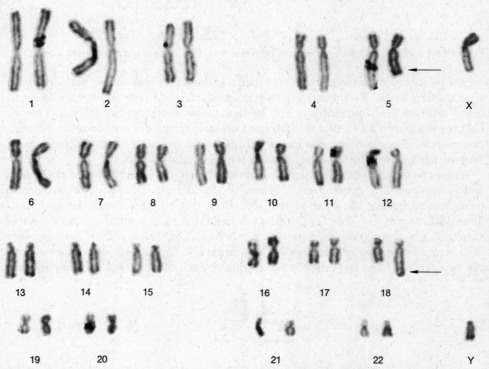

Figure 18-15 Karyotype of heterozygote for a eucentric reciprocal translocation between autosomes 5 and 18. (Courtesy of K. Hirschhorn.)

[9] Figure 18-15 shows the karyotype of a man heterozygous for a eucentric reciprocal translocation between autosomes 5 and 18.

Some children with Down's syndrome have 46 chromosomes, including—in addition to two normal number 21's—an autosomal pair (from group 13–15 or from group 16–18) which is heteromorphic, one member being longer than usual. The extra piece is probably the long arm of 21, so the individual is hyperploid for 21, having almost three 21's. In some cases the mother is phenotypically normal although heterozygous for a eucentric reciprocal translocation between 21 and, for example, 15. Her chromosome constitution can be represented by 15, 15.21 (centromere of 15), 21.15 (centromere of 21), 21. An egg containing 21 and 15.21 (the half-translocation) fertilized by a normal sperm (containing 21 and 15) produces the almost-three-21 mongoloid under discussion (Figure 18-16). (The break in 15 must have been so close to the end that the hypoploid segment in the half-translocation mongoloid individual was not lethal.) In other cases such half-translocational mongoloids have half-translocational nonmongoloid mothers with 45 chromosomes. These mothers have, for example, only one normal 21, one normal 15, and the half-translocation 15.21. The hypoploidy for both 21 and 15 must be small enough to be viable in the mother, who produces the aneuploid gamete that makes her child mongoloid. Note that no relation exists between mother's age and the occurrence of half-translocational mongoloid children.

Some persons with the *cri-du-chat* ("*cat-cry*") *syndrome* have a similar origin. This syndrome, which is characterized by a cat-like cry during the first year of life, numerous head defects, and mental retardation, is due to the presence in heterozygous condition of a chromosome 5 missing a segment of the short arm. About 13 per cent of children with this syndrome carry a half translocation of a reciprocal translocation involving chromosome 5 present in a parent.

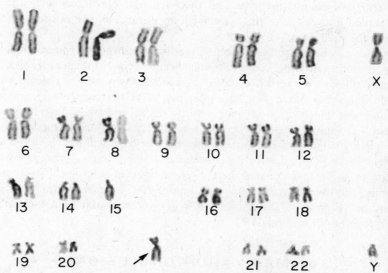

Figure 18-16   Karyotype containing a 15.21 half-translocation (arrow) among 46 chromosomes. This male has Down's syndrome as a result of being nearly trisomic for chromosome 21. (Courtesy of K. Hirschhorn.)

When each member of a pair of homologs is broken once, the breaks are usually at different loci. Hence, a eucentric reciprocal translocation will produce two eucentric chromosomes, one with a deficiency and the other with a duplication; reciprocal translocation of the aneucentric type produces a dicentric and an acentric chromosome.

The frequency of various types of chromosomal rearrangement induced by high-energy radiation and various factors which modify this frequency are discussed in Sections S18.13a, S18.13b, and S18.13c. Radiation-induced rearrangements have contributed significantly to the advancement of genetics (Section S18.13d). (R)

18.14   Structural changes in nuclear chromosomes can be detected genetically or cytologically. Cytological identification is aided especially when homologous regions synapse.

Structural changes in chromosomes may be detected initially by cytological examination, or they may be noted first by their effects on the phenotype (in plants, often by decreased fertility). Thus, detection and identification of structural changes can be made cytologically, or genetically, or by a combination of both methods.

When heterozygous, deficiencies can sometimes be recognized genetically since they permit the expression of all loci present in one dose in the nondeficient chromosome. Inversions and translocations can be suspected when mutant heterozygotes show a marked reduction in offspring carrying crossovers (the case of paracentric inversion heterozygotes is discussed in Section 25.4). Using appropriate genetic markers, inversion homozygotes show some genes in the reverse of normal order, whereas in heterozygotes or homozygotes for translocations genes normally not linked are found linked. Sometimes a cytological study is preceded by genetic studies, indicating the class of structural change involved and the particular chromosome(s) affected. Of course, detailed knowledge of the cytological appearance of the normal genome is a prerequisite for such work.

The prophase I chromosomes of some organisms and the interphase giant salivary gland chromosomes of Diptera are particularly suited for cytological studies, because in both cases synapsis between homologs helps locate the presence, absence, or relocation of chromosome parts. For example, inversion heterozygotes show either a reversed segment which does not pair with its nonreversed homologous segment (if the inversion is small), or (if the inversion is larger) show one homolog twisting in order to synapse (Figure 18-17). A deficiency heterozygote will buckle in the region of the deficiency (see Figure 9-9 for a molecular example). Since a chromosome with a duplication may also buckle when heterozygous, careful cytological study is needed to distinguish this case from deficiency (see Figure 18-18). Heterozygotes for reciprocal translocations (Figure 18-19) show two pairs of nonhomologous chromosomes associated together in synapsis. (R)

SUMMARY AND CONCLUSIONS

Gross chromosomal changes in nuclear chromosomes are either euploid or aneuploid.

Gross euploid changes include bringing different types of genomes together (allopolyploidy, somatic cell fusion), and increasing the number of multiples of the genome information present (allopolyploidy, autopolyploidy, and polynemy). The modes of origin and breeding behavior of autopolyploids, and the origin and structure of the giant polynemic chromosomes in the salivary glands of *Drosophila* larvae are considered in detail.

Gross aneuploid changes include the addition or subtraction of one or more whole chromosomes from a genome due to nondisjunction, chromosomal segregation in polyploids, or chromosome breakage. Chromosome or chromatid breakage, which is usually followed by restitutional union, can also cause other gross aneuploid changes

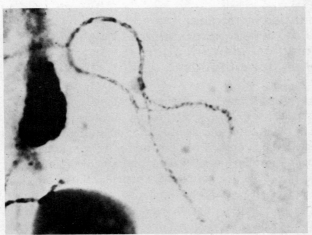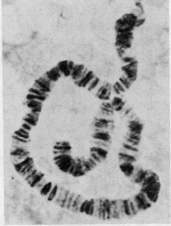

Figure 18-17 Inversion heterozygote (left) in maize (pachynema) (courtesy of D. T. Morgan, Jr.) and (right) in *Drosophila* (salivary gland) (courtesy of B. P. Kaufmann).

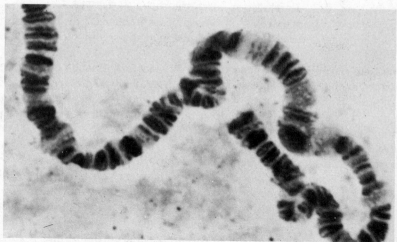

Figure 18-18   Salivary gland chromosomes heterozygous for a shift within the right arm of chromosome 3 of *D. melanogaster*. A piece from map region "98" is inserted into map region "91." The rightmost buckle is due to the absence of the shifted segment; the leftmost buckle is due to its presence. (Courtesy of B. P. Kaufmann.)

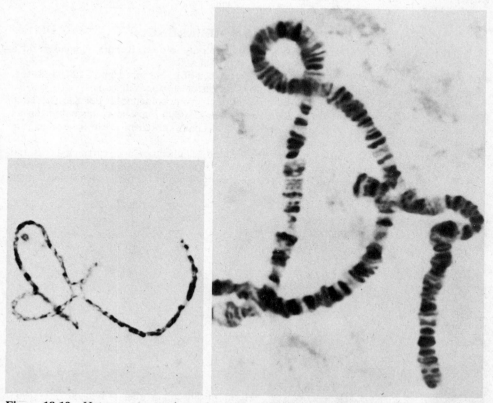

Figure 18-19   Heterozygous reciprocal translocation (left) in maize (pachynema) (courtesy of M. M. Rhoades) and (right) in *Drosophila* (salivary gland) (courtesy of B. P. Kaufmann.)

involving the gain, loss, or relocation of chromosome parts. The occurrence of two nonrestituting breaks in one or two chromosomes is discussed specifically in relation to the production of deficiencies, duplications, inversions, and reciprocal and half-translocations.

Although chromosomes that have undergone structural change may be classified as euploid or aneuploid, the nuclei in which these changes arise are euploid until mitosis or meiosis, and may give rise to progeny nuclei that are aneuploid. The addition of part or all of a chromosome to the genetic content of a nucleus is usually less detrimental than its subtraction.

All types of gross chromosomal change can (1) occur mosaically, in somatic or germinal tissue; (2) occur spontaneously (although rare examples are probably mutations, others that occur frequently or routinely are probably genetically programmed recombinants); (3) be induced experimentally by various means, including chemical mutagens and, especially, high-energy radiations; and (4) be detected genetically or cytologically at metaphase and, especially when homologous regions synapse, at prophase I and at interphase of nuclei with polynemic chromosomes.

GENERAL REFERENCES

Muller, H. J. 1954. The nature of the genetic effects produced by radiation. In *Radiation biology*, Hollaender, A. (Editor), New York: McGraw-Hill Book Company, Chap. 7, pp. 351–473.
Russell, L. B. 1962. Chromosome aberrations in experimental animals. Progr. Med. Genet., 2: 230–294.

SPECIFIC SECTION REFERENCES

18.3   Schindler, A.-M., and Mikamo, K. 1970. Triploidy in man. Report of a case and a discussion on etiology. Cytogenetics, 9: 116–130.
18.4   Gibson, D. A. 1970. Somatic homologue association. Nature, Lond., 227: 164–165. (Somatic pairing in the Tasmanian rat kangaroo during mitosis.)
       Heitz, E., and Bauer, H. 1933. Beweise für die Chromosomennatur der Kernschleifen in den Knäuelkernen von *Bibio hortulanus* L. (Cytologische Untersuchungen an Dipteren, I). Z. Zellforsch, 17: 67–82. (Giant polynemic chromosomes are described.)
       Painter, T. S. 1933. A new method for the study of chromosome rearrangements and plotting of chromosome maps. Science, 78: 585–586. Reprinted in *Classic papers in genetics*, Peters, J. A. (Editor), Englewood Cliffs, N.J.: Prentice-Hall, Inc., 1959, pp. 161–163.

Hermann Joseph Muller (1890–1967) in 1963. Dr. Muller was the recipient of a Nobel prize in 1946. (Photograph by Scientific Products.)

18.5   Griffen, A. B., and Bunker, M. C. 1964. Three cases of trisomy in the mouse. Proc.
       Nat. Acad. Sci., U.S., 52: 1194–1198.

       Neurath, P., De Remer, K., Bell, B., Jarvik, L., and Kato, T. 1970. Chromosome loss
       compared with chromosome size, age, and sex of subjects. Nature, Lond., 225:
       280–281. (In man.)

18.6   Blakeslee, A. F. 1934. New Jimson weeds from old chromosomes. J. Hered., 25:
       80–108.

       Blakeslee, A. F., and Belling, J. 1924. Chromosomal mutations in the Jimson weed,
       Datura stramonium. J. Hered., 15: 194–206.

18.8   Ephrussi, B., and Weiss, M. C. 1965. Interspecific hybridization of somatic cells.
       Proc. Nat. Acad. Sci., U.S., 53: 1040–1042.

       Ephrussi, B., and Weiss, M. C. 1969. Hybrid somatic cells. Scient. Amer., 220 (No. 4):
       26–35, 146.

       Harris, H. 1970. *Cell fusion*. Cambridge, Mass.: Harvard University Press.

       Stone, W. H., Friedman, J., and Fregin, A. 1964. Possible somatic cell mating in twin
       cattle with erythrocyte mosaicism. Proc. Nat. Acad. Sci., U.S., 51: 1036–1044.

       Volpe, E. P., and Earley, E. M. 1970. Somatic cell mating and segregation in chimeric
       frogs. Science, 168: 850–852. (Another example *in vivo*.)

18.12 Dubinin, N. P., and Nemtseva, L. S. 1970. The phenomenon of "vesting" in ring
       chromosomes and its role in the mutation theory and understanding of the
       mechanism of crossing-over. Proc. Nat. Acad. Sci., U.S., 66: 211–217. (X-rayed
       dry *Crepis* seeds can contain an internally deleted rod chromosome which is
       encircled by or vested in the deleted segment whose ends have joined to form a ring.)

       Kristenmacher, M. L., and Punnett, H. H. 1970. Comparative behavior of ring
       chromosomes. Amer. J. Human Genet., 22: 304–318.

18.13 Kadotani, T., Ohama, K., Sofuni, T., and Hamilton, H. B. 1970. Aberrant karyotypes
       and spontaneous abortion in a Japanese family. Nature, Lond., 225: 735–736.
       (Probably due largely to half-translocations in the F_1 both of whose parents are
       reciprocal translocation heterozygotes.)

       Nusbacher, J., and Hirschhorn, K. 1969. Autosomal anomalies in man. Adv. in
       Teratology, 3: 1–63.

18.14 Rowley, J. D. 1969. Cytogenetics in clinical medicine. J. Amer. Med. Assoc., 207
       (No. 5): 914–919.

Lewis John Stadler (1896–1954) is noted for his
studies on the nature of mutation and of the
gene. He and H. J. Muller discovered independently the mutagenic effect of X rays. [From
Genetics, 41: 1 (1956).]

SUPPLEMENTARY SECTIONS

S18.9a The absorbed energy of radiation occurs in the form of heat and of activated and ionized particles. Many chromosome breaks are caused by ion clusters produced by highly energetic radiations.

Chromosome breakage is an energy-requiring biochemical event. Radiation can provide this energy, the particular biochemical consequences depending upon the form and amount of energy absorbed. Less energetic radiations (such as visible light) leave energy in the form of *heat*; more energetic radiations (such as ultraviolet light) leave energy in the form of heat and *activation*; the latter type of energy makes an electron move from an inner to an outer orbit of an atom. The more energetic the radiation, the greater the likelihood that the energy absorbed will lead to chemical change. For example, ultraviolet light produces more breaks in chromosomes than does visible light.

Radiations of energy higher than ultraviolet light (X rays and gamma rays; alpha and beta rays; electrons, neutrons, protons, and other fast-moving particles) are even more capable of causing breaks. Although such high-energy radiations also leave energy in the form of heat and activation, most of the energy left in the cells is in the form of electrically charged particles, or *ions*, produced by *ionization*. When a highly energetic wave is stopped (or a fast-moving particle is captured or slowed down), energy absorbed by the atoms of the medium can cause an atom to lose an orbital electron, creating an ion. Such an electron, torn free of the atom, goes off at great speed and can, in turn, cause other atoms to lose orbital electrons—to be ionized. All atoms losing an electron, of course, become positively charged ions, and atoms that capture free electrons become negatively charged ions. Since each electron lost from one atom is eventually gained by another atom, ions occur as pairs. In this way a path or track of ion pairs, or an *ion track*, is produced which often has smaller side branches. The length of the main or primary ion track and its side branches and the density of ion pairs differ with the type and energy of the radiation involved. Fast neutrons make a relatively long, rather uniformly thick ion track; fast beta rays or electrons make a relatively long, uniformly thin or interrupted track of ions; ordinary X rays make a relatively short track sparse in ions at its origin becoming only moderately dense at its end. All known ionizing radiations produce clusters of ion pairs within microscopic distances. In other words, no amount or kind of high-energy radiation presently known can produce only single ions, or single pairs of ions evenly spaced over microscopic (hence, relatively large) distances.

Since one ion or a pair sufficiently separated from the next does not exist, the genetic effects of ionization must be determined from the activity of clusters of negatively and positively charged ions. Ions undergo chemical reactions to neutralize their charge to reach a more stable configuration. It is during this process that ion clusters are able to produce chromosome breaks (Figure 18-10A).

S18.9b The roentgen (r) unit measures the amount of energy absorbed in the form of ions; the rad unit measures the total amount of absorbed energy.

The amount of ionization produced by radiation is measured in terms of an ionization unit called the *roentgen*, or *r unit*, one r being equal to about 1.8×10^9 ion pairs per cubic centimeter of air. A sufficiently penetrating radiation (such as fast electrons), producing this 1.8×10^9 ion pairs in a given cubic centimeter of air, can also produce this amount in successive cubic centimeters of air because only a very small fraction of the incident radiation is absorbed at successive depths. If not very energetic X rays are used, all radiation may be absorbed near the surface of the medium, keeping the deeper regions free from ionization. The amount of energy left at any level depends not only upon the energy of the incident radiation, but also upon the density of the medium through which the radiation passes. Thus, in tissue, which is approximately 10 times as dense as air, a penetrating high-energy radiation produces about 1,000 times the number of ion pairs per cubic centimeter as it does in air. It is calculated that one r is able to produce, on the average, less than one ion pair in a *Drosophila* sperm head. Since ions occur in clusters, one r may place dozens of ion pairs in one sperm head and none in dozens of other sperm heads. The r unit measures only the absorbed energy which produces ions; another unit, the *rad*, measures the total amount of radiant energy absorbed by the medium. In the case of X rays, about 90 per cent of the energy left in the tissue is used to produce ions; the rest produces heat and excitation. Since ultraviolet radiation is nonionizing, its dosage is measured in rads and not r units.

S18.9c Since the thickness and length of an ion track vary with the type of ionizing radiation, these variables determine the number and location of the breaks. The number of breaks increases linearly with the dose as measured in r units. Ion clusters must occur close to, or within, the chromosome that they break.

The number of chromosome breaks produced by X rays increases linearly with the radiation dose (r) (Figure 18-20). This relationship means

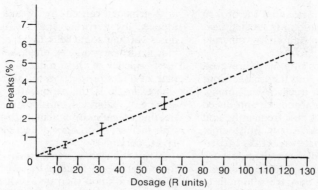

Figure 18-20   Relation between X-ray dosage and the frequency of breaks induced in grasshopper chromosomes. (See J. G. Carlson, 1941. Proc. Nat. Acad. Sci., U.S., 27:46.)

that X rays always produce at least some ion clusters large enough to cause a break. Moreover, clusters of ions from different tracks of ions do not combine their effects to cause a break. (If there were such cooperation between clusters, the break frequency at low doses would be lower than what has been found because of the waste of clusters too small to break; the frequency at higher doses would be higher because of the cooperation among such clusters.) Certain radiations, like fast neutrons, produce fewer breaks per r than X rays because one r of these radiations produces larger—and, hence, fewer—clusters, of ions than do X rays. These larger clusters more often exceed the size needed to produce a break, and therefore, because they waste ions are relatively less efficient in breakage than X-ray-induced clusters.

Ion clusters can produce breaks either directly by attacking the chromosome itself, or indirectly by attacking oxygen-carrying molecules (which, in turn, react with the chromosomes) or other chemical substances (which in turn, affect the chromosome or oxygen-carrying molecules). In any case, this indirect pathway must be of nearly submicroscopic dimensions; otherwise, different ion clusters would be able to cooperate in causing breakage. Thus, only ion clusters in or very close to the chromosome can produce breaks in it, as has been visibly demonstrated by using beams of penetrating radiation of microscopic diameter. Such a beam passing through a metaphase chromosome can break it, but fails to do so when directed at the protoplasm adjoining the chromosome.

Bacq, Z. M., and Alexander, P. 1961. *Fundamentals of radiobiology,* second edition. New York: Pergamon Press, Inc.
Ionizing radiation. 1959. Scient. Amer., 201:No. 3.
Muller, H. J. 1958. General survey of mutational effects of radiation. In *Radiation biology and medicine,* Claus, W. D. (Editor), Reading, Mass.: Addison-Wesley Publishing Company, Inc., Chap. 6, pp. 145–177.

S18.13a   Whether they result from one or two breaks, all chromosomal rearrangements induced by a single ion track increase linearly with r dose, have no threshold dose, and therefore, are unaffected by protracting or concentrating the dose.

Since, under given conditions, the number of breaks increases linearly with an ionizing dose—each part of the dose independently producing its proportional number of breaks—clearly, the number of breaks produced is also independent of the rate at which a given total dose is administered. It also follows that all structural changes in chromosomes resulting from single breakages are also independent of the radiation dose rate. Radiations such as fast neutrons which produce long, densely packed ion tracks can frequently induce two chromosome breaks with the same track. In this case, if the same chromosome—having folded or coiled tightly—is broken twice by being twice in the path of the track, then large and small structural changes of inversion, deficiency, and duplication types can be produced. The frequency of these rearrangements increases linearly with fast neutron dose and is independent of the dose rate.

A single fast neutron-induced track of ions can also break two different chromosomes when chromosomes are closely packed together, as they are in the sperm head. The linear increase with dose in the frequency of reciprocal translocation obtained after sperm are treated with fast neutrons provides evidence for concluding—as was done in Section 18.9—that proximity of sticky ends favors their union. Such a linear dose-effect can be obtained only if both breaks are produced by the same track and if the broken ends capable of exchange union are located near each other—broken ends produced by different tracks being too far apart.

When ordinary X rays are employed, however, the ion clusters are smaller, and the track of ions is shorter than fast neutron tracks. Accordingly, two breaks in the same chromosome are produced by the same X-ray ion track less frequently, and if they do occur, they are usually quite close together. Note, however, that two breaks occurring within submicroscopic distances in successive gyres of a coiled chromosome produce structural changes whose size ranges only from minute to small. Nevertheless, a small proportion of single X-ray tracks—in the treatment of sperm, for example—do cause two breaks, each in a different chromosome. Therefore, for X-ray doses that produce fewer than two tracks per sperm, gross chromosomal rearrangement frequency increases linearly with dose. So, actually every dose of X rays has some chance of producing a gross rearrangement. In other words, no matter how small a dose of ionizing radiation is received, the possibility of a chromosomal break and a gross chromosomal mutation always exists.

Abrahamson, S., Gullifor, P., Sabol, E., and Voigtlander, J. 1971. Induction of translocations in mature *Drosophila* oocytes over a dose range of 10–500 roentgens of X-rays. Proc. Nat. Acad. Sci., U.S., 68: 1095–1097.

S18.13b   Two-or-more-break structural changes produced by ion clusters in separate, independently occurring tracks increase in frequency faster than the amount of dose and have a threshold dose. If joining of ends can take place during the course of irradiation, such rearrangements are reduced in frequency by protracting the delivery of the total dose.

In the case of X rays or fast electrons, two breaks that occur in the same nucleus usually result from the action of two ion clusters, each derived from a different, independently arising track, so that each break is induced independently. Two-break gross rearrangements of this origin are dose dependent, for when a small enough dose is given, a nucleus is traversed by only one track and, therefore, only one-track—not two-track—gross rearrangements ordinarily result. But when the dose is large enough for a nucleus to be traversed by two separate tracks, the two breakages required for two-break gross rearrangements are readily produced independently. The higher the dose of X rays used, therefore, the greater the efficiency in producing multibreak gross re-

arrangements caused by breaks independently induced by separate tracks. Accordingly, for doses causing some cells to experience two such independently produced breaks and higher doses, the frequency of these mutations increases more than in direct proportion to the amount of dose. One example is the exponential rise in the frequency of reciprocal translocation obtained after treating sperm in inseminated *Drosophila* females with increasing dosages of fast electrons (Figure 18-21, curve T).

X-ray induced rearrangements involving two (or more) breaks induced by separate tracks may also depend upon the rate at which a given dose is administered. When a suitably large dose is given over a short interval, the ends produced by separate breaks exist simultaneously and are able to cross-unite. But when the same dose is given more slowly, the pieces of the first break may restitute before those of the second are produced, thus eliminating the opportunity for cross union. In this event, the same dose produces fewer gross rearrangements when given in a protracted manner than when given in a concentrated manner. Although this dose-rate dependence for X rays is true for most cells—at least during part of the interphase stage—it does not apply to mature sperm of animals, probably including man. In these gametes and during most of nuclear division in other cells, the broken pieces cannot join each other, and therefore, accumulate. For this reason, it makes no difference how quickly or slowly the dose is given to the chromosomes in such a sperm head, since the breaks remain unjoined at least until the sperm head swells after fertilization.

Brewen, J. G. 1963. Dependence of frequency of X-ray-induced chromosome aberrations on dose rate in the Chinese hamster. Proc. Nat. Acad. Sci., U.S., 50: 322–329.
Herskowitz, I. H., Muller, H. J., and Laughlin, J. S. 1959. The mutability of 18MEV electrons applied to *Drosophila* spermatozoa. Genetics, 44: 321–327.

S18.13c   The frequencies of both breakage and joining can be modified by the physical–chemical state of the chromosomes and by other cellular structures and functions.

As already mentioned, the spatial arrangement of chromosomes with respect to each other influences the number of breaks and the kinds of structural changes they produce. The possibilities for multiple breakages and for joinings are quite different for chromosomes packed into the tiny head of a sperm than they are for chromosomes located in a large nucleus. But even within a given

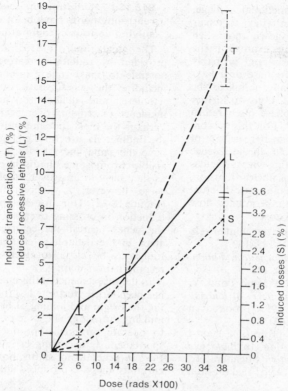

Figure 18-21 / Percentage of mutation, ± 2 times the standard error, recovered from *Drosophila* sperm exposed to different dosages of 18-meV electrons. The X-limited recessive lethal frequencies (L) are joined by solid lines and are adjusted for the control rate; sex chromosome loss frequencies (S) are connected by dashed lines and are corrected for the control rate; reciprocal translocation frequencies (T) between chromosomes II and III are connected by dot–dash lines. (See I. H. Herskowitz, H. J. Muller, J. S. Laughlin, 1959. *Genetics*, 44: 326.)

type of cell, other factors can influence breakage or rejoining, such as the presence or absence of a nuclear membrane, the degree of spiralization of the chromosomes, the stress or tension under which the parts of a chromosome are held, the degree of hydration, the amount of matrix in which the genes are embedded, protoplasmic viscosity and the amount of fluid and particulate movement around the chromosomes, gravity, centrifugal force, and vibration.

In cells whose DNA duplexes have just replicated and in somatic or meiotic cells where homologs are synapsed, a special restriction on the movements of the pieces is produced when only some of the apposed strands are broken (as mentioned in Section 18.11). In this situation, the forces that keep parts of one strand adjacent to the corresponding parts of its sister or homolog may prevent the broken pieces from moving apart freely, so that the unbroken strand or strands serve as a splint for the broken one(s) and reduce

the opportunities for cross union. Many factors exist, therefore, which determine to what degree chromosome and chromatid fragments can separate from each other; those affecting the distances between different chromosomes or the parts within a chromosome also affect chromosome and chromatid breakability.

The frequencies and types of structural changes depend also upon the total amount of chromosomal material present in the nucleus and the number and size of the chromosomes into which this material is divided. The rearrangements that occur in different cells of a single individual depend upon whether the cell is haploid, diploid, or polyploid, and upon whether or not particular chromosome regions have already replicated.

Radiation can produce important nonmutating effects upon the chromosomes by damaging nonchromosomal cellular components, which, in turn, affect chromosomal behavior and function. If the cells are capable of repairing such nonchromosomal, structural or functional damage, they will have a longer time in which to repair when a radiation dose is given slowly than when given quickly. The most obvious example is the effect of radiation upon mitosis (and probably meiosis). Cells at about midprophase or a later stage in nuclear division usually complete the process even though irradiated. Cells no further advanced than about midprophase often return to interphase when irradiated. For this reason, ionizing radiation causes a greater degree of synchromy in division than occurs in the absence of radiation. Accordingly, starting with a population of cells in various stages of nuclear division, the chromosomal targets for mutation are different in the later stages of receiving a protracted dose and of receiving a concentrated dose.

Puck, T. T. 1960. Radiation and the human cell. Scient. Amer., 202 (No. 4): 142–153.

Sobels, F. H. 1963. *Repair from genetic radiation*. New York: Pergamon Press, Inc.

Sparrow, A. H., Binnington, J. P., and Pond, V. 1958. *Bibliography on the effects of ionizing radiations on plants, 1896–1955*. Brookhaven Nat. Lab. Publ., 504 (L-103).

Tazima, Y. 1971. Problems of protection against the genetic effect of radiation. In *Biological aspects of radiation protection*, Sugahara, T., and Hug, O. (Editors), Tokyo: Igaku Shoin Ltd., pp. 5–15.

S18.13d Radiation-induced chromosomal rearrangements have been valuable in solving various cytogenetic problems.

The great supply of rearrangements readily provided by radiation treatment has made it possible to make many important discoveries, including the genetic basis of the centromere, telomere, and collochore; and the reduced incidence of crossing over near the centromere. Perhaps the most fundamental contribution was the finding, via structural changes, that the genes have the same linear order in the cytologically visible chromosome, that is, in *chromosome maps*, as they have in crossover maps. The spacing of these, however, is different in the two cases (Figure 18-22). Thus, for example, because of the reduction in crossing over near the centromere, the genes nearest the centromere—spaced far apart in the metaphase chromosome map—are found to be close together in the crossover recombination map.

In the supplements of this chapter our attention has been largely restricted to the factors influencing the origin and joining of breaks produced by ionizing radiation. These factors are also expected to operate on breaks produced by any other spontaneously occurring or induced mechanism. For, in general, no matter how broken nuclear chromosomes are produced, all possess the same properties.

QUESTIONS AND PROBLEMS

1. At least seven viral infections in man are associated with an increased incidence of chromosome rearrangements in white blood cells, for example chromosome loss, chromosome breakage, and other gross structural rearrangements. Apparently, the frequency with which these mutations involve different chromosomes is not random. What molecular explanation can you offer for such viral effects?

2. For an ordinarily diploid individual, parthenogenetic development as a haploid usually produces abnormalities. Development is sometimes less abnormal, however, if chromosome doubling occurs at an early developmental stage. Explain both observations.

3. Which is more likely to have an abnormal distribution of chromosomes during meiosis, an autotetraploid or an allotetraploid? Explain.

4. Describe at least two different ways that the trisomy causing Down's syndrome may originate.

5. The only presently known case of trisomy for a chromosome of the 19–20 group occurred mosaically in a 6-year-old boy. To what do you attribute this?

6. Discuss the statement: All somatic cells from diploid zygotes are chromosomally identical.

7. Do you suppose that the human species will benefit from a discovery that certain of its members are trisomic? Explain.

8. What genetic explanation can you offer for the fact that the seed capsule of the Datura haploid is smaller than that of the triploid?

9. What do you consider to be the advantages and disadvantages of polynemy?

10. Unfertilized mammalian eggs can contain ploidies of 1N, 2N, 3N, or 4N. Explain how each of these could be produced.

11. How can you explain the fact that persons with Down's syndrome are more susceptible to leukemia than normal diploids?

12. Explain why individuals with Down's syndrome show a wide variety of phenotypic differences as well as similarities in their abnormalities.

13. Would you expect a correlation between

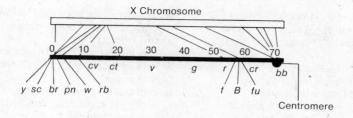

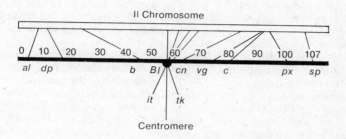

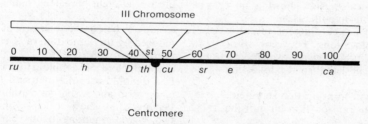

Figure 18-22   Comparison of chromosome (hollow bar) and crossover (solid bar) maps in *D. melanogaster*.

producing a child with Down's syndrome and the frequency with which the mother has abortions? Subsequent children with Down's syndrome? Explain.

14. Should a woman with a trisomic mongoloid sibling be more than ordinarily concerned about having a child of this type? Explain.

15. The terms euploid and aneuploid (hypo- or hyperploid) have been applied to both individual chromosomes and to whole nuclei. Give an example of
   a. a hypoploid chromosome in a euploid nucleus.
   b. a hyperploid chromosome in a hyperploid nucleus.
   c. an aneuploid nucleus containing all structurally normal chromosomes.

16. Given the chromosome AB/CDE/F.GHI/J, where the period indicates the centromere and the slanted lines the positions of three simultaneously produced breaks, draw as many different outcomes as possible. Indi-

cate which one is most likely to occur.

17. Discuss the origin of monosomics among human zygotes.

18. In human chromosomes at mitotic metaphase, discuss the detectability of the following:
   a. Paracentric inversion.
   b. Pericentric inversion.
   c. Deficiency.
   d. Duplication.
   e. Half-translocation.

19. What characteristics of cells undergoing oogenesis favor the production and viable transmission of half-translocations?

20. In *Drosophila*, a male, dihybrid for the mutants *bw* and *st*, when crossed to *bw bw st st*, normally produces offspring whose phenotypes are in a 1:1:1:1 ratio. On exceptional occasions, this cross produces offspring having only two of the four phenotypes normally obtained. How can you explain such an exception?

21. Explain how you could cytologically determine the position of the locus for *white* on the X chromosome of *Drosophila* by each of the following:
   a. Deficiencies of various sizes.
   b. Inversions of various sizes.
   c. Various reciprocal translocations.

22. Suppose you had a self-maintaining strain of *Drosophila* in which all females were yellow-bodied and males, gray-bodied. How would you explain this consistency if the egg mortality were always 50 per cent? Low, as it is normally? How would you test your hypothesis cytologically?

23. a. Several X-linked mutants in *Drosophila* cause notched wings. One of these mutants is lethal in the male and also in the mutant homozygote female. How do you suppose such a homozygote is produced?
   b. A female heterozygous for this mutant ($N/+$) is mated to a facet, fa/Y, male. In F_1 all sons are normal, half the daughters are normal, and half are both notched and faceted. Explain this result showing how you might test your hypothesis.

24. Make a diagram of the different eucentric reciprocal translocations between autosomes 2 and 3 in *Drosophila* which you would expect to be lethal in the following cases:
   a. When either half-translocation is present.
   b. When one half-translocation but not the other is present.
   c. Under no circumstances.

25. Does the absence of crossing over in male *Drosophila* facilitate the detection of heterozygous reciprocal translocations? Explain.

26. Given a *Drosophila* heterozygous for a eucentric reciprocal translocation between chromosomes 2 and 3 and assume both half-translocations are lethal when present separately. Discuss the nature of the recombinational linkage maps one would obtain from mating
   a. genetically marked females of this type with appropriately marked nontranslocation males.
   b. genetically marked males of this type with appropriately marked nontranslocation females.

27. A chromosome A.BCDEEDCFG has a reverse repeat, or duplication, for CDE. Compare the stability of this chromosome with A.BCDECDEFG, which carries a tandem repeat or duplication for the same region.

28. Do you suppose that chromosomes exposed to X rays are more likely to undergo structural change when they are densely spiralized than when relatively uncoiled? Why?

29. Discuss the relative efficiency, per r, of small doses of X rays and of fast neutrons in producing structural changes in chromosomes.

30. Do you suppose that the mutability of ultraviolet light threatens man's survival? Explain.

31. Compare the number and fate of breakages induced by the same dose of X rays administered to
   a. a polyploid and a diploid liver cell in man.
   b. a diploid neuron in man and *Drosophila*.
   c. a sperm and a spermatogonium in man.

32. Persons that show a loss–gain involving two whole nonhomologous chromosomes (for example, persons who are both monosomic X and trisomic 21) are more frequent than expected from the chance simultaneous occurrence of the separate events. Show how the two events are dependent in their occurrence if synapsis occurs between nonhomologs, especially in the meiosis of XYY individuals.

Chapter 19

Of Nonmendelian Genes in Nucleated Cells

In Chapter 1 we noted that DNA and RNA are found not only in nuclei and nuclear areas, but in other parts of the cell as well. At the start of Chapter 5 we decided that before we can consider such nucleic acids to be genetic material, they must be shown to be replicas that have been (or are expected to be) replicated or transcribed. Let us now consider the occurrence and properties of nucleic acids in organelles outside the nucleus to see whether they are genetic material. We will also consider such genetic material's function, organization, distribution, and recombination.

19.1 As in procaryotes, genes that are not distributed to progeny cells by means of a spindle during mitosis and meiosis are nonmendelizing, and are called nonmendelian genes.

We have seen that eucaryotic cells use a spindle mechanism in mitosis and meiosis to distribute nuclear chromosomes in specific ways. The genes of these nuclear chromosomes, therefore, are also distributed in specific ways; for example, they undergo segregation during meiosis. Such genes are called *mendelian genes* since their distribution follows the segregation principle first discovered by Mendel for nuclear genes in meiotic organisms. Because a procaryote such as *E. coli* does not have a spindle for such segregation, its chromosomes are said to carry *nonmendelian genes*, which nonetheless are distributed in a regular manner during bacterial division and can segregate from a diploid to a haploid condition.

19.2 The cytoplasm and nucleus of eucaryotic cells may contain nonmendelizing genes from other organisms.

Eucaryotic cells may contain genetic material from other organisms such as viruses, rickettsiae, and bacteria which is nonmendelizing because it does not use the host's spindle apparatus to be distributed to host daughter nuclei. Some of this nonmendelian genetic material is restricted to the cytoplasm—for example, the genetic material of DNA viruses such as rabbit pox virus, some RNA viruses, and certain rickettsiae. Cytoplasmic nonmendelian genes are also present in the bacteria or their derivatives that infect *Paramecium* (see Section S19.2) and other protozoa.

The genetic material of viruses located in the nucleus also may be distributed in a nonmendelian manner. For example, the RNA genetic material of TMV found in the nucleus (and also in chloroplasts) seems to be independent of the spindle of the tobacco cell.

Foreign or dispensable nonmendelian genes have been found in many eucaryotic organisms, including *Drosophila*.[1] It should be noted that the mendelian genetic material of eucaryotic intracellular parasites such as certain protozoa, algae, and yeasts may be distributed in a nonmendelian manner when their host cells divide. (R)

19.3   By integrating into nuclear chromosomes, nonmendelian genetic material of viruses and bacteria may become mendelian.

Considerable evidence has been obtained that the DNA's of viruses such as polyoma and SV40 can integrate into the nuclear chromosomes of their host cells, in which condition they behave as mendelian genetic material. Since these DNA's probably also exist off the chromosome in dividing cells, they are probably sometimes nonmendelian genes. In this connection it should be recalled that although the RNA genetic material of Rous sarcoma virus seems to be nonmendelian, its DNA complement is apparently integrated into a host chromosome where it probably acts as mendelian genetic material.

The experiments discussed in Section S19.3 provide evidence that nonmendelian bacterial DNA can enter barley nuclei where it can integrate with barley DNA, thereby possibly becoming mendelian genetic material. (R)

19.4   Among an organism's own genes some, nuclear in origin, may be distributed in a nonmendelian manner. Other nonmendelian genes may be in the DNA of extranuclear organelles.

We should note that a gene which does not segregate from an allele during meiosis is not necessarily an extranuclear or a typical nonmendelian gene, since certain loci (for example, loci that are X- or Y-limited) occur in nuclear chromosomes and have no alleles from which to segregate. Furthermore, a nuclear chromosome with a centromere abnormality may be distributed in a nonmendelian manner. In organisms still evolving a meiotic mechanism or ones in which meiosis has degenerated, gene distribution may be somewhat irregular as compared with normal meiosis.

Copies of some nuclear genes, for example those coding for the nucleolus in certain oocytes, are released from chromosomes and are either retained free in the nucleus or liberated to the cytoplasm (see Chapter 24). Some of these genes continue to be transcribed, and cells containing these may undergo division. In such cases copies of mendelian genes are distributed in a nonmendelian manner.

Various organelles outside the nucleus, some of which contain DNA, are not distributed to daughter cells by the spindle mechanism. Such DNA may be extranuclear nonmendelian genetic material and is the subject of the remaining sections in this chapter.

[1] CO_2 sensitivity in *Drosophila* is due to the presence of a particle called *sigma*. Sigma contains DNA, is mutable, and has many of the characteristics of a virus including infectivity by experimental means. Certain sigma and episome characteristics are similar. Some melanotic tumors in *Drosophila* may also depend upon the presence of an episome-like particle.

19.5   Plastids are cytoplasmic bodies that seem to contain genetic material.

Many plant cells, but not bacteria and blue-green algae, contain cytoplasmic bodies called *plastids*. Some, the *chloroplasts* (Figure 19-1), are green because they contain chlorophyll; others, the *leucoplasts*, are white. The number of chloroplasts per cell varies from 1 (in the alga *Spirogyra*) to 30 to 50 (in a leaf cell). Chloroplasts lose their pigment in the dark to become leucoplasts, but revert to chloroplasts upon exposure to sunlight. In maize, several mutations of nuclear genes affect the sequence of reactions leading to the manufacture of chlorophyll. One such mutation prevents plastids from producing any chlorophyll at all, so they become leucoplasts, which cannot function in photosynthesis.

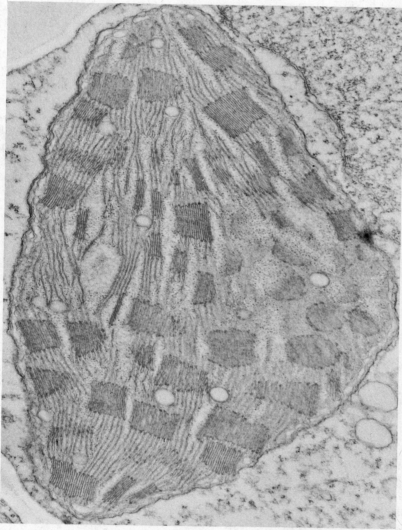

Figure 19-1   Electron micrograph of a cross section of a maize chloroplast. (Courtesy of A. E. Vatter; from G. Becker, 1972. *Introductory concepts of biology*, New York: Macmillan.)

Certain maize plants have mosaic leaves; that is, some leaves are striped green and white. The white parts, which contain leucoplasts that cannot become green, can survive by receiving nourishment from the green parts. This mosaic phenotype is apparently not due to a nuclear gene transmitted through a gamete, since striping persists even when all paternal and maternal nuclear chromosomes are replaced by means of matings with nonstriped individuals. The cause of this mosaicism is indicated by the following experiment. Sometimes a green-and-white striped portion of a plant gives rise to an ovary which develops into an ear of maize. When the kernels in such an ear are planted in rows that correspond to their positions in the cob, white and green seedlings occur in groups (Figure 19-2), as though a pattern of striping that occurred in the ovary had persisted in the cob. The greenness of whiteness of a seedling thus seems to be maternally determined. Support for this hypothesis is that the color of the parental part which forms the pollen (and, hence, the male gamete) has no influence on seedling color. Since pollen grains are not known to carry plastids and since the one key factor proves to be the color of the tissue giving rise to the ovary, it appears that only the plastids within an ovum determine seedling color.

Cells located at the border between green and white tissues contain plastids of both fully green and completely white types. These two kinds of plastids within the same cell seem to have no influence upon each other, and appear to develop according to their intrinsic capacities. When a zygote (or other cell) containing both kinds of plastids produces daughter cells which receive only white or only green plastids, these daughter cells give rise to sectors only of white or only of green tissue. Plastids thus seem to arise only from preexisting plastids; and daughter plastids appear to be of the same color type as their parent. Since they are self-replicating, mutable (capable

Figure 19-2   Groups of albino and nonalbino seedlings from kernels planted in rows corresponding to their positions in a cob produced by a green–white striped plant. (Courtesy of M. M. Rhoades.)

of being changed), and capable of replicating their mutant condition, plastids seem to contain genetic material.[2] (R)

19.6   Chloroplast DNA is probably genetic material.

Chloroplasts contain DNA which has the following general characteristics. It has a MW greater than 10^7, is double-stranded, rod-shaped, not complexed with histone, and contains no detectable amount of 5-methylcytosine. That chloroplast DNA has and retains an individuality is also indicated by the following. *Chlamydomonas reinhardi* is a one-celled alga with two flagella and a single chloroplast. Nonnuclear DNA of *Chlamydomonas*—including chloroplast DNA—is conserved through mitotic and meiotic divisions; *Chlamydomonas* chloroplast DNA has a lower guanine + cytosine content than cellular DNA as a whole, and has unique dinucleotide sequences. In *Euglena* only 15 per cent of chloroplast DNA (reported to be circular and 40 nm long) hybridizes with nuclear DNA when both are single-stranded.

Supporting the idea that chloroplast DNA is self-replicating is the finding, in 1-week-old seedlings of tobacco, that chloroplast DNA replicates several times faster than nuclear DNA. This hypothesis is also supported by finding DNA polymerase in tobacco chloroplasts whose newly synthesized chloroplast DNA hybridizes 45 per cent with chloroplast DNA but only 7 per cent with nuclear DNA. It is likely, therefore, that chloroplast DNA is self-replicating, hence genetic material. It should be noted, however, that the DNA polymerase in the chloroplast, of *Chlamydomonas* at least, seems to be neither coded nor the result of translation in the chloroplast. This is indicated from the continued division of the chloroplast (hence the continued replication of chloroplast DNA via a polymerase) despite treatment with rifampicin which causes loss of chloroplast ribosomes. (R)

19.7   Some transcripts of chloroplast (and nuclear) DNA may be translated in the chloroplast.

Since DNA-dependent RNA polymerase is found in chloroplasts, transcription is expected to occur there. The effect of rifampicin in causing loss of ribosomes is attributed to its effect in inhibiting the functioning of chloroplast (as it does bacterial, but not nuclear) DNA-dependent RNA polymerase, which in turn results in the loss of synthesis of chloroplast rRNA.

Some translation may also occur in chloroplasts since these organelles contain ribosomes. Chloroplast and cytoplasmic ribosomes differ; the former is similar to the "70s" procaryotic type,[3] whereas the latter is 80s.

---

[2] In another study, a cross of two all-green maize plants produced some green-and-white-striped progeny. These striped plants prove to be homozygous for a mutant nuclear gene, *iojap* (*ij*), for which their parents were heterozygous. Since colorless plastids in ova of striped plants remain colorless in subsequent generations, even in homozygotes for the normal nuclear allele, the plastids' lack of color is not due to interference by *ij ij* in the biosynthetic pathway leading to the production of chlorophyll pigment. The simplest explanation for this effect is that, in the presence of *ij ij*, a plastid gene essential for chlorophyll production is mutated to a non-functional form.

[3] This ribosome is actually 68s, composed of 33s and 28s subunits, containing 22s and 16s RNA, respectively.

It is possible that some structural proteins and enzymes of the chloroplast, some proteins of chloroplast ribosomes, etc., are also coded in chloroplast DNA. Note, however, that the DNA polymerase in chloroplasts may be neither coded nor translated in chloroplast DNA (as mentioned in the previous section), and that the mRNA for ribulose-1,5-diphosphate carboxylase is apparently transcribed from nuclear DNA and translated in the chloroplast. (R)

19.8   *Chlamydomonas* seems to possess an extensive system of nonmendelian genes that are transmitted usually by one sex type only, can recombine postmeiotically, and are probably located in chloroplast DNA.

A single haploid *Chlamydomonas* can reproduce asexually by means of mitotic cell division to produce a clone. No sexual reproduction is observed between members of a single clone, which are all of the same mating type (either + or −). When individuals of different mating type are mixed together, they can pair, fuse, and produce diploid zygotes. After two meiotic divisions, the zygote produces four haploid cells which, when isolated, give rise to two clones of the + mating type and two of the − mating type. It thus appears that mating type is determined by a single mendelian gene having *mt*⁺ and *mt*⁻ alleles.

The wild-type *Chlamydomonas* is genetically sensitive to streptomycin (*sm–s*). Somehow this drug acts as a mutagen to induce certain streptomycin-resistant (*sm–r*) individuals. When such *sm–r* individuals are crossed with *sm–s* essentially all progeny become streptomycin resistant when the *sm–r* parent is *mt*⁺ (Figure 19-3). Essentially none of the progeny become *sm–r*, however, when the *sm–r* parent is *mt*⁻. In other words, only *mt*⁺ parents ordinarily seem to transmit an allele determining streptomycin sensitivity to the zygote; moreover, all meiotic products ordinarily seem to receive a copy of whatever streptomycin-sensitivity allele persists in the zygote. Thus, *sm–s* and *sm–r* do not seem to be distributed to the zygote or its meiotic products in the expected mendelian manner. These and other results indicate that streptomycin sensitivity is due to a nonmendelian gene. Streptomycin also causes a large number of *Chlamydomonas* prototrophs to become auxotrophs by mutating other genes having the same nonmendelian characteristics.

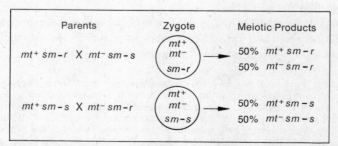

Figure 19-3 Distribution of genes of mendelian (*mt*⁺, *mt*⁻) and nonmendelian (*sm–r, sm–s*) types in *Chlamydomonas*. In this case, persisting nonmendelian genes are ordinarily contributed to a zygote uniparentally, and to all the meiotic products of a zygote.

In rare cases, zygotes retain nonmendelian genes from both parents rather than just from the mt^+ parent. The progeny of such zygotes from crosses involving one or more nonmendelian loci show that the nonmendelian genes can recombine postmeiotically, that is, in the mitotic divisions that follow meiosis. Some of the loci are recombinationally linked, and two different, seemingly allelic, mutants can recombine to produce either the wild-type allele or the corresponding "double" mutant.

Such studies indicate the existence of an extensive nonmendelian genetic system in *Chlamydomonas*. Various indirect lines of evidence indicate these genes are probably located in semiconservatively-replicating chloroplast DNA. (R)

19.9   A genetic recombination linkage map of nonmendelian genes in *Chlamydomonas* is circular.

In *Chlamydomonas*, when one of the parents (mt^+) is treated with ultraviolet radiation just before mating, the zygote routinely retains the nonmendelian genomes of both parents. Such zygotes provide progeny that can be isolated and classified with regard to two or more nonmendelian markers for which the parents differed. Figure 19-4 summarizes the procedure for obtaining progeny to be classified for all markers. Thus, for example, $ac2^+\, ac1 \times ac2\, ac1^+$ produces $ac2^+\, ac1/ac2\, ac1^+$ zygotes. Mitotic progeny of the zygotes are scored as being (1) dihybrid heterozygotes (containing all four alleles), (2) segregants that contain parental combinations of alleles only (having the markers $ac2^+\, ac1$, or $ac2\, ac1^+$), or (3) what are apparently primary-structure recombinants (for example, containing $ac2^+$ and $ac1^+$ only). Recombination

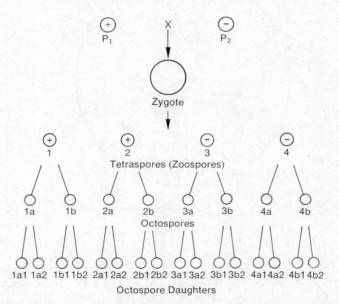

Figure 19-4 Procedure for pedigree analysis. Gametes are mated and zygotes plated. After germination, progeny of individual zygotes are replated at the octospore stage and after one more doubling each pair of octospore daughter cells is separated and allowed to form colonies. The 16 colonies, representing the first two doublings of each zoospore, are then classified for all segregating markers. Sex type is marked as + or −. (After R. Sager.)

frequency is expressed as the number of primary-structure recombinants per total progeny scored.

Recombination frequencies have been obtained in this way for nine nonmendelian loci. These frequencies show that all nine loci are linked and, moreover, can be arranged in a circular map based on relative frequency of recombination (Figure 19-5). The map seems to show polarity as indicated by a postulated *attachment point* (*ap*). The data indicate that the zygote and its progeny are diploid for this linkage group, implying a regular mechanism for its distribution. (R)

19.10   Mitochondria seem to contain genetic material.

Mitochondria (Figure 19-6) are organelles, found in all cells except bacteria and blue-green algae, consisting of a smooth outer membrane that is probably continuous with the endoplasmic reticulum and an inner membrane that forms double-layered folds, or cristae. The outer membrane is, in general, permeable to substances with a molecular weight up to 10,000. The cristae with attached elementary particles contain the enzymes that catalyze the process of oxidative phosphorylation—the major pathway for energy production in aerobic cells. The number of mitochondria

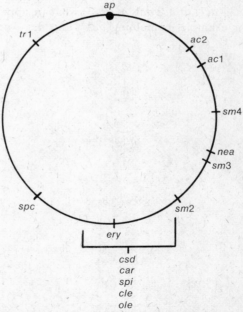

Figure 19-5 Circular genetic map of nonmendelian genes in *Chlamydomonas* based on recombination frequencies. (Courtesy of R. Sager.) *ap*, attachment point; *ac2* and *ac1* acetate-requirement; *sm4*, streptomycin dependence; *nea*, neamine resistance; *sm3*, low-level streptomycin resistance; *sm2*, high-level streptomycin resistance; *ery*, erythromycin resistance; *csd*, conditional streptomycin dependence; *car*, carbomycin resistance; *spi*, spiramycin resistance; *cle*, cleasine resistance; *ole*, oleandomycin resistance; *spc*, spectinomycin resistance; and *tr1*, temperature sensitivity.

per cell varies from one (in a unicellular alga) to hundreds (in a kidney cell) to the thousands (in giant cells).

When a cell divides the daughters by chance receive approximately equal numbers of mitochondria. Mitochondria, which have been seen to divide transversely, probably always arise from preexisting mitochondria. Moreover, since mitochondria undergo phenotypic modifications (including those affecting membrane morphology and protein content) which are replicated and seem to be based upon mutations in non-mendelian genes,[4] mitochondria seem to contain genetic material. (R)

19.11   Mitochondrial DNA is probably genetic material.

Mitochondria contain double-stranded DNA which is not complexed with histone and seems to be located inside the inner membrane and to be attached to the membrane at one point. In higher organisms this DNA is usually circular, about 5 μ long, with a MW of 9 to 10×10^6, which is lower than that of chloroplast DNA, containing about 14,000 base pairs. A mitochondrion contains one to three nuclear areas, or *nucleoids*. Since each area can contain more than one circular molecule of DNA, a mitochondrion can average four to five circular molecules of DNA, the range being two to eight. Even though higher organisms have circular mitochondrial DNA about 5 μ long, careful measurements indicate that they are all slightly different in length from each other. The total amount of DNA in the approximately 250 mitochondria in a mouse fibroblast is only about 0.15 per cent of the amount in the nucleus of that cell.

Although some circular mitochondrial DNA is found in yeasts and molds, these as well as other microorganisms such as protozoans (*Tetrahymena* and *Paramecium*) usually have mitochondrial DNA that is rod-shaped and of higher molecular weight.[5]

Five kinds of cytological–chemical evidence support the hypothesis that mitochondrial DNA is genetic material.

[4] Several mutant yeast strains (called "petite" mutants) form tiny colonies on agar. When such individuals are crossed with normal-sized ones, a 1:1 ratio of normal:petite results after segregation. These strains, which are caused by mutant nuclear genes, are called *segregational petites*. When normal yeast cells are treated with the acridine dye euflavin, or with ethidium bromide—dyes known to intercalate in double-stranded DNA—numerous petite colonies arise that do not segregate regularly when crossed with normal yeast. The ease with which these *vegetative petites* are induced and the subsequent failure of the petite gene to segregate properly indicate that they are caused by a mutant nonmendelian gene. Some change in mitochondrial membrane morphology has been detected for petites; the slow growth of petites is due largely to the absence of respiratory enzymes, cytochromes a, a_3, b, and c, and a deficiency in some dehydrogenases, known to reside in mitochondria.

In *Neurospora* a slow-growing strain, "poky," fails to show segregation when crossed with a wild-type strain. The trait is not linked to any nuclear chromosome and is apparently due to a maternally transmitted mutant nonmendelian gene. Poky individuals have morphologically abnormal mitochondria, in which an amino acid substitution has occurred in a structural protein. Young cultures of poky have no cytochromes a and b, but make an excess of a cytochrome c. As the culture ages, it starts producing cytochromes a and b, the excess cytochrome c, which seems to be coded in the nucleus, is diluted out, and the phenotype approaches that of the wild type.

Another maternally transmitted mutant in *Neurospora* has a defective respiratory metabolism even though all the normal respiratory enzymes are present. This strain also has been found to have defective mitochondrial structural protein.

[5] In *Tetrahymena*, for example, each mitochondrion has about seven open DNA duplexes each about 17.6 μ long. Some of the open molecules in yeast have single-stranded ends which can base-pair to circularize the molecule.

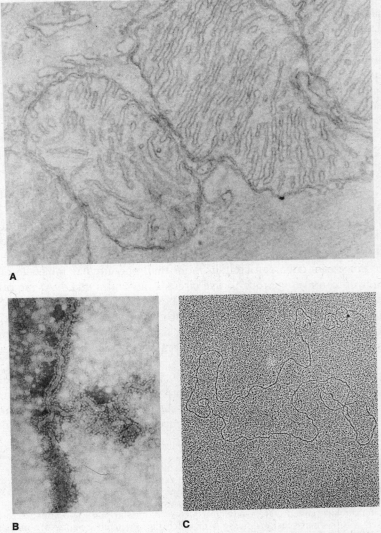

A

B   C

Figure 19-6   Electron mierographs of (A) mouse heart mitochondria ($\times 38,000$), (B) *Neurospora* mitochondria prepared to show cristae with elementary particles attached ($\times 35,000$), and (C) the outline of *Neurospora* mitochondrial DNA ($\times 16,000$). (Courtesy of Dr. Walther Stoeckenius.)

1. In *Neurospora*, mitochondrial DNA is conserved, that is, is not disintegrated and dispersed, during vegetative multiplication and sexual reproduction. In the latter case, the DNA is transmitted predominantly by the maternal parent.
2. The integrity and individuality of mitochondrial DNA is supported by finding that its base composition and melting temperature differ from that of nuclear DNA; little base pairing occurs between nuclear and mitochondrial DNA when both are single-stranded (in the mouse, however, 40 to 70 per cent of the mitochondrial DNA hybridizes with nuclear DNA); mitochondrial

DNA has 5-methylcytosine, but less than does nuclear DNA. Certain yeasts, mutant in nonmendelian genes, have mitochondria with altered DNA base ratios and buoyant densities.

3. In *Saccharomyces*, as in *Tetrahymena* and *Physarum*, mitochondrial DNA synthesis is discontinuous and occurs, in the cell cycle, slightly before nuclear DNA synthesis. (Mitochondrial DNA replicates semiconservatively.)

4. Electron micrographs show circular molecules of mitochondrial DNA which are apparently self-replicating (and/or are being transcribed) within the mitochondrion.

5. Intact duplex mitochondrial DNA undergoes one-complement transcription *in vitro*. *In vivo*, however, both the heavy (H) and light (L) complements are transcribed—all of the H and at least part of the L strand.

These findings, together with the ones mentioned previously, lead us to conclude that mitochondrial DNA is probably a copied copy, and, therefore, genetic material. (R)

19.12   Mitochondrial DNA undergoes primary and quaternary structure recombination, as detected in cytochemical, cytological and, probably, gene-action studies.

Whereas most mitochondrial DNA occurs in the form of single circles, an appreciable amount also occurs normally in doubled condition, that is, as double circles—either as double-length (2 to 4 per cent) or as interlocked pairs of the single-length circle (5 to 10 per cent). Larger concatemers are also found. By certain chemical treatments, especially protein starvation, as much as 70 per cent of mitochondrial DNA can be induced to occur in double circles. Return to normal physiological culture conditions returns the tissue to normal double-circle frequency, suggesting that the generation of circular dimer and higher multiple forms of mitochondrial DNA is reversible. This is cytochemical evidence of recombination, some of which apparently involves mitochondrial DNA primary structure.

Quaternary structure genetic recombination of the DNA's in different mitochondria is also indicated by cytological observations of mitochondria dividing and fusing together.

Studies of gene action have provided evidence for intermitochondrial recombination which probably involves DNA primary structure. In yeast erythromycin (E), spiramycin (S), and paromomycin (P) are drugs that affect protein synthesis in the mitochondrion only. Whereas the normal yeast is sensitive (s) to these drugs, nonmendelian mutant strains have been obtained which are resistant (r) to each of these drugs individually. The genes involved seem to be located in mitochondrial DNA. When two different yeast strains are mated and cultured anaerobically, for example, $E^s P^r \times E^r P^s$, zygotes yield progeny not only of parental types ($E^s P^r$ 25; $E^r P^s$ 19), but of recombinant types also ($E^s P^s$ 31; $E^r P^r$ 5). Although the double-resistant clones ($E^r P^r$) can be explained as the result of the survival of both parental genotypes in some progeny, the large number of double sensitives ($E^s P^s$) as well as further tests of recombinants strongly support the view that recombination has occurred at the level of primary DNA structure and that, at least under anaerobic conditions, segregation occurs to produce cells that are haploid with respect to these loci. The frequency of recombinants has been used to make a linear linkage map for these loci, presumably in mitochondrial DNA. (R)

19.13.   Some mitochondrial components are (1) imported, (2) unique, (3) exported.

Imported components

The mitochondrial DNA of higher organisms is less than 15,000 base pairs long. If all this DNA were used to code for protein, it would furnish information for approximately 5,000 amino acids, or only about 50 proteins each 100 amino acids long. Since mitochondria are known to contain some 70 enzymes, including respiratory enzymes and at least 20 different aminoacyl-tRNA synthetases, plus various other structural and ribosomal proteins, it is clear that some mitochondrial protein components are coded in extramitochondrial genetic material. Specific evidence has been obtained for the involvement of nuclear genes in the production of several proteins found in mitochondria.[6]

Unique components

Since the mitochondrial DNA of higher and lower organisms differ in length, these DNA's may differ in the number and kinds of mitochondrial components they code —higher organisms, with shorter mitochondrial DNA's, coding fewer mitochondrial components. The fact that an appreciable portion of mitochondrial DNA does not hybridize with nuclear DNA suggests, moreover, that mitochondrial DNA codes for unique RNA's and proteins. This is supported by the following:

1. Mitochondrial ribosomes differ from cytoplasmic ribosomes. For example, in *Neurospora* the mitochondrial ribosome is of the "70s" type[7] and the cytoplasmic ribosome is of the "80s" type[8]. In most higher animals (which have 80s cytoplasmic ribosomes) the mitochondrial ribosome is 60s.[9] Hybridization studies show that these mitochondrial rRNA's are unique and coded in the mitochondrial DNA. Mitochondrial rRNA–mitochondrial DNA hybridization studies reveal that the genes for the two kinds of rRNA are repeated at least four times in mitochondrial DNA.

2. At least 17 tRNA's for different amino acids, including fMet tRNA, are found in mitochondria, and the results support the hypothesis that these comprise a unique set, differ-

[6] This evidence consists of finding a nuclear mutant in *Neurospora* whose mitochondria have no or little Leu-tRNA synthetase. The type of malic dehydrogenase found in mitochondria seems to be under nuclear gene control in maize. In yeast, cytochrome c is synthesized on 80s ribosomes in the cytoplasm, using mRNA transcribed from nuclear DNA, then imported by mitochondria.

[7] This ribosome is 73s, composed of a 50s-like and a 37s subunit, containing, respectively, 23s and 16s RNA.

[8] This ribosome is 77s, composed of a 60s-like and a (different) 37s subunit, containing, respectively, 25s and 17s RNA.

[9] This ribosome is composed of 43s and 32s subunits, containing "21s" and 13s RNA, respectively.

ing from those coded in the nucleus.

3. At least three different aminoacyl-tRNA synthetases have been found to be exclusive to mitochondria. These may be coded in mitochondrial DNA.

4. Mitochondria contain a DNA polymerase that is distinct from nuclear DNA polymerase and may be coded in mitochondrial DNA.

5. Present evidence indicates that in yeast, at least, mitochondrial DNA codes for a portion of the inner mitochondrial membrane.

Exported components

Transcripts of some mitochondrial information seem to be shipped and used outside of mitochondria. This conclusion is supported by finding RNA complementary to mitochondrial DNA associated with cytoplasmic ribosomes of nuclear origin that are attached to the endoplasmic reticulum. (R)

19.14   The properties of centromeres, centrosomes, and kinetosomes indicate that they are structurally and functionally related. The DNA's they contain seem to be homologous.

A granular structure, the *centriole*, is sometimes seen within the *centrosome*, the organelle that serves as a pole at each end of the spindle in animal cells. The centriole is cylindrical and in cross section appears to be composed of nine sets of three tubules each (Figure 19-7). The inner tubule of each set is connected to the outer tubule of an adjacent set. When two centrioles are together (as after the centriole "divides") they are usually oriented perpendicular to each other.

Likewise, granules are sometimes seen within the *centromere* (Figure 19-8), an organelle structurally somewhat similar to the centriole. Furthermore, both centrosome and centromere granules appear to contain double-stranded DNA. The DNA

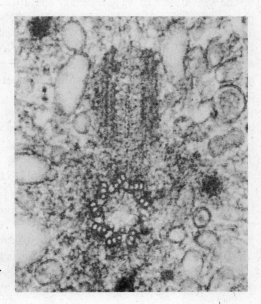

Figure 19-7   Electron micrograph of a pair of centrioles in a human cell grown in tissue culture. (Courtesy of A. E. Vatter; from G. Becker, 1972. *Introductory concepts of biology*, New York: Macmillan.)

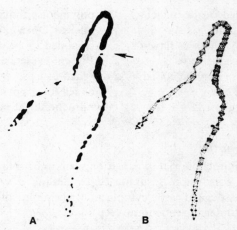

Figure 19-8 Centromere and its granules in maize. (Courtesy of A. Lima de Faria, 1958. J. Hered., 49: 299.)

of the centromere is apparently a coiled thread which passes from one chromosome arm to the other.

Centromeres and centrosomes both are motile. Centromeres are sometimes attracted to each other, and are attracted to the centrosomes at anaphase. During the meiotic divisions preceding sperm formation in a particular mollusk, some chromosomes degenerate and release "naked" centromeres. These bodies group together at the centrosome and thereafter mimic centrosomal behavior and appearance exactly. Assuming that the structural and functional properties common to centromeres and centrosomes are coded in their own DNA's, the DNA's of these two organelles would seem to be homologous. Evidence indicates that the *kinetosome*, the granular body at the base of each cilium or flagellum responsible for ciliary and flagellar motion, also contains DNA which may be homologous to the DNA's in centrioles and centrosomes.

The *kinetoplast* of *Trypanosoma* contains a significant amount of DNA, 40 to 70 per cent of which hybridizes with nuclear DNA, as well as a histone-like protein. Such large cytoplasmic organelles, which are associated with mitochondria, are (like kinetosomes) involved with motility. DNA replication occurs synchronously in nucleus and kinetoplast; the latter can be damaged irreversibly by treatment with acridine dyes. The information stored in kinetoplast DNA is presently under investigation.

Further information about the DNA's in centrosomes, kinetosomes, and kinetoplasts is needed before they can be classified as genetic material. (R)

SUMMARY AND CONCLUSIONS

Although most of the genetic information in a eucaryotic cell is contained in nuclear DNA which is distributed to progeny nuclei by a mendelian (spindle-utilizing) mechanism that assures the constancy of chromosomal content generation after generation via mitosis, meiosis, and fertilization, other nonmendelian genetic material is usually, probably always, present in the cell.

Such genetic material may be infective, comprising the DNA or RNA genomes of viruses or other microorganisms which may replicate in the nucleus, the cytoplasm, or in cytoplasmic organelles. Although these genomes can replicate independently of host chromosomes and undergo nonmendelian distribution, parts or all of some of them or their DNA copies may be able to integrate with host nuclear chromosomes and become mendelian genetic material. Such behavior by genetic material would be, therefore, episomal.

Eucaryotic cells contain nonmendelian DNA, in such normally present organelles as chloroplasts and mitochondria, which in view of various evidences presented is probably genetic material. Chloroplasts and mitochondria seem to be (1) procaryotic, and (2) endosymbiotic. They are procaryote-like because each seems to contain only one kind of chromosome which can replicate and be distributed to progeny in a regular, but nonmendelian, manner (this apparently involves a mesosomal-type bacterial mechanism in mitochondria at least) and whose primary structure recombination yields linkage maps. Moreover, they contain ribosomes that differ from those free in the cytoplasm but resemble those of bacteria.

Chloroplasts and mitochondria are symbiote-like because the "host" cannot exist without their products or functions; and because their limited genetic material does not code for all their characteristic substances (for example, proteins), some of which, therefore, must be coded in "host" genetic material. In this connection various examples are given of the importation by these two organelles of (1) nucleic acid and protein components needed for the replication, transcription, and translation of organellar information, or (2) substances coded in nuclei that are needed for the special structures or functions of these organelles.

Even though chloroplasts and mitochondria can be recognized to be procaryotic endosymbiotes at present, we do not know whether they arose as degenerate derivatives of free-living bacteria, or had an origin that was independent of bacteria. We also do not know to what extent primary structure recombination occurs between the DNA's of different types of organelles (including that in centromeres, centrosomes, and kinetosomes, which seem to be homologous, and in kinetoplasts); nor do we know to what extent primary structure recombination occurs between organellar DNA's and infective nucleic acids.

GENERAL REFERENCES

Charles, H. P., and Knight, B. C. J. G. (Editors). 1970. *Organization and control in prokaryotic and eukaryotic cells.* Cambridge: Cambridge University Press.

Cohen, S. 1970. Are/were mitochondria and chloroplasts microorganisms? Amer. Scientist, 58: 281–289.

Ephrussi, B. 1953. *Nucleo-cytoplasmic relations in micro-organisms.* Oxford: Clarendon Press.

Goodenough, U. W., and Levine, R. P. 1970. The genetic activity of mitochondria and chloroplasts. Scient. Amer., 223 (No. 5): 22–27, 132.

Granick, S., and Gibor, A. 1967. The DNA of chloroplasts, mitochondria, and centrioles. Progr. Nucleic Acid Res. and Mol. Biol., 6: 143–186.

Miller, P. L. (Editor). 1970. *Control of organelle development.* Sympos. Soc. Exp. Biol., No. 24. Cambridge: Cambridge University Press.

Sager, R. 1972. *Cytoplasmic genes and organelles.* New York: Academic Press, Inc.

SPECIFIC SECTION REFERENCES

19.2   Barigozzi, C. 1963. Relationship between cytoplasm and chromosome in the transmission of melanotic tumours in *Drosophila.* In *Biological organization*, pp. 73–89, New York: Academic Press, Inc.

Lanham, U. N. 1968. The Blochmann bodies: hereditary intracellular symbionts of insects. Biol. Rev., 43: 269–286.

L'Héritier, P. 1958. The hereditary virus of *Drosophila*. Adv. Virus Res., 5: 195–245. (Describes sigma.)

Preer, L. B. 1969. Alpha, an infectious macromonuclear symbiont of *Paramecium aurelia*. J. Protozool., 16: 570–578.

Wolstenholme, D. R. 1965. A DNA and RNA-containing cytoplasmic body in *Drosophila melanogaster* and its relation to flies. Genetics, 52: 949–975.

19.3   Sambrook, J., Westphal, H., Srinivasan, P. R., and Dulbecco, R. 1968. The integrated state of viral DNA in SV40-transformed cells. Proc. Nat. Acad. Sci., U.S., 60: 1288–1295.

19.5   Kirk, J. T. O., and Tilney-Bassett, R. A. E. 1967. *The plastids*. San Francisco: W. H. Freeman and Company, Publishers.

Rhoades, M. M. 1946. Plastid mutations. Cold Spring Harbor Sympos. Quant. Biol., 11: 202–207.

Rhoades, M. M. 1955. Interaction of genic and non-genic hereditary units and the physiology of non-genic inheritance. In (Vol. 1) *Encyclopedia of plant physiology*, Ruhland, W. (Editor), Berlin: Springer-Verlag, pp. 19–57.

19.6   Chiang, K.-S. 1968. Physical conservation of parental cytoplasmic DNA through meiosis in *Chlamydomonas reinhardi*. Proc. Nat. Acad. Sci., U.S., 60: 194–200.

Surzycki, S. J. 1969. Genetic functions of the chloroplast of *Chlamydomonas reinhardi*: effect of rifampsin on chloroplast DNA-dependent RNA polymerase. Proc. Nat. Acad. Sci., U.S., 63: 1327–1334.

Wells, R., and Sager, R. 1971. Denaturation and renaturation kinetics of chloroplast DNA from *Chlamydomonas reinhardi*. J. Mol. Biol., 58: 611–622. (A major fraction seems to be repeated about 24 times.)

19.7   Hoober, J. K., and Blobel, G. 1969. Characterization of the chloroplastic and cytoplasmic ribosomes of *Chlamydomonas reinhardi*. J. Mol. Biol., 41: 121–138.

19.8   Sager, R. 1965. Genes outside the chromosome. Scient. Amer., 212 (No. 1): 70–79, 134.

19.10 Rifkin, M. R., and Luck, D. J. L. 1971. Defective production of mitochondrial ribosomes in the *poky* mutant of *Neurospora crassa*. Proc. Nat. Acad. Sci., U.S., 68: 287–290.

Roodyn, D. B., and Wilkie, D. 1968. *The biogenesis of mitochondria*. London: Methuen & Company, Ltd.

Tracy M. Sonneborn, about 1966. (Photograph by Dellenback.)

Smoly, J. M., Kuylenstierna, B., and Ernster, L. 1970. Topological and functional organization of the mitochondrion. Proc. Nat. Acad. Sci., U.S., 66: 125–131.

19.11   Aloni, Y., and Attardi, G. 1971. Symmetrical *in vivo* transcription of mitochondrial DNA in HeLa cells. Proc. Nat. Acad. Sci., U.S., 68: 1757–1761.

Borst, P., and Kroon, A. M. 1969. Mitochondrial DNA: physiochemical properties, replication, and genetic function. Intern. Rev. Cytol., 26: 107–190.

Chèvremont, M. 1963. Cytoplasmic deoxyribonucleic acids: their mitochondrial localization and synthesis in somatic cells under experimental conditions and during the normal cell cycle in relation to the preparation for mitosis. Sympos. Int. Soc. for Cell Biol., 2: 323–331.

Nass, M. M. K. 1969. Mitochondrial DNA: advances, problems, and goals. Science, 165: 25–35.

19.12   Nass, M. M. K. 1969. Reversible generation of circular dimer and higher multiple forms of mitochondrial DNA. Nature, Lond., 223: 1124–1129.

Sarkissian, I. V., and McDaniel, R. G. 1967. Mitochondrial polymorphism in maize, I. Putative evidence for *de novo* origin of hybrid-specific mitochondria. Proc. Nat. Acad. Sci., U.S., 57: 1262–1266.

Thomas, D. Y., and Wilkie, D. 1968. Recombination of mitochondrial drug-resistance factors in *Saccharomyces cerevisiae.* Biochem. Biophys. Res. Commun., 30: 368–372.

19.13   Dawid, I. B., and Chase, J. W. 1972. Mitochondrial RNA in *Xenopus laevis.* II. Molecular weights and other physical properties of mitochondrial ribosomal and 4s RNA. J. Mol. Biol., 63: 217–231.

Gross, S. R., McCoy, M. T., and Gilmore, E. B. 1968. Evidence for the involvement of a nuclear gene in the production of the mitochondrial leucyl-tRNA synthetase of *Neurospora.* Proc. Nat. Acad. Sci., U.S., 61: 253–260.

Küntzel, H. 1969. Mitochondrial and cytoplasmic ribosomes from *Neurospora crassa*: characterization of their subunits. J. Mol. Biol., 40: 315–320.

19.14   Brinkley, B. R., and Stubblefield, E. 1966. The fine structure of the kinetochore of a mammalian cell *in vitro.* Chromosoma, 19: 28–43. (Centromere structure.)

Friedländer, M., and Wahrman, J. 1970. The spindle as a basal body distributor: a study in the meiosis of the male silkworm moth, *Bombyx mori.* J. Cell Sci., 7: 65–89. (Accurate distribution of centrioles.)

Laurent, M., and Steinert, M. 1970. Electron microscopy of kinetoplastic DNA from *Trypanosoma mega.* Proc. Nat. Acad. Sci., U.S., 66: 419–424.

Lima de Faria, A. 1956. The role of the kinetochore in chromosome organization. Hereditas, 42: 85–160. (Evidence that the centromere contains DNA.)

Pollister, A. W., and Pollister, P. F. 1943. The relation between centriole and centromere in atypical spermatogenesis of viviparid snails. Ann. N.Y. Acad. Sci., 45: 1–48.

Simpson, L., and da Silva, A. 1971. Isolation and characterization of kinetoplast DNA from *Leishmania tarentolae.* J. Mol. Biol., 56: 443–473.

SUPPLEMENTARY SECTIONS

S19.2   The DNA genetic material of the extranuclear endosymbiote kappa is transmitted nonmendelianly to *Paramecium* progeny via fission and conjugation.

Kappa particles (and the similar lambda or mate-killer particles) are infective apparently different Gram-negative bacteria located in the cytoplasm of certain strains of the protozoan *Paramecium.* Hundreds of kappa particles can be easily seen in a single cell (Figure 19-9). They contain double-stranded DNA (and very probably RNA) and are self-reproducing. Individuals containing kappa are called *killers,* since animal-free fluid obtained from cultures of killer paramecia will kill sensitive (kappa-free) individuals.

Mutant kappa particles are known to produce modified poisons. Kappa is liberated into the medium once it develops a highly refractile granule, which sometimes appears as a "bright spot" under the microscope. One "bright-spot" kappa particle is enough to kill a sensitive individual. Kappa has a specific relationship to its host, in that a particular host gene (K) must be present for kappa to maintain itself, that is, reproduce. Killer individuals homozygous for the host allele (k) cannot maintain kappa, and after 8 to 15 divisions, kappa particles are lost and sensitive individuals result.

Although kappa can be transmitted from one generation of *Paramecium* to the next, its distribution to the next generation depends upon

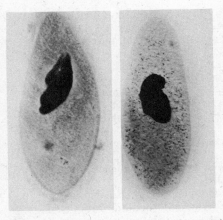

Figure 19-9 Normal (left) and kappa-containing (right) *Paramecium*. (Courtesy of T. M. Sonneborn, 1950. Heredity, 4: facing p. 26.)

the mechanism by which the new generation is initiated. Two such mechanisms—asexual and sexual—are described briefly, with special reference to kappa transmission.

A typical *Paramecium* contains a diploid *micronucleus* and a highly polyploid (about 1,000N) *macronucleus* (or *meganucleus*). When the parent divides asexually by *fission*, two daughter paramecia are produced. Both micronucleus and macronucleus replicate and separate; when fission is completed, both daughter cells are chromosomally identical to each other and to their parent cell. Although the cytoplasmic contents are not equally apportioned to the daughters, a killer parent will normally produce two killer daughters since each receives some of the hundreds of kappa particles present in the parental cytoplasm. Successive fissions by the killer daughters will produce a clone of chromosomally identical killer individuals. Similarly, successive fissions of a sensitive *Paramecium* will produce a clone of sensitive individuals.

A new generation can also be formed sexually. When clones of different mating type are mixed, a *mating reaction* occurs which involves individuals of different mating types sticking together to form larger and larger clumps of paramecia. After this clumping, members of different mating types undergo *conjugation* in pairs. During conjugation (Figure 19-10) the micronucleus of each mate undergoes meiosis to produce four haploid products, three of which subsequently disintegrate. The remaining nucleus divides mitotically to produce two haploid nuclei. Next, one of the two haploid nuclei in each conjugant migrates into the other conjugant, where it joins the nonmotile haploid nucleus to form a single

diploid nucleus in each conjugant. The macronucleus disintegrates during conjugation.

After conjugation the two paramecia separate and produce the exconjugants of the next generation. Since each conjugant contributes an identical haploid nucleus to each fertilization micronucleus, both exconjugants are identical with respect to micronuclear chromosomes—as can be proved by employing various marker genes. (When the conjugants are homozygous for different alleles, the exconjugants are identical heterozygotes.) The diploid micronucleus in each exconjugant divides once mitotically; one product forms a new macronucleus, while the other remains as the micronucleus.

Since all conjugants happen to be resistant to killer action, we can study the consequence upon kappa transmission of mating a killer with a sensitive individual. The cytoplasmic interiors of conjugants are normally kept apart by a boundary probably penetrated only by the migrant haploid nuclei so that little or no cytoplasm is exchanged. Consequently, the exconjugants have the same kappa condition as the conjugants; that is, one is a killer and one is a sensitive individual. Under certain experimental conditions, however, a wide bridge forms between the conjugants allowing the

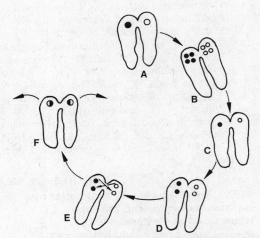

Figure 19-10 Simplified representation of micronuclear events occurring during conjugation in *Paramecium*. Each conjugant has a single diploid micronucleus (A), which following meiosis produces four haploid nuclei (B). Three of these disintegrate (C), and the remaining nucleus divides once mitotically (D). The conjugants exchange one of the haploid mitotic products (E), after which fusion of haploid nuclei occurs (F); so each of the conjugants, which later separate, contains a single diploid micronucleus.

cytoplasmic contents of both mates to flow and mix (Figure 19-11). When the cytoplasmic mixing between killer and sensitive conjugants is extensive, kappa particles flow into the sensitive conjugant and both exconjugants are killers.

Consider how specific nuclear genes are distributed in conjugation. If each conjugant is a micronuclear heterozygote, *A a*, which one of the four haploid nuclei produced by meiosis—*A*, *A*, *a*, or *a*—will survive depends on chance. Accordingly, whether the cytoplasms of the conjugants mix or not, both exconjugants will be *A A* 25 per cent of the time, *A a* 50 per cent of the time, and *a a* 25 per cent of the time. Note again that both exconjugants are identical with respect to micronuclear genes, and that both will give rise to clones phenotypically identical with respect to the micronuclear gene-determined trait under consideration. When dealing with a trait determined by a cytoplasmic particle like kappa, however, the result can be different. In this particular example, the cross of a sensitive individual with a killer produces exconjugants whose type depends upon the occurrence or nonoccurrence of cytoplasmic mixing.

Figure 19-11 Silhouettes of conjugating *Paramecium*. (A) Normal, no cytoplasmic mixing. (B) Wide bridge, permitting cytoplasmic mixing.

Beale, G. H., Jurand, A., and Preer, J. R. 1969. The classes of endosymbiont of *Paramecium aurelia*. J. Cell Sci., 5: 65–91.

Sonneborn, T. M. 1959. Kappa and related particles in *Paramecium*. Adv. Virus Res., 6: 229–356.

Sonneborn, T. M. 1960. The gene and cell differentiation. Proc. Nat. Acad. Sci., U.S., 46: 149–165.

S19.3   Nonmendelian bacterial DNA may become integrated with barley chromosomes in barley seedlings.

Barley DNA is less dense than *Micrococcus lysodeikticus* DNA. If barley seedlings are grown in culture medium containing radioactively labeled DNA isolated from this bacterium, label appears in the nuclei of root cells. If, 24 hours after exposure to this DNA, DNA is isolated from the barley seedling, large pieces of labeled DNA of intermediate density are recovered in the ultracentrifuge. These pieces appear to be approximately one-third bacterial to two-thirds barley in composition. The bacterial DNA portion seems to occur as a duplex attached end to end to duplex barley DNA since (1) sonication of the complex releases DNA of the original bacterial and barley densities, and (2) heat denaturation of the unsonicated complex does not produce single strands of the densities of single-stranded bacterial or barley DNA's. Denatured or sonicated bacterial DNA is not incorporated in the seedling; native bacterial DNA is also incorporated in the barley seedling shoot, although less rapidly than in the root.

When normal barley seedlings are exposed to tritiated deoxythymidine, this label is incorporated into barley DNA and serves as an index of DNA synthesis (DNA, we recall, showing little, if any, turnover). When the seedlings are exposed to this label after having incorporated unlabeled bacterial DNA, the label is also incorporated, preferentially in the DNA of bacterial density. This furnishes evidence that the incorporated bacterial DNA is still self-replicating, that is, genetic material. The basis for the relative lack of incorporation into barley DNA when bacterial DNA is incorporated with it is unknown.

These results strongly suggest that bacterial DNA and barley DNA are integrated together, perhaps accomplished by the same kind of mechanism used for integrating episomes. Confirmation and extension of these results are highly desirable.

Ledoux, L., and Huart, R. 1969. Fate of exogenous bacterial deoxyribonucleic acids in barley seedlings. J. Mol. Biol., 43: 243–262.

Stroun, M., Anker, P., and Auderset, G. 1970. Natural release of nucleic acids from bacteria into plant cells. Nature, Lond., 227: 607–608. (Bacterial RNA found in shoot cells is either taken up directly or transcribed from bacterial DNA taken up directly.)

QUESTIONS AND PROBLEMS

1. Criticize the statement that the same episome may be a mendelian gene at one time and a nonmendelian gene at another.

2. What is your opinion of the text's restriction of mendelian genes to eucaryotic cells that produce a spindle?

3. Do you expect that RNA extranuclear genes will be found to be normal components of nucleated cells? Explain.

4. What evidence would you require for proof that the kinetosome contains genetic material?

5. Calculate the approximate molecular weight of 17.6-μ-long mitochondrial DNA.

6. Keeping in mind the difficulties of proving the existence of extranuclear genes, which do you think represents the primary genetic material in cellular organisms, nuclear or extranuclear genetic material? Explain.

7. Do you think the evidence presented that sex in *Chlamydomonas* is based primarily upon a single pair of genes is conclusive? Justify your answer.

8. Discuss the permeability of mRNA through cellular and organellar membranes.

9. A variety of antibiotics react with 70s ribosomes (but not 80s ribosomes), causing them to malfunction. How can such antibiotics cure eucaryotes of an infection by procaryotes if all eucaryotes also contain the antibiotic-sensitive 70s ribosomes?

10. State two possible reasons why mitochondrial and chloroplast DNA's have not been replaced by additional nuclear DNA.

11. Do you think that the study of nucleocytoplasmic interrelations in *Paramecium* has any bearing upon differentiation processes in multicellular organisms? Explain.

12. Certain paramecia are thin because of a homozygous nuclear gene, *th*. What is the phenotypic expectation for the clones derived from exconjugants of a single mating of th^+th^+ by th^+th? How would cytoplasmic mixing affect your expectation? Why?

13. How do mendelian and nonmendelian genes in *Chlamydomonas* differ with respect to location, transmission, segregation, and chemical composition?

PART V

Genetic Interaction

Chapter 20

Interaction of Phenotypic Effects of Alleles and Nonalleles

The success of an organism does not depend only on the physical–chemical quality and quantity of its genetic material, and how this material is replicated, transcribed for translation, varied, recombined and transmitted. Although these suborganismal features are important components for determining biological success, the phenotype as expressed at the level of the smallest naturally occurring functional unit—the cell—also helps determine whether the whole unit is successful. (No matter how good a muscle cell is in all genotypic respects, it is a failure if, phenotypically, it cannot contract.) This means that to understand the contributions of genes to organisms we need know the principal ways that genes and their products interact to produce the phenotype of a cell, and, in the case of multicellular organisms, the phenotypes of tissues, organs, organ systems, and the integrated whole.

Although later chapters will be concerned with the control of which genes are functional, this chapter and the next three will deal with how the products of functional mendelian genes interact to produce the phenotype. In the present chapter we consider the interaction of the phenotypic (posttranslational) effects of alleles and nonalleles.

20.1 Products of the functioning of the genotype of one organism may be used more or less directly as part of the phenotype of another organism.

Before considering how normally present mendelian genes interact at the post-translational level, we should note that the phenotype of one organism can directly incorporate or utilize the products of functional genes of another organism. Thus, virions of one genotype may have the protein coat of another genotype. For example, one can produce in the test tube infective TMV that have the coat of one genotype and the genetic material of another (see footnote to Section 1.2). Similarly, a mixed infection of ϕT2 and ϕT4, which differ in tail structure, produces some progeny that have ϕT4 tails and ϕT2 genomes and others that have ϕT2 tails and ϕT4 genomes. In this case, therefore, the phage coat sometimes contains a normal but noncorresponding phage chromosome, so the phenotype of the phage does not match its genotype.

Bacterial phenotype can depend upon the presence or absence of a phage genotype. For example, an *E. coli* lysogenic for $\phi\lambda$ is immune to infection by $\phi\lambda$, whereas a nonlysogen is sensitive to such infection. Similarly, although *rII* mutants of ϕT4 can grow in *E. coli* strain K12, they cannot grow in *E. coli* K12(λ)—the same strain lysogenic for λ (see Section S10.4a). Another example of *phage conversion* of a bacterial trait involves the lipopolysaccharides of *Salmonella*, substances which, at the cell surface, serve as receptor sites for certain viruses. These compounds consist of a lipid core to which polysaccharide side chains are attached; the side chains change when the bacterium is lysogenized; the particular modification depends upon the genotype of infecting phage and changes the nature of the phage receptor sites. The production of diphtheria toxin by *Corynebacterium diphtheriae* is also a cooperative effort that requires the bacterium to be lysogenized by particular phages of the β group. Phage genes can also modify the colonial morphology or pigmentation of their bacterial hosts.

The above principles apply also to eucaryotic organisms infected, for example, by viruses. (R)

20.2   Dominance occurs when the phenotype of a heterozygote resembles one homozygote more than the other homozygote.

Suppose, in certain kinds of plant, gene *A* codes for red flower color and allele *A'* for no red color in flowers; and that the *A A* homozygote has red, the *A' A'* homozygote, white flowers. What will be the phenotypic expression of the two alleles in the heterozygous condition, *A A'*? Depending upon the kind of plant under study, all heterozygotes may be red, almost red, pink, pale pink, or white. If a gene causes the phenotype of the heterozygote to appear more like its homozygote than that of its allele, the gene is said to show a *dominant effect* (show *dominance*, or be dominant) and its allele is said to show a *recessive effect* (to show *recessiveness*, or be recessive). Contrary to the best usage of the term, mutants are also said to be dominant when they are expressed phenotypically in heterozygous condition but have an unknown phenotypic effect in homozygous condition because the mutant is too rare or is lethal when homozygous.

In the present case *A* would be completely dominant to completely recessive *A'* if all *A A'* were red; *A* would be partially dominant and *A'* partially recessive in almost-red *A A'*; *A* and *A'* would show no dominance or recessiveness in pink *A A'*; and *A* would be completely recessive to completely dominant *A'* if *A A'* were white. Note that genotypes are masked in cases of complete or almost complete dominance since, in the absence of further crosses, one cannot decide between the heterozygous and a homozygous genotype. Although, for convenience, dominant and recessive are often used in reference to genes, it should be remembered that these terms refer to the phenotypic expression of genes in heterozygous condition and have no relation to their chemistry, integrity, replication, or mode of transmission.

Whenever one is dealing with complete dominance, a cross to an individual recessive for the pairs of mendelian genes involved will always serve to identify the genotype of the other parent, since the phenotypic types and frequencies of the offspring will correspond to the genotypic types and frequencies occurring in the gametes of the latter. This kind of cross is, therefore, called a *test cross*, or a *backcross* when the test-crossed individual had an ancestor recessive for the mendelian genes under study.

20.3   Relative to the normal (wild-type) allele, mutant alleles usually have hypomorphic or amorphic phenotypic effects.

The differences between the phenotypic effect of a mutant allele and its wild-type alternative, the one normally found in the population, can be studied by adding more representatives of the mutant allele to the genotype and examining the effect. In *Drosophila*, for example, the normal fly has long bristles when the normal, dominant gene bb^+ is present. A mutant strain has shorter, thinner bristles because of the recessive allele bb (bobbed bristles), which—it should be recalled—has a locus both in the X and Y chromosomes. We might suppose that the male, or female, homozygous for bb has bobbed bristles because this allele results in thinning and shortening the normal bristle. Since otherwise-diploid XYY males and XXY females can be obtained which carry three bb alleles, according to this view, one would expect the bristles formed to be even thinner and shorter than they are in ordinary mutant homozygotes. But, on the contrary, in the presence of three representatives of bb—that is, three doses of bb—the bristles are almost normal in size and shape. This finding demonstrates that bb functions in the same way as bb^+ does, but to a lesser degree. Mutant alleles whose phenotypic effect is similar but less than the normal gene's effect are called *hypomorphs*. Many *point mutants*, for example, mutants with changes in one or a few genetic nucleotides, are hypomorphs, since, in the absence of the normal gene, additional doses cause the phenotype to become more normal. One can imagine that such point mutations change one or two amino acids in the protein coded, which, nevertheless, still functions structurally or enzymatically, although less efficiently than the normal protein.

Of the remaining mutant alleles, most are *amorphs*; these produce no phenotypic effect even when present in extra dose. One example is the gene for white eye (*w*) in *Drosophila*. In this case a single amino acid change may have sufficed to inactivate the protein completely; or a single base substitution may have terminated the protein prematurely; or, the addition or substraction of a nucleotide gave rise to a phase shift that produced nonsense protein.

Some mutant alleles, *neomorphs*, produce a new effect—adding more doses of a neomorphic mutant causes more departure from normal, whereas adding more doses of the normal alternative has no effect.

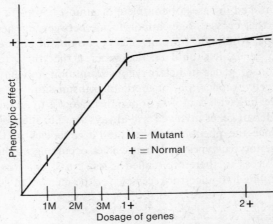

Figure 20-1   Relationship between dosage of normal and mutant alleles and their phenotypic effect.

The relationship between the normal, wild-type gene and its hypomorphic mutants is indicated diagrammatically in Figure 20-1. The vertical axis represents phenotypic effect; the normal, wild-type effect is indicated by " + ." The horizontal axis refers to the dosage of either the normal gene or a hypomorphic mutant. Notice that a single + gene itself produces almost the full normal phenotypic effect (and often the difference between its effect and the normal effect is not readily detected). Two + genes reach the wild-type phenotypic level. In the case of the hypomorphic mutant, however, even three doses may not reach the phenotypic level produced by one + gene (recall the discussion of *bb*). Note also that genetic modifiers or environmental factors, which can shift the position of the genes on the horizontal axis and thereby shift the phenotypic effect, have a decreasing influence as one proceeds from individuals carrying only one dose of mutant toward individuals carrying two + genes.

20.4   Dominance is the natural consequence of one wild-type allele producing almost all the phenotypic effect required and of most mutant alleles being · hypomorphs or amorphs. Most mutants with phenotypic effects, therefore, lower the reproductive potential when pure.

Natural selection would clearly favor alleles that result in phenotypic effects close to wild type—that is, near the curve's plateau (Figure 20-1)—for such alleles assure phenotypic stability. Any mutant that produced such a phenotypic effect would, in the course of time, become the normal gene in the population and would automatically be dominant when heterozygous with a hypomorphic gene alternative. This model illustrates how the heterozygote with one + and one mutant gene has practically the same effect as the normal homozygote, and it seems to best explain most cases of complete or almost complete dominance. Since the normal gene alternative already produces a near-optimum phenotypic effect, this scheme also illustrates why, other things being equal, so few mutants are beneficial, that is, increase the *reproductive potential*—the organism's ability to produce surviving offspring.[1]

Although it is understandable from the preceding discussion that hypomorphic and amorphic mutants are usually detrimental when pure, one may still wonder what effects these mutants have when heterozygous with the normal gene. If the mutant is an amorph, the mutant heterozygote can fall short of producing the wild-type phenotypic effect and, therefore, such mutants are expected to be slightly detrimental when heterozygous. Hypomorphs are expected to be less or not at all detrimental when heterozygous, at least with respect to the trait for which they are classified as hypomorphic. But since each gene affects many different biochemical processes, a mutant hypomorphic in respect to one trait may be amorphic in respect to another. In *Drosophila*, for example, the normal allele *apr*$^+$ which results in dull-red eye color also pigments the Malpighian tubules. One of its alleles, *apr*, causes a lighter eye color (being hypomorphic in this respect) but no color in the Malpighian tubules (being amorphic in this respect). We will postpone until Section 34.3 consideration of examples of mutant heterozygotes whose reproductive potential is greater than that of both the wild-type and the mutant homozygote.

20.5   Dominance can cause the number of phenotypic classes to be less than the number of genotypic classes.

When identical mendelian monohybrids, $A A' \times A A'$, are crossed, the genotypic ratio in F_1 expected under ideal conditions is $1 A A : 2 A A' : 1 A' A'$ (Figure 16-1). If A is completely dominant to A' the expected phenotypic ratio is 3 "A" (composed of $1 A A$ and $2 A A'$):1 "A'" individuals, and the three genotypic classes become only two phenotypic classes.[2]

Consider again next the genotypic consequences of crossing two identical mendelian dihybrids, alleles A and A' being recombinationally unlinked to alleles B and B'. Thus, in the mating $A A' B B' \times A A' B B'$, each parent produces four equally frequent types of haploid gametes (Figure 20-2). Since male and female gametes fertilize each other at random we obtain all the possible gametic unions by using either the branching track or the checkerboard methods of combining gametes at random,

---

[1] The biological fitness of a mutant gene—pure or hybrid—is best described in terms of its effect upon reproductive potential, which includes the mutant-carrying individual's capacity to reach the reproductive stage and its fertility and fecundity during this period, as well as the viability of its offspring until reproductive maturity. In terms of the past evolutionary history of a species, it is understandable that in the great majority of cases, mutants affecting a trait or organ cause its degeneration. All the genotypes in a species have been subjected to selection for many generations, those producing the greatest reproductive potential having been retained. Although point mutation at any locus is a rare event, many of the possible alternatives for each gene must have occurred at least several times in past history. Of these alternatives, only the more advantageous alleles were retained, and these are the ones found in present populations. So, a point mutation today is likely to produce one of the genetic alternatives that occurred also in the past but had been eliminated because of its lower reproductive potential. It should be realized, moreover, that reproductive potential is the result of coordinated action of the whole genotype. The genotype may be likened to the machinery that makes modern automobiles—the automobile representing the phenotype—with the environment furnishing the necessary raw materials. Present genotypes, like the machines that manufacture automobiles, are complex and have had a long evolutionary development. The chance that a newly occurring point mutation will increase reproductive potential is probably smaller than the chance that a random local change in the present machinery will result in a better automobile.

[2] This is the kind of phenotypic ratio Mendel observed in the progeny of self-fertilized monohybrid garden peas.

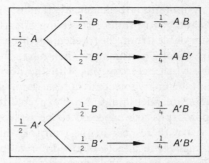

Figure 20-2   Genotypes of gametes formed by a dihybrid, $A\,A'\,B\,B'$, undergoing independent segregation of the two gene pairs.

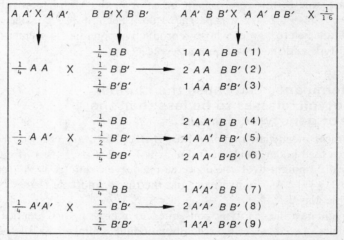

Figure 20-3   Genotypic results of segregation and random fertilization occurring independently for the two gene pairs in the cross $A\,A'\,B\,B' \times A\,A'\,B\,B'$. (See also the legend of Figure 16-4.)

as was done in Figure 16-3. Figure 20-3 obtains the same zygotic products a different way, that is, by having the segregation and random fertilization for $A\,A' \times A\,A'$ and for $B\,B' \times B\,B'$ occur independently of each other (the method used earlier in Figure 16-4).

Recall that among every 16 offspring, on the average, there would be nine different genotypes in the ratio of $1:2:1:2:4:2:1:2:1$. *If neither gene pair shows dominance, and if each pair acts both independently and on different traits,* two $1:2:1$ phenotypic ratios will be produced, and these, when distributed at random, will result in the $1:2:1:2:4:2:1:2:1$ phenotypic ratio (Figure 20-4). Here, because no genotype is masked phenotypically by any other, the phenotypic and genotypic ratios are the same.[3] (This would also be true of the following crosses: $A\,A'\ B\,B' \times A\,A\ B\,B$, $A\,A'\ B\,B' \times A'\,A'\ B'\,B'$, $A\,A'\ B\,B \times A\,A\ B\,B'$.)

When, however, the aforementioned conditions are changed so that one of the

---

[3] This kind of result is illustrated in the progeny of parents both of whom have thalassemia minor ($T\,t$) and MN ($M\,N$) "blood type." ($T\,T$ is phenotypically normal, $t\,t$ has thalassemia major; $M\,M$ is phenotypically M, $N\,N$ is phenotypically N, as discussed in Section S16.1a.)

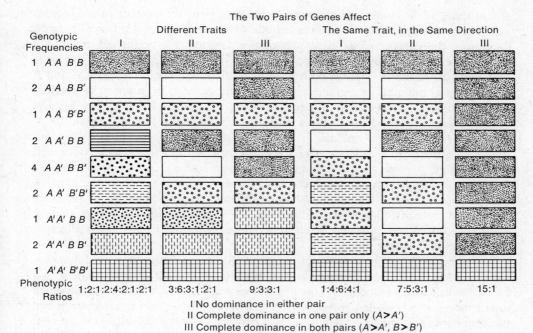

The Two Pairs of Genes Affect

Different Traits — The Same Trait, in the Same Direction

Figure 20-4 Some phenotypic ratios obtainable from crosses between identical dihybrids.

two pairs of genes shows "complete" dominance, two different genotypes will produce the same phenotype, and fewer than nine phenotypes are expected. Thus, if B is completely dominant to B' genotypes 1 and 2 (in Figure 20-3) are expressed as one phenotype, genotypes 4 and 5 as another, and 7 and 8 as another, so that the phenotypic ratio becomes $3:1:6:2:3:1$[4] (Figure 20-4). If both gene pairs show "complete" dominance, one phenotype is expressed by genotypes 1, 2, 4, 5 (both dominants expressed), another by genotypes 3 and 6 (one dominant expressed), another by 7 and 8 (the other dominant expressed), and another by genotype 9 (neither dominant expressed), producing the $9:3:3:1$ ratio[5] (Figure 20-4). Dominance, therefore, causes a reduction in the number of phenotypic classes.

20.6   When epistasis or "dominance between nonalleles" occurs among two or more gene pairs that affect the same trait, the number of phenotypes observed is less than the number of genotypes.

What phenotypic ratios are expected when two different, independently active, pairs of mendelian genes affect the same trait in the same manner or direction? If one or more allelic combinations for one gene pair produce the same phenotype as

---

[4] This is the phenotypic ratio expected in the progeny of parents both having MN blood type ($M\,N$) and heterozygous for albinism ($A\,a$)—$A\,A$ and $A\,a$ are normal, $a\,a$ is albino, as discussed in Section S16.1a.

[5] This is the kind of phenotypic ratio Mendel observed in the progeny of self-fertilized dihybrid garden peas.

one or more allelic combinations for the other gene pair, the number of phenotypes will also be reduced from the maximum (nine when identical dihybrids are crossed). Of course, the number of different phenotypes detected will be further reduced if the absence of dominance in both gene pairs is changed to dominance in one gene pair, and still further reduced if both gene pairs show dominance. Thus, if A and B produce equal amounts of melanin pigment in human skin, the amount of pigment being cumulative, and A' and B' produce none, dominance being absent, a cross between identical mendelian dihybrids yields the ratio 1 "black" (type 1, Figure 20-3): 4 "dark" (types 2, 4): 6 "mulatto" (types 3, 5, 7): 4 "light" (types 6, 8): 1 "white" (type 9), instead of nine different phenotypes, as seen also in Figure 20-4. Moreover, if both A and B show complete dominance, for example either gene producing full flower color, the phenotypic ratio becomes 15 colored (types 1–8): 1 colorless (type 9), as seen also in Figure 20-4. Note that when different pairs of genes act on the same trait in the same direction or way, they have a common phenotypic background on which their effects *superpose* and the effect of one gene pair interferes with the detection of the effect of the other pair.

Sometimes different gene pairs act independently on the same trait in different—antagonistic or cooperative—ways. For example, in *Drosophila* (Figure 20-5), A' is a recessive allele which reduces the wing to a stump, whereas B' is a recessive allele which causes the wing to be curled, the dominant allele A making for normal sized wings and the dominant allele B straight wings. A cross between two identical dihybrids does not produce the expected 9:3:3:1 ratio. In the present case, the ratio becomes 9 flies with long, straight wings: 3 with long, curled wings: 4 whose wings are mere stumps (of which one fourth would have had curled wings if the full wing had formed). Here, then, the phenotypic expression of one gene pair can prevent detection of the phenotypic expression of another gene pair.

In another case, either of two pairs of genes may prevent a given phenotype from occurring. Suppose the dominant alleles A and B each independently contribute something different but essential for the production of red pigment, whereas their corresponding recessive alleles A' and B' fail to make the respective independent contributions to red pigment production. Then crosses between two identical dihybrids will produce 9 red: 7 nonred (composed of 3 homozygotes for A' only, 3 homozygotes for B' only, and 1 homozygote for both A' and B'). Notice that if the recessive

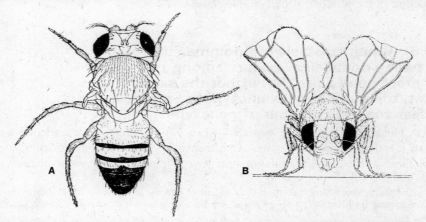

Figure 20-5 *D. melanogaster* mutants showing the no-wing (left) and the curled wing (right) phenotypes. (Drawn by E. M. Wallace.)

alleles are considered, we have just dealt with examples of unilateral and mutual opposition to phenotypic expression, respectively, but if the dominant alleles are considered these become cases of unilateral and mutual cooperation in phenotypic expression.

In all cases where two pairs of genes affecting the same trait interact phenotypically by superposition, antagonism, or cooperation, one pair of genes has had an influence upon distinguishing the effects of the other. The general term *epistasis* is used in these cases to describe the interference with—suppression or masking of—the phenotypic expression of one pair of genes by the members of a different pair. Genes whose detection is hampered by nonallelic genes are said to be hypostatic, or to exhibit *hypostasis*. As dominance implies recessiveness, so epistasis implies hypostasis. There need be no relationship between the dominance of a gene to its allele and the ability of the gene to be epistatic to nonalleles. In theory, then, epistatic action may depend upon the presence of A, A', or $A A'$; moreover, hypostatic reactions may depend upon the presence of B, B', or $B B'$. Consequently, it should be noted that in crosses between identical dihybrids, epistasis–hypostasis can produce phenotypic ratios still different from those already described.

20.7 The interaction of nonallelic genes can sometimes change the kind, and not the number, of phenotypes obtained.

Consider another example of a dihybrid in which both pairs of genes show dominance but no epistasis. In *Drosophila*, the dull-red color of the multifaceted compound eye of flies found in nature is due to the presence of both brown and red pigments. The brown pigment or *ommachrome* is found at the periphery and the red pigment or *pteridine* at the center of each facet or *ommatidium*. Let A be the allele which produces the red pigment and A' its recessive allele which produces no red pigment; let B be the nonallele producing the brown pigment whose allele B' makes no brown pigment. A mating between two dull-red dihybrid flies (from a cross of pure red, $A A B' B'$, by pure brown, $A' A' B B$) produces offspring in the proportion 9 dull red (containing $A - B -$): 3 red (containing $A - B' B'$): 3 brown (containing $A' A' B -$): 1 white ($A' A' B' B'$). The last phenotypic class, resulting from the absence of both eye pigments, is new in this series of crosses. This case illustrates that the interaction of nonallelic genes may result in *apparently novel phenotypes*. Such interactions change not the number but the kind of phenotypes obtained.[6]

The preceding discussion suggests that any given phenotypic trait may be the result of the interaction of several gene pairs. One is even led to conclude that the total phenotype is the product of the total genotype acting together with the environment. The difference between phenotypic and genotypic ratios is often due to products of gene action—by alleles and nonalleles—which superpose, cooperate, or conflict at the physiological or biochemical level.

[6] We see, therefore, that a phenotypic ratio that differs from the expected genotypic one does not necessarily violate either segregation or independent segregation. In fact, gene segregation and independent segregation were first proved by Mendel despite the misleading phenotypic simplifications of genotypic ratios wrought by the occurrence of dominance; moreover, the principle of independent segregation could also have been first proved from crosses involving epistasis or apparently novel phenotypes.

SUMMARY AND CONCLUSIONS

The phenotype of a cell depends upon the translational products of gene action. Although some phenotypic traits of a eucaryotic organism are the products of action of its nonmendelian genes or of the genes of other organisms, most seem to result from the action of its own mendelian genes. Interactions can occur among the translational products of nuclear alleles and nonalleles.

When loci are paired, some degree of dominance is usually found in heterozygotes, recurring mutants usually being hypomorphic or amorphic to the wild-type allele previously selected in nature. When pure, most point mutants are detrimental to reproductive potential.

When little or no interaction of phenotypic effects occurs between nuclear alleles and nonalleles, observed genotypic ratios directly represent expected mendelian genotypic ratios. The occurrence of such interaction, however, between alleles (dominance) or nonalleles (epistasis—including superposition, cooperation, and antagonism) can reduce the observed number of phenotypic classes relative to the expected number of genotypic classes. Other interactions between nonalleles change the kind, not the number, of phenotypic classes. All these phenotypic interactions produce phenotypic ratios that are consistent, however, with expected mendelian genotypic ratios.

GENERAL REFERENCES

Bateson, W. 1909. *Mendel's principles of heredity*. Cambridge: Cambridge University Press.
Lynch, H. T., Mulcahy, G. M., and Krush, A. J. 1970. Genetic counseling and the physician. J. Amer. Med. Assoc., 211: 647–651.
Wagner, R. P., and Mitchell, H. K. 1964. *Genetics and metabolism*, second edition. New York: John Wiley & Sons, Inc.
Wright, S. 1963. Genic interaction. In *Methodology in mammalian genetics*. Burdette, W. J. (Editor). San Francisco: Holden-Day, Inc., pp. 159–192.

William Bateson (1861–1926). [From Genetics, 12: 1 (1927).]

SPECIFIC SECTION REFERENCES

20.1   Losick, R., and Robbins, P. W. 1969. The receptor site for a bacterial virus. Scient.
       Amer., 221 (No. 5): 120–124, 166.

Novick, A., and Szilard, L. 1951. Virus strains of identical phenotype but different
genotype. Science, 113: 34–35.

QUESTIONS AND PROBLEMS

1. A mating of a black-coated with a white-coated guinea pig produces all black offspring. Two such offspring when mated produce mostly black but some white progeny. Explain these results genetically.

2. A cross of two pink-flowered plants produces offspring whose flowers are red, pink, or white. Defining your genetic symbols, give all the different kinds of genotypes involved and the phenotypes they represent.

3. What bearing have the following facts relative to the generality of the phenomenon of dominance?

    When pure lines of smooth-seeded plants and shrunken-seeded plants are crossed, the F_1 seeds are all smooth. Microscopic examination reveals that the margins of the starch granules in the seeds are smooth in the smooth P_1, highly serrated or nicked in the shrunken P_1, and slightly serrated in all the F_1.

4. What conclusions could you reach about the parents if the offspring had phenotypes in the following proportions?
    a. 3:1
    b. 1:1
    c. 9:3:3:1
    d. 1:1:1:1

5. Suppose a particular garden pea plant is a septahybrid. Assuming independent segregation, what proportion of its gametes will carry all seven recessive nonalleles? All seven dominant nonalleles? Some dominant and some recessive nonalleles?

6. In rabbits the following alleles produce a gradation effect from full pigmentation to white: agouti (C), chinchilla (c^{ch}), and albino (c). Another allele, c^h, produces the Himalayan coat color pattern (like that of a Siamese cat). C is completely dominant to all these alleles, c^h is completely dominant to c, whereas c^{ch} shows no dominance to c^h or c.
    a. How many different diploid genotypes are possible with the alleles mentioned?
    b. A light chinchilla mated to an agouti produced an albino in F_1. Give the genotypes of parents and F_1.
    c. An agouti mated to a light chinchilla produced in F_1 one agouti and two Himalayan. Give the genotypes possible for parents and F_1.
    d. An agouti rabbit crossed to a chinchilla rabbit produced an agouti offspring. What genotypic and phenotypic results would you expect from crossing the F_1 agouti with an albino?

7. Two green maize plants are crossed and produce offspring of which approximately $\frac{9}{16}$ are green and $\frac{7}{16}$ are white. How can you explain these results?

8. A chicken from a pure line of "rose" combs is mated with another individual from a pure line of "pea" combs (see the accompanying illustration). All the F_1 show "walnut" combs. Crosses of two F_1 walnut-type individuals provide F_2 in the ratio 9 walnut: 3 rose: 3 pea: 1 "single." Choose and define gene symbols to provide a genetic explanation for these results.

9. Three walnut-combed chickens were crossed to single-combed individuals. In one case the progeny were all walnut-combed. In another case one of the progeny was single-combed. In the third case the progeny were either walnut-combed or pea-combed. Give the genotypes of all parents and offspring mentioned.

10. Matings between walnut-combed and rose-combed chickens gave 4 single, 5 pea, 13 rose, and 12 walnut progeny in F_1. What

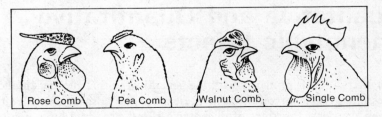

Rose Comb   Pea Comb   Walnut Comb   Single Comb

11. A mating of two walnut-combed chickens produced the following F_1 with respect to combs: 1 walnut, 1 rose, 1 single. Give the genotypes of the parents.

12. A hornless, or polled, condition in cattle is due to a completely dominant gene, P, normally horned cattle being $p\ p$. The gene for red color (R) shows no dominance to that for white (R'), the hybrid ($R\ R'$) being roan color. Assuming independent segregation, give the genotypic and phenotypic expectations from the following matings:
   a. $Pp\ RR \times pp\ RR'$
   b. $Pp\ RR' \times pp\ R'R'$
   c. $Pp\ RR' \times Pp\ RR'$
   d. Hornless roan (whose mother was horned) × horned white.

13. When dogs from a brown pure line were mated to dogs from a white pure line, all the numerous F_1 were white. When the progeny of numerous matings between F_1 whites were scored there were 118 white, 32 black, and 10 brown. How can you explain these results genetically?

14. Using your answer to the preceding question, give the phenotypic and genotypic expectations from a mating between the following:
   a. A black dog (one of whose parents was brown) and a brown dog.
   b. A black dog (one parent was brown, the other was black) and a white dog (one parent was brown, the other was from a pure white strain).

15. When one crosses pure White Leghorn poultry with pure White Silkies, all the F_1 are white. In the F_2, however, large numbers of progeny occur in a ratio approaching 13 white : 3 colored. Choosing and defining your own gene symbols, explain these results genetically.

16. a. In the yellow daisy the flowers typically have purple centers. A yellow-centered mutant was discovered which when crossed to the purple-centered type gave all purple-centered F_1, and among the F_2 47 purple and 13 yellow. Explain these results genetically.
   b. Later, another yellow-centered mutant occurred which also gave all purple F_1 from crosses with purple-centered daisies. When these F_1 were crossed together, however, there were 97 purple and 68 yellow. Explain these results genetically.
   c. How can you explain that a cross between the two yellow-centered mutants produced all purple-centered F_1?

17. Give a single genetic explanation that applies to all the following facts regarding human beings:
   a. One particular deaf couple has only normal progeny.
   b. One particular deaf couple has only deaf progeny.
   c. One particular normal couple has many children; about $\frac{3}{4}$ are normal and $\frac{1}{4}$ deaf.
   d. One particular normal couple has all normal children.
   e. Normal, monozygotic twins marry normal, monozygotic twins and have a total of 9 normal and 9 deaf children.

18. When two plants are crossed it is found that $\frac{63}{64}$ of the progeny are phenotypically like the parents, and $\frac{1}{64}$ of the progeny are different from either parent but resemble each other. Give a genetic explanation for this.

Chapter 21

Qualitative and Quantitative Phenotypic Effects

Chapter 20 dealt primarily with the general ways that mendelian alleles and non-alleles interact phenotypically. The present chapter, also concerned with such interactions, considers the kinds of phenotypic effects produced by mutants.

21.1   Mutant genes with a translational effect can affect viability to different degrees.

Base-substitution or other mutants that produce no change in the quantity or quality of a translational product ("protein-silent" mutants) also produce no change in the phenotype of the cell or higher levels of organization. Mutants that have a translational effect can produce large–small–indetectable effects on viability.

In the snapdragon (*Antirrhinum*) one finds two kinds of full-grown plants, green and a paler green called *auria*. Green crossed by green produces only green, but auria by auria produces seedlings of which 25 per cent are green ($A\ A$), 50 per cent auria ($A\ a$), and 25 per cent white ($a\ a$). The last type of seedling dies after exhausting the food stored in the seed because it lacks chlorophyll. Among full-grown plants, the phenotypic ratio observed is $\frac{1}{3}$ green: $\frac{2}{3}$ auria. In this case, the absence of dominance gives the $1:2:1$ phenotypic ratio characteristic of a cross between monohybrids in the seedling stage which, following the death of the albino, becomes a $2:1$ ratio among the survivors.

In mice, matings between yellow-haired individuals produce F_1 in the ratio 2 yellow: 1 nonyellow. It is found after this mating that $\frac{1}{4}$ of the fertilized eggs which should have completed development fail to do so and abort early in embryogenesis. Since crosses between nonyellows produce only nonyellows, the nonyellow phenotype must be due to one type of homozygote, yellow must be the heterozygote, and the aborting individuals must be due to the other type of homozygote. The gene symbols usually employed are not satisfactory here, for we now must describe two effects for each gene—color and viability. Moreover, the allele that is dominant for the first effect is recessive for the second, and vice versa. This problem is solved by using base letters with superscripts for each gene (Figure 21-1), where the base letter refers to one trait and the superscript refers to the other trait. Let the superscript l be the recessive lethal effect of the gene dominant for yellow, Y, and the superscript L be the dominant normal viability effect of the allele recessive for nonyellow, y. Accordingly, the F_1 from crossing two yellow mice ($Y^l y^L \times Y^l y^L$) are 1 $Y^l Y^l$ (dies): 2 $Y^l y^L$ (yellow): 1 $y^L y^L$ (nonyellow).

In both the snapdragon and mouse cases described, death results from the presence of a gene in homozygous condition. Genes that kill the individual before maturity are called *lethal genes* or *lethals*—those usually doing so only when homozygous are *recessive lethals*, and those acting in this way when heterozygous are *dominant lethals*. Lethals may act very early or very late in development, or at any stage in between. Sometimes a lethal effect is produced not by one gene or a pair, but by the combined effect of several nonallelic genes. In such a case, some of the nonalleles are contributed

P_1	yellow	X	yellow
	$Y^l y^L$		$Y^l y^L$
G_1	$\frac{1}{2} Y^l, \frac{1}{2} y^L$		$\frac{1}{2} Y^l, \frac{1}{2} y^L$
F_1	$\frac{1}{4} Y^l Y^l$ dies	$\frac{1}{2} Y^l y^L$ yellow	$\frac{1}{4} y^L y^L$ nonyellow

Figure 21-1   Results of matings between yellow mice.

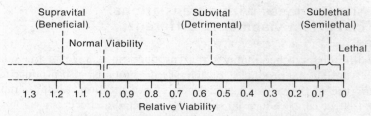

Figure 21-2   Classification of effects that mutants have on viability.

by each parent, and the offspring dies because the nonalleles, viable when separate, are lethal when together.

Different alleles, recessive or dominant, have been shown to affect viability in different degrees. These effects cover the entire spectrum—ranging from those which are lethal, through those which are greatly or slightly detrimental, to those which are apparently neutral or even beneficial (Figure 21-2). When different combinations of alleles or nonalleles have different viabilities, the phenotypic ratios observed may differ significantly from those expected. (R)

21.2 Point mutants with small phenotypic effects are more frequent than those with large phenotypic effects; point mutants which are detrimental when pure are also, to a lesser extent, detrimental when heterozygous.

Point mutants with small phenotypic effects occur much more frequently than those with large effects. For instance, pure (homo- or hemizygous) mutants which lower the viability of males without being lethal are at least three to five times more frequent than those which are recessively lethal (Figure 18-21).

Experience confirms the expectation that most "recessive" lethal point mutants— these are lethal when homozygous—also have some detrimental effect on reproductive potential when heterozygous. Such mutants are not completely recessive, therefore, and when heterozygous in *Drosophila* cause death before adulthood in about 5 per cent of individuals. Usually mutants that are detrimental but not lethal when pure also show a detrimental effect when heterozygous; this effect is somewhat less than that produced by heterozygous recessive lethal point mutants.

Elegant techniques have been developed to detect the spontaneous and induced frequencies of point mutants in mendelian chromosomes and to test their phenotypic effects in pure and heterozygous condition. One such procedure employed for X-limited genes in *Drosophila melanogaster* is described in detail in Section S21.2. (R)

21.3 Various phenotypic aspects of differentiation and development depend upon the intercellular effects of gene action.

In addition to causing intracellular phenotypic effects, many mutants produce intercellular effects which are important for development and differentiation. Various embryological experiments have shown the following:

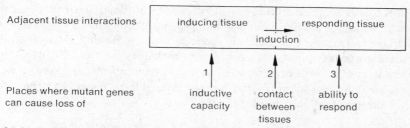

Figure 21-3   Interaction between adjacent tissues and its prevention by mutants.

1. Specific regions of the early embryo (at the gastrula stage, for instance) will become specific kinds of tissues in the mature organism.
2. Cell type can be modified by transplantation of cells into different regions. (The cell type sometimes has been determined before the time of transplantation; such cells are said to have lost their *competence*.)
3. The differentiation of competent cells can be changed through interaction with other cells or cell layers, a process called *induction* (Figure 21-3).

Each of these and other differentiating processes can be adversely affected by mutant alleles (as we shall see in the examples that follow), producing a profound detrimental effect on development. In each case we can attribute the normally occurring process as being at least in part the phenotypic consequence of the action of the normal allele, assuming that the mutants concerned are hypomorphs or amorphs rather than neomorphs (see Section 20.3).

Mutant genes can cause a loss of inductive capacity (Figure 21–3.1)

In the mutant chick *wingless*, wing buds are made up of an inner core of mesoderm covered by ectoderm. After the buds develop somewhat, the ectodermal parts degenerate; and development of the wings stops. Even when normal ectoderm is placed around *wingless* mesoderm, the ectoderm soon degenerates. Hence, *wingless* mesoderm seems to have lost the inductive capacity to maintain the surrounding ectoderm.

Mutant genes can prevent induction by preventing contact of the inducing and responding tissues (Figure 21–3.2)

A mutant gene in mice sometimes prevents the optic vesicle from making contact with the overlying ectoderm. Consequently, the ectoderm is not induced to form a lens. In mutant individuals in which the optic vesicle does contact the ectoderm, a lens is induced, indicating that the induction–response system is present but fails when the reactants are not in contact.

Mutant genes can cause a tissue to lose its ability to respond to induction (Figure 21–3.3)

Mesoderm must be induced by presumptive notochordal tissue, that is, tissue which develops into the notochord, in order to differentiate. When the mesoderm from normal mouse embryos is wrapped around presumptive notochordal tissue from either normal embryos or embryos homozygous for the *Brachy* mutant, the mesoderm develops into cartilage and vertebral segments in tissue culture. Under similar conditions, however, mesoderm from homozygous *Brachy* embryos does not form cartilage or vertebrae when in contact with presumptive notochord from normal embryos. It appears, therefore, that the mesoderm of the mutant is unable to respond to the inductive stimuli of presumptive notochordal tissue.

Mutant genes can cause a general slowdown of growth

In both homozygotes and heterozygotes for the chick mutant *Creeper* (*Cp*) the differentiation of cartilage is abnormal and their overall development is slower than in + + individuals. The *Cp* in single or double dose apparently causes a general slowing down in growth; the structures most affected seem to be those growing most rapidly at the time of the mutant gene's activity. Such a genetically induced slowdown in growth rate causes a reduction in the size of the hind limbs and the long bones of fore limbs (Figure 21-4).

Dwarf mice homozygous for a particular mutant gene have all body parts proportionally reduced in size. During early development, both dwarf and normal mice grow at the same rate; later, however, the dwarf suddenly stops growing and never reaches sexual maturity. The anterior pituitary gland of the dwarf is considerably smaller than that of the normal mouse and lacks certain large cells normally present. Since dwarfs can grow to normal size after injection of an extract from a normal pituitary gland (Figure 21-5), it appears that dwarfs lack a growth hormone. Here, then, we are dealing with a chemical messenger, a pituitary hormone, which regulates growth in general. Recombination studies indicate that the presence of this hormone is determined by a single pair of segregating genes. (R)

21.4   The alternatives for discontinuous or qualitative traits can be separated into discrete classes; those for continuous or quantitative traits cannot.

Up to now, the traits chosen to study genetic interaction in higher organisms occur in clearcut, qualitatively different alternatives like plant color in snapdragons, wing

Figure 21-4   Creeper (A) and normal (B) roosters.

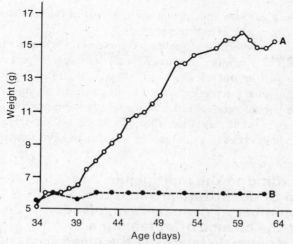

Figure 21-5   Effect of injecting pituitary gland extracts into dwarf mice. Starting at about 30 days of age, each day for 30 days dwarf mice were injected with a pituitary gland extract from normal mice (A) whereas their dwarf litter mates were injected with a pituitary gland extract from dwarf mice (B).

morphology in *Drosophila*, and colorblindness in human beings. These are called *discontinuous* or *qualitative traits* because in each case an individual belongs clearly to one phenotypic class or another. Although the interaction of many or all genes may ultimately be involved in the appearance of a given phenotype, the phenotypic alternatives previously considered have been effected primarily by only one or a few pairs of genes. Moreover, in these cases the nongenetic environment had much less or no effect upon the phenotypic differences involved.

For practical and theoretical reasons one may also be interested in the genetic basis for certain *continuous traits* like height of maize or intelligence in man, for which there are so many grades that individuals are not separable into discrete types or classes. Such traits are also called *quantitative traits* because the continuous range of phenotypes observed requires that an individual be measured in some way in order to be classified.

21.5   It is hypothesized that quantitative traits are due to the combined effects of many gene pairs, each gene pair contributing only slightly (and the environment relatively more) toward the expression of the phenotype.

Are quantitative traits also determined genetically? Let us make the simplest assumption that quantitative traits differ from qualitative ones only in degree, the former being due to the combined effects of many gene pairs. In the case of *multigenic* (*polygenic*) *traits*, although many phenotypic classes would be made possible by the action of multiple gene pairs, the effect of any single pair would be difficult to distinguish. Consequently, since each pair of genes would contribute only slightly toward the expression of the quantitative trait, one would expect the effect of environment to be relatively larger than that of any single gene or gene pair. The large effect of fertilizer upon maize ear size and of diet upon height in human beings illustrate the importance of environment in multigenic traits.

A given trait may be determined qualitatively in certain respects and quantitatively in other respects. For example, in garden peas one pair of genes may determine whether the plant will be normal or dwarf, the actual size of a normal plant being determined by multigenic interaction with the environment playing a significant role. Similarly, a single pair of genes can determine whether a human being has a serious mental deficiency or normal mentality, although nearly all individuals have a degree of mental ability which varies in a continuous way due to environment and polygenes.

21.6   According to the multigenic explanation of quantitative traits, the larger the number of gene pairs involved, the smaller the chance of obtaining a phenotype a given distance off the mean phenotype.

If quantitative traits are determined multigenically, it ought to be possible to derive other characteristics of them which are consistent with actual observations by considering the same trait, first as a qualitative trait (that is, determined by one or two or three gene pairs), and then as a quantitative trait (that is, determined by many gene pairs). Let the trait be color, and the alternatives in P_1 be black and white. Assume first that there is no dominance at all; then, whether one, two, three, or many gene pairs are involved, the F_1 will be uniform and phenotypically intermediate (medium gray) between the two P_1. Examine, in Figure 21-6, results of matings

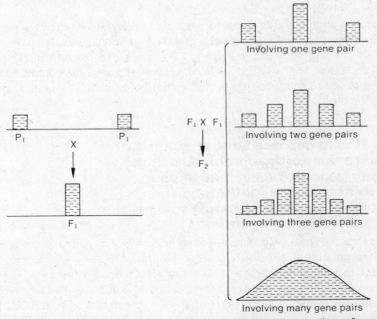

Figure 21-6 Dependence of number of phenotypic classes upon number of gene pairs in the complete absence of dominance. Horizontal axis shows classes, vertical axis indicates relative frequencies.

between F_1 (by cross- or self-fertilization) in each case. As the number of F_2 classes becomes large, one would expect environmental action to cause individuals to fall out of their phenotypic class, so to speak, and into the space between classes or into an adjacent phenotypic class. And so, as gene-pair number increases, classes become more numerous, then indiscrete, resulting finally in a continuum of phenotypes.

Note also that as the number of gene pairs determining the trait increases, the fraction of all F_2 resembling either P_1 becomes smaller. Thus, with one pair of genes $\frac{1}{2}$ of F_2 are black or white, with two pairs $\frac{1}{8}$, with three pairs $\frac{1}{32}$, etc. Consequently, as the number of genes increases from 10 to 20 and more, the continuous distribution of phenotypic types gives rise to an F_2 curve which becomes narrower and narrower. In other words, the chance of recovering in F_2 any phenotype a given distance off the mean decreases as gene-pair number increases. Although it may be relatively easy to identify whether one, two, or three gene pairs cause a given characteristic, it is much more difficult to determine exactly how many pairs are involved whenever more than three are involved. In multigenic cases, measurement of how the population varies relative to the average phenotype can give information as to the approximate number of polygenes involved.

The variability of a trait can be measured statistically as follows (see also the appendix on biometrics at the end of the book). First, the *mean*, *m* (the simple arithmetic average), is found. The *variance*, *v* (the measure of variability from the mean), for a group of measurements is determined by finding the difference between each measurement and the mean, squaring each such difference, adding all the values obtained, and dividing the total by 1 less than the number of measurements involved. With a given sample size, all other things being equal, the greater the variance, the smaller the number of gene pairs involved, as would be expected from Figure 21-6. One may find detailed statistical procedures for using variance this way in any standard textbook on elementary statistical methods.

21.7 Since dominance reduces the number of phenotypic classes, it leads one to underestimate the number of gene pairs interacting to produce a quantitative trait.

Consider next the effect of dominance upon the expression of quantitative traits. When a qualitative trait is determined by one, two, or three pairs of heterozygous genes not showing dominance, there are (as in Figure 21-6) three, five, or seven possible phenotypic classes, respectively. As a result of dominance, however, the number of classes is reduced (cf. Sections 20.5 and 20.6). Since the estimated number of gene pairs responsible for a phenotype is directly related to the number of phenotypic classes, the number of gene pairs involved in a quantitative trait is underestimated whenever dominance occurs. This effect is important because many genes show complete or partial dominance.

One can construct a hypothetical case in which two pairs of genes both showing dominance can give much the same phenotypic result as one pair with no dominance. Suppose gene *A* (as *A A* or *A a*) adds 2 units of effect and its recessive allele *a* (as *a a*) adds only 1 unit; suppose *B* (as *B B* or *B b*) subtracts 1 unit of effect and its recessive allele *b* (as *b b*) has no effect at all. Then a 2-unit individual (*A A b b*) mated with 0-unit one (*a a B B*) will give all intermediate 1-unit F_1 (*A a B b*). The F_2 from the

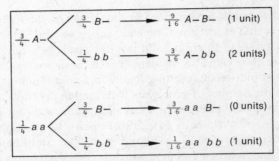

Figure 21-7 Results of crossing together the dihybrids described in the text.

mating of the F_1 can be derived by a branching track as shown in Figure 21-7. The phenotypic ratio obtained in F_2 of $3:10:3$ might be, in practice, difficult to distinguish from the $1:2:1$ ratio obtained from crossing monohybrids showing no dominance.

21.8　Dominance causes regression; that is, parents which are phenotypically extreme for a quantitative trait have progeny which are, on the average, less extreme.

Dominance has a second effect with regard to quantitative traits; this can be illustrated by means of two crosses involving the genes just described. In the first, two 0-unit individuals are crossed, $a\,a\,B\,b \times a\,a\,B\,b$, yielding $\frac{3}{4}\,a\,a\,B-$ (0 unit) and $\frac{1}{4}\,a\,a\,b\,b$ (1 unit). In this case the parents, which are at one phenotypic extreme (0 unit), produce offspring which are, on the average, less extreme (0.25 unit). In the second case, two 2-unit individuals are crossed, $A\,a\,b\,b \times A\,a\,b\,b$, yielding $\frac{3}{4}\,A-\,b\,b$ (2 units) and $\frac{1}{4}\,a\,a\,b\,b$ (1 unit). Here the parents are at the other phenotypic extreme (2 units) but produce offspring which are, on the average, less extreme (1.75 units). These results demonstrate *regression*, the consequence of dominance which causes

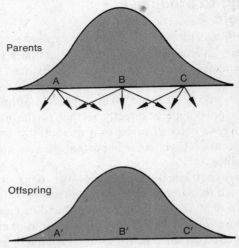

Figure 21-8 Principle of regression.

individuals phenotypically extreme in either direction to have progeny less extreme.

Figure 21-8 illustrates the principle of regression in polygenic situations. When no dominance occurs, the average offspring from parents at A, B, and C will be at the corresponding points A′, B′, C′, respectively, in the offspring curve. (The environment will cause some fluctuation around these phenotypic mean points in the offspring curve.) In the case of dominance, however, the offspring of A will be, on the average, to the right of A, as shown by arrows, whereas the offspring of C will generally be to the left of C. Contrary to what one might expect, this loss of extreme individuals generation after generation will *not* make the entire population more and more homogeneous phenotypically; there will be a closely counterbalancing tendency for the average members, B, of the population to produce offspring more extreme than themselves in either direction. The result is that, as in cases of no dominance, the distribution curve for the offspring will be the same as for the parent population.

21.9 Because dominance is widespread, selection of individuals of one extreme expression of a quantitative trait must be continued for several to many generations to obtain offspring whose average phenotype is closer to the desired extreme.

To obtain a line of phenotypically extreme individuals from a population showing a quantitative trait, one would choose the extreme individuals as parents (Figure 21-9). If dominance were absent, the very first offspring generation would have the same mean as the group selected as parents. Some degree of dominance usually occurs, and hence regression will usually occur; and the mean size of the first-generation offspring will be somewhat less extreme than that of the selected parents, but somewhat more extreme than the original mean. As one continues to select appropriately extreme individuals as parents, the offspring in successive generations will, on the average, approach more and more closely the extreme phenotype desired.

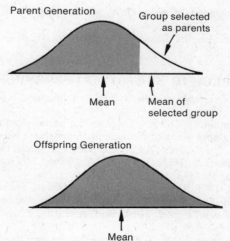

Figure 21-9 Selection for a quantitative character.

SUMMARY AND CONCLUSIONS

Mutant genes have a variety of effects on the phenotype. These effects can be detected on specific morphological and biochemical traits during the adult and developmental stages. Sometimes the effect on viability is scored. Different mutants can produce detectable viability effects at any stage in the life cycle and can modify phenotypic ratios so that certain classes of offspring are in excess, reduced frequency, or are absent. Mutants which, in pure condition, cause a reduction in frequency of a class of offspring are much more frequent than recessive lethals which (like dominant lethals) cause the absence of a class of offspring. Most mutants have a smaller detrimental effect on reproductive potential when heterozygous than when pure.

In addition to their intracellular effects, many mutants produce intercellular effects which are important for development and differentiation. These effects include loss of inductive capacity or response, loss of contact between inducing and responding tissues, and changes in general growth rate.

Genes are the basis not only of discontinuous, qualitative traits, but of continuous, quantitative traits. Continuous traits are determined by many gene pairs, each of which has a phenotypic effect that is small and often matched or exceeded by the action of the environment.

The variability of a quantitative trait is such that the larger the number of heterozygous genes determining it, the narrower is the distribution curve and the smaller the chance of recovering either of the extreme phenotypes in the offspring. When genes are heterozygous, dominance has the effect of reducing the number of phenotypic classes and of placing proportionally more offspring in extreme classes. Consequently, dominance usually causes one to underestimate the number of genes determining a quantitative trait. Dominance also causes regression, so selection must be continued for a number of generations to obtain a line that approaches the desired extreme phenotype.

GENERAL REFERENCES

Edwards, J. H. 1960. The simulation of Mendelism. Acta Genet., Basel, 10: 63–70.
Falconer, D. S. 1961. *Introduction to quantitative genetics.* New York: The Ronald Press Company.
Mather, W. B. 1964. *Principles of quantitative genetics.* Minneapolis: Burgess Publishing Company.
Wright, S. 1941. The physiology of the gene. Physiol. Rev., 41: 487–527.

SPECIFIC SECTION REFERENCES

21.1 Hadorn, E. 1961. *Development genetics and lethal factors.* New York: John Wiley & Sons, Inc.
21.2 Crow, J. F., and Temin, R. G. 1964. Evidence for partial dominance of recessive lethal genes in natural populations of *Drosophila*. Amer. Nat., 98: 21–33.
      Muller, H. J. 1954. The nature of the genetic effects produced by radiation. In *Radiation biology*, Hollaender, A. (Editor), Vol. 1. New York: McGraw-Hill Book Company, Inc., Chap. 7, pp. 351–473.
      Sigurbjörnsson, B. 1971. Induced mutations in plants. Scient. Amer., 224 (No. 1): 86–95, 122. (Radiation and chemicals used to obtain rare beneficial mutations.)
21.3 *Differentiation and development.* 1964. Boston: Little, Brown and Company and J. Exp. Zool., 157, No. 1.
      Ebert, J. D., and Sussex, I. M. 1970. *Interacting systems in development*, second edition. New York: Holt, Rinehart and Winston, Inc.

Grüneberg, H. 1963. *The pathology of development.* Oxford: Blackwell Scientific Publications, Ltd.

Waddington, C. H. 1962. *New patterns in genetics and development.* New York: Columbia University Press.

SUPPLEMENTARY SECTION

S21.2   Point mutants occurring in X-limited loci of *Drosophila* can be detected by means of elegant breeding schemes.

Special techniques have been developed to detect point mutants from their effects on reproductive potential. We shall consider in detail one such procedure employed in *Drosophila melanogaster* for this and other purposes.

The commonly used technique for detecting recessive lethals is called "*Basc*" (see Figure 21-10) and was designed to discover such mutants arising in the male germ line, in hemizygous X-chromosome loci, that is, X-limited loci. This technique makes use of the fact that when an X-limited recessive lethal mutant is present in a sperm that is used to produce a daughter, it will cause all this daughter's sons which receive this paternally derived mutant to be missing from her progeny. Such sons can be identified by the absence of one of two phenotypic classes of males if, as described below, the sons expected are of only two possible genotypes (and phenotypes)—one type having copies of the paternally derived X and the other type having copies of the maternally

derived X, crossover X's having been prevented from appearing in the progeny.

The P_1 males used are wild-type, having all normal characteristics including ovoid, dull-red compound eyes. The P_1 females have X chromosomes homozygous for *Bar eye* (*B*) (see Figure 28-6), for *apricot eye color* (*apr*), and for two paracentric *inversions* inside the left arm. The smaller inversion (*In S*) lies inside the larger inversion (*In sc^{S1} sc^8*, whose left point of breakage is designated sc^{S1} and right, sc^8), which includes almost the entire left arm. *Basc* derives its name from *B*ar, *a*pricot, *sc*ute inversion. Stock *Basc* females (or males) have bar-shaped eyes of apricot color. The genotype of the *Basc* female is written $sc^{S1}\ B\ In\ S\ apr\ sc^8/sc^{S1}\ B\ In\ S\ apr\ sc^8$. When the wild-type male is mated with the *Basc* female, the F_1 daughters obtained are $+/sc^{S1}\ B\ In\ S\ apr\ sc^8$ and have kidney-shaped eyes (characteristic of *Bar* heterozygotes) but are otherwise wild type.

Since the right arm of the X is very short it is of no concern here. Because each F_1 female is heterozygous for two paracentric inversions, almost all crossing over between the left arms of

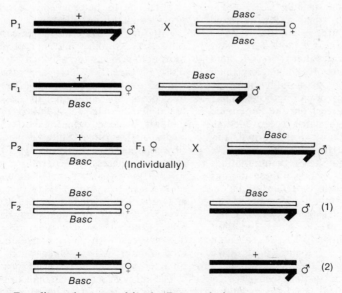

Figure 21-10   Breeding scheme used in the Basc technique.

her X's produces dicentric or acentric crossover strands which fail to enter the gametic nucleus (see Section 25-4). Accordingly, F_1 females produce eggs having an X that is, for our purposes, either completely maternal (sc^{S1} B In S apr sc^8) or completely paternal ($+$) in derivation. If this F_1 daughter mates with her $Basc$ brothers, half of the sons in the next generation (F_2) receive the $+$ maternal X and half receive the $Basc$ maternal X. So, if the progeny of a single F_1 female are examined, it is a simple matter to detect the presence of both types of sons among the scores of F_2 progeny usually produced. Note that each wild-type F_2 son carries an identical copy of the X which the mother (the F_1 female) received from her father (the P_1 male). Even when the sperm used to form the F_1 female carries an X-limited recessive lethal mutant, the F_1 female usually survives because she carries its $+$ allele in her $Basc$ chromosome. Each wild-type F_2 son, however, carries this mutant in hemizygous condition and usually dies before adulthood, so no wild-type sons appear in F_2. It becomes clear, then, since an F_1 female is formed by fertilization with a wild-type X-carrying sperm, that the absence of wild-type sons among her progeny is proof that the particular P_1 sperm carried a recessive lethal, X-limited mutant.

Such a lethal mutant must have occurred in the germ line after the fertilization that produced the P_1 male—he would not have survived had it been present at fertilization. It is unlikely that many of the X-limited lethals present in sperm originate very early in development, for in this case a large portion of the somatic tissue would also carry the lethal and usually cause death before adulthood. Even when a few hundred sperm from one male are tested, only one is usually found to carry an X-limited recessive lethal mutant. This indicates that most X-limited lethals present in sperm involve only a very small portion of the germ line. Occasionally, however, the mutation occurs early enough in the germ line so that several sperm tested from the same male carry what proves to be the same recessive lethal.

When a thousand sperm from normal, untreated males are tested for X-limited recessive lethals by means of a thousand separate matings of F_1 females, approximately two of these matings are found to yield no wild-type sons. This X-limited recessive lethal mutation frequency of 0.2 per cent is fairly typical in $D.$ $melanogaster$. For every 1,000 r of X rays to which the adult male is exposed, approximately 3.1 per cent more sperm are found to carry X-limited recessive lethals (see Figure 18-21, for the similar frequency obtained after exposure to fast electrons).

When used as described, the Basc technique detects only those recessive lethals which kill before adulthood. Other recessive lethals that produce wild-type adult males which are sterile or die before they can mate are not detected. No recessive lethals are detected unless they are hemizygous in the F_2 male, as mentioned. Since a considerable number of X-linked mutants whose lethality is prevented by genes normally present in the Y chromosome is known to occur, this sex-linked group is missed because each F_2 male is normally provided with a Y chromosome. Suitable modifications of the Basc procedure can be made to detect this special kind of Y-suppressed recessive lethal. On the other hand, the advantages and applications of the Basc technique as described are numerous.

For example, the presence or absence of wild-type males in F_2 is easily and objectively determined. Since the recessive lethal detected in F_2 is also carried by the heterozygous-Bar F_2 females, further study of the recessive lethal is possible in F_2 and subsequent generations. Such studies reveal that certain lethals are associated with intergenic changes—lethals unassociated with intergenic changes being designated recessive lethal point mutants. The Basc technique can also be used to detect recessive lethals that occur in a P_1 $Basc$ chromosome, the absence of $Basc$ males among the F_2 progeny indicating such a mutation. Moreover, if the environmental conditions are standardized, it becomes possible to detect hemizygous mutants which either lower the viability of the F_2 males without being lethal or raise their viability above normal. The opportunity for studying the viability effects of recessive lethals in heterozygous condition is also provided by this technique.

Although the Basc technique can also be used to detect X-linked mutants producing visible morphological changes when hemizygous, all those "$visibles$" which are also hemizygous lethals are missed. The "$Maxy$" technique overcomes this difficulty. In this method, the tested female has 15 X-linked recessive point mutants on one homolog and their wild-type alleles on the other. Suitable paracentric inversions maintain the individuality of these chromosomes in successive generations. Mutants are detected when such females show one or more of the recessive traits. Maxy detects, therefore, any mutation involving the wild-type alleles of the 15 recessives, provided that the mutant does not produce the wild-type phenotype when heterozygous with the recessive allele and is not a dominant lethal. Once such mutants are obtained, they can be screened for point mutants.

The study of recessive lethals in the X chromosome and in the autosomes shows that there are hundreds of loci whose point mutations may be recessively lethal. It should be noted that the recessive lethals detected by Basc and the visibles detected by Maxy are not mutually exclusive types of mutants, for some Maxy-detected visibles are lethal when hemizygous, and about 10 per cent of Basc-detected hemizygous lethals show some morphological effect when heterozygous. It can be stated, in general, that any mutant in homo- or hemizygous condition which is a "visible" will produce some change in viability, and, conversely, that any mutant which affects viability will produce a "visible" effect, "visible" at least at the biochemical level.

Muller, H. J. 1954. A semi-automatic breeding system ("Maxy") for finding sex-linked mutations at specific "visible" loci. Drosophila Information Service, 28: 140–141.

Muller, H. J., and Oster, I. I. 1963. Some mutational techniques in Drosophila. In Methodology in basic genetics, Burdette, W. J. (Editor), San Francisco: Holden-Day, Inc., pp. 249–278.

Schalet, A. 1958. A study of spontaneous visible mutations in Drosophila melanogaster. (Abstr.) Proc. X Intern. Congr. Genetics, Montreal, 2: 252.

Wallace, B. 1970. Spontaneous mutation rates for sex-linked lethals in the two sexes of Drosophila melanogaster. Genetics, 64: 553–557.

QUESTIONS AND PROBLEMS

1. How can genes be lethal to a genotype without producing a corpse?

2. In *Drosophila*, a mating of ♂ A × ♀ B or of ♂ C × ♀ D produces F_1, ¼ of which turn brown and die in the egg stage. If, however, the matings are ♂ A × ♀ D or ♂ C × ♀ B, none of the F_1 eggs turn brown and die. How can you explain these results genetically?

3. In the Japanese quail (*Coturnix coturnix*) matings between normal-appearing individuals of certain strains produce some micromelic embryos, having a short broad head with bulging eyes, which die between 11 and 16 days of incubation. How would you proceed to determine whether these abnormal embryos are homozygotes for a single recessive lethal gene?

4. Two curly-winged, stubble-bristled *Drosophila* are mated. Among a large number of adult progeny scored the ratio obtained is 4 curly stubble : 2 curly only : 2 stubble only; 1 neither curly nor stubble (therefore normal, wild type). Explain these results genetically.

5. In *Drosophila* each of the genes for curly wings (*Cy*), plum eye color (*Pm*), hairless (*H*), and dichaete wings (*D*) are lethal when homozygous. A curly, hairless male mated to a plum, dichaete female produces 16 equally frequent types of sons and daughters. One curly, plum, hairless, dichaete F_1 son is irradiated with X rays and then crossed to a plum, dichaete female. Three F_2 sons phenotypically like the father, collected and mated separately with wild-type females, produce the following males and females in the F_3 progeny:

PHENOTYPE	SON 1	SON 2	SON 3
Cy H	140	120	76
Cy D	120	—	81
Pm H	135	—	84
Pm D	154	117	79

Explain these results, using cytogenetic diagrams for all individuals mentioned.

6. Using pure stocks of *Drosophila*, yellow-bodied male by gray-bodied (wild-type) female produced 1,241 gray-bodied daughters, 1,150 gray-bodied sons, and 2 yellow-bodied sons. The reciprocal mating produced 1,315 gray daughters, 924 yellow sons, and 1 yellow daughter. Give the genetic and chromosomal makeup of each type of individual mentioned. Discuss the relative viability and fertility of the different chromosomal types.

7. Females of *Drosophila* having a notch in their wing margins mated to wild-type males gave the following F_1 results: 550 wild-type ♀♀, 472 notch ♀♀, 515 wild-type ♂♂. Explain these results genetically.

8. A line of *Drosophila* pure for the X-limited gene, *coral* (w^{co}), was maintained in the laboratory for many generations. To demonstrate sex linkage to a class, a coral male was mated to a wild-type female, and all the F_1 were as expected. The reciprocal cross between a coral female and wild-type male, gave 62 coral females and 59 wild-type males. Present a hypothesis to explain this

unusual result. How would you test your hypothesis?

9. The wild-type eye shape in *Drosophila* is ovoid. A certain mutant, *X*, narrows the eye. Using pure lines, and ignoring rare exceptions, mutant ♀ × wild-type ♂ produces mutant sons and daughters in F_1; wild-type ♀ × mutant ♂ produces wild-type sons and mutant daughters in F_1. Another mutant, *Y*, also narrows the eye. Using pure lines of *Y* and wild-type, mutant ♂ or ♀ × wild-type ♀ or ♂ produces 2 mutant ♂♂ and ♀♀:1 wild-type ♂♂ and ♀♀. Discuss the genetics of mutants *X* and *Y*.

10. Do the genes for quantitative traits show epistasis? Explain.

11. Does the environment have a more important role in determining the phenotype in cases of quantitative than in cases of qualitative traits? Explain.

12. Suppose each gene represented by a capital letter causes a plant to grow an additional inch in height, *a a b b c c d d e e* plants being 12 inches tall. Assume independent segregation occurs for all gene pairs in the following mating: *A a B B c c D d E E* × *a a b b C C D d E e*.
    a. How tall are the parents?
    b. How tall will the tallest F_1 be?
    c. How tall will the shortest F_1 be?
    d. What proportion of all F_1 will be the shortest?

13. In selecting for a quantitative trait, is the desired phenotype established in a pure line more easily when dominance does or does not occur? Explain.

14. Measure the length of 10 lima beans to the nearest millimeter. Calculate the variance of this sample. To what can you attribute the variance?

15. Is it of any advantage to an organism to have a trait determined quantitatively, that is, by many gene pairs, rather than qualitatively, that is, by principally one or a few gene pairs? Why?

16. How would you prove that you were dealing with multiple alleles rather than multiple pairs of genes?

17. In cattle a cross of a solid-coat breed and a spotted-coat breed produces a solid coat in F_1. Among the individuals of the spotted breed there is considerable variation, ranging from individuals that are solid-colored except for small white patches to those that are white with small colored patches. Selection within this breed can increase or decrease the colored areas. Discuss the genetic basis for coat color in these two breeds of cattle.

18. Discuss the number of gene pairs involved in the following case: Golden Glow corn has 16 rows of kernels to the ear; Black Mexican has 8 rows. The F_1 is phenotypically intermediate, having an average of 12 rows. The F_2 is phenotypically variable, ranging from 8 to 18 rows, with approximately one of each 32 ears being as extreme as either P_1.

19. The Sebight Bantam and Golden Hamburgh are pure lines of fowl which differ in weight. Although the F_1 of crosses between these lines are fairly uniform and intermediate in weight, one in about every 150 F_2 is clearly heavier or lighter than either P_1 pure line. Suggest a genetic explanation for these results.

20. Are all the mutants detected by the Basc or Maxy techniques point mutants? Explain.

21. Suppose, in the Basc technique, that an F_2 culture produced both of the expected types of daughters but no sons. To what would you attribute this result?

22. How can you determine whether a recessive lethal detected in the F_2 by the Basc technique is associated with an inversion or a reciprocal translocation?

23. A wild-type female produces 110 daughters but only 51 sons. How can you test whether this result is due to the presence, in heterozygous condition, of a recessive X-linked lethal?

24. How can you explain the phenotype of a rare female in the Maxy stock that produces only unexceptional progeny but has compound eyes distinctly lighter than normal?

Chapter 22

Genotypic and Environmental Contributions to Phenotype

We noted in Chapter 21 that environment plays a large role, relative to a single gene, in the expression of quantitative traits. In this chapter we consider the number of qualitative phenotypic effects that are produced by one gene, the roles the rest of the genotype and the environment have in gene expression, and estimate the relative importance of genotype and environment in the production of qualitative phenotypic traits whose genetic basis is unknown.

22.1 Since the protein coded by a gene has an indirect effect on a variety of metabolic reactions, many genes have multiple phenotypic effects.

A gene may code for a protein that has only one primary structural or enzymatic use. Since, in cell metabolism, many chemical reactions lead to and from any given chemical reaction, it is obvious that even such proteins will have numerous biochemical consequences, each ultimately influencing a somewhat different aspect of the phenotype. We expect, therefore, that genes affecting translational products will have *multiple*, *manifold*, or *pleiotropic effects* on the phenotype.

Several examples of pleiotropism in higher organisms are described next.

1. Pleiotropism can be observed in *Drosophila* using two strains which are practically identical genetically (*isogenic*), except that one is pure for the gene for dull-red eye color (w^+) and the other is pure for its allele white (w). Another trait, apparently unconnected with eye color, is also examined in these two strains—the shape of the spermatheca, an organ found in females which is used to store the sperm received. When the ratio of the diameter to the height of this organ is determined for each strain, this index of shape is found to be significantly different in the dull-red as compared to the white strain. From this result it can be concluded that the eye-color gene studied is pleiotropic. Other studies show that many different genes for other morphological traits are also pleiotropic.[1]

2. In *Drosophila* a recessive lethal gene called *lethal-translucida* causes pupae to become translucent and die. Using suitable techniques, one can compare the kinds and amounts of chemical substances in the blood

---

[1] In the case of the yellow mouse, the allele producing yellow coat color as a dominant effect also has a recessive lethal effect. On the presumption that homozygotes for this allele would have yellow body color had they survived, and on the basis that there is no obvious relation between coat color and viability, it could be concluded that this, too, is a case of pleiotropism.

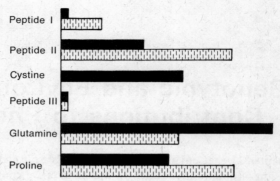

Figure 22-1 Pleiotropism at the biochemical level. Black, normal individuals; dashed, *lethal-translucida* homozygotes. (After E. Hadorn.)

fluid of normal larvae and pupae with those found in the recessive lethal homozygotes (Figure 22-1). Some substances are found in equal amounts in both genotypes (peptide III), others are more abundant in the lethal than in the normal individual (peptide I, peptide II, and proline), still others are less abundant (glutamine) or absent (cystine) in the lethal. Thus it is clear that pleiotropism is also detectable at the biochemical level.[2]

3. A genetic disease in man called *sickle-cell anemia* is due to homozygosity for a certain allele. This disease involves the following morphological effects, either singly or in any combination: anemia, enlarged spleen, skin lesions, heart, kidney, and brain damage. As a consequence, homozygotes for the gene for sickling usually die as adolescents or young adults; this allele, therefore, almost always acts as a recessive lethal.

It is also found that the red blood cells of these homozygotes may become sickle-shaped instead of being disc-shaped (Figure 22-2). Sickle-shaped cells can clump together and clog blood vessels in various parts of the body, leading to the malfunctions of all the organs already mentioned; in addition, these defective corpuscles are readily destroyed by the body, with consequent anemia.

We see, then, that the apparently unrelated phenotypic effects of the gene for sickling are merely consequences of the sickling of red blood cells. Moreover, biochemical studies (see Section 32.2) show that sickling itself is the result of the presence of an abnormal type of hemoglobin (having a slightly lower oxygen-carrying capacity than normal hemoglobin) which sickle-cell homozygotes carry in their red blood cells. There is, therefore, a *pedigree of causes* for the multiple effects of the gene for sickling. The first cause is the gene, the second is the

---

[2] The coat color of Himalayan rabbits ($c^h c^h$) is usually mosaic, that is, black at the extremities and white elsewhere. Because individuals with this genotype are completely black when grown under cold temperatures, we suspect that the gene has only one primary effect. This hypothesis is supported by the finding that this genotype produces an enzyme, necessary for pigment formation, which is temperature-sensitive, being inactivated by temperatures above about 34°C. Thus, in a cool climate, the body temperature is less than 34°C at the extremities, and pigment is produced there; on the warm parts of the body no pigment is formed because the enzyme is inactivated by heat. The Himalayan pattern is attributed, then, to a single product of gene action which, because it is subject to modification by the environment, can result in two different phenotypic alternatives of the same trait.

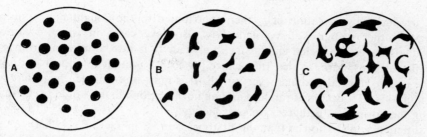

Figure 22-2   Silhouettes showing various types of human red blood cells: normal, in normal homozygote (A), sickle-cell trait, in mutant heterozygote (B), sickle-cell anemia, in mutant homozygote (C).

abnormal hemoglobin it produces, the third is the sickling that follows, and the fourth is the subsequent red cell clumping and destruction which produce gross organic defects and anemia. (R)

22.2   A genotype may not always be expressed phenotypically; when it is expressed the phenotype may be variable.

Consider a family tree or pedigree for *polydactyly* (Figure 22-3), a rare condition in which human beings have more than five digits on a limb. In the figure, the topmost female is affected, having five fingers on each hand and six toes on each foot. Her husband is normal in this respect. This couple has five children, three affected. This suggests that polydactyly is due to a single dominant gene, *P*, and that the mother is *P p*, the father *p p*. Consistent with this hypothesis is the result of the marriage of one of their affected daughters to a normal man. This marriage produced two sons, one of whom is affected, and this affected son, in turn, has five children including some affected and some unaffected.

But now examine the left side of this pedigree. Note the firstborn son who is unaffected yet has an affected daughter. How may this be explained? It might be supposed that this son is genotypically *p p* and that his daughter is *P p*, the *P* having

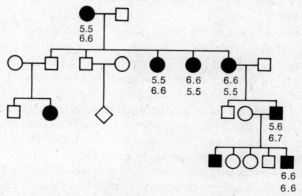

Figure 22-3   Pedigree of polydactyly in man. Circle, ♀; square, ♂; diamond, undetermined sex; filled-in symbol, affected. Individuals dropped from the same horizontal line are children of the same parents. (See also Figure 16-11.)

been produced by mutation of *p*, then contributed to the daughter at conception. However, other pedigrees for polydactyly also have cases in which two normal individuals have an affected child. Since polydactyly is rare, mutations from *p* to *P* must be still more rare, so that the chance for such a mutant to appear in a sex cell of one of two normal parents is very small. It is most improbable, then, that such a rare mutation, if it occurs at random among normal individuals, would occur so often among the normals in pedigrees for polydactyly.

A different explanation is that the firstborn son is, in fact, *P p*, where *P* is not expressed in any detectable way, although it is expressed in his daughter. This interpretation is supported by the kind of expression that the *P* gene produces in different affected individuals in this pedigree. These may have the normal number of fingers but have extra toes, or they may have the reverse; they may have different numbers of toes on the two feet, or they may have extra fingers on one hand and the normal number on the other. The expression of polydactyly, as far as the number of extra digits is concerned, is clearly quite variable. Accordingly, since it is possible to have no expression on one limb of an individual known to be *P p*, it must also occur that, on occasion, expression fails on all four limbs of an individual with this genotype.

The ability of a given gene or gene combination to be expressed phenotypically in one way or another is called *penetrance*. The *P* gene is heterozygous condition, therefore, has a penetrance of less than 100 per cent, sometimes failing to produce any detectable phenotypic effect when present. Although a polydactylous person is certain to carry *P*, a normal phenotype can represent either the *P p* or *p p* genotype. Since polydactyly is rare, it is usually quite safe to score as *p p* the genotype of a normal individual who marries into a line of descent containing *P*.

The expression of *P* when heterozygous is not only quite variable with respect to the number and position of extra digits, but further variability of expression is demonstrated by the different degrees of development which the extra digits show. The term *expressivity* is used to refer to the kind or degree of effect produced by a penetrant genotype. In individuals where *P* is nonpenetrant when heterozygous there is no expressivity, and when *P* is penetrant its expressivity is variable. (R)

22.3   Variations in penetrance or expressivity can have an environmental or genetic basis.

What factors are involved in the production of variable penetrance, or, in cases of penetrance, of variable expressivity? A study of a genetically uniform line of guinea pigs shows that polydactyly occurs more frequently in the litters from younger than from older mothers. In this case the physiological changes accompanying age modify penetrance. In another case, a genetically uniform line of *Drosophila* flies shows a greater percentage of penetrance of an abnormal abdomen phenotype when moisture content during development is high than when it is low. Both these examples illustrate that variations in penetrance can be produced by variations in the environment of different individuals with essentially identical genotypes.

We are already familiar with the effect of genotypic variations upon penetrance under essentially constant environmental conditions. The penetrance of an allele may depend upon the nature of its partner allele in cases of complete or partial dominance, and the penetrance of one or a pair of alleles may be modified by its epistatic–hypostatic relations to nonallelic genes (Chapter 20). Similarly, it can be shown that variable expressivity may be the consequence of differences in either or both the environment and the genotype.

The terms *penetrance* and *expressivity*[3] were used to compare the phenotypic events that occur in different individuals genetically identical in one particular respect. That is, once any phenotypic expression occurred within an individual, the genotype was said to be penetrant, and all other phenotypic comparisons between penetrant individuals were considered matters of expressivity. In fact, however, one can also correctly speak about penetrance within an individual for those cases in which the particular genotype has two or more occasons to express itself. Thus, for example, the gene for polydactyly has two apparently equal chances to be penetrant in the case of the hands, and two apparently equal chances to be penetrant in the case of the feet. The genotype may be penetrant in one hand (six fingers) and not in the other (five fingers); it may be penetrant in the feet (each foot having six toes—represented as 6.6) and not in the hands (5.5). When differences in penetrance (or expressivity) are shown by essentially duplicate parts of the same individual (one hand having seven and the other six digits, or one hand having a large and the other a small extra digit), one can be reasonably certain that these differences have an environmental and not a mutational basis. When different individuals are compared with respect to penetrance or expressivity, however, it is often impossible to attribute, with assurance, similarities or differences among them to genotype or to environment, if both of these factors can vary in uncontrolled ways. (R)

22.4   One can estimate the relative contributions of genotype and environment in the production of a trait by means of studies with human twins.

In organisms other than man experimental conditions can be controlled so that a standard genotype exposed to different environments shows to what extent environment is responsible for phenotypic variability, whereas a standard environment to which different genotypes are exposed reveals to what extent these genotypes produce different phenotypes. Since neither the environment nor the genotypes of human beings are subject to experimental control, how can we determine to what extent a particular human trait is controlled by genotype (nature) and by environment (nurture)? Fortunately, this nature–nurture problem can be studied using the results of certain naturally occurring phenomena.

An individual contains many different parts which presumably have the identical genotype. Accordingly, as mentioned in the previous section, one can attribute to nurture any phenotypic differences in expressivity or penetrance found among parts that are essentially duplicates of each other. For example, a heterozygote for polydactyly with six fingers on one hand and five on the other illustrates the extent to which environment can affect this trait. When, however, a trait involves the entire body, or only one or several different nonduplicate parts of the body, the contribution

---

[3] One should be careful to differentiate between penetrance and expressivity on one hand and dominance and epistasis on the other. Suppose, with respect to height, that $T\,T$ always produces tall, $T'\,T'$ always short, and $T\,T'$ always (1) near-tall, or (2) medium. Although the hybrid shows (1) partial, or (2) no dominance, there is 100 per cent penetrance for each of the three genotypes. If among the heterozygotes there was some variability in size (owing to variations in environment or the rest of the genotype), we would have different expressivities for the 100 per cent penetrant $T\,T'$ genotype.

of nurture can be learned only by comparing different individuals which have identical genotypes.

Since each human individual is heterozygous for a relatively large number of genes, the chance of obtaining genetic identity in two *siblings* (children of the same parents) is very small indeed. However, two or more siblings with identical genotypes can be produced in man by asexual reproduction, which occurs in the following manner. A single fertilized egg starts development normally by undergoing a series of mitotic divisions. At some time, however, the cells produced fail to adhere to each other, as they would normally do, and separate into two or more groups, each of which may be able to develop into a complete individual. Each individual thus produced is, barring mutation, genetically identical to all others formed from the same fertilized egg. The separation referred to may occur at different stages of early development, and the number of cells in the two or more groups formed may be unequal. Separation may even occur more than once, at different times in the development of a particular zygote. The individuals produced in this asexual manner are *monozygotic* or *identical* twins, triplets, quadruplets, etc. We need consider only monozygotic twins here, since multiple births of greater number are usually too infrequent to be useful for a general study of the nature–nurture problem.

Multiple births can also be produced directly by sexual reproduction. When twins are produced in this way they start as two separate eggs, each fertilized by a separate sperm. Such twins are genetically different—being in this respect, no more similar than siblings conceived at different times—and are *dizygotic*, or *nonidentical* (*fraternal*) twins.

These two kinds of twins provide natural experimental material for determining the relative influence of genotype and environment upon the phenotype. Barring mutation, monozygotic twins furnish the identical genotype in two individuals, and both kinds of twins share similar environments before birth and, when raised together, after birth.

The phenotypic differences between monozygotic twins reared together are essentially the consequence of environment (Figure 22-4). One can compare the average difference between such monozygotic twins with the average difference between monozygotic twins who, for one reason or another, were reared apart. This comparison yields information regarding the influence of greater, as compared with lesser, environmental differences upon the phenotype. Since dizygotic or monozygotic twins reared together are exposed to environments which, on the average, vary to the same extent, a comparison of the average difference between monozygotic twins and the average difference between dizygotic twins will give an index of the genotype's role in causing the differences observed. In order to collect valid data from twin studies it is essential, of course, that one be able to recognize in each case whether the twins are monozygotic or dizygotic in origin.[4] (R)

---

[4] The best way to identify dizygotic twins is to compare the siblings with reference to a large number of traits known to have a basis in genes showing 100 per cent penetrance and fairly uniform expressivity—such traits as sex, eye color, and ABO, MN, Rh, and other blood-group types. Naturally, only traits for which at least one parent is heterozygous are of use in testing the dizygotic origin of twins. Assuming the absence of mutation, any single difference in such traits would prove the twins dizygotic. (On this basis, twins of opposite sex are classified immediately as dizygotic.) Of course, two such differences would make the decision practically infallible, since two mutations involving genes for the limited number of traits compared in a pair of monozygotic twins would be so rare as to be beyond any reasonable probability of occurrence. When the number of traits serving to test the genotypes of twins is sufficiently large, therefore, it becomes nearly certain that they would have shown one or more differences had they been dizygotic in origin. Failure to show any such differences, then, may be attributed to identical genotypes derived from a single zygote, that is, to monozygotic twinning.

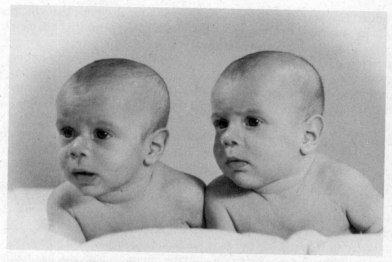

Figure 22-4 Monozygotic twins, Ira and Joel, at $3\frac{1}{2}$ months and at 19 years of age. (Courtesy of Mrs. Reida Postrel Herskowitz, July 14, 1946.)

22.5 The genotypic and environmental contributions to various physical traits have been investigated using the twin method.

Let us outline the procedure one might follow in using twins to study the relative roles of genotype and environment in producing specific qualitative traits. The objective is to score separately cases of monozygotic and dizygotic twin pairs reared together in which one sibling and in which both siblings have the alternative of the trait under consideration. This furnishes for monozygotic and for dizygotic pairs the percentage of *concordance*, that is, the percentage of all affected pairs in which both members have the phenotypic alternative under consideration.

In determining concordance for dizygotic twins one usually scores only pairs in which the twins are of the same sex. This convention is necessary because the postnatal environment of twins of opposite sex is likely to be more different than that of twins of the same sex. (If the environment differed for the two kinds of twins, one would not be able to specify whether the environment or the genotype was the cause of a phenotypic difference that is greater among dizygotics than monozygotics.) Only twins of the same sex are used in the twin studies discussed here.

It is theoretically possible to obtain a result in which concordance is lower for monozygotics than it is for dizygotics. Such a difference in concordance could be ascribed to environmental differences being greater among the monozygotics than among the dizygotics.

The results of concordance studies for some physical traits in twins reared together are summarized in Figure 22-5. In each case monozygotics have a higher concordance than dizygotics, the difference being roughly the minimal chance of having the phenotype for genotypic reasons.[5]

Concordance for clubfoot is 32 per cent for monozygotics, but only 3 per cent for dizygotics (Figure 22-5). The extra concordance of 29 per cent (32 per cent minus 3 per cent) found among monozygotics must be attributed to their identical genotype. The 3 per cent concordance found among dizygotics might be due entirely to similarity in genotype, or entirely to the environment, or to a combination of these two factors. Since we cannot decide from these data, we conclude that in twins or other individuals exposed to the same environment that twins are, the occurrence of clubfoot can be attributed to genotype approximately 29 per cent of the time, with 32 per cent as the approximate upper limit.

In the case of the monozygotics, 68 per cent of the time the second twin failed to have clubfoot when the first twin did. The failure of concordance is called *discordance*.

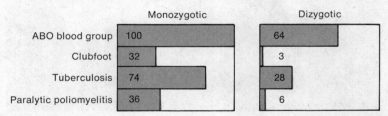

Figure 22-5   Percentage concordance for various physical traits in twins reared together.

[5] The concordance for ABO blood type is 100 per cent for monozygotics and approximately 64 per cent for dizygotics. Had concordance been 100 per cent for both types of twins, we would conclude that there is no net genetic or environmental differences for ABO blood group in the two types of twins. The concordances observed do differ, however, and do so in a particular direction. Because of this difference the 100 per cent concordance for monozygotics must mean that this trait is determined genetically with a penetrance of 100 per cent despite the environmental fluctuations normally occurring between monozygotic twins. Since an equivalent amount of environmental fluctuation caused no differences in the case of monozygotics, the lower percentage of concordance for dizygotics cannot be attributed in any part to environment. This lower concordance must be attributed, therefore, to the differences in genotype which dizygotics can have in this respect. Of course, we could have predicted such a result from the previous knowledge that ABO blood type is genetically determined and is known to have complete penetrance. The lower concordance for dizygotics, therefore, must be due to their receiving different genotypes from parents, one or both of whom were heterozygous.

The 68 per cent discordance between monozygotics is attributable to differences in their environment. It is concluded, then, that in twins or other individuals exposed to the same environment that twins are, the occurrence of clubfoot is the result of the environment approximately 68 per cent of the time, with 71 per cent as the approximate upper limit.

Concordance–discordance studies reveal only the relative contributions of genotype and environment to a particular phenotype (clubfoot, for example, as in the case just discussed). Such studies do not teach us anything about the kinds of environment involved when the genotype determines the phenotype under consideration, nor do they teach us anything about the genotypes involved when the environment decides the phenotype. The clubfoot twin studies also tell us nothing about the effect upon the penetrance of clubfoot of environmental differences greater than those occurring between twins reared together. Application of the conclusions from twin studies to the general population assumes that environments for twins and nontwins are the same. Such an assumption may be invalid.

In the case of *tuberculosis*, concordance is 74 per cent for monozygotics and 28 per cent for dizygotics. Accepting the supposition that both types of twins have the same average exposure to the tubercle bacillus, the susceptibility to this disease is determined genetically 46 to 74 per cent of the time and environmentally 26 to 54 per cent of the time. In support of the view that the extra concordance among monozygotics has a genetic basis is the finding that concordant monozygotics usually have the same form of this disease, affecting corresponding organs with the same severity, whereas this similarity is less fequent among concordant dizygotics.

In earlier studies, *paralytic poliomyelitis* was 36 per cent concordant for monozygotics and 6 per cent concordant for dizygotics. As in the case of tuberculosis, the occurrence of the disease probably did not depend upon the infective organisms because most human beings were exposed to them normally. Accordingly, the incidence of this disease depended upon the rest of the environment 64 to 70 per cent of the time and the genotype 30 to 36 per cent of the time. (In the case of *measles*, the finding that concordance is very high among both types of twins simply means that any genetic basis for susceptibility to this disease is quite uniform throughout the population from which the twin samples were obtained.)

22.6   The genotypic and environmental contributions to various mental traits have been investigated using the twin and family methods.

The relative contributions of genotypes and environment to personality and other mental traits can be studied by using the twin and family methods separately or together. When a metronome is run at a series of different speeds, the tempo preferred by different persons is different. *Tempo preference* may be considered to be one aspect of the general personality. When tests are made to compare the tempo preferred by monozygotic twins, the difference in their scores is found to be 7.8 of the units employed (Figure 22-6). This is, as might be expected, not significantly different from the difference in score of 8.7 units obtained by testing a given individual on different occasions. However, dizygotic twins have a difference in score of 15, which is significantly different, being about twice that of the monozygotics. Since nontwin siblings have a difference in score of 14.5, they prove to be as similar in this respect as are

Individuals	Difference in Score
Same person on different occasions	8.7
Monozygotic twins	7.8
Dizygotic twins	15.0
Siblings	14.5
Unrelated	19.5

Figure 22-6   Variation in preferred tempo. (After C. Stern.)

dizygotic twins. Finally, unrelated persons show a difference in score of 19.5 units. Since the greater the genetic similarity, the smaller the difference in score, there is clearly a genotypic contribution to this personality trait.

Studies of twins for the mental disease *schizophrenia* show concordance of 36 per cent for monozygotics and 14 per cent for dizygotics. It is likely, however, that differences in social environment cause more discordance in the case of dizygotics than in the case of monozygotics. Nevertheless, in support of the view that the concordance for monozygotics is not entirely the result of similar environment but is partially genotypic in origin are two cases of monozygotic twins who were separated, raised in different environments, yet were concordant at about the same age.

Different people, of course, score differently on IQ examinations. The differences in ability to answer questions on these examinations can be used to measure what may be called *test intelligence*. Although the scores of nonsiblings vary widely above and below 100, the difference between the scores of twins reared together is only 3.1 for monozygotics but 7.5 for dizygotics. Clearly identity in genotype makes for greater similarity in score. Monozygotics reared apart have scores that differ by 6. In this case the greater difference in environment makes for a greater difference in performance of monozygotics, but this is still not so great a difference as is obtained between dizygotics reared together. Therefore, both genotypic and environmental factors affect the trait, test intelligence.

It should be noted that although the twin and family methods used in this and previous sections tell whether genotypic differences are associated with the occurrence of certain phenotypic differences, they provide no information regarding the genes involved. (R)

SUMMARY AND CONCLUSIONS

Since the product of a protein-coding gene is expected to affect many different biochemical reactions, genes affecting translational products should have many different effects on the phenotype. In some cases the pleiotropic effects of a mutant are, indeed, traceable by a pedigree of causes back to a single action on the part of the gene.

The production by a genotype of some phenotypic effect (penetrance) and its nature (expressivity) depend upon both the genotype and the environment. In human beings the occurrence of essentially duplicate parts within an individual, and of monozygotic and dizygotic twins, provides an especially favorable opportunity to test the effect of environment and of genotype upon the penetrance and expressivity of a given qualitative phenotypic alternative. Using the twin and family methods, a considerable number of physical and mental traits in man were found to be determined by the joint action of genotype and environment whose relative importance varies for different traits. The twin and family methods do not, however, tell us anything about the nature of the genotypes or environments involved.

SPECIFIC SECTION REFERENCES

22.1   Dobzhansky, Th., and Holtz, A. M. 1943. A re-examination of manifold effects of genes in *Drosophila melanogaster*. Genetics, 28: 295–303.

Hadorn, E. 1956. Patterns of development and biochemical pleiotropy. Cold Spring Harbor Sympos. Quant. Biol., 21: 363–374.

22.2   Woolf, C. M., and Woolf, R. M. 1970. A genetic study of polydactyly in Utah. Amer. J. Human Genet., 22: 75–88.

22.3   Sang, J. H. 1963. Penetrance, expressivity and thresholds. J. Heredity, 54: 143–151.

22.4   Newman, H. H. 1940. *Multiple human births*. Garden City, N.Y.: Doubleday & Company, Inc.

Osborn, R. H., and DeGeorge, F. V. 1959. *Genetic basis of morphological variation*. Cambridge, Mass.: Harvard University Press.

22.6   Kallman, F. J. 1953. *Heredity in health and mental disorder*. New York: W. W. Norton & Company, Inc.

QUESTIONS AND PROBLEMS

1. Most of the genes studied in *Drosophila* affect the exoskeleton of the fly. Do you suppose these genes also have effects on the internal organs? Why?

2. Would you expect to find individuals who are homozygous for polydactyly? Explain. What phenotype would you expect them to have? Why?

3. Why are genes whose penetrance is 100 per cent and expressivity is uniform particularly valuable in a study of gene properties?

4. Would you expect the mutation rate to polydactyly, P, from normal, p, to be greater among normal individuals in a pedigree for polydactyly than it is among normals in general? Explain. How might you test your hypothesis?

5. Two normal people marry and have a single child who is polydactylous on one hand only. How can you explain this?

6. A certain type of baldness is due to a gene that is dominant in men and recessive in women. A nonbald man marries a bald woman and they have a bald son. Give the genotypes of all individuals and discuss the penetrance of the gene involved.

7. A man has one brown eye and one blue eye. Explain.

8. How could you distinguish whether a given phenotype is due to a rare dominant gene with complete penetrance or a rare recessive gene of low penetrance?

9. In determining whether or not twins are dizygotic, why must one study traits for which one or both parents are heterozygotes?

10. Are mistakes ever made in classifying twins as dizygotic in origin? Why?

11. What would be the probability of twins being dizygotic in origin if both have the genotype $a\,a\;B\,b\;C\,C\;D\,d\;E\,e\;F\,f$, each pair of alleles segregating independently, if the parents are genotypically $A\,a\;B\,b\;C\,C\;D\,D\;E\,e\;F\,f$ and $A\,a\;B\,B\;C\,C\;d\,d\;e\,e\;F\,F$?

12. Is tuberculosis "inherited"? Explain.

13. Is it valid to apply the conclusions from twin studies to nontwin members of the population? Explain.

14. What conclusions can you draw from the data of B. Harvald and M. Hauge (J. Amer. Med. Assoc., 186: 749–753, 1963) obtained from an unbiased sample of Danish twins?

	TWIN PAIRS	ONE TWIN CANCEROUS	BOTH TWINS CANCEROUS AT SAME SITE	BOTH TWINS CANCEROUS AT DIFFERENT SITES
Monozygotic	1528	143	8	13
Dizygotic	2609	292	9	39

15. One child is hemophilic; its twin brother is not.
    a. What is the probable sex of the hemophilic twin?
    b. Are the twins monozygotic? Explain.
    c. Give the genotypes of both twins and of their mother.

Chapter 23

Sex Determination

Meiosis and the fusion of nuclei produced by meiosis are the two most important features of the sexual mechanism for genetic recombination in eucaryotes. This sexual process, however, also involves another, and in some organisms, separate, kind of differentiation. This is the differentiation that produces phenotypically different gametes or sexes—the cellular and organismal vehicles for accomplishing meiosis and nuclear fusion. In this chapter we will consider the relation that genes and environment have in determining such sexual differentiations.

23.1 Some genes for sex determination are permanently linked to one type of sex chromosome.

In Section 16.4, it was mentioned that in addition to two sets of autosomes the ordinary *Drosophila melanogaster* female is XX and the male XY. By knowing the sex of flies that carry—besides the two sets of autosomes—either XXY (female), XXYY (female), or X0 (male), we can see that the Y is not sex-determining in this organism (although the Y is necessary for fertility, X0 males having nonmotile sperm). Knowing that sex in *Drosophila* is correlated with the chromosomal alternatives of XX versus X, one can ask: What is the detailed genetic basis for sex in terms of genes located in the X chromosome? To answer this question two assumptions must be made, in *Drosophila* and in other species having heteromorphic sex chromosomes, to correlate the genetics with the cytology of sex.

1. That X- and Y-limited sex genes must be located in regions of the X and Y which distinguish them cytologically.
2. No crossing over may occur between X and Y within these cytologically different segments.

These postulates are necessary to preserve the exact correspondence between the morphology of the X and Y and their chromosome-specific sex-gene content. Consequently, even though a crossing over occurs between the X and Y in a segment which they share, the resultant strands that appear cytologically as X will carry X-limited sex genes, whereas those that appear as Y will not. These requirements are reasonable since synapsis does not occur between noncorresponding regions of homologous chromosomes, and, in the absence of pairing, crossing over cannot occur. (Note that no crossing over ordinarily occurs in the *Drosophila* male, homologous chromosomes, including X and Y, being held together in prophase I by homologous collochores.)

In the case of the bug *Protenor*, males are X0 and females XX. Although genes for sex determination are usually located in single kinds of X or Y chromosomes, these genes are sometimes distributed among several kinds of X's and Y's. Thus, for example, the beetle *Blaps polychresta* has, besides 9 pairs of autosomes, 12 X's and 6 Y's in the male.

23.2 Some genes for sex determination are autosomal.

One laboratory strain of *D. melanogaster* produces about 75 per cent males and 25 per cent females (Figure 23-1A), instead of the normal sex ratio of approximately 50 per cent males and 50 per cent females. Since just as many egges become adult in this unusual strain as in a normal one, the abnormal result cannot be due to a gene that affects the viability of one sex.

In this exceptional case an autosomal gene is found to be affecting the determination of sex. This gene, called *transformer*, has two alleles, tra^+ and tra. Homozygotes for tra always form males regardless of the X genes present ($tra\ tra$ is epistatic and the X genes hypostatic), whereas heterozygotes or homozygotes for tra^+ have their sex determined by the presence of sex genes on the X (in this case the X sex genes are epistatic). Accordingly, XX individuals that are also $tra\ tra$ appear as (sterile) males (*transformed females*), explaining the excess number of males in the progeny. Thus, a cross of XY $tra\ tra$ (male) by XX $tra^+\ tra$ (female) (Figure 23-1B) produces one-fourth each XY $tra\ tra$ (males), XY $tra^+\ tra$ (males), XX $tra\ tra$ (males, transformed females), XX $tra^+\ tra$ (females)—accounting for the numerical results. These results, confirmed by others, prove that autosomal genes are also concerned with sex determination. Note, however, that the tra allele is very rare; almost all *Drosophila* found in nature are homozygous tra^+. (R)

23.3 *Drosophila* with an abnormal number of chromosomes are often of abnormal sex type; that is, they are often intersexes or supersexes.

So far we have described only two sex types in *Drosophila*. Occasionally, however, individuals occur which have, over all, an intermediate sexual appearance; that is, they are both male and female in certain respects. Such sexual intermediates, called

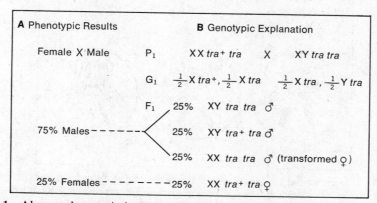

Figure 23-1 Abnormal sex ratio in *Drosophila*.

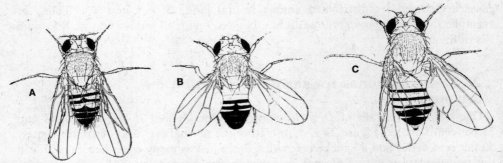

Figure 23-2 Some abnormal sex types in *Drosophila*: A, superfemale; B, supermale; C, intersex. (Drawn by E. M. Wallace.) Compare with normal male and female in Figure 15-6.

intersexes (see Figure 23-2), are sterile. Intersexes are relatively frequent among the progeny of triploid (3N) females (whose chromosomes at mitotic metaphase are diagrammed in Figure 23-3).

Some of the gametes of triploid females are haploid and some diploid; still others contain one, two, or three nonhomologs with or without a haploid set. Whereas haploid eggs produce normal males and females when fertilized by sperm from a normal male, diploid eggs produce triploid females when fertilized by X-bearing sperm. Diploid eggs produce XXY individuals with three sets of autosomes, however, when fertilized by Y-bearing sperm. Some intersexes have this chromosomal constitution; other intersexes carry three autosomal sets and XX—one X derived from an egg containing two autosomal sets and the other from an X-bearing sperm.

Close observation reveals two additional sex types among the progeny of triploid *Drosophila* (Figures 23-2 and 23-3). These do not appear as intersexes but as sterile "supersexes"—one type, called a *superfemale*, shows characteristic female traits even

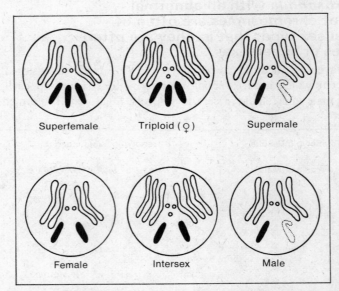

Figure 23-3 Chromosomal complements of the sexual types found among the progeny of triploid females of *D. melanogaster*. X chromosomes are represented by filled-in blocks, autosomes by blanks, and Y by a dashed line.

more strongly than does the normal female, the other type, *supermale*, shows character-istic male traits even more strongly than does the normal male. Chromosomally, the superfemale contains two sets of autosomes and three X's (derived from an egg which carries one set of autosomes plus XX fertilized by an X-carrying sperm). The super-female usually dies before adulthood (see Section 16.6). The supermale contains three sets of autosomes plus XY (derived from an egg which carries two sets of autosomes plus X fertilized by a Y-bearing sperm).

23.4 In *Drosophila* sex type is determined by the balance between genes located in the X chromosome and those located in autosomes.

What conclusions can we draw about sex determination from a knowledge of the chromosomal composition of different sex types in *Drosophila*? Since we know that genes in the X and in the autosomes are sex-determining, let us refer to Figure 23-4, which tabulates the number of X's and sets of autosomes present for each sex type and also the ratio of X's to sets of autosomes—a *numerical sex index*. This index ranges from 0.33 for supermales to 1.5 for superfemales. Note that an index of 0.50 makes for male and that adding a set of autosomes can be interpreted as creating more maleness, producing the supermale. When the sex index is 1.0, essentially normal females are produced, indicating that the female tendency of one X over-powers the male tendency of one set of autosomes. But if the index is between 0.50 and 1.00, intersexes are produced, indicating, by the same line of reasoning, that the effect of two X's is partially overpowered by the extra autosomal set present. Finally, when the sex index is 1.5, the female tendency of the X's becomes so strong that super-females result.

These results strongly suggest that sex determination in *Drosophila* is due to the balance of genes located in the X on the one hand, in the autosomes on the other. According to this view, only the balance of the genes involved is important, so that a

Phenotypes		Number of X Chromosomes	Number of Sets of Autosomes (A sets)	Sex Index $\dfrac{\text{Number X's}}{\text{Number A sets}}$
Superfemale		3	2	1.5
Normal female	Tetraploid	4	4	1.0
	Triploid	3	3	1.0
	Diploid	2	2	1.0
	Haploid	1	1	1.0
Intersex		2	3	0.67
Normal male		1	2	0.50
Supermale		1	3	0.33

Figure 23-4 Sex index and sexual type in *D. melanogaster*.

sex index of 1.0 should (and does) produce a typical female, whether the individual is diploid (2X + 2 sets of A), triploid (3X + 3 sets of A), or tetraploid (4X + 4 sets of A). Individuals that contain haploid (1X + 1A set) sections have been found and, as expected from their sex index of 1.0, these parts were female. Since all known facts support the exact correspondence between chromosomal constitution and sexual types, we can accept chromosome balance as the typical basis of sex determination in *Drosophila*.

What is the relationship between X-autosome balance and *tra*, the sex-transforming gene? Sex is determined by the usual X-autosome balance when the individuals carry *tra*$^+$, which they normally do. When *tra* is homozygous, however, the balance is shifted and 2X + 2A sets produce a sterile male. (R)

23.5   In insects mosaicism in sexual phenotype accompanies mosaicism in sex-chromosome constitution.

On relatively rare occasions abnormal *Drosophila* appear with some of their parts typically male and the remainder typically female. Such individuals are said to be mosaic for sex traits; *sex mosaics* are also called *gynandromorphs* or *gynanders* (Figure 23-5). The male and female parts are clearly demarcated in such flies, sometimes the front and hind halves, at other times the right and left sides are of different sex. The sharp borderline between male and female parts in an insect gynander is due to the relatively small role that hormones play in insect differentiation, so that each body part is formed according to the genotype it contains. In view of the preceding discussion, one would predict that the diploid cells in the female part of a gynander contain XX and those in the male part X, the number of autosomes being normal. If this prediction is correct, then approximately half-and-half gynanders could originate as follows. The individual starts as a zygote containing XX—that is, as a female. The first mitotic division of the zygotic nucleus is abnormal—one daughter nucleus contains XX and is normal, the other daughter nucleus contains X and is defective because one of the X's failed to be included in this nucleus, degenerated, and was lost. However, subsequent nuclear divisions are normal—cells produced following mitosis of the XX nucleus and its descendants giving rise to female tissue and cells derived

Figure 23-5   *D. melanogaster*; the gynandromorph whose left side is female and right side is male (Drawn by E. M. Wallace.)

from the X nucleus giving rise to male parts. In this case the gynander has about half its body male and half female. If, however, the X is lost at some later mitosis, a correspondingly smaller portion of the body will be male, explaining gynanders one fourth or less male.[1]

Gynanders also occur in moths. Whereas male moths usually have large, beautifully colored wings and females small stumps of wings, gynanders have been found with wings like the male on one side and those like the female on the other side. The explanation for these exceptions is similar to that given for *Drosophila*. In the case of the moth, however, the gynander usually starts as a male zygote (XX). (R)

23.6   Although sex type in human beings is determined at fertilization, the sex differentiated depends largely upon sex hormones.

In human beings also sexual type is determined at fertilization, XY zygotes becoming males; XX zygotes, females. In early development, however, all sex organs or *gonads* are neutral; that is, they give no macroscopic indication whether they will later form testes or ovaries. The early gonad has two regions, an outer one, the *cortex*, and an inner one, the *medulla*. As development proceeds, the cortex degenerates in those individuals that carry a Y (male), and the medulla forms a testis; in individuals genetically determined to be females, the medulla degenerates and the cortex forms an ovary.

Once the testis and ovary are formed, they take over the regulation of further sexual differentiation by means of the hormones they produce. The hormones direct the development or degeneration of various sexual ducts, the formation of genitalia, and other secondary sexual characteristics. Since sexual differentiation is largely controlled by the sex hormones, it is not surprising that genetically normal individuals are morphologically variable with regard to sex. Any change in the environment that can upset the production of, or tissue response to, sex hormones can produce effects which modify the sex phenotype. So, the phenotypes normally considered male and female show some variability—providing some of the spice of life. Genetically normal persons exposed to abnormal environmental conditions can differentiate phenotypes

---

[1] We can test in *Drosophila* whether this explanation of gynandromorphism is sometimes correct by making use of an X-limited gene which produces a phenotypic effect over a large portion of the body surface, that is, a gene that affects the size and shape of the bristles and hairs. Such a gene is *forked*, two of its mutant alleles being f^{34b} and f. In homozygotes (females) and hemizygotes (males), f^{34b} produces bristles and hairs of normal length and shape; f causes them to be shortened, split, and gnarled. The f^{34b}/f heterozygotes have bristles and hairs slightly abnormal in these respects, showing a "weak forked" phenotype. If a cross is made to produce female offspring that are f^{34b}/f heterozygotes, the following predictions can be made regarding the phenotype of the gynanders occasionally present among the siblings: All gynanders, originating as postulated, will be weakly forked in their female parts; their male parts will have either normal or strongly forked bristles and hairs, depending upon whether the lost X carried f or f^{34b}, respectively. Experimental results obtained confirm exactly these expectations.

Although most gynanders in *Drosophila* and other insects in which the male has the heteromorphic sex chromosomes can be explained in this manner, some gynanders originate another way. In extremely rare cases, an abnormal egg is produced after meiosis which contains not one but two haploid gametic nuclei. Because polyspermy sometimes occurs in insects—that is, more than the one sperm normally involved in fertilization enters an egg—one of the two haploid egg nuclei may be fertilized by an X-carrying sperm, the other by a Y-carrying one. The resultant individual is approximately a half-and-half gynander. This type of gynander can be identified if the two paternal (or the two maternal) haploid gametic nuclei are marked differently for a pair of autosomal genes.

that lie between the two normal ranges of sex type and, therefore, are intersexual in appearance. Although it is sometimes easy to classify an individual as being an intersex because the person is clearly between the two sex norms, other individuals at the extremes of normality cannot readily be labeled normal, or intersex, or supersex. Intersexual phenotypes due to environmental factors can result either from genotypic males who have developed partially in the direction of female, or from genotypic females partially differentiated in the direction of male.

23.7   Human beings with an abnormal number of sex chromosomes are often of abnormal sex type.

Persons are known who have different numbers of sex chromosomes but are otherwise diploid. Only one viable type has a single sex chromosome; this is the X0 individual, who is female. The typical phenotypic effect of this condition is called *Turner's syndrome* (after its discoverer) and is characterized by the failure to mature as a woman. Turner-type females usually do not develop breasts, ovulate, or menstruate. Because of variability in the genotypic details and in the environment (including medical treatment), considerable variation occurs in the phenotypic consequences of the X0 condition. Although one woman apparently of this constitution is known to have given birth to a normal (XY) son, sterility occurs almost invariably, and short stature invariably, in X0 individuals. (The X0 mouse is apparently less variable phenotypically since it always seems to produce a fertile female.) The other single-sex-chromosome type, Y0, is presumably lethal in man (and is lethal in mouse).

Otherwise-diploid persons having three sex chromosomes are of three types: XXX is female (sometimes mentally defective); XYY is male (sometimes associated with impulsive and antisocial behavior; aggressiveness); XXY is male. Any excess of a sex chromosome (especially the Y) makes the person taller than expected from the family pedigree. The XXY individual, who is invariably sterile, may have undersized sex organs, and may develop various secondary sexual characteristics of females, possesses *Klinefelter's syndrome* (named after its discoverer). Along with the X0 female, he is phenotypically variable; for instance, some Klinefelter males are mentally retarded, others are not; although all those presently known are sterile, some show normal sexual drive and behavior. (In the mouse, too, XXY is a sterile male.)

The approximate frequencies among liveborn individuals is 1 per 1,000 ♀♀ for XXX; 1 per 700 ♂♂ for XYY; 1 per 800 ♂♂ for XXY; and 1 per 3,000 ♀♀ for X0. In accordance with the view that the loss of a chromosome is more deterimental than its gain, the X0 condition is fairly common among abortuses, perhaps only 1 X0 embryo in 40 surviving to term.

Otherwise-diploid persons of the following additional types are also known: XXXX (♀); XXXY (♂); XXYY (♂); XXXXX (♀); XXXXY (♂); XXXYY (♂). Contrary to the situation in *Drosophila*, it is clear from all these results that the Y chromosome is the primary sex-determining chromosome in man (and mouse). Presence of a single Y determines the sex as male; absence of a Y produces the female. All individuals require an X in order to be viable.

The Y versus no Y sex-determining mechanism in human beings and mice implies that the Y must carry one or more genes for maleness in that portion which makes it cytologically unique, the X having no corresponding allele(s). Admitting that the presence of gene(s) for maleness on the Y makes for male, what is genetically responsible for the femaleness produced in the absence of the Y? Clearly other genetic factors are present—not limited in location to the Y chromosome—which affect sex and, therefore, femaleness. The female tendency often shown by the human XXY suggests that the X contains genes affecting normal sexual differentiation which, when present in excess, cause a shift toward femaleness. Presumably, the X also has this capacity when Y is absent.

All cases in which the entire body seems to contain an abnormal number of sex chromosomes can be explained as the result of nondisjunction leading to chromosome loss or gain which occurs either during meiosis or at an early cleavage division—probably the first—of the fertilized egg. Such sex-chromosome nondisjunctions are correlated in human beings, at least in the production of XXY's, with the mother's advanced age at the time of pregnancy.

By following the distribution of X-linked mutants, it has been shown, however, that the nondisjunction which produces an abnormal sex-chromosome number sometimes involves the paternally contributed sex-chromosome material. This origin is exemplified by a red-green colorblind father having an X0 daughter of normal vision. In fact, about 70 per cent of X0 individuals contain a maternally derived X, the paternal sex chromosome being absent. Since certain aged *Drosophila* eggs cause the loss of paternal chromosomes after fertilization, it is important to recognize the possibility that the loss of a paternal chromosome in man can occur post- as well as premeiotically. Owing to a premeiotic paternal nondisjunction, colorblind women can, of course, have XXY Klinefelter sons of normal vision.

Although half of sperm are normally expected to be male-determining and half female-determining, the *sex ratio* in man favors males over females and shifts with parental age. This bias and shift in sex ratio are discussed in more detail in Section S23.7, which also considers various genetic and nongenetic factors that may be responsible. (R)

23.8   Rearrangements are known involving the sex chromosomes of human beings.

If an X chromosome is broken once within or near the centromere, replication and joining of sister ends will produce *isochromosomes*, chromosomes composed of identical lengthwise halves (Figure 23-6). The transmission of such chromosomes in

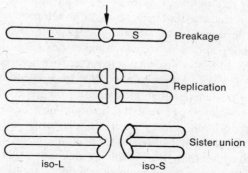

Figure 23-6 Formation of isochromosomes following centromeric breakage and chromosome replication.

man is expected to be normal, or almost normal, as it is in other species having isochromosomes or chromosomes that contain partial deletions of the centromere or two centromeres close together.

Persons are known that contain besides a normal X, the long-arm isochromosome of X ($X^L.X^L$) or the short-arm isochromosome of X ($X^S.X^S$). Both types are sterile females, showing that the genes missing have sexual effects. Since the $X^L.X^L$ carrier has typical Turner's syndrome whereas the $X^S.X^S$ carrier does not (short stature, neck webbing, etc., being absent), the nonsexual portion of Turner's syndrome is attributed to the loss of genetic material in X^S, the short arm of the X (see also Figure 29-6).

Isochromosomes $Y^L.Y^L$ and $Y^S.Y^S$ also occur for the Y chromosome. Loss of the long arm of Y (in X $Y^S.Y^S$ individuals) produces phenotypic males with many of the nonsexual characteristics of Turner's syndrome (including short stature), indicating that some of the genes in Y^L are also located in X^S. Loss of the short arm of Y (in X $Y^L.Y^L$ individuals) produces phenotypic females with no nonsexual abnormalities, indicating that the genes for male sex determination are mainly in Y^S (see also Figure 29-6).

Phenotypic Klinefelter's males that seem to be XX may have received an X from their mother and a half-translocation containing most of the X plus Y^S ($X.Y^S$) from their father. If the piece of X missing were approximately the size of Y^S, the $X.Y^S$ chromosome would be morphologically indistinguishable from an X. A half-translocation containing Y^L plus a small piece of X would appear like a Y. Such a chromosome plus a normal X apparently produces females with abnormally developed gonads which seem to have an XY sex chromosome constitution.

Still other rearranged X chromosomes occur which are rings or have deletions in the short arm or long arm. The Y chromosomes of phenotypically normal males vary considerably in size—there being no correlation with virility. (R)

23.9 Human beings who are mosaics for sex chromosomes are intersexes or infrasexes, not gynandromorphs.

A considerable number of persons having different chromosomal compositions in different body parts are mosaic for sex chromosomes. These include the following mixed constitutions: XX/XY, XXX/X0, XX/X0, XY/X0, XXY/XX, XXXY/XY. Such cases are usually due to one or more errors in chromosome distribution among the daughter nuclei produced after fertilization, although most, if not all, XX/XY are derived from double fertilization of binucleate eggs. Although such individuals are sex-chromosome mosaics, and some may even have one ovary-like and one testis-like gonad, they are not gynanders in superficial characteristics because of their whole-body distribution of sex hormones. Although the XXY male is often clearly an intersex, the X0, XXX, and so on females that show incomplete maturity are best considered infrafemales, being underdeveloped sexually. It should now be clear that some specific phenotypic sexual abnormalities may be based primarily either on an abnormal environment or on an abnormal chromosomal composition (recognizing also the possibility that mutants other than those involving an abnormal number of sex chromosomes can affect sex). Accordingly, chromosomal counts are often desirable in order to determine the cause—and, hence, the treatment—of sexual abnormality.

23.10   In Hymenoptera the sexes usually differ in ploidy.

In Hymenoptera (for example, bees, ants, wasps, and sawflies) unfertilized eggs develop as males (haploids) and fertilized eggs, usually, as females (diploids). Haploid males produce haploid sperm via suitable modifications of the meiotic process, and all gametes of males and females have morphologically identical chromosomal compositions.

In the parasitic wasp, *Habrobracon juglandis*, when the parents are closely related, some of the sons are haploid, but others are diploid having 10 pairs of chromosomes like their sisters. Genetic study shows that such diploid males have a biparental origin. A study of intrastrain and interstrain breeding supports the interpretation that a multiple allelic series determines sex in this form. With respect to this sex-determining locus or chromosome region, haploids are males, diploid heterozygotes are females, and diploid homozygotes are relatively inviable semisterile males. (R)

23.11   In some species one genotype codes for two kinds of gametes or sexes; the environment determines which of these phenotypes are expressed.

In certain organisms, male and female gametes are produced in the same individual. Animals of this type are said to be *hermaphroditic* (after Hermes and Aphrodite), and plants, *monoecious*. The hermaphrodite snail, *Helix*, has a gonad that produces both eggs and sperm from cells which sometimes lie very close together. In the earthworm, eggs and sperm are produced in separate gonads located in different segments of the body. In certain mosses, egg- and sperm-like gametes are also produced in separate sex organs (located on the same haploid gametophyte).

In all these cases, the two types of gametes are produced by an organism that has but a single genotype, that is, one that is not genetically mosaic. Nevertheless, it might be supposed, at first, that the haploid genotype carried by eggs and by the sperm is different and causes the difference in phenotype and behavior. In the case of the gametophyte of mosses, however, the individual is haploid and so are both types of gametes it forms. Accordingly, in such organisms we cannot expect differences in gene content to be the basis either for the formation of gametes or for the different types of gametes produced.

Gamete formation in hermaphroditic and monoecious organisms, therefore, must depend primarily upon environmental differences. Such differences must exist even between cells that lie close together, as is the case in *Helix*. It is reasonable to suppose that the same kinds of environmental factors which can direct one group of cells to form muscle cells and an adjacent group to form bone cells can direct the differentiation of still other cells to make gonadal tissue in which adjacent cells can further differentiate as sperm and egg.

In the examples already mentioned, the type of gamete differentiated depends upon the different positions which cells have within a single organism; consequently, they are subject to differences in internal and external environments. In the marine annelid *Ophryotrocha*, the two sexes are in separate individuals, and the sex type formed is determined by the size of the organism. When the animal is small, because of youth or because it was obtained by amputation from a larger organism, it manufactures sperm;

when larger, the same individual shifts to the manufacture of eggs. In this case the environment of the gonad is changed by the growth of the organism.

Finally, consider sex determination in the marine worm *Bonellia*, in which the separate sexes are radically different in appearance and activity—females being walnut-sized and having a long proboscis, males being microscopic ciliated forms that live as parasites in the body of the female. Fertilized eggs grown in the absence of adult females develop as females; they develop as males in the presence either of adult females or simply an extract of the female's proboscis. In this case, then, differentiation as a whole, including sexual differentiation, is regulated by the presence or absence of a chemical messenger manufactured by females.

Nothing has been stated about the specific genetic basis for the determination or differentiation of sex in any of the examples given in this section because different sexes or gametes are determined not by genetic differences among cells, organs, or individuals, but by environmental differences acting upon a uniform genotype. The genes, nevertheless, must play a role in all these cases by making possible different sexual responses to variations in the environment.

SUMMARY AND CONCLUSIONS

The formation of different types of gametes or sexes always has a genetic basis. In some species, including hermaphroditic animals and monoecious plants, for example, a given genotype produces different gametes or sexes in response to differences in internal or external environment. In other species different genotypes produce different gametes or sexes independently of normal variations in the internal or external environment. In these cases sexual differences can often be correlated with genetical and cytological differences, as described next.

Genes responsible for sex determination are located not only in sex chromosomes but in autosomes as well. Although sex type may be changed through the action of a single pair of genes, a given sex is usually the result of the interaction of several, and probably many, pairs of genes. Sex behaves, therefore, like a qualitative trait in its grosser details and like a quantitative trait in its finer details.

Chromosomal differences found among zygotes serve as visible manifestations of differences in the balance of genes concerned with sex. Whenever, as in female *Drosophila*, genic balance is unaffected by the addition or subtraction of whole sets of chromosomes, sex type also is unaffected. Changes in chromosome number which produce intermediate genic balances, however, also produce intermediate sex types—intersexes; those which make the balance more extreme than normal produce extreme sex types—supersexes.

These principles of sex determination apply also to human beings. In man and many other organisms, a large part of sexual differentiation is controlled by sex hormones produced by the gonads. This type of control rarely, if ever, permits the occurrence of individuals who are typically male in one part and typically female in another part; it may also contribute to the formation of abnormal sex types for nongenetic reasons.

GENERAL REFERENCES

Goldschmidt, R. B. 1955. *Theoretical genetics.* Berkeley: University of California Press.
Levitan, M., and Montagu, A. 1971. *Textbook of human genetics.* New York: Oxford University Press.

Richard Benedict Goldschmidt (1878–1958). [From Genetics, 45: 1 (1960).]

McKusick, V. A. 1964. *Human genetics.* Englewood Cliffs, N.J.: Prentice-Hall, Inc.
Stern, C. 1968. *Genetic mosaics and other essays.* Cambridge, Mass: Harvard University Press.

SPECIFIC SECTION REFERENCES

23.2 Sturtevant, A. H. 1945. A gene in *Drosophila melanogaster* that transforms females into males. Genetics: 30: 297–299.
23.4 Bridges, C. B. 1925. Sex in relation to chromosomes and genes. Amer. Nat., 59: 127–137. Reprinted in *Classic papers in genetics*, Peters, J. A. (Editor), Englewood Cliffs, N.J.: Prentice-Hall, Inc., 1959, pp. 117–123.
23.5 Hannah-Alava, A. 1960. Genetic mosaics. Scient. Amer., 202: 118–130.
23.7 *Lancet*, No. 7075, Vol. 1, 1959, pp. 709–716.
     Polani, P. E. 1969. Abnormal sex chromosomes and mental disorder. Nature, Lond., 223: 680–686.
23.8 Ferguson-Smith, M. A. 1970. Chromosome abnormalities II. Sex chromosome defects. Hospital Practice, April: 88–100.
23.10 Whiting, P. W. 1943. Multiple alleles in complementary sex determination in *Habrobracon*. Genetics, 28: 365–382.

SUPPLEMENTARY SECTION

S23.7 Despite the meiotic expectation, the sex ratio in man favors males over females and shifts with parental age. Various genetic and nongenetic factors are invoked to explain these facts.

Consider how the genotype is related to the *sex ratio*, that is, to the relative numbers of males and females born. On the average, 106 boys are born for each 100 girls. This statistic might be surprising at first, since half the sperm are expected to carry X, half Y, and all eggs, an X, the ratio of boy to girl expected at conception is 1:1. Even if the four meiotic products of a given cell in spermatogenesis usually carry X, X, Y, Y, there is the possibility that during or after *spermiogenesis* (conversion of the telophase II cell into a sperm) some X-bearing sperm are lost. Some evidence suggests that at conception males are much more numerous than females; since more male fetuses normally abort than female, the numbers of boys and girls are more nearly equal at the time of birth than they were at conception.

A study of the sex ratio at birth shows that the ratio 1.067 : 1.000 is found only among young parents, and that it decreases steadily until it is about 1.036 : 1.000 among the children of older parents. How may this significant decrease be explained? Perhaps in older mothers there is a greater chance for chromosomally normal male babies to abort, or for chromosome loss in the earliest mitotic divisions of the fertilized egg. If the chromosome lost is an X and the zygote is XY, the loss is expected to be lethal, so that a potential boy is aborted. If the zygote losing an X is XX, a girl can still be born. Moreover, if the chromosome lost in the XY individual is a Y, a girl can be born instead of a boy. Part of the effect may be due to the increase in meiotic nondisjunction with maternal age (zygotes of XXX type form viable females, whereas zygotes of Y0 type are expected to abort).

We must include the possibility that the fathers may also contribute to this shift in sex ratio. Postmeiotic selection against Y-carrying sperm may increase with paternal age. Or, as fathers become older, the XY tetrad may be more likely to undergo nondisjunction to produce sperm containing respectively, X, X, YY, 0. The first two can produce normal daughters; the last one can produce an underdeveloped X0 daughter; and only the YY is capable of producing males. Even though the XYY individual is male, it may sometimes abort. Other genetic and nongenetic explanations for the shift in sex ratio with age are also possible. This discussion merely demonstrates how the basic facts of sex determination, chromosome loss, and nondisjunction may be used to formulate various hypotheses whose validity is subject to test.

When many pedigrees are examined for sex ratio, several consecutive births of the same sex occasionally occur. This phenomenon could, of course, happen purely as a matter of chance when enough pedigrees are scored. One family, however, is reported to have only boys in 47 births and, in another well-substantiated case, out of 72 births in one family, all were girls. In both these cases the results are too improbable to be attributed to chance.

We do not know the basis for such results in man, but two different cases of almost exclusive female progeny production in *Drosophila* might suggest an explanation for those human pedigrees in which only one sex occurs in the progeny. In the first case, an XY male carrying a gene called *sex ratio* is responsible. Because of this gene almost all functional sperm carry an X. In the second case, a female transmitting a spirochaete microorganism to her offspring through the egg is responsible. Such a female mated to a normal male produces zygotes which begin development; soon thereafter the XY individuals are killed by the spirochaete, leaving almost all female survivors.

The sex ratio can be controlled if the genotypes of the zygotes formed can be controlled. Since X- and Y-bearing sperm of men must differ in various respects because the X and Y differ in size, it should be possible to separate the two types and thereby control the sex of progeny. Using various animal forms, such experiments have been performed with some success by Russian, American, and Swedish workers, using electric currents or centrifugation. Although these experiments have been encouraging, the results are not yet consistent, and the techniques not yet suitable for practical use.

Bangham, A. D. 1961. Electrophoretic characteristics of ram and rabbit spermatozoa. Proc. Roy. Soc., Ser. B, 155: 292–305.

Ikeda, H. 1970. The cytoplasmically-inherited "sex-ratio" condition in natural and experimental populations of *Drosophila bifasciata*. Genetics, 65: 311–333.

QUESTIONS AND PROBLEMS

1. If sexual reproduction is advantageous, why do so many organisms still reproduce asexually?

2. Give the genotypes and phenotypes of the unexceptional, the nondisjunctional, and the gynandromorphic offspring expected from a mating of f^{34b}/f with f *Drosophila*.

3. Using first the autosomal alleles e and e^+ and then the X-limited alleles y and y^+, devise crosses by which you could identify gynanders in *Drosophila* resulting from two fertilizations of a single egg.

4. Compare the genotypes and phenotypes of sex chromosome mosaics of flies, moths, and men.

5. All human beings have the same number of chromosomes in each somatic cell. Discuss this statement giving evidence in support of your view.

6. The following types of mosaics are known in human beings:

XXX/X0	XXY/XX
XX/X0	XXXY/XY
XY/X0	

    Give a reasonable explanation for the probable origination of each.

7. In human beings, can the members of a pair of monozygotic twins ever be of different sexes? Explain.

8. Assuming that each homolog carried a different allele, a^1, a^2, a^3, of the same gene, make a schematic representation of a triva-

lent as it might appear during synapsis. Show diagrammatically the chromosomal and genetic content of the four meiotic products that could be obtained from your trivalent diagram.

9. a. *Scurfy*, *sf*, is an X-linked recessive gene that kills male mice before they reproduce. How is a stock containing this gene maintained normally?

    b. Occasionally, the stock containing this gene produces scurfy females which also die before reproductive age. Suggest a genetic explanation for these female exceptions.

10. List the types of human zygotes formed after maternal nondisjunction of the X chromosome. What phenotype would be expected from each of the zygotes that these, in turn, may produce?

11. List specific causes for the production of abnormal sex types in human beings.

12. How can you explain that only one "X0" individual is known to have had a successful pregnancy, whereas all other X0's are sterile?

13. Discuss the general applicability of the chromosomal balance theory of sex determination.

14. In *Drosophila*, why are gynanders not intersexes? Is this true in man also? Explain.

15. What chromosomal constitution can you give for a triploid human embryo that is "male"? "Female"?

16. A nonhemophilic man and woman have a hemophilic son with Klinefelter's syndrome. Describe the chromosomal content and genotypes of all three individuals mentioned.

17. Klinefelter-type males occur who are XXXYY. Give a possible origin of this chromosomal constitution.

18. In the plant genus *Melandrium*, one observes individuals of the following types:

Diploid: XX + 11 AA = ♀
               XY + 11 AA = ♂
Triploid: XXX + 11 AAA = ♀
               XXY + 11 AAA = ♂
Tetraploid: XXXX + 11 AAAA = ♀
               XXYY + 11 AAAA = ♂
                    or
               XXXY + 11 AAAA = ♂

Discuss the cytogenic basis for sex determination in *Melandrium*.

19. Compare the self-sterility alleles in *Nicotiana* (see Section S16.1b) with the sex-determination alleles in *Habrobracon*.

20. How can you explain the following changes in chromosomal mosaicism in man?
    1. XY/X0 mosaics become more XY with time.
    2. Triploid/diploid mosaics become more diploid with time.

21. What evidence would support the view that XX/XY mosaicism in human beings is the result of double fertilizations of binucleate eggs?

22. How can you explain that in human beings X0/XY mosaics seem to have a greater chance for gonadal tumors and XXY males a greater chance for mammary tumors than XY individuals?

23. R. A. Turpin reported two cases of monozygotic twins. One set contains an XY male and an X0 female; the other set is composed of a disomic-21 male and a trisomic-21 male. Discuss the mechanisms probably involved in producing such twins. Include in your hypothesis the additional fact that one X0 cell is also found in the first XY individual mentioned.

PART VI

Genetic Regulation

Chapter 24

Regulation of Gene Synthesis and Destruction

In the preceding chapters we have examined the structural, functional, mutational, recombinational, and phenotypic properties of genetic material. We have not yet considered, however, all the kinds of information which must be contained in the genetic material of an organism. For the term "organism" implies an organization, an orderliness in structure and function, by which are coordinated not only the parts of a cell but the cells themselves. This ordering requires that specific genes act in specific patterns and sequences. We will consider in the next several chapters how genetic material is able to regulate its own function. In the first two chapters we will see how the organism chooses which parts of the total genetic material are present and in how many replicas. We shall look first at the genetic basis for the regulation of gene synthesis and destruction.

24.1 DNA gene chemistry is under genetic regulation.

Organisms can exert some "choice" over the exact chemical composition of their genetic nucleic acids. Known choices involve the ways that already synthesized DNA is modified by enzymatic means, as mentioned in Section 8.8. For example, T-even phages code for phage-specific enzymes, glucosyl transferases, that glucosylate some of the hydroxymethylcytosines present. The pattern of glucosylated and nonglucosylated bases is different for different phages. Different phages and other organisms code for species-specific DNA methylases which add methyl groups to cytosine or adenine. Again, only some of these bases are methylated, the pattern being species-specific.

Modification of gene chemistry is advantageous because it makes DNA species-specific. This specificity permits an organism to recognize (1) its own normal DNA (which is, therefore, subject to replication and transcription by its own DNA and RNA polymerases), (2) its own DNA which has become abnormal (which is, therefore, subject to degradation and repair synthesis), as well as (3) foreign DNA (which is, therefore, subject to degradation, unless that DNA has mimicked the host DNA pattern). On the other hand, RNA genetic material does not seem to be modified in these ways, since ribosomes cannot usually read messenger nucleic acids that are methylated, and RNA genetic material is usually translated.

We do not know how the enzymes involved specify different patterns of gluco-sylation or methylation. We do have some information, however, regarding the synthesis and persistence of certain of these enzymes relative to their time of need, that is, shortly after DNA synthesis.

24.2   DNA replication in bacteria apparently occurs in units called replicons.

In our discussion of transformation (Chapter 11), we implied that donor DNA does not replicate unless it is integrated into the host chromosome. The host chromosome seems to be a complete replicating unit, or *replicon*, whereas the donor DNA fragment does not seem so. A replicon must carry a site at which replication can begin; once started, it continues to completion regardless of the nature or origin of the DNA base sequence that follows. Episomes such as the DNA of temperate phages, sex factors, and substituted sex factors must also be replicons since they themselves contain the information necessary for independent replication. In abortive transduction, however, the transducing phage contains genetic material that must be a defective replicon since the unintegrated loci cannot replicate. Mutant types of F are known which cannot replicate when free but which are replicated when integrated in the *E. coli* chromosome, where they are part of a functioning replicon. When a normal episome is integrated, apparently only one replicon in the episome-host chromosome is operative. (R)

24.3   Gene replication is regulated within a chromosome.

That replication is regulated within a chromosome is suggested by the observation in many organisms that chromosome replication is initiated at specific, not random, positions.

Procaryotes

Such control is definitely known in bacteria, where replication ordinarily begins at only one site in a bacterial chromosome; this site (or gene) is a specific one; replication being completed in a single sequential synthesis. We believe, therefore, that each bacterial chromosome is a single replicon. In regularly dividing *E. coli*, F⁻, F⁺, and Hfr normally initiate replication at about the 8 o'clock position (or at about 60 min) of the genetic map, as seen in Figure 13-8. When Hfr is undergoing conjugation, however, replication starts at or near the locus of integrated F. This suggests that the active DNA polymerase starts synthesis at one *recognition gene* in nonconjugating Hfr males and a different one in conjugating Hfr males. Each bacterial chromosome seems to have a single functioning recognition, or *replication initiator*, *gene*.

Initiation also seems to depend upon an initiator substance or membrane rather than upon cell division. In fact, under special circumstances, chromosome replication can be initiated again before the chromosome has finished replication (Figure 24-1). For example, replication is initated prematurely when thymine starvation or exposure to nalidixic acid is terminated. In this connection we should mention a report that a low-molecular-weight, possibly protein, bacterial-coded factor seems to be necessary for the initiation of DNA polymerase action on *E. coli* DNA.

Phages

Such regulation would apply to virulent phage if replication starts simultaneously with the injection into the host of one end of a rod phage chromosome. Note that when phage T4 chromosomes deficient for one third of their length are tested, they initiate replication but do not initiate a second replication. This suggests that replication initiation depends upon the presence of genes not located at the replication start point.

Vegetative lambda DNA seems to have a preferred replication start point (*ori*, in Figure 26-5). Some evidence has been obtained that lambda codes for a factor which, when joined to a DNA polymerase coded in *E. coli*, recognizes free lambda DNA (and presumably no longer recognizes *E. coli* DNA).

Eucaryotes

In higher organisms the chromosomes are much longer than in bacteria. For example, in man the average chromosome (all 23 contain about 2.8×10^9 base pairs) is at least 25 times larger than the *E. coli* chromosome (which contains about 4×10^6 base pairs). That the chromosomes of insects contain numerous start points for DNA synthesis is shown by the incorporation of radioactive DNA precursors into giant polynemic chromosomes at several places at the same time. Such chromosomes are considered to be composed of a large number of longitudinally arranged replicons. Even if all replicons within a chromosome started replicating at the same time, which

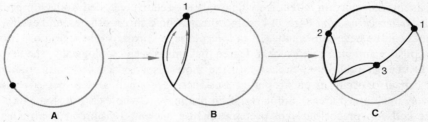

A   B   C

Figure 24-1   Replication of *E. coli* chromosome. A DNA duplex is represented by a single line. (A) Point of replication or growing point (dot) is at initiator position. (B) First growing point has advanced to 1. (C) Second and third initiations of replication have occurred, under special circumstances, and their growing points have advanced to 2 and 3, even though the first growing point at 1 has not finished replicating the chromosome.

they do not (see Section 24.5), it is clear that the chromosome of a higher organism is synthesized in separate pieces which (1) must be held in place, and (2) then linked together.[1] (R)

24.4 Nuclear chromosome morphology and replication can be regulated by cytoplasmic factors.

The conformations of genes and chromosomes are varied at specific times. For example, the hydration and dehydration associated with phage chromosome functioning and transmission, respectively, occur at specific times and are expected to be dependent upon enzymatic action indirectly, if not directly. Similarly, the dehydration and hydration and the folding–coiling versus unfolding–uncoiling that occurs in the nuclear chromosomes of mitotic organisms must also be explained in like manner, that is, as involving enzymatic action.

When an ovum receives in its cytoplasm via experimental transplanation the nucleus of another cell of the same organism, the transplanted nucleus enlarges, its chromatin becomes dispersed, and cytoplasmic protein enters it. (Recall that the compact sperm nucleus also swells upon entering the egg cytoplasm.) When adult brain nuclei, which are in a nonmitotic, metabolic state, are transplanted into maturing oocytes, groups of chromosomes on spindles are formed.

DNA replication in the nucleus is similarly dependent upon cytoplasmic factors. This is shown by experiments in which adult brain nuclei, which are not synthesizing DNA, are transplanted into parthenogenetically activated eggs of the same species, which are starting DNA synthesis. Within 1 to 2 hours the transplanted nuclei begin DNA synthesis. Also, when midblastula nuclei, which are active in DNA synthesis, are transplanted into growing oocytes, which are not synthesizing DNA, the transplanted nuclei stop synthesizing DNA.

Such findings show that nuclear phenotype, including nuclear chromosome morphology and replication, is subject to regulation by cytoplasmic factors. (R)

24.5 Chromosomes or chromosome regions that are heterochromatic replicate after those that are euchromatic.

At any given time in a metabolic nucleus, some chromatin is relatively diffuse in appearance, being relatively uncoiled and unclumped, and is called *euchromatin*; whereas another portion is relatively dense, being relatively coiled and clumped and is called *heterochromatin*. Parts of chromosomes, whole chromosomes, and even whole genomes can be heterochromatic. If, in interphase, a chromosome region or chromosome coils up and clumps to such a degree that this is seen cytologically, the material is said to be heterochromatic relative to the more dispersed euchromatin. (Clumped areas can also occur in euchromatin, but these are small and dispersed between relatively unclumped areas.) Similarly, if, in prophase, a whole chromosome or a part of one coils up precociously in preparation for nuclear division, it is also heterochromatic. In *Drosophila* chromosomes, for example, the regions adjacent to the

---

[1] Perhaps the chromosomes of higher organisms consist of fibers made up of a series of circular DNA duplexes—each one, say, about the size of the *E. coli* chromosome—joined linearly by means of polypeptide linkers.

centromeres are intrinsically heterochromatic since they routinely become condensed and stain darkly earlier in mitotic prophase than the other chromosomal regions. In the polynemic chromosomes of larval salivary gland cells, which are permanently at interphase, the same regions adjacent to centromeres are intrinsically heterochromatic because they routinely stain differently (darker, with fewer bands) as compared to other regions of the chromosomes. Since it is possible to study in detail the lengthwise appearance of polynemic chromosomes, it is also possible to identify short regions of such intrinsic or *constitutive heterochromatin* that are interspersed among the euchromatic regions by (1) their similarity in appearance and stainability to, and (2) their synapsis with the heterochromatin of the chromocenter (Section 18.4).

When exposure to radioactive precursors of DNA is initiated at different times during the S stage of interphase, it is found as a general rule that heterochromatic chromosomes or chromosome regions replicate after euchromatic ones. We can suppose that the clumped condition inhibits, delays, or prevents replication—perhaps by making the DNA template relatively unavailable to DNA polymerase and DNA precursors. In human beings autosomes 13, 14, and 15 cannot be distinguished from each other at metaphase. However, autosome 13 is late-replicating throughout its length; autosome 14 is late-replicating in the region near its centromere; autosome 15 is early-replicating throughout.

The Y chromosome of *Drosophila melanogaster*, which is mainly heterochromatic, replicates later than the other chromosomes. Since all the parts of the Y involved in three different reciprocal translocations with mainly euchromatic chromosomes are still late-replicating, it is concluded that the Y segments contain information that regulate their time of replication. Nothing is known at present about the genetic mechanism for the intrachromosomal and whole-chromosomal regulation of the timing of gene replication in eucaryotes. (R)

24.6   Gene replication is regulated at the cellular level in procaryotes.

That bacteria ordinarily have a characteristic number of nuclear areas per cell, whether they are derived asexually (by fission of a parent) or sexually (from an exconjugant), suggests that chromosome or gene replication is regulated at the level of the cell. (Recall from Section 24.4 and Figure 24-1, however, that chromosome replication can be experimentally asynchronized with cell division in *E. coli*.)

A bacterial episome free in the cytoplasm is in its autonomous state. This state does not guarantee that the episome replicates unrestrainedly, since it is dependent upon the raw materials and the transcription–translation machinery of the host cell. Moreover, in the case of free F and F', episome replication is regulated by a *repressor* coded in the episome itself; this repressor permits, on the average, one replication per bacterial cell division or conjugation. Since an F^- cell newly accepting a free sex factor contains no repressor, F multiplication proceeds at an accelerated pace for a time, permitting the rapid conversion of all the members of an F^- culture to F^+ after the introduction of a single F^+ male. As F functions in its new host, regulation is established via the repressor and, presumably, other chemical regulators, so that the episomal chromosome, like the bacterial chromosome, replicates only once a generation. Note, however, that although $F^+ \times F^-$ conjugation releases free F from repression so that it can replicate, the bacterial chromosome is apparently not replicated then; so that the once synchronized number of replications of F and host chromosome is asynchronized by this conjugation.

24.7   Gene replication is also regulated at the cellular level in eucaryotes.

Regulation of the replication of nuclear and extranuclear genes at the cellular level in eucaryotic cells is implied from the following observations:

1. Nuclear DNA replication occurs only during a particular part of interphase and early prophase I of meiosis. A specific example of control at this level is seen in the lily, in which the microspore, which contains DNA, remains in interphase for several weeks. During this time *thymidine kinase* activity starts at a specific time and ends within 24 hours. Thus, it appears that this enzyme, needed for DNA replication before mitosis, is formed for this purpose and is destroyed or inactivated after its task is completed.

2. DNA synthesis ceases when the the nucleus is euploid for DNA— even if the nucleus fails to divide and contains one or more extra genomes. Human liver cells, for example, are diploid or polyploid. That different cells of the same tissue seem to be stabilized at different ploidies suggests that some regulation of DNA replication is occurring at the cellular level. We do not know how such regulation is accomplished.

3. We have already seen in Section 14.8 that nuclear replication occurs without cell replication in early development of certain yolk-filled eggs. In the mosquito *Culex pipiens*, the chromosome number in the epithelial cells of the larval ileum increases from the diploid number of 6 to as high as 48 and 96 without nuclear or cell division. Sister chromosomes tend to synapse (and so do homologous chromosomes) so that there can be 6 groups of 8 or 16 elements each in the largest nuclei. During pupation these groups individually go to metaphase and without further chromosome replication produce daughter nuclei and cells with half the chromosome composition. This somatic reduction division is repeated until the mature pupal ileum cells have only 12 or 6 chromosomes. All cases of endoreplication, polyploidy, and polynemy, of course, also illustrate the divorce of gene replication from cell or nuclear division.

4. Studies of cells in tissue culture show that the initiation of DNA synthesis is regulated at the cell level by the arrangement of cells relative to each other. Release of a cell from contact with neighboring cells promotes the initiation of DNA synthesis, although the way this is accomplished is still unknown.

5. The DNA's in mitochondria and chloroplasts are probably replicons. The limited range in the number of chromosomes per mitochondrion and the specific timing of DNA replication in chloroplasts relative to the whole cell cycle are evidence that extranuclear chromosome replication is regulated at the organellar–cellular level. (R)

24.8 Nuclear genome number is regulated at the tissue and organ levels.

The following evidence indicates that nuclear DNA replication is regulated at the tissue and organ levels.

Differentiated nuclei which normally undergo a series of chromosomal endo-replications, expressed as increasing multiples of polynemy, are found in several tissues, including the salivary gland, Malpighian tubule, and gastric caecum, of larval Diptera such as *D. melanogaster*. Using the increase in nuclear volume as a sufficiently precise measure of an increase in the number of genomes, it is found during larval development (1) all the cells of such tissues (but none of others) increase in genome multiple, (2) the range in genome multiple within a tissue is relatively narrow, (3) increases in genome multiple occur synchronously and repeatedly in the three different tissues studied, and (4) some tissues continue to increase in genome multiple (salivary gland) even after others (Malpighian tubule, gastric caecum) have ceased to do so. These results indicate that nuclear genome replication in different organs is co-ordinately regulated, even though some organs exercise some independence from control.

24.9 Gene destruction is normally programmed.

The same genes that survive under one set of organismal circumstances are chosen to be destroyed under another. Several examples can be given at different levels of organization in eucaryotic and procaryotic cells.

1. *Organ-system level.* Metamorphosis in the frog involves the resorption of the tadpole tail. Insect metamorphosis involves digestion of single and groups of larval organs.
2. *Tissue or cell-group level.* Polar bodies produced by meiosis are sometimes digested. Nurse cells for insect oocytes are destroyed and their nuclear contents digested and transferred to the growing oocyte. In the grasshopper *Melanoplus differentialis* whole bundles of spermatocytes in certain testicular tubes are digested, liberating DNA presumably for some nutritional purpose. Gene loss at this level does not always mean immediate death to the cell groups involved, however, since in mammals red blood cells lose their nuclei and function in respiration as red blood corpuscles; in plants, sieve cells function even though they have lost their nuclei.
3. *Intranuclear level.* Whole chromosome loss routinely occurs in *Miastor* and the germ and somatic lines of *Sciara*. Parts of chromosomes are routinely lost from *Cyclops* and from somatic cells of *Ascaris* (the latter case is described in Section 25.2).

   Some DNA which is selectively replicated (and is apparently genetic; described in the next two sections) is also selectively eliminated. This is the fate of the extra nucleolar DNA in amphibian oocytes. In the dipteran *Tipula*, the oocyte nucleus has a body (containing 50 per cent of all DNA present) which disappears at diplonema.

   Up to 41 per cent of the DNA in

Aedes aegypti mosquito larvae is double-stranded and has a molecular weight of about 5×10^5. This DNA, apparently nuclear in origin, is essentially absent in pupae and adults. The DNA content of the salivary gland cell of the snail *Helix* decreases as a particular secretion product is made. Germinating wheat seeds and growing roots of wheat and maize contain double-stranded, presumably genetic, DNA of low molecular weight (around 1×10^5) which has a higher G + C content than the high-molecular-weight DNA present and is metabolically labile.

After conjugation *Paramecium aurelia* contains about 35 fragments of old macronucleus besides two new macronuclei. Under starvation conditions the macronuclear fragments are selectively autolyzed, their DNA being digested to supply precursor material for the new macronucleus and surviving old fragments.

4. *Procaryotic-cell level.* Genes that are introduced into a bacterial cell by transformation and conjugation are often normal to the biological system. Those that are neither integrated into the host genome nor functional are apparently degraded. Genes do not have to be part of a potentially functional replicon to persist— donor genes in an abortive transduction persist without being replicated. (R)

24.10 Disproportionate nuclear gene replication occurs and is presumably regulated genetically.

Although eu- and heterochromatin replicate at different times, nuclear chromosomes and their parts ordinarily eventually complete the same number of replications —one, in preparation for normal mitosis and meiosis; more than one, in cases of endoreplication leading to polyploidy or polynemy. Many examples exist, however, where some nuclear chromosomes or parts replicate more often than others. Such differential or disproportionate replication of DNA in the somatic or germ line results in *amplification* of the DNA made in extra copies and, of course, in *under-replication* of DNA not made in extra copies.

Amplified genomes

Amplification can involve whole chromosome sets. For example, in the coccid *Phanocoecus* the male ordinarily has 5 pairs of chromosomes per somatic nucleus. The 5 maternally derived chromosomes are euchromatic and the 5 paternally derived chromosomes are heterochromatic. In certain cells called oenocytes *differential polyploidy* occurs—the maternal but not the paternal chromosomes are replicated, so that the cell comes to contain up to 80 euchromatic maternal-type but only 5 hetero-chromatic paternal-type chromosomes.

Amplified chromosome parts
(see also Section 24.11)

Examples of amplification involving only parts of chromosomes include:

1. *Extra replications of DNA that appear to remain integrated in the chromosome.*
   a. In one abnormal human family, some cells show one chromosome with an extra duplication of one of its arms, so that at metaphase it appears as a three-armed chromosome.
   b. Hybrids between *Nicotiana tabacum* and *N. octophora* occasionally have cells whose nuclei contain one or a few *megachromosomes*. These can be attributed to one region of a chromosome selectively undergoing repeated replications while the rest of the genome replicates once.
   c. In *Drosophila*, measurements of chromocentral and nonchromocentral DNA in larval cells of different polynemies strongly suggest that chromocentral DNA is less polynemic than nonchromocentral DNA. Recall that chromocentral DNA is heterochromatic.
   d. In *Rhynchosciara* and *Sciara* certain bands in the giant larval salivary gland chromosomes puff out. This puffing is associated with a differential replication of DNA such that the puff can have as much as a 15-fold greater relative DNA content than a nonpuff region. Several chromosome regions are involved. Several agents (for example, ecdysone) cause puffing to occur earlier; others (microsporidian infection) delay or suppress puffing. Infections can cause extra chromosome replications and specific puffs.

2. *Extra replications of DNA that are released from the chromosome.*
   a. In *Hybosciara fragilis* the extra DNA is released from polynemic chromosomes as the cores of *nucleoloids* (free nucleolus-like bodies) and are normally transferred to the nucleoplasm. Several chromosome regions are involved. A similar phenomenon occurs in the polynemic chromosomes of *Sarcophaga*.
   b. The protozoan *Stylonychia mytilis* has a macronucleus which releases small pieces of DNA which are maintained in the cytoplasm without being denatured.
   c. Embryonic muscle cells are reported to have *I somes* in their cytoplasm. These bodies are composed of DNA attached to ribosomes probably via their mRNA which is being translated into one of the special proteins needed by this cell type. I-DNA is assumed to be produced by amplification of nuclear genes.
   d. The DNA associated with yolk platelets in certain eggs may be an example of amplification of nuclear genes.

The preceding suggests that when cells are to become specialized and require an unusually large amount of a protein or other metabolic product, the nuclear genes leading to the production of such substances often undergo amplification. This is supported by finding that DNA puffs incorporate RNA precursors—presumably forming mRNA. It is still unknown how amplified genes are able to remain integrated with the regular chromosomal DNA sequence or by what process released amplified DNA is deintegrated. It is not difficult to hypothesize mechanisms for both types of events based upon earlier sections of this book. The next section describes a particular nuclear amplification that often occurs in the female germ line. (R)

24.11   Amplification often occurs in oocytes for nuclear genes involved in the synthesis of rRNA.

Extra replications of nucleolus organizer DNA occur in many oocytes and the resultant DNA is (as in the previous section) either (1) retained as an integrated portion of the nuclear genome, or (2) released from the regular genome, remaining in the nucleus as the cores of free nucleoli.

1. In the oocyte of the dipteran *Tipula*, the nucleus contains a body (containing 50 per cent of all the DNA present) which disappears at diplonema. This body is due to the amplification and retention in integrated form of the DNA of the nucleolus organizer. This giant puff is similar to the DNA puffs formed in *Rhynchosciara* and *Sciara*.

The same kind of amplification of nucleolus organizer DNA occurs also in other Diptera (*Pales quadristriata* and *P. scurra*), in Coleoptera (*Dytiscus marginalis*), and in the cricket *Acheta domesticus*.

2. In amphibians such as *Xenopus* and *Triturus*, the nucleus of each oocyte has several hundred extra nucleoli, each of which is free of the main chromosomal body and contains the DNA of the nucleolus organizer region. This DNA is transcribed to rRNA. The typical free nucleolus consists of a compact fibrous core, containing the DNA, surrounded by a granular matrix. Both regions contain RNA and protein. After removing some material, the fibrous core can unwind and is found (Figure 24-2B) to consist of a thin circular axial DNA-containing fiber periodically coated with matrix material which can be removed by proteases and RNase. The ribonucleoprotein matrix shows a thin-to-thick gradation, each *matrix unit* in a core showing the same direction of orientation. Each matrix unit in a core is separated from its neighbors by matrix-free segments of the core axis which range from $\frac{1}{3}$ (usually) to 10 times the length of the matrix unit (Figure 24-3). The length of each matrix unit (about 2.5 μ) corresponds closely to the length of DNA needed to code for a 40s pre-rRNA molecule. Each ribonucleoprotein fiber appears, therefore, to contain a growing pre-rRNA molecule; since there are 100 or so fibers per matrix unit, there must be the same number of RNA polymerase molecules functioning in this region, which is presumed to be just one DNA duplex thick. The function of the apparently nontranscribed "spacer" DNA is unknown (see "silent DNA" in Section 8.3).

In *Xenopus* the number of matrix units per core varies considerably—from 8 to

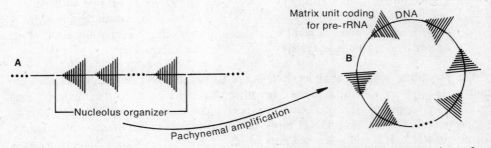

Figure 24-2   Amplification of nucleolus organizer DNA in Amphibia. (A) Portion of a chromosome in a somatic or prepachynemal nucleus showing the nucleolus organizer region and 3 of about 450 hypothesized matrix units. (B) One of hundreds of fibrous cores containing ring chromosomes composed of nucleolus organizer DNA produced by amplification during pachynema. See the text for a description.

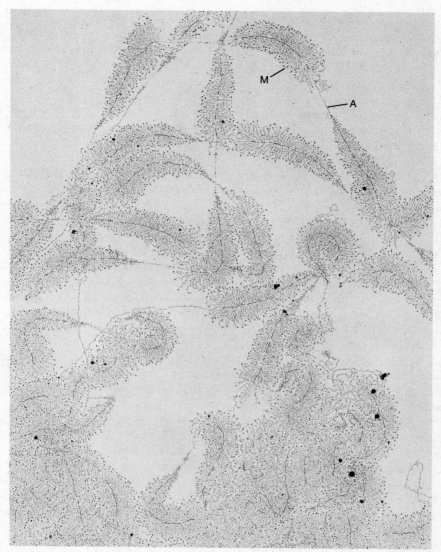

Figure 24-3 Electron micrograph of a portion of a fibrous core containing a ring chromosome produced by amplification of nucleolus organizer DNA. A, DNA-containing axis; M, matrix unit. (Courtesy of O. L. Miller, Jr., and B. R. Beatty, Biology Division, Oak Ridge National Laboratory. From cover photo of Science, 164: 23 May 1969. Copyright 1969 by the American Association for the Advancement of Science.)

175 matrix units have been counted; larger cores have an estimated 1,000 matrix units. It is likely that the haploid nucleolus organizer region contains an estimated 450 matrix units and that this value is amplified 1,500 times in the mature oocyte (Figure 24-2A). Thus the amplified cores may contain less or more matrix units than the number hypothesized for the nucleolus organizer region of the chromosome.

It should be noted that amplification of *rDNA* (DNA complementary to rRNA) does not occur in somatic tissues of *Xenopus*, at least in the embryo and erythrocytes. (R)

SUMMARY AND CONCLUSIONS

Among organisms having DNA as genetic material, some can regulate their chromosome morphology; all seem able to modify the chemical composition of their DNA through enzymatically directed, unique modifications of the bases. Organisms having DNA genetic material also use various means to regulate the synthesis of DNA, as follows.

Although additional support for the following generalization is desirable, the normal genetic material of procaryotes seems to be a single replicon that codes for a DNA polymerase, a replication initiator substance (which may or may not attach to the DNA polymerase), and a recognition gene (comparable to that in phage Qβ RNA, Section 5.3) which active DNA polymerase recognizes as the synthesis start point. Bacteria may also have genes that regulate the frequency of chromosome replication.

Bacterial episomes free of the host chromosome are also replicons; they probably code for factors which direct the host's DNA polymerase to preferentially recognize the episome's recognition gene, and therefore, to preferentially replicate the episome. Episomes also code for repressors which usually prevent episomal DNA from acting as a replicon. Thus, the integrated episome represses the replication of homologous free episomes. This suppression also applies to integrated episomes, which are usually replicated only as part of the host chromosome replicon. Sometimes, as during conjugation with Hfr, however, the recognition gene of the episome and not that of the host chromosome is used.

The replication of the chromosomes of mitochondria and chloroplasts is expected to be regulated in ways similar to those employed by procaryotes and their episomes. The chromosomes in nuclei, however, seem to contain several to many linearly arranged replicons. The activity of these replicons is coordinated so that the entire chromosome is replicated once a nuclear division, cytologically detected heterochromatin usually replicating after euchromatin. Replication is regulated not only within a chromosome but also at the cell, tissue, and organ system levels.

Gene destruction is normally genetically programmed for homologous (as well as foreign) DNA entering but not integrating with the genetic material of a procaryote. Organisms—multicellular or unicellular—with two or more nuclei sometimes genetically program the loss of part or all the genetic material in somatic nuclei (but not in germinal nuclei, which are used to bridge generations).

Disproportionate nuclear gene replication can occur in the somatic or germ lines to amplify whole genomes or part of a chromosome. The extra replicas of a chromosome part may remain attached to the parental chromosome region or may be liberated. Amplification seems to occur only in cells that are specialized and require unusually large amounts of a protein or other metabolic product. Although the amplified DNA is genetic material, it is ordinarily not transmitted to future cell generations either because it is produced in cells which will not subsequently divide (for example, giant polynemic cells of certain insect larvae) or is eventually destroyed in cells which will subsequently divide (as is apparently true for the rDNA in the extra nucleoli of amphibian oocytes).

GENERAL REFERENCES

Jacob, F. 1966. Genetics of the bacterial cell. Science, 152: 1470–1478. (Nobel prize lecture, discusses the replicon.)

Jacob, F., Brenner, S., and Cuzin, F. 1963. On the regulation of DNA replication in bacteria. Cold Spring Harbor Sympos. Quant. Biol., 28: 329–348. Reprinted in *Papers on bacterial genetics*, second edition, Adelberg, E. A. (Editor), Boston: Little, Brown and Company, 1966, pp. 403–436.

Lima-de-Faria, A., and Jaworska, H. 1968. Late DNA synthesis in heterochromatin. Nature, Lond., 217: 138–142.

Miller, O. L., Jr., and Beatty, B. R. 1969. Visualization of nucleolar genes. Science, 164: 955–957.

Pavan, C., and Da Cunha, A. B. 1969. Gene amplification in ontogeny and phylogeny of animals. Genetics, 61 (Suppl. 1/2): 289–304.

Plaut, W., Nash, D., and Fanning, T. 1966. Ordered replication of DNA in polytene chromosomes of *Drosophila melanogaster*. J. Mol. Biol., 16: 85–93. (Evidence for a longitudinal array of starting points for DNA synthesis.)

SPECIFIC SECTION REFERENCES

24.3   Lark, K. G., and Renger, H. 1969. Initiation of DNA replication in *Escherichia coli* 15T⁻: chronological dissection of three physiological processes required for initiation. J. Mol. Biol., 42: 221–235.

Mosig, G., and Werner, R. 1969. On the replication of incomplete chromosomes of phage T4. Proc. Nat. Acad. Sci., U.S., 64: 747–754.

Nishimura, Y., Caro, L., Berg, C. M., and Hirota, Y. 1971. Chromosome replication in *Escherichia coli*, IV. Control of chromosome replication and cell division by an integrated episome. J. Mol. Biol., 55: 411–456. (By F.)

24.4   Gurdon, J. B. 1968. Transplanted nuclei and cell differentiation. Scient. Amer., 219 (No. 6): 24–35, 144.

Johnson, R. T., and Rao, P. N. 1971. Nucleo-cytoplasmic interactions in the achievement of nuclear synchrony in DNA synthesis and mitosis in multinucleate cells. Biol. Rev., 46: 97–155.

24.5   Halfer, C., Tiepolo, L., Barigozzi, C., and Fraccaro, M. 1969. Timing of DNA replication of translocated Y chromosome sections in somatic cells of *Drosophila melanogaster*. Chromosoma, 27: 395–408.

24.7   Berger, C. A. 1938. Multiplication and reduction of somatic chromosome groups as a regular developmental process in the mosquito, *Culex pipiens*. Johns Hopkins Univ. Contributions to Embryol., No. 167, pp. 211–232.

Degani, Y., and Atsman, D. 1970. Enhancement of non-nuclear DNA synthesis associated with hormone-induced elongation in the cucumber hypocotyl. Exp. Cell Res., 61: 226–229. (Most of the hormone-induced DNA synthesis occurs in organelles outside the nucleus.)

Dulbecco, R., and Stocker, M. G. P. 1970. Conditions determining initiation of DNA synthesis in 3T3 cells. Proc. Nat. Acad. Sci., U.S., 66: 204–210. (Cells in tissue culture.)

Hancock, R., and Weil, R. 1969. Biochemical evidence for induction by polyoma virus of replication of the chromosomes of mouse kidney cells. Proc. Nat. Acad. Sci., U.S., 63: 1144–1150. (Virus seems to activate a regulatory system controlling chromosome replication.)

Hotta, Y., and Stern, H. 1963. Molecular facets of mitotic regulation, II. Factors underlying the removal of thymidine kinase. Proc. Nat. Acad. Sci., U.S., 49: 861–865.

24.9   Bostock, C. J., and Prescott, D. M. 1972. Evidence of gene diminution during the formation of the macronucleus in the protozoan, *Stylonychia*. Proc. Nat. Acad. Sci., U.S., 69: 139–142. (More than 60 per cent of the DNA sequences in the micronucleus are not present in the macronucleus.)

Lang, C. A., and Meins, F., Jr. 1966. A soluble deoxyribonucleic acid in the mosquito *Aedes aegypti*. Proc. Nat. Acad. Sci., U.S., 55: 1525–2531.

Lima de Faria, A., and Moses, M. J. 1966. Ultrastructure and cytochemistry of metabolic DNA in *Tipula*. J. Cell Biol., 30: 177–192.

24.10   Bell, E. 1969. *I*-DNA: its packaging into *I*-somes and its relation to protein synthesis during differentiation. Nature, Lond., 224: 326–328.

Crouse, H. V. 1968. The role of ecdysone in DNA-puff formation and DNA synthesis in the polytene chromosomes of *Sciara coprophila*. Proc. Nat. Acad. Sci., U.S., 61: 971–978.

Nur, U 1966. Nonreplication of heterochromatic chromosomes in a mealy bug, *Planococcus citri* (Coccoidea: Homoptera). Chromosoma, 19: 439–448.

Rudkin, G. 1969. Non replicating DNA in *Drosophila*. Genetics, 61 (Suppl. 1/2): 227–238.

Swift, H. 1969. Nuclear physiology and differentiation. A general summary. Genetics 61 (Suppl. 1/2): 439–461.

24.11   Brown, D. D., and Dawid, I. B. 1968. Specific gene amplification in oocytes. Science, 160: 272–280. Reprinted in *Papers on regulation of gene activity during development*, Loomis, W. F., Jr. (Editor), New York: Harper & Row, Inc., 1970, pp. 201–209.

Gall, J. G. 1968. Differential synthesis of the genes for ribosomal RNA during amphibian oögensis. Proc. Nat. Acad. Sci., U.S., 60: 553–560. Reprinted in *Papers on regulation of gene activity during development*, Loomis, W. F., Jr. (Editor), New York: Harper & Row, Inc., 1970, pp. 210–217.

Miller, O. L., Jr., and Beatty, B. R. 1969. Extrachromosomal nucleolar genes in amphibian oocytes. Genetics, 61 (Suppl. 1/2): 133–143.

QUESTIONS AND PROBLEMS

1. Is the statement "Every normal event involved in gene synthesis and destruction is regulated genetically" a self-evident truth or a hypothesis that must be tested extensively before being accepted? Explain.

2. Give an example of regulation of gene replication whose mechanism is relatively well understood and another that is not.

3. Do you expect that rDNA is amplified in human oocytes? Explain.

4. Discuss the future of specific cells having amplified nuclear DNA's with respect to nuclear division and the fate of the amplified DNA.

5. What do you suppose is the chemical connection between still-integrated amplified DNA and the nonamplified DNA at each of its ends? Can you suggest a way to test your ideas experimentally?

6. Give two examples of programmed gene destruction. What specific advantages do you suppose such destruction has?

7. Discuss the interconversion of heterochromatin and euchromatin.

8. How does a bacterial episome regulate or control its replication?

9. Hypothesize a role for reverse transcription in the amplification of oocytic rDNA.

10. Give an example in *Chlamydomonas* of non-mendelian genetic material that is apparently routinely destroyed.

Chapter 25

Regulation of Gene Distribution and Variation

Chapter 24 began our discussion of the regulation by the genotype of the kinds and amounts of genetic material that are present in an organism. The present chapter continues with a consideration of two additional ways such regulation can be achieved: (1) control of the distribution of genetic material among the cells of an organism, and (2) control of the amount and kinds of variations that occur in genetic material. The six chapters that follow this one will deal primarily with the ways that the genetic material regulates which of the genes present are functional.

25.1   Some aspects of mitosis and, probably, amitosis are under genetic control.

Procaryotes

Bacteria and blue-green algae seem to have a special mechanism, already described, for gene distribution to progeny cells. In *E. coli*, for example, chromosome replication and distribution apparently involve a replicon whose activity is synchronized with the replication of the portion of cell membrane to which it is attached.

Eucaryotes

Unicellular organisms. Single-celled eucaryotic organisms usually divide by mitosis, in which a spindle separates the chromosomes. Although in most cases the nuclear membrane breaks down and the spindle makes direct connection with the centromeres, this is not the situation in certain Protozoa. For example, in some parasitic flagellates condensed chromosomes attach to the inside of a persistent nuclear membrane by their centromeres, and anaphase movement of daughter chromosomes is accomplished by elongation of the nuclear membrane attached on the outside to the cytoplasmically located spindle. In these cases a spindle is used to separate chromosomes that are attached to membranes, whereas in procaryotes such a separation is accomplished without a spindle.

Many ciliate Protozoa such as *Paramecium* contain, in addition to a diploid micronucleus which divides mitotically, a highly polyploid *macronucleus* (about 1,000 N) which divides amitotically, that is, without forming a spindle, by pinching into two parts. Since the macronucleus apparently does not become aneuploid even after many successive divisions, some mechanism must regulate the separation of complete genomes from one another when daughter macronuclei are formed. This mechanism may involve the separation of chromosomes attached to the persistent nuclear membrane. The genetic bases for such amitosis and its control is as yet unknown.

Multicelullar organisms.   Nuclei of multicellular organisms usually divide mitotically. In such divisions the orientation of the spindle relative to other cells or nuclei is under genetic control. In the snail *Limnaea*, for example, a single gene pair in the diploid mother determines the orientation of the spindle during the first two cleavage divisions of the fertilized egg. When the mother is homozygous or heterozygous for one allele, the spindle is oriented in one particular direction, and a snail is formed whose shell is coiled right-handedly. When the mother is homozygous for another, recessive, allele, however, the spindle is in the opposite direction and gives rise to a snail whose shell has a left-handed coil.

The control of gene distribution is clearly important in cells whose chromosomes become polyploid (as in the human liver) or polynemic (as in the dipteran larval salivary gland). The strands of a polynemic chromosome may be prevented from separating by histones which bind them together. The rate of mitosis, an important aspect of gene distribution, is also under genetic control. (R)

25.2   Differences in gene distribution in somatic and germinal cells can occur for genetic reasons.

In one species of the roundworm *Ascaris*, each nucleus in mitotic cells of the germ line has a single pair of chromosomes. In the nuclei of the cells that initiate the somatic line, however, these chromosomes break up into a number of small rod-shaped fragments, some of which are lost. Some fragments persist in the somatic line as chromosomes, however, whose ends are sealed off and whose movements during mitosis are normal because each has one or more centromeres. (The germ-line chromosome is *polycentric*; that is, it has numerous centromeres along its length, the action of all but one of them being suppressed.) Because chromosome fragmentation in *Ascaris* takes place only in somatic cells, there must be a gene-based physiological difference between cells entering the somatic line and those remaining in the germ line.

Other unusual phenomena associated with gene distribution are also under genetic control. Mutant genes are known in *Drosophila* and maize which give rise to spindles whose fibers do not converge at the poles during meiosis (although they converge normally during mitosis). The divergent spindles lead to chromosome loss because, at telophase, one or more of the spread out chromosomes fails to be included with the others in a daughter nucleus. In *Sciara*, the fungus gnat, whole chromosomes are eliminated in somatic nuclei during early cleavage stages. Moreover, paternally derived chromosomes are eliminated in males during meiosis.

In maize plants that have a particular rearrangement of chromosome 10, the centromeres of most chromosomes are functional during mitosis but not meiosis. These chromosomes are still able to migrate to the poles during meiotic anaphase because of new, functional centromeric regions which appear near each end. Such *neocentromeres* are also formed in mutant strains of rye and other cereal plants.

The preceding illustrates that germ and somatic cell lines can differ in nuclear genetic composition because genetic factors, acting on the spindle, on centromeres, and on the linear arrangement of chromosome segments, cause chromosome loss or fragmentation in one cell line but not the other. (R)

25.3   Crossing over and synapsis are under genetic control.

Crossing over usually occurs at exactly corresponding points in two nonsister strands.[1] Consequently, no deficient or duplicated segments are produced and euploidy is maintained even though recombination between homologs occurs. Not only must the machinery for crossing over be genetically specified, but it must also be possible to genetically prevent this machinery from working in those cases where crossing over

[1] Since we do not know the exact mechanism of crossing over we cannot tell whether, for example, breakpoints needed to start the crossing-over process occur at different positions in nonsister strands and some repair process subsequently makes the exchange take place at exactly corresponding points on the nonsister strands, or whether symmetry occurs throughout the process. Nonreciprocal exchanges are, however, not uncommon (see Section 17.12).

occurs during meiosis in one sex and not in the other. In *Drosophila*, for example, the female but not the male undergoes meiotic crossing over.

Synapsis and chiasma formation in meiosis help distribute the homologs in such a way as to prevent the gain or loss of whole chromosomes. Specific mutant genes are known (one occurring in maize) which not only lack synaptic attraction for their alleles but also prevent or destroy synapsis at other loci. In contrast to such genes are those (collochores, for example) which assist the synapsis of homologs (see Section 16.6). (In the *Drosophila* male, which has no crossing over and hence no typical chiasmata, the collochores serve to hold homologs together until anaphase I.)

25.4   Gene distribution during meiosis is influenced by meiotic drive.

In organisms heterozygous for sufficiently large paracentric inversions (Figure 25-1), the partner chromosomes can synapse during meiosis at all regions except those adjacent to the points of breakage. Synapsis requires one partner to twist in the inverted region while the other partner does not. Should one crossing over occur anywhere within the inverted region—for example, between *C* and *D*—the two non-crossover strands of the tetrad will each contain one centromere and will thus be *eucentric*—one with and one without the inversion. The two crossover strands will be *aneucentric*; that is, one will be the acentric (duplicated for *A* and deficient for *G.HIJ*), and the other, dicentric (deficient for *A* and duplicated for the other region).

Individuals heterozygous for a large paracentric inversion are often at a reproductive disadvantage, since crossing over within the inverted region results in genetically defective gametes. This reproductive disadvantage would be avoided, however, if some mechanism prevented the dicentric produced by such a crossing over from entering a gamete. Any mechanism that causes the products of meiosis to occur in functional gametes in abnormal frequencies is said to produce a *meiotic drive* in favor of certain genotypes and against others. (The term "meiotic drive" is usually restricted to instances in which an *A A'* individual does not produce functional *A* and *A'* gametes in a 1 : 1 ratio.)

A meiotic drive against the dicentric chromosome mentioned above is produced when the two meiotic divisions in a female occur in tandem, as they do in *Drosophila*. In a *Drosophila* oocyte heterozygous for a paracentric inversion, a single crossing over

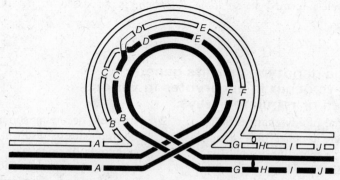

Figure 25-1   Single crossing over in the inverted region in a paracentric inversion heterozygote. (See the text for a discussion of the consequences.)

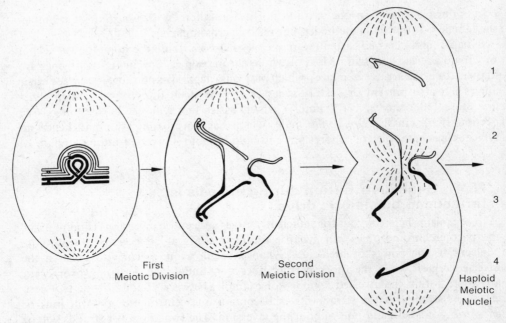

First
Meiotic Division

Second
Meiotic Division

1

2

3

4

Haploid
Meiotic
Nuclei

Figure 25-2 Distribution of strands during meiotic divisions after a single crossing over in the inverted region in a paracentric inversion heterozygote in *Drosophila*.

within the inverted region likewise produces the dicentric chromosome at anaphase I (Figure 25-2). But this dicentric serves to hold the dyads at metaphase II so that the two eucentric monads, which did not undergo exchange, proceed to the outermost two of the four poles at anaphase II. Therefore, at the end of telophase II the four meiotic products are arranged in a row: (1) one eucentric, (2) part of the dicentric, (3) the remainder of the dicentric, and (4) the other eucentric. Since one of the two end nuclei becomes the egg nucleus, the dicentric strand is prevented from entering the gametic nucleus. Consequently, in *Drosophila*, paracentric inversions rarely give rise to aneuploid gametes of either sex type.

Many other examples of meiotic drive are known which are produced by preferential segregation to the functional pole of one of two genetic alternatives present during oogenesis in animals and megasporogenesis in plants. An example of meiotic drive in *Drosophila* males, termed *segregation distortion*, is discussed in detail in Section S25.4.

25.5 The genotype permits genetic changes to occur in eucaryotes in various controlled or regulated ways.

1. The normal ploidy changes in a sexual cycle in eucaryotes—from diploid to haploid to diploid (or in polyploids, for example, from 4N to 2N to 4N)—are under genetic control.

2. Normally occurring somatic endoreplications result in somatic polyploidy or polynemy. These changes are under genetic control.

3. The number of mutations increases with mitotic activity. Since the rate

of mitosis is under genetic control, the genotype controls its variability in this way. Thus, the smaller the number of mitotic cell divisions needed for growth and maintenance, the smaller will be the number of mutations which occur due to mitosis. (Note that many cancer cells are mutants whose mitotic rate has increased.)

4. We have already mentioned in Section 25.2 that certain mutants modify meiosis and thereby produce aneusomic gametes.

5. The frequency of nondisjunction leading to aneusomy has been shown to depend both on the amount and distribution of heterochromatin and on the types of chromosomal rearrangements present. Therefore, to the extent that the genotype regulates its heterochromatin and rearrangements, it is also regulating the incidence of nondisjunction.

6. Similarly, the arrangement of meiotic products in *Drosophila* oogenesis (Section 25.4) acts to eliminate dicentrics produced by crossing over in paracentric-inversion heterozygotes.

7. Finally, the arrangement of the chromosomal material and the metabolic activity of the cell (as it influences the amount of water and oxygen present, for example) are other ways in which genetic changes depend upon the genotype itself.

25.6   The genotype controls or regulates the occurrence of point mutation.

The preceding section dealt mainly with the prevention or regulated occurrence of changes involving large numbers of genes in eucaryotes. We have already described in Sections 9.10 and 9.11 how the frequency of point mutations in procaryotes is controlled or regulated by gene-coded mutagens and antimutagens as well as mutator and antimutator DNA polymerases. It is obvious (or it will be from Chapter 34) that the allele of DNA polymerase selected in nature is one which provides some, but not too much, genetic variability. A mutator gene in *E. coli*, which preferentially causes $A:T \to C:G$ point mutations, is notable in this connection. Even after 7,000 or so such mutations have accumulated, the mutator strain is still viable. The viability of a strain containing such a large number of changes can be explained by one or a combination of factors: degeneracy in the code; DNA that functions other than as recognition or as protein-coding genes; redundancy.

The occurrence of point mutation is genetically regulated in eucaryotes also. Consider the spontaneous point-mutation frequencies for two lines of the same species of *Drosophila*—one living in a tropical and the other in a temperate climate. If the genotype were at the mercy of temperature in the wild, we would expect the tropical form to have a higher frequency of spontaneous point mutation than the temperate form (see the footnote to Section 9.10). When both lines are grown at the same temperature in the laboratory, however, the tropical form has a lower mutation rate than the temperate one. This result provides good evidence that the tropical form has genetically suppressed (or the temperate form has genetically enhanced) its mutational response to temperature. Consequently, in nature the two forms probably show less difference in mutation frequency than would be expected with the difference in temperature.

Other strains of *Drosophila melanogaster* collected from various regions have different spontaneous point-mutation frequencies. Some of this may be due to differences in the mutability of otherwise identical alleles (isoalleles, see Section S16.1b); part may be due also to a general control of mutability by the genotype, for some strains contain mutator genes which can increase the general point-mutation frequency as much as tenfold. Of course, other alleles of mutator genes can be considered antimutators. Since the organisms most advanced in evolution contain more genetic material per cell than less advanced forms, the most advanced forms apparently have selected genotypes which reduce their spontaneous mutation rate to avoid over-mutation, and a ploidy (for example, diploidy) in which the detrimental effects of mutant genes are suppressed by the presence of homologous loci that usually carry normal alleles.

25.7 The regulation of mutability involves cell susceptibility to viruses and episomes as well as the relationship between nuclear and extranuclear genes.

Procaryotes

The frequency of spontaneous mutation from auxotrophy to prototrophy is known for a large number of alleles for various markers in *Salmonella*. When auxotrophic bacteria are infected with transducing phage grown on the same genetic strain or on a bacterial strain carrying a deletion (deficiency) for the gene under test, the frequency of prototrophs is significantly increased. Genes induced to revert to prototrophy in this way are called *selfers*. Although the mechanism of reversion is unknown, the presence of a transducing fragment which presumably synapses in a region near a selfer gene somehow stimulates the mutability of the selfer. Consequently, phage enhances the mutability of bacterial genes.

Eucaryotes

The results in the following list involve viral infections of higher animals, including man:

1. Both Rous sarcoma virus (containing Rous associated virus 2) and sigma virus increase mutation rate in *Drosophila*.
2. The addition of Rous sarcoma virus to normal rat cells in tissue culture produces an increased incidence of chromosome breakage over the control level.
3. After infection of human cell lines *in vitro* with the simian virus SV40, large numbers of chromosomal mutants are detected including chromosome loss, chromosome breakage, and gross chromosomal changes like dicentrics, rings, and (probably) translocations. The frequency with which these involve different chromosomes is apparently not random.
4. All patients with clinical measles (rubeola) have a high incidence of chromosome breakage in the white blood cells by the fifth day after onset of the rash. Chromosome breaks occur in 33 to 72 per cent of the cells examined, and all chromosomes are breakable at numerous positions, although the unions between ends produced by

breakage resulting in structural rearrangements are of low frequency. At least seven other viral infections in man are associated with an increased incidence of various gross chromosomal changes in white blood cells.

We do not know whether these mutational effects in procaryotic and eucaryotic cells are due to a general metabolic effect of the presence, functioning, or replication of viral nucleic acids; to a specific episomal-like feature of these viruses; or to some other factor or combination of factors. In any case, since viruses can induce mutations in cells of higher organisms *in vitro* and *in vivo*, it is possible that mutants of normally present extranuclear genes can also do so. Clearly, then, the genetic control of mutability involves plasmids and episomes as well as normally present nuclear and extranuclear genes; each is hypothetically capable of affecting its own mutability as well as each other's (see Section 19.5 footnote 2).

In view of the finding that a variety of intracellular infecting organisms (including rickettsia) can increase the mutation rate of the host, all mechanisms for the destruction of genetic invaders are potentially mechanisms for the regulation of mutability. Such mutation-regulating mechanisms might involve, therefore (1) phagocytosis, (2) lysosomes, (3) *interferons* (proteins which prevent the replication of viruses), (4) antibodies, and (5) recognition and degradation of foreign nucleic acids.

SUMMARY AND CONCLUSIONS

Various ways of distributing genes in procaryotes (including cell division, transformation, transduction, and conjugation) and in eucaryotes (including mitosis, meiosis, fertilization, and infection) have been described in previous chapters. Each of these gene-distribution mechanisms must be either programmed or influenced— hence, each is to some extent regulated—by cellular genetic material. The present chapter illustrates the genetic control or regulation of some specific aspects of gene distribution, in eucaryotes primarily. For example, genetic regulation is implied (1) when chromosomes are distributed by the division of nuclei having persistent nuclear membranes (using a spindle, as in certain parasitic flagellates, or not, as in the amitotic division of macronuclei in ciliates), and (2) when chromosomes are distributed differently in different tissues (as in the germ and somatic tissues of *Ascaris*). The normal progress of mitosis, meiosis, and crossing over requires the presence of normal genes, whose mutants (1) cause synapsis to be defective, (2) produce spindles which vary in position or shape, (3) cause abnormal centromeric behavior, or (4) result in a meiotic drive.

Various regularly occurring and mutational variations in amount or kind of genetic material that are programmed or influenced by cellular genetic material have also been described in previous chapters. The present chapter includes examples of regulation of (1) normally occurring gross changes in nuclear genetic material, and (2) the frequency of point mutations in nuclear chromosomes. Since viruses and other intracellular infecting organisms can induce mutations in host genetic material, genetic control of susceptibility to infection also genetically regulates the occurrence of mutation. We expect that normally present nonmendelian and mendelian genes probably have a mutational interaction which is controlled by the genetic material of the organism.

SPECIFIC SECTION REFERENCES

25.1 Boycott, A. E., and Diver, C. 1923. On the inheritance of sinistrality in *Limnaea peregra*. Proc. Roy. Soc. Lond., 95B: 207–213.

DuPraw, E. J. 1970. *DNA and chromosomes*. New York: Holt, Rinehart and Winston, Inc.

25.2 Rhoades, M. M., and Vilkomerson, H. 1942. On the anaphase movement of chromosomes. Proc. Nat. Acad. Sci., U.S., 28: 433–436. (By neocentromeres.)

25.4 Rhoades, M. M., and Dempsey, E. 1966. The effect of abnormal chromosome 10 on preferential segregation and crossing over in maize. Genetics, 53: 989–1020. (An example of meiotic drive.)

Zimmering, S., Sandler, L., and Nicoletti, B. 1970. Mechanisms of meiotic drive. Ann. Rev. Genetics, 4: 409–436.

25.6 Magni, G. E. 1963. The origin of spontaneous mutations during meiosis. Proc. Nat. Acad. Sci., U.S., 50: 975–980.

25.7 Baumiller, R. J. 1967. Virus induced point mutation. Nature, Lond., 214: 806–807. (Sigma virus in *Drosophila*.)

Burdette, W. J., and Yoon, J. S. 1967. Mutations, chromosomal aberrations, and tumors in insects treated with oncogenic virus. Science, 154: 340–341.

Demerec, M. 1963. Selfer mutants of *Salmonella typhimurium*. Genetics, 48: 1519–1531.

Halkka, O., Meynadier, G., Vago, C., and Brummer-Korvenkontio, M. 1970. Rickettsial induction of chromosomal aberrations. Hereditas, 64: 126–128.

Nichols, W. W., 1970. Virus-induced chromosome abnormalities. Ann. Rev. Microbiol., 24: 479–500.

SUPPLEMENTARY SECTIONS

S25.4 Segregation distortion in *Drosophila* is an example of meiotic drive.

Drosophila melanogaster homozygous for the II chromosome mutants *cinnabar* (*cn*) and *brown* (*bw*) have white eyes because *cn/cn* and *bw/bw* prevent the formation of the brown and the red pigments, respectively, which together comprise the dull-red eye color of the wild type. When the test cross $cn^+bw^+/cn\ bw\ \male$ by $cn\ bw/cn\ bw\ \female$ is made, the progeny typically occur in the approximate phenotypic ratio of one white to one dull red. If, however, the unmarked II chromosome comes from certain natural populations, this cross produces 93 to 99 per cent (instead of about 50 per cent) dull-red progeny. Moreover, this atypical ratio is not associated with any increase in egg mortality. It is concluded, therefore, that the two kinds of male gametes ($cn^+\ bw^+$ and $cn\ bw$) must be functionally unequal in number at the time of fertilization, suggesting that the segregation ratio $1\ cn^+\ bw^+ : 1\ cn\ bw$ is somehow distorted prezygotically.

Analysis of the segregation distortion phenomenon reveals a genetic factor, *Segregation-Distorter*, *SD*—present in the unmarked (wild-type) II chromosome—located in the heterochromatic region of the right arm near the centromere. The presence of *SD* in one homolog seems to produce a physiological effect which tends to prevent sperm containing the other homolog from functioning in fertilization. The sperm dysfunc-tion explanation is supported by (1) the number of progeny increasing while, as males age, distortion is decreasing; (2) the gain in SD^+-containing progeny as SD/SD^+ males age; (3) the ability of the female genotype to affect distortion ratio; and (4) the reduced fecundity of SD/SD males, as though each *SD* independently causes dysfunction of sperm carrying the other member of the allelic pair.

The *segregation ratio* (*k*), defined here as the proportion of all progeny of SD/SD^+ that contain the *SD* homolog, is constant (0.93 to 0.99) in the laboratory stock that carries the *SD* homolog found in nature. This homolog normally carries two other localized genetic elements affecting segregation ratio, revealed by the following results. Every *SD*-bearing chromosome recombinant for the (probably heterochromatic) tip of the right arm of the II chromosome becomes less stable. The decrease in stability is reflected by variations in ability to distort ($k = 0.7$ to 0.9). Consequently, the stable line must have a modifying gene, *Stabilizer of SD*, *St(SD)*, at the tip of the right arm of II. Stabilization occurs whether *St(SD)* is in *cis* or *trans* position relative to *SD*.

Since the markers *purple* (*pr*) and *cn* closely span both the centromere and the *SD* locus, one can study recombinants for the regions near *SD*. The results show that a locus is present in the right arm of II—near *SD* but farther from the centromere—whose presence seems to be essential for

SD operation since chromosomes that carry *SD* alone show only weak distortion, *k* being approximately 0.6. This locus is *Activator of SD, Ac(SD)*, which must be in *cis* position for *SD* to function. Since it is found that crossing over in the *SD-Ac(SD)* region is reduced, it is hypothesized that a small rearrangement exists in this region.

Although the F_1 of the usual heterozygous *SD* male occur in a distorted ratio (the father distorts, or shows segregation distortion via his progeny), the F_1 from heterozygous *SD* females do not. An *SD/SD$^+$* male can distort when outcrossed to an attached-X female (footnote to Section 17.3). Surprisingly, when his *SD*-containing sons are tested (these receive the father's X), they do not distort. It would appear that a distorting male conditions his X chromosome so that sons receiving it cannot distort. When a distorting male is mated to an unrelated *SD$^+$/SD$^+$* female having separate X's, all the *SD*-containing sons distort since each receive an unchanged maternal X. (Note that the daughters carry one unchanged maternal and one changed paternal X.) Among the *SD*-containing sons the daughters produce, the half receiving the unchanged maternal X can distort, whereas those receiving the changed paternal X cannot. (When either of these kinds of males are outcrossed to *SD$^+$/SD$^+$* females, all *SD*-containing sons receive an unchanged maternal X and, therefore, can distort.) Females producing *SD*-carrying sons of which only half distort, are said to be *conditioned* and to show *conditional distortion*; the mechanism of conditional distortion is unknown.

SD causes a distortion in the recovery of sex chromosomes as well as of second chromosomes. In one case, for example, *SD/SD$^+$* males produced a frequency of 0.992 *SD*-containing offspring and 0.008 *SD$^+$*-containing offspring. The sex ratio (proportion of all progeny that are males) was 0.524 among the *SD*-containers but only 0.190 among the *SD$^+$*-containers. As second chromosome distortion decreases so does sex chromosome distortion (that is, the proportion of males among *SD$^+$* offspring increases). The results support the hypothesis that sex-chromosome constitution has no effect on the functioning of *SD*-bearing sperm but does have an effect on *SD$^+$*-bearing sperm which is greater the greater the distortion for second chromosomes.

SD was initially obtained from a natural population that showed no second chromosome distortion because *SD*'s detrimental effect on the transmission of its homolog was suppressed by a combination of factors. One was X-chromosome conditioning fostered by inbreeding. Another factor in this population was that selection apparently favored the retention of *SD$^+$* alleles resistant to distortion. *SD* is an actively investigated example of meiotic drive, a force capable of altering gene frequencies in natural populations by the production of functional gametes which do not carry segregants in a 1 : 1 ratio.

Dennell, R. E., and Judd, B. H. 1969. Segregation Distorter in *D. melanogaster* males: an effect of female genotype on recovery. Molec. Gen. Genetics, 105: 262–274.

Hartl, D. L. 1969. Dysfunctional sperm production in *Drosophila melanogaster* males homozygous for the segregation distorter elements. Proc. Nat. Acad. Sci., U.S., 63: 782–789.

Hiraizumi, Y., and Watanabe, S. S. 1969. Aging effect on the phenomenon of segregation distortion in *Drosophila melanogaster*. Genetics, 63: 121–131.

S25.6   Although different genes within a species differ in spontaneous mutability as do the genes in different species, perifertilization stages are relatively rich in spontaneous point mutations.

Because only one member of a pair of genes in a nucleus mutates at one time, point mutation is a very localized, submicroscopic event. Although many point mutants occur singly, point mutants at a given locus sometimes appear in a cluster of cells or individuals. The mutants in a cluster often seem to be identical and can usually be explained by assuming a single cell has undergone mutation, having divided a number of times before the tests to detect the mutants were performed. Such data indicate that point mutation is usually completed within one cell generation, after which the new genetic alternative is just about as stable as the old.

Although all allelic and nonallelic genes do not have the same spontaneous mutation frequency, within a species, different loci have about the same order of mutability. Study of a representative sample of specific loci in *Drosophila* reveals an average of one point mutation at a given locus in each 200,000 germ cells tested. In mice the per locus frequency is about twice this, or 1 in 100,000. In man, by scoring the mutants detected in heterozygous condition, the per locus rate is found to be one per 50,000 to 100,000 germ cells per generation. Even though some genes are definitely more mutable than others, the average spontaneous point mutation rate per genome per generation can be estimated for *Drosophila*, mouse, and man. In one *Drosophila* generation 1 gamete in 20 (or 1 zygote in 10) contains a new detectable point mutant. In mice, this frequency is about 1 in 10 gametes, whereas in man it is about 1 in 5 gametes (or 2 in 5 zygotes).

Point mutation is not restricted to the genes of any particular kind of cell, occurring in males and females, in somatic tissues of all kinds, and in the diploid and haploid cells of the germ line. Later stages in gametogenesis and very early developmental stages—*perifertilization stages*—are found to be relatively rich in spontaneous point mutations. Despite the great differences in life span, one does not find correspondingly great differences in the spontaneous germ-line-mutation frequencies of flies, mice, and men. This similarity in mutation frequency is not surprising if most of these mutations occur in the perifertilization stages, since each of these organisms spends a comparable length of time in these stages. Still another similarity among these species is the comparable number of cell divisions required for each to progress from a gamete of one generation to a gamete of the next. In fact, the differences in mutation frequency for these organisms are approximately proportional to the differences in the number of germ-cell divisions per generation.

QUESTIONS AND PROBLEMS

1. Why do you expect the distribution of replicated genetic material to be under genetic control?

2. Compare the advantages and disadvantages of a ring versus a rod chromosome with respect to the regulation of chromosome replication.

3. When homozygous, the mutant gene *claret-nondisjunctional* (*ca^nd*) in *Drosophila* causes nondisjunction of one or more chromosomes in meiosis but not in mitosis. What gene in maize acts like this mutant? How might you determine the similarity of these two genes?

4. Why can very small paracentric or pericentric inversions survive in populations even when they usually occur in heterozygous condition?

5. What are the meiotic products of a two-strand double crossing over within a heterozygous paracentric inversion such as shown in Figure 25-1?

6. Do you expect meiotic drive to occur in *Neurospora*, in which the meiotic divisions occur in tandem as they do in the *Drosophila* female? Explain.

7. Criticize the following statement: Maize chromosomes are normally polycentric.

8. In certain organisms that have several large and several small chromosomes, the smaller ones regularly are located in the center of the metaphase plate, the larger ones at the periphery. In what respect is this observation relevant to the present chapter?

9. What can you conclude about the time and place of phenotypic action of the mutant gene in maize, *polymitotic divisions*, which causes extra mitotic divisions of the haploid pollen grain when the diploid parent is homozygous, but not when it is heterozygous, for the mutant?

10. How is the precision of the mitotic and meiotic processes related to the mutability of the genetic material?

11. Do you suppose that the state of metabolic activity of a chromosome influences mutability? Explain.

12. Do you suppose that all viruses cause a significant increase in the frequency of chromosomal breakage? Explain.

13. Discuss the mechanisms by which segregation distortion is suppressed in natural populations of *Drosophila*.

14. What possible explanations can you present for the action of X and Y chromosomes in producing sex-chromosome distortion in progeny of *Drosophila* males heterozygous for *SD*?

Chapter 26

Gene-Action Regulation—
Operons in Procaryotes

In Chapters 24 and 25 we have seen how an organism regulates the amount and quality of its genetic material. This chapter begins a study of how an organism regulates which of the genes present are functional in the transcription–translation sequence. The regulation of replication and of distribution of genetic material entails the regulation of protein synthesis such that different polypeptides are made at different times and in different amounts. In this chapter we will see in procaryotes how this control of gene action depends upon different kinds of genes.

26.1 Gene-action regulation can occur due to factors that affect the start and stop of transcription by DNA-dependent RNA polymerase.

We have already noted that mRNA, tRNA, and rRNA are separate transcripts of different segments of a chromosome, for example that of *E. coli*. It is obvious, therefore, that DNA-dependent RNA polymerase must recognize "transcription start points" and, since less than a whole chromosome is transcribed as a unit, probably also "transcription stop points."

Transcription-initiation (sigma and psi) factors

Escherichia coli DNA-dependent RNA polymerase can be separated by chromatography into a *core enzyme* and a factor called *sigma* (σ). *In vitro*, the core enzyme transcribes calf thymus DNA and ϕT4 DNA less efficiently than the whole enzyme, the *holoenzyme*, the efficiency of transcription being restored if σ is added to the core enzyme. The $1\sigma + 1$ core enzyme makes up a *transcription initiation complex*. Since only the core portion is needed for continuation of RNA synthesis, σ can be liberated after initiation and be reused several times. (Rifampicin, which inhibits initiation of transcription, binds to the core enzyme, not to σ). In *E. coli* the DNA-dependent RNA polymerase holoenzyme can be described as $\alpha_2\beta\beta'\sigma$; that is, 2 α chains (each 39,000 MW) + 1 β chain (155,000 MW) + 1 β' chain (165,000 MW) + 1 σ molecule (90,000 to 95,000 MW).

The role of sigma in the selection of transcription initiation sites has been studied in *E. coli in vitro* using the duplex replicative form (RF) of the single-stranded DNA ϕfd. (The base sequence at the 5' end of the RNA normally synthesized in *E. coli* starts with adenine or guanine and is followed by a pyrimidine.) When only the core enzyme is used (1) the RNA begins with unusual 5' terminal sequences, (2) either DNA strand is copied, and (3) the length of the RNA is more variable than usual. Such a random initiation of RNA synthesis by the core enzyme is in contrast with the results obtained with the holoenzyme—this transcribes only the − strand at certain points, and produces more uniform lengths of RNA having a greater percentage of typical starting base sequences.

Much has still to be learned about the operation of σ on the *E. coli* chromosome—including whether variants occur and are used to transcribe different portions of the bacterial chromosome differentially. We do know that certain genes in *E. coli* are normally preferentially transcribed not because of a modification in sigma but of the RNA polymerase holoenzyme. For example, the synthesis of large amounts of rRNA is regulated in *E. coli* by a factor called *psi*$_r$ (Ψ_r) which when combined with DNA-dependent RNA polymerase holoenzyme preferentially transcribes rRNA. (Ψ_r also seems to be a bacterium-coded portion of the RNA-dependent RNA polymerase of $\phi Q\beta$.)

That the specificity of transcription in *E. coli* resides in the types of factor, not in the core enzyme, is illustrated in the role of sigma in the differential transcription of the phage genome. In the case of ϕT4, during the first minute of infection the core enzyme plus *E. coli* σ transcribes "pre-early" phage genes. One of the translation products is a T4σ which begins to function 3 to 4 minutes after infection, apparently replacing the *E. coli* σ and thereby stopping the transcription both of *E. coli* DNA and of ϕ pre-early genes. One of the translation products of these newly made transcripts of "early" ϕ genes is a different (or rearranged) T4σ, which initiates transcription of "late" phage genes.

Transcription–termination (rho) factors

Factors have been discovered which attach to the core polymerase to stop transcription. In *E. coli*, for example, a *terminator* factor, *rho* (ρ), an 8 to 10s protein of 200,000 MW, is needed to make *in vitro* the same short mRNA's as are made *in vivo*. Without ρ the mRNA's made *in vitro* are too long! Thus, with λ DNA as template and no ρ, the RNA made is widely heterogeneous in size—5s to 35s; with ρ, one half the RNA is 7s and 12s—common *in vivo* sizes—indicating that the transcription now starts and stops at the right places.

The preceding discussion of protein factors that can start and stop RNA synthesis illustrates one mode of regulating gene action by which only a portion of the DNA information present in a procaryotic cell is transcribed at any given time. Sometimes, this regulation involves the synthesis of different types of core enzyme.[1]

26.2 Bacterial mRNA's are sometimes several protein-coding genes long. Such mRNA's are the transcripts of operons.

The RNA viruses that attack *E. coli* are used as mRNA in their host and code for three proteins—phage maturation (A) protein, phage coat protein, and phage-specific

[1] Evidence has been obtained that, in addition to coding for phage-specific sigmas, ϕT4 also codes for modifications in the core enzyme. After infection with ϕT7, only four phage genes are transcribed by the *E. coli* holoenzyme. One of these genes has as its translation product a new T7-specific DNA-dependent RNA polymerase which transcribes the remaining 25 to 30 phage genes. Other work indicates that the RNA polymerase changes with cell stage in other procaryotes. In *Bacillus subtilis*, for example, the RNA polymerase isolated from the sporulating cell and the RNA polymerase isolated from the vegetative cell differ in their subunits—the former enzyme being unable to transcribe a certain phage DNA *in vitro*, whereas the latter can.

RNA-dependent RNA polymerase. Some naturally occurring mRNA in *E. coli* also codes for more than one protein. For example, when lactose is added to *E. coli's* culture medium an mRNA is newly produced which is too long to code only for one of the three enzymes whose synthesis is induced by the lactose. Similarly, other conditions cause the production of mRNA's of 33s or 38s; the latter being the mRNA equivalent of about 11,000 DNA base pairs; the 3,300 or so amino acids coded by it surely comprising several separate proteins. We conclude, therefore, that *E. coli* mRNA's sometimes code for more than one protein. The DNA sequence that codes for the transcription of an mRNA containing the information for more than one protein is called an *operon*.

26.3   In an operon the transcription of the structural genes is coordinated by the action of functional genes—the promoter and operator genes. The promoter locus binds the transcription holoenzyme; the operator locus determines whether or not transcription of the structural genes in an operon may occur.

Genes transcribed to RNA which is translated into proteins are called *structural genes* since they contain the information to order or structure the amino acid sequence of proteins. Before the beginning of the sequence of the structural genes of an operon —the end from which the mRNA synthesis starts—is found the DNA sequence for two *functional genes*,[2] the *promoter* and the *operator* genes (Figure 26-1). The promoter locus serves as the site that binds the transcription initiation complex, that is, the DNA-dependent RNA polymerase holoenzyme; the operator gene determines the

---

[2] Promoters and operators are referred to here as genes, although they are often referred to in the literature as "sites." The term "gene" was originally used in the literature to denote the informational basis for phenotypes which were ultimately found to be based upon protein. Although an organism is no more than its genes (in a favorable environment), an organism is more than its protein, and usage of the term gene in this book includes all types of organismal information coded or contained in genetic nucleic acid (Section 2.12). Accordingly, the following DNA sequences are considered genes here:

1. Those whose transcripts are translated into polypeptides. Note that the polypeptide may be modified during or after synthesis —for example, by the removal of part of the N-terminal end or digestion of internal peptides. Hence, the DNA for the initiator codon AUG is not a gene, but only part of one.
2. Those whose transcripts are not translated but yield rRNA's or tRNA's.
3. Those which DNA polymerase recognizes as replication start or stop points (for example, those genes essential to a replicon).
4. Those which DNA-dependent RNA polymerase recognizes as promoter, operator, or transcription stop points. It is estimated that promoter and operator genes need to be at least 10 to 20 nucleotides long to contain suitable specificity.
5. Those which contain information other than that above. These may hypothetically include genes which control the number of times a ribosome can attach to a given mRNA, and those which signal the termination of translation of a polypeptide in a multiple protein-coding mRNA (these probably contain more information than is transcribed into a single nonsense triplet).

Single-stranded nucleic acids may contain genes that give certain portions of the molecule secondary structure which in turn influences replication, transcription, and translation. Still other genes could conceivably affect or regulate tertiary structure, mutability, recombination, etc. It should be noted, however, that part or all of a gene which contains one type of organismal information may be utilized for another type of information.

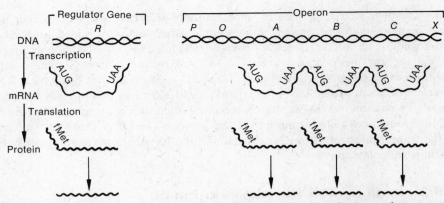

Figure 26-1 Generalized operon and its regulator gene in *E. coli. R*, regulator gene; *P*, promoter; *O*, operator; *A, B, C*, structural genes; *X*, hypothetical transcription-ending gene. The modes of interaction between the regulator and operator genes are described in Section 26.4 and illustrated in Figure 26-2.

possibility or impossibility of forming the mRNA for the structural genes that follow it in the operon. Although it is not known whether these functional genes are transcribed by RNA polymerase, they are probably not translated. Whether an operator gene permits transcription often depends upon the activity of a *regulator gene*, a structural gene that is not part of the operon but whose functioning it helps to regulate. The relationships between the operon and a regulator gene are described next.

26.4 Many operator genes permit transcription to occur only when they are unbound by extrinsic regulating substances. The reverse may be true for some operators.

For many operons control of gene action is a negative process. That is, the conformation of the operator gene is such that transcription is permitted until an *active repressor* substance combines with the operator gene to change the conformation to a form not permitting transcription. Removal of the active repressor restores the operator's transcription-active conformation.

Such negatively controlled operons have been observed to be of two general types: (1) those that are usually nonfunctional or turned off (Figure 26-2A), and (2) those that are usually able to be transcribed (Figure 26-2B). In the former case the protein coded by the regulator gene serves as an active repressor, combines with the operator gene sequence, and turns off the operon. Removal of the repressor from the operator gene allows transcription of the operon. This is usually accomplished by the action (either direct or indirect) of an *inducer* of the particular operon. In the latter case the regulator gene produces an inactive repressor protein, and the operon is usually able to be transcribed continuously. If a certain metabolite combines with the inactive repressor, it can become an active repressor which can combine with the operator gene and turn the operon off. (Note that negative control of operon function may conceivably occur because a repressor protein bound to the operator interferes with the functioning of the adjacent promoter, or vice versa.)

For some other operons control of gene action is reported to be a positive process.

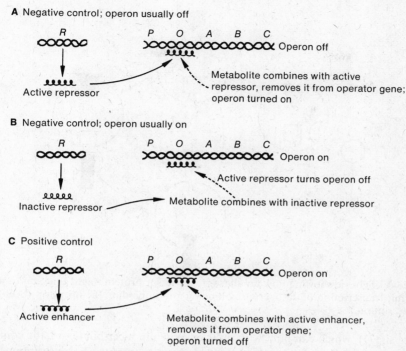

Figure 26-2 Some simple types of operons regulated negatively (A and B) or positively (C). Gene symbols as in Figure 26-1.

In such cases the operator gene may have the wrong conformation for transcription until it has bound an active enhancer. One form of such a positive control of an operon is shown in Figure 26-2C.

Recall that positive control of operon function is demonstrated whenever sigma factors are required for RNA polymerase to initiate transcription at the promoter. In one case *cyclic-AMP* plus a *cyclic-AMP protein* factor must join and attach to the DNA before the RNA polymerase holoenzyme can transcribe. Glucose breakdown products, however, lower cyclic-AMP concentration and, therefore, RNA initiation at certain promoters. (R)

26.5   The reversibility of the binding between repressor and operator seems to depend upon the allosteric properties of the protein.

Repressor proteins may function by being *allosteric*, that is, by having two or more separate sites for binding with different smaller molecules, each different combination causing a different change in the conformation of the protein. Thus, for purposes of illustration (Figure 26-3), an inactive repressor protein (P) can combine with an activator (A) to produce active repressor (R) whose changed conformation exposes (or generates) a separate site (O) which can bind to the operator, thereby preventing transcription of the operon. As the result of O binding with the operator, the conformation of the protein is changed to R', which now has exposed (or generated) a

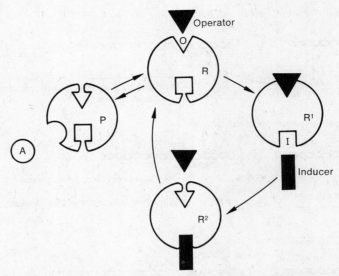

Figure 26-3 Scheme showing how an allosteric repressor protein might function to prevent and permit transcription of an operon by binding and unbinding the operator. (See the text for a description.)

separate site (I), which can bind with inducer. When inducer binds to I, the conformation changes to R^2, liberating the operator, thereby permitting transcription of the operon; when inducer is removed, the conformation returns to R. An operon can be negatively controlled, therefore, by this, or similar, schemes involving an allosteric repressor.

The above allosteric hypothesis of repressor protein function is reasonable in view of the finding that hemoglobin and many enzymes have allosteric properties that control their functioning. (R)

26.6   The *lac* operon of *E. coli* illustrates negative control of a usually nonfunctional (inducible) operon.

The normal *lac* operon of *E. coli* (Figure 26-4) consists of the following linear sequence of genes: p^+ (promoter), o^+ (operator), z^+ (structural gene for the enzyme β-galactosidase, which occurs free in the cytoplasm), y^+ (structural gene for the enzyme galactoside permease, or M protein, which is located in the cell membrane), and a^+ (structural gene for the enzyme thiogalactoside transacetylase, which occurs free in the cytoplasm). The permease helps lactose get into the bacterial cell and the galactosidase cleaves lactose (a β-galactoside) into galactose and glucose. (The

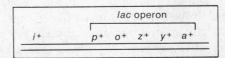

Figure 26-4 Wild-type or normal *lac* region of the *E. coli* genetic map. i^+, regulator gene; p^+, promoter gene; o^+, operator gene; z^+, gene for β-galactosidase; y^+, gene for galactoside permease; a^+, gene for thiogalactoside transacetylase.

function of transacetylase is unknown.) Another locus, i^+, the regulator gene, is located outside the operon close to the promoter. This regulator gene codes for an active repressor protein which is diffusible, binds to the o^+ operator gene, and prevents transcription of the mRNA for the structural loci z, y, and a.

In the presence of lactose, however, the active repressor no longer binds to o^+, the operon is transcribed, and the enzymes needed for penetration and digestion of lactose are made. Lactose (or a metabolite of it) functions therefore as an inducer.[3] In other words, E. coli of genotype i^+ p^+ o^+ z^+ y^+ produces indetectable amounts of permease and galactosidase constitutively (in the absence of lactose) but can produce large amounts of both enzymes inducibly (in the presence of lactose). The lac operon provides a model for the explanation of the genetic basis for many instances of induced enzyme formation. Section S26.6 discusses the phenotypic expression in E. coli of normal and mutant, haploid and diploid, lac regions in the absence and presence of inducer. (R)

26.7   The his operon of Salmonella illustrates negative control of a usually functional (repressible) operon.

The operon coordinates the expression of its structural genes by permitting or preventing the functioning of all of them. The genes of the lac region in E. coli are further related functionally since they all involve a pathway of lactose utilization. Operons such as lac, whose gene products are special structural proteins or enzymes needed for degradative (catabolic) reactions, are ordinarily inactive.

Ten of the enzymes in the pathway of histidine biosynthesis in Salmonella typhimurium are also coordinately controlled and map in a gene cluster. In this case, control of the functioning of the his operon (Figure 12-7, where O is the operator gene) involves the production of an inactive repressor which must be activated in order to facilitate binding with the operator and thereby keep the operon from functioning. This kind of control is especially suitable for regulating synthetic (anabolic) reactions. In an environment which lacks the end product of the pathway, the operon is allowed to function and direct the synthesis of catalysts that make this substance. If this metabolite is synthesized or taken into the cell exogenously, the repressor is activated and synthesis stops. Subsequent withdrawal of the metabolite (derepression) causes the active repressor to become inactive and allows the operon to function once again. Such operons are usually functional. (R)

26.8   Transcription of lambda phage DNA is under both negative and positive controls.

Bacteriophage lambda DNA can be maintained stably in a bacterial host, in which case the cell is immune, that is, superinfecting phages can no longer grow. The lysogenic cell, that is, one which carries lambda in prophage state, makes a repressor (an acidic protein, 2.8s, with a MW 30,000)—the product of lambda's cI gene—which blocks transcription of lambda DNA by binding to the operator sites, O_L and O_R, of

---

[3] There is a basal level of lac operon function in the absence of inducer which is so low, however, as to be indetectable in the experiments considered here and in Section S26.6.

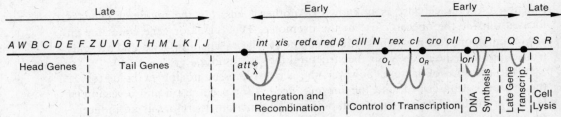

Figure 26-5 Physical and genetic map of vegetative λ. Black arrows indicate direction of transcription but not necessarily individual mRNA species. Dots indicate sites of action of λ DNA. Gray arrows indicate where the gene products act. Genes *A* through *J* are involved in morphogenesis of phage heads and tails; *att*$_λ^φ$, site of insertion of phage DNA into host DNA; *int*, *xis*, integration and excision of λ DNA; *red* α (exonuclease) and *red* β, λ recombination system; *cIII*, *cII*, required for expression of *cI* gene; *N*, required for efficient expression of early genes; *rex*, restriction of growth of T4rII; *cI*, λ repressor which binds to O_L and O_R; *cro*, negative regulator of *cI* transcription; *O*, *P*, required for λ replication initiated at *ori* (origin of replication); *Q*, stimulates transcription of late genes at late gene promoter between genes *Q* and *S*; *S*, *R*, required for lysis of host. (Courtesy of Ira Herskowitz.)

two operons which are transcribed to the left and right, respectively (Figure 26-5). (Evidence that different operons are transcribed to mRNA in opposite directions, that is, RNA is made which is complementary to either strand of duplex DNA, is discussed in Section S26.8.) For transcription of genes *O*, *P*, and *Q* (transcribed to the right), as well as genes *int* and *red* (transcribed to the left), therefore, this repressor must be inactivated. However, inactivation of the repressor is not sufficient for transcription of these genes. Certain phage gene products are required as positive regulators. Namely, transcription of the *O-P-Q* and *int-red* regions requires action of gene *N* product. Transcription of late genes *S-R* and *A-J* require *Q* product (which probably is lambda sigma). These positive control elements may act as initiation or antitermination factors for transcription. (R)

26.9 Transcription of structural genes can be controlled by separating them from or joining them to their promoter. Regulator genes are often near the genes they control.

Genes which function late in the lytic cycle of lambda phage are located at both ends of vegetative lambda DNA ("late genes" in Figure 26-5). Deletion of a site between genes *Q* and *S*, late gene promoter, prevents not only expression of genes *S* and *R* in the right arm, but also genes *A-J* in the left. Accordingly, the late genes at both ends of the recombination map are expressed as though they belonged in the same transcriptional unit. This *functional linkage* (see the footnote in Section 10.3) is evidence for a physical linkage between two groups of late genes, apparently brought about by the circularization of the λ chromosome or the linking up of separate λ DNA molecules end to end.

Control of late gene expression in lambda is another example in which the regulator gene maps near its site of action. In this case, *Q* seems to code for lambda σ factor which acts on the promoter gene located between *Q* and *S*. Other examples of close linkage of regulator genes and the genes they control include *i*[+] and *o*[+] of the *lac* operon and the *cI* gene and its operators (Figure 26-5). (R)

26.10   Transcription is also controlled by DNA replication and DNA conformation.

In addition to the several ways already described, gene action is also affected or controlled at the level of transcription both by DNA replication and DNA conformation.

The sequence of the structural genes in an operon determines the order of appearance of their gene products. Accordingly, the structural genes in an operon are usually arranged relative to their operator in the same sequence as their protein products are needed in a series of biochemical reactions. Because the genes within a replicon are synthesized sequentially, the first genes replicated offer twice as many templates for RNA synthesis as those replicated last. In *Bacillus subtilis*, moreover, during chromosome replication the points of maximum transcription exhibit the same sequenciality as observed for gene synthesis. (After chromosome replication, however, mRNA is produced by different regions in different amounts.) In other words, in an operon as well as in different chromosome regions, the genes replicated first seem to be those whose translational products are needed first.

When the DNA of ϕX174 is a double-stranded, circular helix, RNA complementary to both single-stranded rods is made after the ring is broken (see Section 5.5). When, however, the duplex ring is intact, RNA complementary to only one strand of the DNA is made. We see, therefore, that one-complement transcription requires that the circular DNA duplex be intact. Other *in vitro* studies indicate that the double-helical structure of DNA is necessary for one-complement transcription to RNA. For example, using a cell-free RNA polymerase system from *E. coli*, one-complement transcription is obtained from unbroken, native, ϕT7 or rat liver mitochondrial DNA, whereas two-complement transcription is obtained if such DNA is denatured or fragmented. Maintenance of DNA secondary structure, therefore, also provides for control over whether one or both complements are transcribed. (R)

26.11   Regulation of gene action can also occur in several ways at the translational level.

Gene action in procaryotes can be regulated in several ways at the level of translation. We will discuss in order controls based upon (1) tRNA's, (2) ribosomes, (3) mRNA's, and (4) other parts of the translation machinery.

tRNA types

All T phages code for phage-specific tRNA's. ϕT2 has little or no CUG codon and, therefore, needs little or no Leu tRNA with the complementary anticodon. The phage apparently codes for its own Leu tRNA and for an RNase that digests the host variety of Leu tRNA (since 2 to 3 minutes after infection the amount of host Leu tRNA is reduced to 60 per cent of its original level). Such a mechanism would reduce the translation of host mRNA and promote that of viral mRNA. In this connection we can note that about 1.2 per cent of herpes simplex virus' double-stranded DNA codes for 10 to 20 molecular species of virus-specific tRNA. tRNA type is used not only to recognize which mRNA's to translate in virus-infected cells, but also which ones to translate at different times in a single uninfected cell. For example, the types of Ser-tRNA change as the growth condition of *B. subtilis* changes.

Ribosome modification and activity

Phage infection seems to lead to a change in the host ribosomes so that they preferentially translate phage mRNA. This is indicated by T4 RNA being selectively translated on uninfected *E. coli* ribosomes which are complexed with a heat-labile factor isolated from ribosomes of T4-infected cells. Other evidence suggests that factors are needed for ribosomes to bind to initiation sites for genes that are translated late, but not those that are translated early, in phage development.

mRNA primary structure, secondary structure, repression, and degradation

Primary structure. RNA has information in its primary and secondary structure that is, or can be, used to regulate gene action at the translation level. One site of information in mRNA primary structure is its nucleotide sequence for ribosome attachment (is this coded in a "gene"?—see footnote to Section 26.3). Since ribosomes can attach to circular nucleic acids, it is no surprise that the mRNA of the *lac* operon, for example, has more than one ribosome attachment point—one at the 5′ end and at least one other internally. A second site of information in mRNA primary structure is its nucleotide sequence for protein termination. Each of these sequences, composed of one nonsense codon at least, may also function as a ribosome dropoff point. Thus, enzymes coded by z^+, y^+, and a^+ of the *lac* operon occur in the relative numbers 10 : 5 : 2 because ribosomes attach to the mRNA at different rates at different places, or because those that attach at the 5′ end drop off after reading protein termination signals, or both.

Secondary structure. Most RNA viruses code for an RNA polymerase and coat protein—products coded once in the genome—which are needed in different amounts and at different times during phage reproduction. Thus, the expression of the genome of an RNA virus must often involve differential, controlled translation. The RNA of phage R17 contains numerous double-stranded regions, so that the molecule has numerous hairpin (base-paired) regions along the length of the single fiber. Protein initiator codons (and presumably ribosome attachment points) are located in the single-stranded regions (codons for internal Mets lie in the double-stranded regions). The RNA of the closely related ϕf2 is also partially double-stranded. *In vitro* studies show that there are several places where protein initiation could occur but does not because of ϕf2 RNA secondary structure. Therefore, prevention of ribosomal attachment by RNA secondary structure results in translation of RNA phages being initiated at preferential sites. It is not known whether secondary structure plays a role in differential translation of normal cellular mRNA's.

Repression. Solution of the problem of producing more coat protein than RNA polymerase from a continuous strip of viral mRNA seems to involve an additional factor in the case of the RNA phage MS2. In this case the coat protein seems to act as a repressor for other loci on the viral RNA. This explanation is suggested by finding *in vitro* that pure MS2 RNA translates into both coat protein (containing no His) and other proteins (containing His); whereas pure MS2 RNA plus MS2 coat protein translates into more coat protein but little other proteins.

Degradation. Evidence indicates that mRNA is degraded by an exonuclease from its 5′ end, that is, the end transcribed nearer to the operator. We have no direct evidence for regulation except that since some mRNA's in a cell are longer lived than others, different mRNA's must be destroyed differentially, probably enzymatically.

It should be noted that especially long messages might be protected from breakdown by special base sequences, some of which provide secondary structure.

Other parts of translation machinery

There are several places in the translation process where, theoretically, other pieces of translation machinery can control gene action:

1. Protein initiation—control might involve the presence and availability of GTP and of the three factors needed to form a protein initiation complex.

2. Protein elongation—control might involve the presence and availability of elongation factors, of the enzymes that form peptide bonds, and of an enzyme which removes the N-terminal fMet.

3. Protein termination—control might involve the presence and availability of factors for termination, including enzymes that release the polypeptide from the ribosome and the carboxyl-terminal tRNA.

Hopefully, results in the near future will indicate to what extent these parts of the translation machinery are used for the genetic control of gene action.

26.12   The interaction of gene products may depend upon the tertiary conformation of the chromosome.

All the enzymes involved in a sequence of biosynthetic activities are not always coded within a single operon. For example, eight genes of the arginine synthetic pathway in *E. coli* are located in three different operons, all under the control of the same regulator gene. As mentioned in Section 14.1, the circular *E. coli* chromosome is folded to attain a tertiary structure. This folding may bring together the genes of the three arginine operons so that, perhaps, their polypeptide products can interact in a manner that would not be possible otherwise. Evidence for this particular folding is that after UV irradiation a significant number of bacteria are obtained with mutations in two not closely linked arginine genes. These double mutants might be the result of pyrimidine dimerization (induced by the UV light) between loci juxtaposed by the folding. To the extent that the tertiary conformation of procaryotic chromosomes is controlled, therefore, so is the interaction between the products of certain genes.

Recent results suggest that genetic material codes for enzymes that degrade abnormal forms of normal proteins. Such enzymes may be part of a system for posttranslational control of the products of gene action. (R)

26.13   Many genes in bacteria are located in operons.

It is estimated that there are at least 100 to 200 operons in the *E. coli* chromosome.[4] More than a half-dozen are known well enough to be positioned in the *E. coli* linkage map (Figure 13-10). Operons are also known in other bacteria such as *Salmonella*,

---

[4] Some evidence has been obtained that many operator genes have similar base sequences (see Section S26.13).

and may be especially adaptive in procaryotes, where they permit rapid adjustment to changing external and internal biochemical environments.

Although at least one operon-like system occurs in lower eucaryotes such as yeasts and molds, typical operons have not been found in lower or higher eucaryotes. Gene arrangement and control in eucaryotes is considered in the six chapters that follow.

SUMMARY AND CONCLUSIONS

The chromosome of the procaryote codes for many different proteins needed in different amounts at different times. Such needs are met via several different regulatory mechanisms coded in genetic material, as follows:

Differential transcription

Protein-coding genes are often transcribed in clusters, each gene group belonging to an operon. The synthesis of mRNA for an operon is regulated by the presence of an appropriate DNA-dependent RNA polymerase core enzyme to which an appropriate sigma factor is joined. In addition to the holoenzyme, the synthesis of certain mRNA's requires cyclic-AMP and cyclic-AMP protein, and the preferential synthesis of rRNA requires a psi factor. Active holoenzyme recognizes the base sequence of a promoter gene to initiate mRNA synthesis. Whether mRNA synthesis will proceed or not depends upon the conformation of an operator gene. In some cases the operator is nonpermissive because it is bound by active repressor produced in active or inactive form by a regulator gene (RNA synthesis being negatively controlled); in other cases the operator is permissive because it is bound by active enhancer (RNA synthesis being controlled positively, as it is at the promoter locus). The termination of mRNA synthesis involves a rho factor that joins to the RNA polymerase core enzyme.

The preferential transcription of phage DNA is accomplished by (1) phage-coded changes in the RNA polymerase core enzyme and/or (2) phage-coded sigma factors. Transcription of some genes may depend upon establishing physical linkage with the promoter and operator genes of an operon. One-complement transcription occurs from a two-complement DNA template only if the template has the correct duplex conformation. The protein-coding genes in already-replicated portions of a genome furnish twice as many templates for transcription as those in as-yet-unreplicated portions.

Differential translation

Different mRNA's may be translated different numbers of times because (1) each requires different aminoacyl-tRNA's present in different amounts, and (2) different mRNA's have different longevities. The number of copies synthesized of each of the proteins coded within a single mRNA will also depend upon the number, location, availability, and efficiency of ribosomal attachment points and dropoff points in the mRNA. Since there are many gene-coded parts of the translation machinery at the protein initiation, elongation, and termination stages, we expect that the genetic control of gene action can operate through any or all of them.

Interaction between genes may be regulated at the translational level by the tertiary configuration of the chromosome. There may also be a genetic regulation of the longevity of proteins—expecially those that are defective upon synthesis or aging.

The preferential translation of phage rather than host RNA seems to be attained through special phage-coded tRNA's, digestion of host (t and m) RNA's by phage-coded RNases, and phage-induced modification of host ribosomes, so these preferentially translate phage RNA. The number of copies synthesized of each of the proteins coded within the same strip of phage RNA can also be regulated by the presence of secondary structure and/or by translation products acting as active repressors of specific loci.

GENERAL REFERENCES

Cellular regulatory mechanisms. Cold Spring Harbor Sympos. Quant. Biol., 26. 1962. New York: Cold Spring Harbor Laboratory of Quantitative Biology.

Hayes, W. 1968. Chap. 23, Genetic expression and its control. In *The genetics of bacteria and their viruses*, second edition. New York: John Wiley & Sons, Inc., pp. 700–745.

Jacob, F. 1966. Genetics of the bacterial cell. Science, 152: 1470–1478. (Nobel prize lecture, gives recent advances on the operon.)

Jacob, F., and Monod, J., 1961. Genetic regulatory mechanisms in the synthesis of proteins. J. Mol. Biol., 3: 318–356.

Lewin, B. M. 1970. *The molecular basis of gene expression.* New York: John Wiley & Sons, Inc.

Martin, R. G. 1969. Control of gene expression. Ann. Rev. Genetics, 3: 181–216. (In bacterial operons.)

Transcription of genetic material, vol. 35. Cold Spring Harbor Sympos. Quant. Biol., 35. 1971. New York: Cold Spring Harbor Laboratory of Quantitative Biology.

SPECIFIC SECTION REFERENCES

26.1   Bautz, E. K. F., Bautz, F. A., and Dunn, J. J. 1969. *E. coli* σ factor: a positive control element in phage T4 development. Nature, Lond., 223: 1022–1024.

Roberts, J. W. 1969. Termination factor for RNA synthesis. Nature, Lond., 224: 1168–1174.

Schmidt, D. A., Mazaitis, A. J., Kasai, T., and Bautz, E. K. F. 1970. Involvement of a phage T4 σ factor and an anti-terminator protein in the transcription of early T4 genes *in vivo*. Nature, Lond., 225: 1012–1016. (An antiterminator seems to stop rho, the terminator, from operating.)

Silvestri, L. G. (Editor). 1970. *RNA-polymerase and transcription.* New York: American Elsevier Publishing Company, Inc.

Sugiura, M., Okamoto, T., and Takanami, M. 1970. RNA polymerase σ factor and the selection of initiation site. Nature, Lond., 225: 598–600.

Travers, A. A. 1970. Positive control of transcription by a bacteriophage sigma factor. Nature, Lond., 225: 1009–1012.

Travers, A. A., Kamen, R. I., and Schlief, R. F. 1970. Factor necessary for ribosomal RNA synthesis. Nature, Lond., 228: 748–751.

26.3   Le Talaer, J.-I., and Jeanteur, Ph. 1971. Purification and base composition of phage lambda early promoters. Proc. Nat. Acad. Sci., U.S., 68: 3211–3215. (The promoters, or adjacent or related sequences, are rich in adenine and thymine.)

26.4   Zubay, G., Schwartz, D., and Beckwith, J. 1970. Mechanism of activation of catabolite-sensitive genes: a positive control system. Proc. Nat. Acad. Sci., U.S., 66: 104–110. (Cessation of glucose metabolism increases cyclic-AMP and RNA initiation at certain promoters.)

26.5   Monod, J., Changeux, J. P., and Jacob, F. 1963. Allosteric proteins and cellular control systems. J. Mol. Biol., 6: 306–329.

Reznikoff, W. S., Miller, J. H., Scaife, J. G., and Beckwith, J. R. 1969. A mechanism for repressor action. J. Mol. Biol., 43: 201–213.

Jacques Monod (1910–   ) in 1965, the year he was the recipient of a Nobel prize.

26.6   Beckwith, J. R., and Zipser, D. 1970. (Editors) *The lactose operon*. New York: Cold Spring Harbor Laboratory of Quantitative Biology.

Ptashne, M., and Gilbert, W. 1970. Genetic repressors. Scient. Amer., 222 (No. 6): 36–44, 152.

26.7   Atkins, J. F., and Loper, J. C. 1970. Transcription initiation in the histidine operon of *Salmonella typhimurium*. Proc. Nat. Acad. Sci., U.S., 65: 925–932.

26.8   Eisen, H., Brachet, P., Pereira da Silva, L., and Jacob, F. 1970. Regulation of repressor expression in λ. Proc. Nat. Acad. Sci., U.S., 66: 855–862. (The gene *cro* regulates the expression of the regulator gene *cI*.)

Pirrotta, V., Chadwick, P., and Ptashne, M. 1970. Active form of two coliphage repressors. Nature, Lond., 227: 41–44. (They attach to DNA as oligomers—possibly as tetramers.)

26.9   Herskowitz, Ira, and Signer, E. R. 1970. A site essential for expression of all late genes in bacteriophage λ. J. Mol. Biol., 47: 545–556.

Mushynski, W. E., and Spencer, J. H. 1970. Nucleotide clusters in deoxyribonucleic acids. VI. The pyrimidine oligonucleotides of strands r and l of bacteriophage lambda DNA. J. Mol. Biol., 52: 107–120. (Indirect support for the view that promoters are rich in pyrimidines.)

26.10   Hayashi, M., Hayashi, M. N., and Spiegelman, S. 1964. DNA circularity and the mechanism of strand selection in the generation of genetic messages. Proc. Nat. Acad. Sci., U.S., 51: 351–359.

Kennett, R. H., and Sueoka, N. 1971. Gene expression during outgrowth of *Bacillus subtilis* spores. J. Mol. Biol., 60: 31–44. (The relationship between gene order on the chromosome and temporal sequence of enzyme synthesis.)

26.11   Fukami, H., and Imahori, K. 1971. Control of translation by the conformation of messenger RNA. Proc. Nat. Acad. Sci., U.S., 68: 570–573. (Using φR17 RNA.)

Ihler, G., and Nakada, D. 1970. Selective binding of ribosomes to initiation sites on single-stranded DNA from bacterial viruses. Nature, Lond., 228: 239–242.

Kano-Sueoka, T., and Sueoka, N. 1969. Leucine tRNA and cessation of *Escherichia coli* protein synthesis upon phage T2 infection. Proc. Nat. Acad. Sci., U.S., 62: 1229–1236.

Lodish, H. F., and Robertson, H. D. 1970. Regulation of *in vitro* translation of bacteriophage f2 RNA. Cold Spring Harbor Sympos. Quant. Biol., 34: 655–673. (Ribosomes from different bacteria differ in recognizing different points in an mRNA for the initiation of polypeptide synthesis.)

McLellan, W. L., and Vogel, H. J. 1970. Translational repression of the arginine system of *Escherichia coli*. Proc. Nat. Acad. Sci., U.S., 67: 1703–1709. (Repression occurs in the presence of excessive arginine, apparently due to accelerated degradation of mRNA for enzymes for arginine synthesis.)

Newton, A. 1969. Re-initiation of polypeptide synthesis and polarity in the *lac* operon of *Escherichia coli*. J. Mol. Biol., 41: 329–339.

Sugiyama, T. 1970. Translational control of MS2 RNA cistrons. Cold Spring Harbor Sympos. Quant. Biol., 34: 687–694.

26.12   Goldschmidt, R. 1970. *In vivo* degradation of nonsense fragments in *E. coli*. Nature, Lond., 228: 1151–1154. (Incorrectly made protein is digested before its correctly made equivalent.)

Platt, T., Miller, J. H., and Weber, K. 1970. *In vivo* degradation of mutant *Lac* repressor. Nature, Lond., 228: 1154–1156. (Evidence for the genetic regulation of protein destruction.)

Vogel, H. J., and Bacon, D. F. 1966. Gene aggregation: evidence for a coming together of functionally related, not closely linked genes. Proc. Nat. Acad. Sci., U.S., 55: 1456–1459.

SUPPLEMENTARY SECTIONS

S26.6   The expression of the *lac* operon can be altered by mutations in the promoter, operator, and structural genes for enzymes or in the regulator gene.

The regulator gene, i^+, can mutate to a form, i^-, that produces modified or no repressor protein. In the presence of only the i^- allele, therefore, o^+ will not be bound by repressor and the *lac* operon will be expressing itself in the unregulated state *constitutively*—at all times. Besides i^-, the *constitutive allele of i^+*, there is i^s, an allele whose repressor is so modified that although it can still bind to o^+, it does not combine with the inducer. Accordingly, this repressor protein is bound to o^+ irreversibly and the *lac* operon is always turned off. The alternative i^s is, therefore, called the *superrepressor allele of i^+*.

Some mutants of p^+, the promoter gene, permanently prevent the function of the *lac* operon. The o^c allele of o^+ is called the *operator constitutive* allele since it does not bind normal repressor protein and the operon is never turned off.

The structural genes in the *lac* operon also may mutate to inactive states. The allele z^- is noteworthy since it produces nonfunctional z protein called *Cz protein* recognized because it serologically crossreacts with z^+ enzyme, that is, β-galactosidase. (Other z alleles do not result in the production of cross-reacting material, probably because they contain nonsense codons that interrupt the synthesis of β-galactosidase.)

By sexduction one can obtain *E. coli* that carry two *lac* regions, one in the bacterial chromosome, and one as part of an F′ particle. We can ignore the promoter locus, which is p^+ in each of the *lac* operons in the following discussion. In one case the bacterial chromosome is i^- o^+ z^- y^-, which by itself could produce Cz protein constitutively. If after F-duction this cell also contains an F-*lac* particle i^+ o^c z^+ y^+, it will produce galactosidase and permease constitutively because of the arrangement of loci on the F-*lac* particle. In the absence of lactose, the *lac* operon in the bacterial chromosome is turned off by the diffusing repressor produced by the i^+ in the F-*lac* particle. In the presence of lactose, however, the cell produces Cz protein besides the galactosidase and permease. Figure 26-6 gives the results of studies involving other F-duced *E. coli*.

Jacob, F., and Monod, J. 1965. Genetic mapping of the elements of the lactose region in *Escherichia coli*. Biochem. Biophys. Res Commun., 18: 693–701. Reprinted in *Papers in biochemical genetics*, Zubay, G. L. (Editor), New York: Holt, Rinehart and Winston, Inc., 1968, pp. 513–521.

Jacob, F., Perrin, D., Sanchez, C., and Monod, J. 1960. The operon: a group of genes whose expression is coordinated by an operator. (In French.) C. R. Acad. Sci. (Paris), 250: 1727–1729. Translated and reprinted in *Papers on bacterial genetics*, second edition, Adelberg, E. A. (Editor), Boston: Little, Brown and Company, 1966, pp. 198–200.

Jacob, F., Ullman, A., and Monod, J. 1967. Le promoteur, élément génétique nécessaire à l'expression d'un opéron. C. R. Acad. Sci. (Paris), 258: 3125–3128.

S26.8   Different operons within a chromosome are transcribed to mRNA in opposite directions. Some mRNA's are complementary to one strand of double-stranded DNA; others are complementary to the other strand.

Not all operons in the circular chromosome of *Salmonella* or *E. coli* are transcribed to mRNA in the same direction; some operons run clockwise and others counterclockwise from their

Genotype		Noninduced Bacteria			Induced Bacteria		
Chromosome	F−lac	P	G	Cz	P	G	Cz
i^+ o^+ z^- y^+	i^+ o^c z^+ y^+	50	110	nd	100	330	100
i^+ o^+ z^+ y^-	i^+ o^c z^- y^+	—	<1	30	—	100	400
i^+ o^+ z^- y^+	i^+ o^c z^+ y^-	nd	60	—	100	300	—

P = Permease
G = Galactosidase
Cz = Cz Protein

Figure 26-6 Functioning of *lac* genes in various hybrid *E. coli*.   nd, not detectable; —, not tested.

operator gene. Under certain conditions, it is possible to transpose the *lac* operon of *E. coli* to a new chromosomal position. In some bacteria it becomes inserted in one direction; in others, the reverse. Let us assume that the double-stranded DNA of the *lac* segment is composed of the single strands L_1 and L_2. Bacteria of type A have L_1 in the chromosome's + strand; B bacteria with *lac* inverted must have L_1 in the − strand because the DNA backbone polarity must be maintained. Since both A and B bacteria produce functional *lac* enzymes, they must specify the same mRNA which we will arbitrarily take to be a complement of L_1. Hence, to produce RNA complementary to L_1 in A bacteria, the complement of the + strand as made; likewise, in B bacteria, the complement of the − strand is made. Thus, some segments of a bacterial chromosome are transcribed to mRNA that is complementary to the + strand, and other segments are transcribed to mRNA complementary to the − strand (see Figures 4-6D and 26-5).

Levinthal, M., and Nikaido, H. 1969. Consequences of deletion mutations joining two

operons of opposite polarity. J. Mol. Biol., 42: 511–520.

S26.13   Operator genes in different operons seem to have similar nucleotide sequences. Part of the nucleotide sequences of different regulator genes also appear to be similar.

Leucine synthesis in *Salmonella* is controlled by the leucine operon and its regulator gene, R_1 (Figure 26-7). A certain mutation in the operator region (from o_1^+ to o_1^x), however, allows the operon to be irreversibly repressed, "superrepressed," by the product of a regulator gene, R_2, which controls another operon. When the bacterial genome with o_1^x also contains a mutation in the foreign regulator gene, R_2^y, the leucine operon is no longer superrepressed. Since both the o_1^x and the foreign regulator gene mutations apparently are transitions of a single base pair only (as determined from reverse mutation studies), the regions of interaction between o_1^+ and its normal repressor and between o_1^x and the foreign repressor must be similar. If these findings

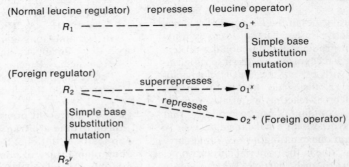

Figure 26-7 Leucine operon in *Salmonella* and its relation to its own (R_1) and a foreign (R_2) regulator gene. The o_1^x mutant is superrepressed by the repressor protein of a foreign regulator gene. A subsequent mutation to R_2^y released o_1^x from superrepression, o_1^x coming partly under the influence of R_1, the o_2^+ operon perhaps becoming constitutive.

are generally true, they would indicate that (1) there are relatively few nucleotide differences between the regions of different regulator genes that code for the operator binding site, and that (2) operator genes for different operons differ from each other by relatively few nucleotides. It is possible, therefore, that many operator genes (and portions of many regulator genes) have a common origin.

Mukai, F. H., and Margolin, P. 1963. Analysis of unlinked suppressors of an o^o mutation in *Salmonella*. Proc. Nat. Acad. Sci., U.S., 50: 140–148.

QUESTIONS AND PROBLEMS

1. Do you suppose that all genes in *E. coli* are part of operons? Explain.
2. *Escherichia coli* grown in nutrient broth are infected with ϕT4. Soon after infection one sample is placed in minimal medium; another is left in nutrient medium. Explain why the bacteria in nutrient medium lyse first.
3. How is gene action affected by changes that involve genetic nucleic acid's
   a. Primary structure?
   b. Secondary structure?
   c. Tertiary structure?
   d. Quaternary structure?
4. D. H. Alpers and G. M. Tomkins, studying the *lac* operon, found that, shortly after adding lactose to the medium, β-galactosidase appears first and reaches a plateau, followed by the appearance of the transacetylase. After removal of the inducer, transacetylase continues to be produced for about 2 minutes longer than the β-galactosidase. How can you explain these findings?
5. How can you define an operon in *E. coli* from an electron micrograph?
6. What evidence can you cite that one strip of messenger RNA can be long enough to contain several structural genes of an operon?
7. How does an operator gene differ from a regulator gene?
8. Describe the regulation of action of the genes of phage lambda during its vegetative and prophage states.
9. What is your present concept of the "gene"?
10. Discuss the view that in *E. coli*, *rII* deletion 1589 involves an operon.
11. Are all regulator genes repressor genes? Explain.
12. Some nonsense mutations are "polar" mutations. These occur near the operator end of the operon, terminating translation at that point, and preventing translation of the codons for subsequent structural genes that are also near the operator end. How can you explain that such polar mutants permit the translation of codons for structural genes close to the opposite end of the mRNA?
13. Why is all regulation of gene action in *E. coli* not at the level of transcription?
14. What can happen to the core DNA-dependent RNA polymerase of *E. coli* to change its specificity?
15. What is allostery and how may it be involved in the regulation of transcription?

Chapter 27

Gene-Action Regulation—
Molecular Basis in Eucaryotes

In Chapter 26 we saw that particular kinds and sequences of genetic information serve to regulate gene action. We saw also how this regulatory information is used at various levels between the start of transcription and the end of translation in bacteria and phage. The present chapter considers the genetic control of gene action in eucaryotic organisms and the molecular basis for such regulation.

27.1   In order to be replicated or transcribed, the template material must be in an appropriate conformation and in the presence of suitable catalysts and precursor materials.

It is obvious that for replication or transcription to occur, the nucleic acid template must be available to the appropriate holoenzyme and substrate. If the template is

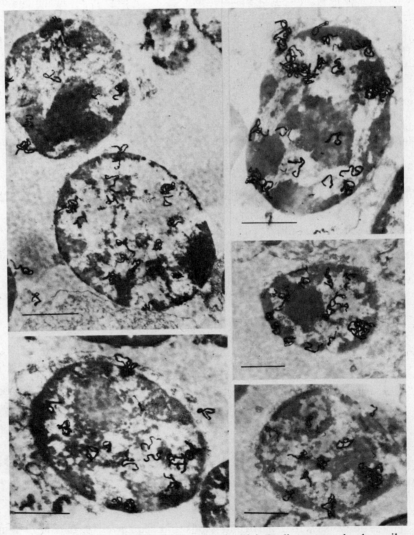

Figure 27-1   Transcription in isolated calf thymus nuclei. Radioautographs show silver grains chiefly over diffuse regions of the nuclear chromatin after incubation in uridine-^{3}H. The line in the lower left corner of each photograph is one micron. (Courtesy of V. C. Littau, V. G. Allfrey, J. H. Frenster, and A. E. Mirsky, 1964. Proc. Nat. Acad. Sci., U.S., 52: 97.)

double-stranded DNA with 10 base pairs per complete turn, then several changes can take place to modify the template and make its major and minor grooves unavailable to DNA polymerase or DNA-dependent RNA polymerase. Undercoiling or overcoiling may prevent the proper copying of template information as can a substance which blocks one or both grooves. Molecules that complex with the DNA can also hinder local denaturation and strand separation. We should not assume, however, that a nucleic acid template in a suitable conformation is necessarily transcribed, since the appropriate enzymes and substrate may not be available.

27.2   Unclumped or diffuse chromatin can be transcribed, whereas clumped or packed chromatin cannot.

Interphase nuclei contain chromatin that is clumped in certain regions (heterochromatin) and unclumped or diffuse in others (euchromatin). It is primarily the genes in diffuse regions that are active in transcription, as illustrated in Figure 27-1.

Chromosomes at metaphase are not transcribing RNA and are poor templates *in vitro*. (R)

27.3   The puffs in polynemic chromosomes are sites of transcription.

At various times during the development of certain dipteran cells, different cross bands of the highly polynemic chromosome " puff " and later " unpuff " in a regular sequence (Figure 27-2). The puffing sequence differs from one larval tissue to another. Puffing is thought to be a local unwinding or unclumping of the chromosome and its DNA so that the degree of coiling is appropriate for transcription. In *Drosophila* and

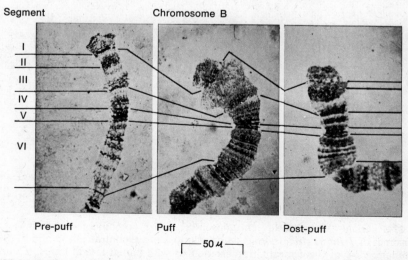

Figure 27-2   Puffing and unpuffing in a region of a salivary gland chromosome of *Rhynchosciara*. (Courtesy of G. Rudkin.)

the midge *Chironomus*, a puff region synthesizes more RNA (probably mRNA) than an equivalent nonpuff region, thus indicating that puffs are sites for transcription.

Injection of *Chironomus* larvae with the pupation hormone *ecdysone* induces specific bands to puff. Later puffs seem to depend on the size and duration of earlier puffs. Apparently, then, this hormone is involved in the control of transcription. Since only about 20 per cent of the bands are ever seen to puff in a dipteran salivary gland cell, a great many genes in a tissue may not be transcribed to RNA.

In a certain species of *Chironomus*, granules occur in the cytoplasm of cells in one lobe of the larval salivary gland. The presence of these granules is associated with a gene as well as a puff near one end of chromosome IV. In cells without granules, this puff is not found. Larvae from a mating of individuals from species which differ in the ability to make these granules are cytogenetically hybrid; that is, one chromosome shows the characteristic puff, but its homolog does not. Moreover, the number of granules in a hybrid individual is approximately half the number in an individual with two puffing chromosomes. These findings correlate puffing with the activity of a specific gene. (R)

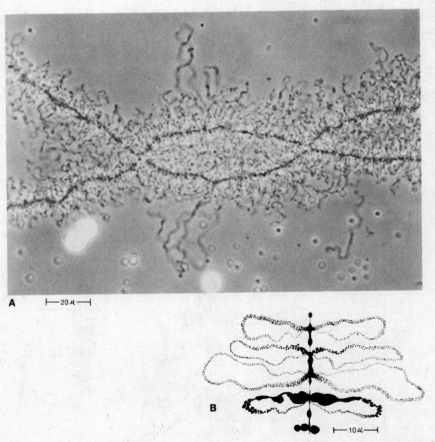

Figure 27-3 Giant "lampbrush" chromosomes of the amphibian oocyte. (A) Unfixed chromosomes of *Triturus viridescens* in saline solution, phase contrast, flash photo. (B) Semi-diagrammatic view of the central chromosome axis with paired lateral loops. (Courtesy of J. G. Gall.)

27.4   The loops of lampbrush chromosomes are sites of transcription. Chromosomal uncoiling allows loop DNA to be used as a template.

Amphibian oocytes have giant chromosomes that look like "lampbrushes" because of the lateral projection of many pairs of loops from the main chromosomal axis (Figure 27-3). Each loop is asymmetric, that is, thin at one point of attachment to the main axis and becoming thicker up to the other point of attachment. Some giant loops can be seen to contain a thin, DNA-containing thread continuous with the main chromosomal axis. Autoradiographs of newt lampbrush chromosomes exposed to radioactively labeled uridine show that incorporation into a giant loop occurs in a definite sequence, starting at the thin end and proceeding around the loop in about 10 days. Thus, RNA is transcribed from different portions of the chromosome at different times. This synthesis is DNA-dependent, since agents such as actinomycin D which inhibit nuclear RNA synthesis lead to disappearance of the loops. From such results comes the hypothesis that a loop (like a puff) is a temporarily unwound portion of the chromosome. As the thick portion of a loop completes its synthetic activity, it is thought to wind up and form part of the nontranscribing, main chromosomal axis. At the same time, a wound part of the main axis unwinds to form the thin end of the loop, which proceeds to synthesize RNA. The presence of many loops in lampbrush chromosomes indicates that a large number of chromosomal sites are available for transcription.

The lampbrush type of chromosome structure has also been reported in the developing oocytes of various mollusks, echinoderms, fishes, reptiles, birds, and mammals (including man), as well as in the onion, the cricket, and the Y chromosome of the *Drosophila* spermatocyte. In summary, then, chromosomal uncoiling seems to be necessary in a wide variety of eucaryotic organisms before DNA can be used as a template. (R)

27.5   The mRNA's of higher animals seem to usually code for only one polypeptide. Eucaryotes, therefore, do not seem to have operons like those in procaryotes.

Contrary to the common situation in bacteria (Section 26.13), mammalian mRNA's seem to routinely code for only a single protein or polypeptide. This has been determined from the size of the polyribosomes that synthesize myosin, tropomyosin, or actin, or one of the two polypeptide chains that make up hemoglobin or a type of gamma globulin. Such results also indicate that no internal protein initiation occurs in mammalian mRNA, which, therefore, can dispense with internal terminator codons. Although several gene clusters occur in fungi such as yeast and *Neurospora* which seem to be coordinately controlled, eucaryotes do not seem to possess procaryote-like operons that produce RNA's coding for several polypeptides.

When long RNA's of pre-rRNA or pre-tRNA types are produced in mammals, they are usually degraded to smaller functional segments. In fact, only about one half of 45s pre-rRNA is used for rRNA. Similarly, a long pre-hemoglobin 60s RNA is degraded to a 10s hemoglobin mRNA before translation. The RNase involved in such degradations is as yet unstudied.

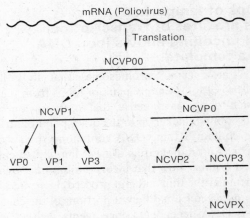

Figure 27-4 Fate of poliovirus mRNA translation product. ------>, expected; ------>, observed. (After M. F. Jacobson and D. Baltimore.)

Viruses that infect mammalian cells show several kinds of adaptation to a host translation system geared for monopolypeptide mRNA's. Some mammalian viruses have RNA genomes composed of a number of fragments, each of which functions as mRNA separately. This is true of reovirus, which is composed of several double-stranded fragments each making a separate mRNA, and is also apparently true of influenza virus which contains several single-stranded RNA fragments. In the case of Newcastle disease virus, an RNA virus, one strand ($+$) is continuous but its ($-$) complement occurs as short pieces which serve as mRNA.

In certain enteroviruses and poliovirus, the RNA phage genome is a single strand and codes for more than one polypeptide. In these cases, the viral RNA is translated into one giant polypeptide, which, however, is then cleaved enzymatically into smaller units (Figure 27-4), comprising virion proteins as well as nonvirion protein (probably including RNA-dependent RNA polymerase).

The DNA virus vaccinia codes for a large polypeptide which after formation is cleaved to form a smaller viral core protein. Even though most mRNA's of higher animals seem to code for only one polypeptide, polypeptide cleavage seems to occur in the formation of certain digestive enzymes, clotting factors, and insulin. (R)

27.6 Various substances that complex with nuclear DNA are likely to affect transcription.

Although a basic protein (which is not a histone) may be associated with *E. coli* DNA, most of the evidence supports the view that the DNA of procaryotic cells is essentially naked.[1] This does not mean that nothing bonds to this DNA; certainly DNA polymerase and DNA-dependent RNA polymerase are bound to it when replication and transcription occur. Moreover, protein repressor or enhancer molecules may be attached at operator loci. Nevertheless, in the greater portion of the bacterial genome the DNA must be free for replication and transcription.

---

[1] It should be noted, however, in this connection that the DNA in the head of phage T2 is complexed with a protein. *In vitro* at least, the inhibition of RNA synthesis from this DNA is linear with the concentration of internal head protein.

Chromatin Source	Nonhistone Protein	Histone	RNA	DNA Template Activity of Chromatin*
Pea				
Embryonic axis	0.29	1.03	0.26	12
Vegetative bud	0.10	1.30	0.11	6
Growing cotyledon	0.36	0.76	0.13	32
Rat				
Liver	0.67	1.00	0.043	20
Ascites tumor	1.00	1.16	0.13	10
Human				
HeLa cells	0.71	1.02	0.09	10
Cow				
Thymus	0.33	1.14	0.007	15
Sea urchin				
Blastula	0.48	1.04	0.039	10
Pluteus stage	1.04	0.86	0.078	20

Figure 27-5   Relative mass of various components of nuclear chromatin relative to that of DNA taken as 1.0. (Adapted from J. Bonner, M. E. Dahmus, D. Fambrough, R. C. Huang, K. Marushiga, and Y. H. Yuan, 1968. Science, 159: 47.)
* Percentage of that displayed by the naked DNA template.

The DNA in nuclei, on the contrary, is usually complexed with one or more of the following: nonhistone (acidic) protein, histone, protamine, RNA. Because these components of chromatin occur in significant mass relative to DNA (Figure 27-5), they are all candidates as substances employed for the regulation of gene action. Just as the unbound nature of bacterial DNA suggests that such DNA is typically available for template usage, the presence of an abundance of substances that can bind to nuclear DNA suggests that this DNA is normally unavailable for template usage. The figure supports this view in that *in vitro* the DNA template activity of whole chromatin is only one third or less of what it is when complexed substances are removed and purified DNA is used.

Although the next seven sections of this chapter will consider each component of chromatin successively with the aim of learning to what extent and by what mechanisms each may be involved in the regulation of gene activity in nuclear chromosomes, we should note beforehand that control of transcription in eucaryotes may involve the use of different RNA polymerases (or their sigma factors). For example, (1) in the rat liver nucleus, the RNA polymerase in the nucleolus (transcribing pre-rRNA) differs from the enzyme found elsewhere in the nucleus; (2) a protein regulatory factor has been reported for the transcription of the ribosomal genes in amphibian oocytes; and (3) the sea urchin has three different RNA polymerases.

27.7   Nonhistone proteins may have a role in regulation of gene action.

The amount of nonhistone, acidic, protein associated with chromatin varies considerably, even within the same organism (Figure 27-5). As might be expected, therefore, this class of protein has a high turnover rate; cells metabolically active in protein synthesis (for example, sea urchin pluteus stage) have larger amounts of nonhistone protein in their chromatin than cells less active in this respect (sea urchin blastula).

Acidic nuclear protein occurs in chromatin as part of the nucleoprotein, the manner in which it is bound to DNA not being clear. The heterogeneity of this protein, however, seems limited. Nevertheless, the melting or denaturation temperature of DNA is raised in the presence of such acidic proteins. In this respect, then, acidic proteins stabilize DNA. Since this stabilization seems to result from the inhibition of strand separation, the nonhistone proteins may have a role in the regulation of gene activity by changing the availability of DNA as a template. (R)

27.8   Histones are relatively small proteins of a relatively small number of types.

The nuclear DNA of eucaryotic cells is complexed with basic proteins such as histone or protamine to form deoxyribonucleoproteins. (Protamine is a rather simple protein rich in the basic amino acid arginine.) Relative to the DNA in chromatin, histones are equivalent in mass and rather constant in amount (Figure 27-5).

Histone isolated from DNA in a nucleohistone can be separated into several subfractions, indicating that a cell probably contains several different types of histones —relatively small molecules (ranging in molecular weight from 3,500 to 74,000)—that differ in amino acid composition. Three main classes exist: (1) *lysine-rich* (relatively very rich in lysine and proline and poor in arginine), (2) *moderately* (or *weakly*) *lysine-rich*, and (3) *arginine-rich* (relatively rich in arginine and poor in lysine). The amino acid sequence of "histone IV," which is 102 amino acids long and rich in Arg and Gly, is known. Histones seem to be coded in about 400 reiterated DNA sequences, some clustered.

The types of basic proteins complexed with DNA vary not only in different organisms but in different tissues of the same organism. For example, although protamine is found in the sperm of certain fish, for example, salmon (where it is called salmine), herring (clupein), mackerel (scombine), and in trout, it is replaced by histone in the somatic cells produced mitotically after fertilization. Many plant histones contain less of the arginine-rich fraction than animal histones. In chickens, the sperm contains protamine, and erythrocyte DNA is complexed with different histones than is liver DNA. In the snail and the squid, three different types of basic protein are associated with the same DNA at various stages in development. Note, in this connection, that the amino acid sequence of histone IV is nearly identical in calf thymus and pea embryo, phylogenetic diversity not being paralleled by histone diversity. We conclude that, despite some variability, histones are of restricted diversity. (R)

27.9   Histones in general seem to serve as repressors of gene activity.

Although there is some variety in the types of basic proteins associated with DNA, this variety is much too small to have each unique gene sequence (or even a significant number of these) bound to a basic protein of unique amino acid sequence. Nevertheless, it is hypothesized that histones, in general, act as repressors of gene activity when they are complexed with DNA. This is supported by the following cytological and cytochemical evidence.

1. Histones seem to be required for proper chromosomal individuality and superstructure as revealed by X-ray diffraction studies of chromosomes and by the effect of selective removal of histones on chromosome organization. Such studies suggest that the histone in a nucleohistone covers the DNA uniformly, if intermittently. Although various other arrangements are possible, arginine-rich histone may be bound spirally around the DNA molecule and occupy positions in one or both grooves of the double helix. Lysine-rich histones may form a bridge between DNA duplexes or between tertiary coils of the same duplex. Thus, metaphase chromosomes seem to have condensed (nontranscribing) chromatin because lysine-rich histone makes cross links between DNA-containing fibrils.[2]

2. The DNA of duck erythrocytes appears to be almost completely complexed with histone, but cells of other organisms have less of their DNA histone-complexed. In peas, for example, the fraction of the total DNA not complexed with histone in the developing cotyledon, embryo, and apices varies from 5 to 30 per cent. As a rule actively growing, protein-synthesizing, tissues have more noncomplexed DNA in their cells than do the cells of differentiated tissues (examine again the last column of Figure 27-5).

3. Isolated nuclei can transcribe RNA from their DNA. Much of this synthesized RNA is mRNA; some is tRNA. In nuclei isolated from the calf thymus, arginine-rich histones *added* to the incubation medium not only reduce the uptake of thymidine into DNA but greatly inhibit the synthesis of RNA. Addition of lysine-rich histones is much less inhibiting.

   Removal of almost all the histone and little nonhistone material from isolated nuclei permits a three- to fourfold increase in RNA synthesis. Moreover, when histone is added to these histone-deficient nuclei, RNA synthesis is immediately suppressed. Removal of *certain* histones from these nuclei also results in a two- to fourfold increase in RNA synthesis (probably mRNA). Thus, transcription of DNA appears to be differentially inhibited by different histones. Furthermore, the removal of histones from DNA apparently can lead to the hitherto-repressed production of messenger RNA.

It appears that the control of genetic activity by histones *in vivo* is essentially preserved not only in isolated nuclei but in isolated chromatin as well, as indicated by the following experiments.

4. Chromatin isolated from pea embryos, 20 per cent of which is not complexed with histone, is able to carry out RNA synthesis with the four usual ribonucleoside triphosphates and DNA-dependent

[2] When clumped chromatin and diffuse chromatin are separated and analyzed, each is found to have about 20 per cent of their total histone as the Lys-rich fraction. Selective extraction of this fraction from the nucleus causes a relaxation of the clumped chromatin. It is not known in what way the disposition of the Lys-rich fraction is different in clumped and unclumped chromatin.

RNA polymerase. Removal of histone increases RNA synthesis about 500 per cent. Reconstituted nucleohistones either do not support DNA-dependent RNA synthesis at all or support it only to a small extent depending upon the histone involved.[3]

5. Pea cotyledons synthesize a specific *pea seed reserve globulin* not produced in other tissues such as buds or roots. Chromatin isolated from pea cotyledons produces mRNA which can be used in a ribosomal system to manufacture this globulin, but chromatin isolated from pea buds does not make RNA coding for this protein. Removal of histones from pea bud chromatin, however, yields DNA which supports globulin synthesis. It, therefore, appears that the gene for globulin synthesis is normally suppressed in bud tissue by histones.

6. Changing the amount of calf thymus histone in a rat tumor cell fraction that contains nucleoli and nucleolus organizers (with adjacent DNA) affects both the amount and the base ratio of the RNA transcripts produced by this fraction *in vitro*.

7. Addition of histones causes the collapse of the loops in lampbrush chromosomes *in vitro*.

The preceding not only indicates that histones may serve as repressors of gene activity, but that different histones show some specificity in their action. (R)

27.10   The general inhibition of gene action by histones is correlated with their ability to affect the denaturation of DNA *in vitro*.

Purified DNA can combine with histones *in vitro* to form reconstituted nucleo-histones of about 35 Å in diameter, whose DNA seems to be as fully complexed with histone as the DNA in native nucleohistones. When DNA is complexed with histones its melting or denaturation temperature rises. In this respect, then, histones stabilize DNA just as do nonhistone acidic proteins. Lysine-rich histones in nucleohistones from peas increase the temperature required to melt half the DNA from 70 to 81°C; half the DNA in arginine-rich nucleohistones melts at 71°C. An approximately linear relationship exists between the lysine content of histone and the melting temperature of DNA in a nucleohistone. DNA fully complexed with protamine, which is rich in arginine and has no lysine, melts at the same temperature as pure native DNA. (R)

27.11   Histones can directly affect the availability of DNA-dependent RNA polymerase.

If DNA polymerase is mixed with either Arg-rich or Lys-rich histones, no effect is noted on the action of this enzyme. On the other hand, mixing Arg-rich histone and

---

[3] DNA fully complexed with protamine, however, is fully active in DNA-dependent RNA synthesis. This suggests that the function of protamine is not the suppression of template activity but the neutralization of the acidic phosphate groups that would cause DNA to repel itself, and prevent the tight chromosome packing required in a sperm nucleus.

DNA-dependent RNA polymerase inhibits RNA synthesis. It is concluded, therefore, that Arg-rich histone can act directly on the RNA polymerase as a regulator of RNA synthesis. Although mixing Lys-rich histone and DNA-dependent RNA polymerase has no effect on RNA synthesis, this synthesis is inhibited when Lys-rich histone is mixed with the DNA template first and then RNA polymerase is added. This supports the view that Lys-rich histone acts as a regulator of gene action at the template level. (R)

27.12 Some of the specificity in the control of gene action by histones may involve chemical modifications of histone structure.

Whether histones repress gene action by interfering with the template, the RNA polymerase, or both, the limited specificity which they have in regulating gene action can be due to

1. Different kinds of histones (as already described in Sections 27.9 through 27.11.).
2. Minor chemical changes in the histones themselves (to be considered in this section).
3. Adapter molecules attached to histones (to be considered in the next section).

Histones can be modified after synthesis by the attachment of acetyl, methyl, and possibly phosphoryl[4] groups. Lysine-rich histones normally have more of their N-terminal ends acetylated than do arginine-rich histones. In one fraction of regenerating liver histone, the acetyl group seems to be added to the N-terminus by N-acetyl-Ser-tRNA which has been reported to act as the polypeptide initiator (instead of the Met-tRNA$_F$ used for typical eucaryotic proteins). When some histones are further acetylated at their ends, they permit complementary RNA synthesis *in vitro*, although the same histones without further acetylation suppress RNA synthesis. It appears that histone acetylation also may be involved in controlling gene action *in vivo*, as shown by finding that (1) nontranscribing clumped chromatin of calf thymus nuclei contains a smaller percentage of acetylated histones than transcribing diffuse chromatin and that (2) acetylation of histones (as well as phosphorylation of proteins associated with chromosomes) appears to precede an increase in nuclear RNA synthesis. For example, a peak of acetylation occurs in the Arg-rich histones before the maximal rates of RNA synthesis occur in regenerating rat liver.

The preceding discussion points up the desirability of knowing more about where and how histones are synthesized.[5] (R)

---

[4] Phosphorylated serine is incorporated at the time of protamine synthesis, which occurs in cytoplasmic ribosomes. After synthesis the protamine is dephosphorylated, in which condition it is hypothesized to precipitate complexed DNA.

[5] Although the thymocyte nucleus contains ribosomes that can synthesize proteins, the nucleus in HeLa cells has no ribosomes and synthesizes no protein. In the latter cell, histone and DNA synthesis start simultaneously in the S phase, the cytoplasm containing polyribosomes bearing 7 to 9s RNA and histone-like polypeptides. If DNA synthesis is arrested, these small polysomes are preferentially disrupted and histone synthesis declines rapidly.

27.13   Some of the specificity in the regulation of gene action by histones may involve adapter molecules, perhaps chromosomal RNA.

The several types of histone and the several ways that each type can be modified chemically would be sufficient to provide some of the specificity needed for the regulation of gene action in eucaryotic cells. The amount of specificity these variations would provide is insufficient, however, for the precise control of the functioning of individual or small groups of genes. It has been suggested that the required precision is mediated by nonhistone acidic protein, which can complex with DNA and histone, acting as an adapter (just as tRNA is the adapter between mRNA and a growing polypeptide). Specific protein-DNA binding can occur, as we know from the protein repressors of transcription in *E. coli*. Nonhistone proteins, however, do not seem to occur in sufficient diversity to play such a role.

RNA has been found complexed with histone in chromosomes (see Figure 27-5). Such RNA, called *chromosomal RNA*, has the following characteristics:

1. It occurs in short chains, 40 to 200 nucleotides long.
2. It has high content (7 to 10 mole per cent) of dihydropyrimidines (dihydro U or dihydro T).
3. In the chromosomes of higher organisms, it is bound to DNA in RNase-resistant form and is bound covalently to chromosomal protein.
4. It hybridizes with 2–5 per cent of homologous denatured and native DNA. (Is the latter property associated with the dihydropyrimidine content?)

5. It has a heterogeneous, organ-specific, base sequence.
6. It is required for the bonding of chromosomal protein to DNA in reconstituting *in vitro* chromatin having sequence-specific characteristics.
7. It binds to the portion of DNA rich in partially redundant sequences (see Section 8.9).
8. It is part of the sequence of huge nuclear informational RNA (Section 6.12), has a high turnover rate, and is restricted to the nucleus.

These properties suggest that chromosomal RNA may have the specificity needed to activate specific loci. (R)

27.14   In eucaryotes translation is regulated genetically in several ways.

Even though eucaryotes do not seem to have typical operons, their translation mechanism is similar to that in procaryotes. Accordingly, one expects to find a spectrum of mechanisms for the genetic regulation of translation in eucaryotes which is similar to that in procaryotes. Several eucaryotic examples of such regulation, whose molecular basis is somewhat understood, will be presented.

The synthesis of a class of protein may depend upon the occurrence of a particular class of ribosome

The ribosomes can differ in different kinds of organisms and in different regions of a given cell (cytoplasmic versus mitochondrion or chloroplast, as described in

Chapter 19). An *in vitro* study of the ribosomes engaged in protein synthesis (having attached mRNA's) obtained from hepatic cells indicates that more than one class of ribosome occurs in the cytoplasm itself. Ribosomes that are attached to the endoplasmic reticulum, that is, *membrane-bound ribosomes*, synthesize serum proteins that are specifically for export, being sent into the lumen or the endoplasmic reticulum membrane; *free ribosomes* synthesize specific nonserum liver proteins which are independent of cytoplasmic organelles.

One hypothesis to explain this finding is that a 60s ribosomal subunit attaches or not to the endoplasmic reticulum. This creates a difference so that certain kinds of 40s subunit with mRNA attached will join to attached 60s and others to unattached 60s subunits. The regulation of types of ribosomes also regulates, therefore, the types of mRNA's translated.

Translation may depend upon factors which inhibit or stimulate ribosomes

Mammalian ribosomes isolated from interphase cells are translationally active *in vitro*, although ribosomes from metaphase cells are relatively inhibited. Treatment of metaphase ribosomes with trypsin restores almost full translational capacity. Likewise *in vivo*, viral RNA (*hence* RNA-dependent RNA polymerase) is synthesized when a mammalian cell is infected with an RNA virus during interphase but not during mitotic metaphase. Ribosomes of unfertilized sea urchin eggs carry a protein, released upon fertilization, which inhibits poly U from functioning as mRNA *in vitro*. These results suggest that at various stages of mitosis and development, protein coats ribosomes and thereby blocks translation.

Translational control by activation of ribosomes may also occur. For example, ribosomes from muscle are more active in protein synthesis when isolated after insulin treatment than after no such treatment. Factors have been reported which attach to the ribosomes and can specify not only the binding of particular mRNA's but the rate at which mRNA is translated. For example, muscle and globin mRNA's preferentially bind to ribosomes containing their respective binding factors, globin mRNA being preferentially translated when ribosomes carry reticulocyte factors. Initiation factors which promote the formation of the 80s ribosome protein-initiation complex in insects seem to be developmental stage-specific since they work only with the mRNA from the same developmental stage.

Translation can be regulated by varying the speed of adding amino acids to growing polypeptide chains

Toadfish that are accustomed to live at 21°C become cold-acclimated when the temperature is dropped at 10°C. Survival at the lower temperature presumably involves changes in one or more of the following:

1. The supply of amino acids.
2. The nature of the protein-synthesizing machinery.
3. The types or amounts of protein synthesized.

In vivo studies show that toadfish acclimated at 10°C synthesize liver protein 75 per cent faster at 21°C than do fish acclimated to 21°C. This cold acclimation seems to be due to an increased aminoacyl transferase activity (due to a change in the conformation or turnover of the enzyme at low temperature) which speeds up the addition of amino acids to growing polypeptides.

Translation may be regulated by tRNA's and aminoacyl-tRNA synthetases

Since the pattern of tRNA's and aminoacyl-tRNA synthetases differs in different tissues of a multicellular organism (as discussed in detail in Section 30.8), translation can be regulated at this point.

Translation may be regulated by suppressing the functioning of mRNA

Even though translation of other mRNA's is occurring, the mRNA for hemoglobin appears in chick development long before it is translated (see Section 30.9). How this prolonged inhibition of translation is accomplished is unknown.

Translation may be regulated by controlling the longevity of mRNA's

(As discussed in detail in Section 30.9.)

SUMMARY AND CONCLUSIONS

Although multiprotein-coding operons are advantageous in procaryotes, eucaryotes seem to have mRNA's that usually code for one polypeptide. Genetic material which infects eucaryotes seems to be adapted to the apparent lack of host machinery for recognizing internal polypeptide start and stop points in RNA by being (or being transcribed to) either monopolypeptide-coding RNA or multiprotein-coding RNA whose multiprotein is cleaved into its component proteins.

Since the mechanisms of transcription and translation are basically similar in procaryotes and eucaryotes, similar mechanisms of genetic control of these processes are expected and found to occur in both types of organisms. For example, one of the transcriptional control mechanisms already known in eucaryotes involves multiple forms of RNA polymerases (or of sigma-like factors). The regulation of translation in eucaryotes seems to involve delayed translation of mRNA; longevity of mRNA; different types of tRNA's, aminoacyl-tRNA synthetases, and ribosomes; and various factors that inhibit or stimulate ribosomes and control the rate of translation.

Transcription in eucaryotes is associated with unclumped chromosomes—as evidenced cytologically by puffs in giant polynemic chromosomes, loops in lampbrush chromosomes, and diffusely distributed chromatin, euchromatin, in ordinary metabolic nuclei. The much larger amount of genetic material per genome in eucaryotes than procaryotes is correlated with the nontranscription of most eucaryotic genes most of the time. This generalized repression of transcription is associated with histones in particular. These basic proteins can interfere directly with RNA polymerase, make the template unavailable, or prevent strand separation in a duplex template. Although some specificity in repression is exhibited by different histones and by acetylation and other chemical modifications of a given histone, histones (and probably nuclear nonhistone proteins) do not exhibit sufficient variety to be able to selectively turn off and on many different kinds of genes. The required specificity may be provided by chromosomal RNA which, bound to chromosomal protein, may turn specific genes on by interacting with partially redundant DNA sequences.

GENERAL REFERENCES

Bonner, J., and Ts'o, P. O. P. (Editors) 1964. *Nucleohistones.* San Francisco: Holden-Day, Inc.

Busch, H. 1965. *Histones and other nuclear proteins.* New York: Academic Press, Inc.,

Davidson, E. H. 1968. *Gene activity in early development.* New York: Academic Press, Inc.

de Reuck, A. V. S., and Knight, J. (Editors) 1966. *Histones: their role in the transfer of genetic information.* Boston: Little, Brown and Co.

Organization and control in prokaryotic and eukaryotic cells. London: Cambridge University Press, 1970.

SPECIFIC SECTION REFERENCES

27.2   Fan, H., and Penman, S. 1971. Regulation of synthesis and processing of nucleolar components in metaphase-arrested cells. J. Mol. Biol., 59: 27–42. (Pre-rRNA synthesis and processing cease at metaphase.)

Lin, H. J., Karkas, J. D., and Chargaff, E. 1966. Template functions in the enzymic formation of polynucleotides, II. Metaphase chromosomes as templates in the enzymic synthesis of ribonucleic acid. Proc. Nat. Acad. Sci., U.S., 56: 954–959.

27.3   Beermann, W. 1963. Cytological aspects of information transfer in cellular differentiation. Amer. Zool., 3: 23–32. Reprinted in *The biological perspective, introductory readings,* Laetsch, W. M. (Editor), Boston: Little, Brown and Company, 1969, pp. 313–325.

Beermann, W., and Clever, U. 1964. Chromosome puffs. Scient. Amer., 210: 50–58, 156. Scientific American Offprints, San Francisco: W. H. Freeman and Company, Publishers.

Laufer, H., and Holt, T. K. H. 1970. Juvenile hormone effects on chromosomal puffing and development in *Chironomus thummi.* J. Exp. Zool., 173: 341–352.

27.4   Davidson, E. H., Crippa, M., Kramer, F. R., and Mirsky, A. E. 1966. Genomic function during the lampbrush stage of amphibian oogenesis. Proc. Nat. Acad. Sci., U.S., 56: 856–863.

Gall, J. G., and Callan, H. G. 1962. H^3 uridine incorporation in lampbrush chromosomes. Proc. Nat. Acad. Sci., U.S., 48: 562–570.

27.5   Baltimore, D., Jacobson, M. F., Asso, J., and Huang, A. S. 1970. The formation of poliovirus proteins. Cold Spring Harbor Sympos. Quant. Biol., 34: 741–746.

Katz, E., and Moss, B. 1970. Formation of a vaccinia virus structural polypeptide from a higher molecular weight precursor: inhibition by rifampicin. Proc. Nat. Acad. Sci., U.S., 66: 677–684.

27.6   Crippa, M. 1970. Regulatory factor for the transcription of the ribosomal genes in amphibian oocytes. Nature, Lond., 227: 1138–1140. (A protein factor with characteristics similar to a bacterial repressor.)

Roeder, R. G., and Rutter, W. J. 1969. Multiple forms of DNA-dependent RNA polymerase in eukaryotic organisms. Nature, Lond., 224: 234–237.

Tocchini-Valentini, G. P., and Crippa, M. 1970. Ribosomal RNA synthesis and RNA polymerase. Nature, Lond., 228: 993–995. (Two enzyme forms are found in *Xenopus*, the one found only in the nucleolus seems responsible for transcribing rRNA *in vivo*.)

27.7   Elgin, S. C. R., and Bonner, J. 1970. Limited heterogeneity of the major nonhistone chromosomal proteins. Biochemistry, 9: 4440–4447. (Of a dozen major types many of which are present in different organs or organisms.)

Gilmour, R. S., and Paul, J. 1970. Role of non-histone components in determining organ specificity of rabbit chromatins. FEBS Letters, 9: 242–244.

27.8   DeLange, R. J., Smith, E. L., Fambrough, D. M., and Bonner, J. 1968. Amino acid sequence of histone IV: presence of ε-N-acetyllysine. Proc. Nat. Acad. Sci., U.S., 61: 1145–1146.

Yamazaki, H., and Kaesberg, P. 1966. Analysis of products of protein synthesis directed by R17 viral RNA. Proc. Nat. Acad. Sci., U.S., 58: 624–631. (The main in vitro product is similar to lysine-rich histone, which may function in vivo to suppress host RNA synthesis.)

27.9   Huang, R. C. C., and Bonner, J. 1962. Histone, a suppressor of chromosomal RNA synthesis. Proc. Nat. Acad. Sci., U.S., 48: 1216–1222.

Johns, E. W., and Hoare, T. A. 1970. Histones and gene control. Nature, Lond., 226: 650–651. (Histones may need to be displaced—not removed—from DNA to free the template to RNA polymerase.)

Littau, V. C., Burdick, C. J., Allfrey, V. G., and Mirsky, A. E. 1965. The role of histones in the maintenance of chromatin structure. Proc. Nat. Acad. Sci., U.S., 54: 1204–1212.

27.10   Olins, D. E. 1969. Interaction of lysine-rich histones and DNA. J. Mol. Biol., 43: 439–460.

27.11   Koslov, Yu. V., and Georgiev, G. P. 1970. Mechanism of inhibitory action of histones on DNA template activity in vitro. Nature, Lond., 228: 245–247. (Histone seems to inhibit movement of RNA polymerase along the DNA, since the RNA made in the presence of histone is shorter than that made in its absence.)

Spelsberg, T. C., Tankersley, S., and Hnilica, L. S. 1969. The interaction of RNA polymerase with histones. Proc. Nat. Acad. Sci., U.S., 62: 1218–1225.

27.12   Pogo, B. G. T., Pogo, A. O., Allfrey, V. G., and Mirsky, A. E. 1968. Changing patterns of histone acetylation and RNA synthesis in regeneration of the rat liver. Proc. Nat. Acad. Sci., U.S., 59: 1337–1344.

Sung, M. T., and Dixon, G. H. 1970. Modification of histones during spermiogenesis in trout: a molecular mechanism for altering histone binding to DNA. Proc. Nat. Acad. Sci., U.S., 67: 1616–1623. (Newly synthesized protamine replaces histones which have become extensively phosphorylated and acetylated, these changes apparently loosening histone binding to DNA.)

27.13   Sivolap, Y. M., and Bonner, J. 1971. Association of chromosomal RNA with repetitive DNA. Proc. Nat. Acad. Sci., U.S., 68: 387–389.

27.14   Fan, H., and Penman, S. 1970. Regulation of protein synthesis in mammalian cells. II. Inhibition of protein synthesis at the level of initiation during mitosis. J. Mol. Biol., 50: 655–670. (In Chinese hamster ovary cells in mitosis, protein synthesis is only 30 per cent the interphase rate apparently due to a lowered rate of initiation of polypeptide synthesis.)

Ganoza, M. C., and Williams, C. A. 1969. In vitro synthesis of different categories of specific protein by membrane-bound and free ribosomes. Proc. Nat. Acad. Sci., U.S., 63: 1370–1376.

Grierson, D., and Loening, U. E. 1972. Distinct transcription products of ribosomal genes in two different tissues. Nature New Biol., 235: 80–82.

Haschemeyer, A. E. V. 1969. Rates of polypeptide chain assembly in vivo: relation to the mechanism of temperature acclimation in Opsanus tau. Proc. Nat. Acad. Sci., U.S., 62: 128–135.

Ilan, J., and Ilan, J. 1971. Stage-specific initiation factors for protein synthesis during insect development. Develop. Biol., 25: 280–292.

Metaforma, S., Felicetti, L., and Gambino, R. 1971. The mechanism of protein synthesis activation after fertilization of sea urchin eggs. Proc. Nat. Acad. Sci., U.S., 68: 600–604.

Tompkins, G. M., Gelehrter, T. D., Granner, D., Martin, D., Jr., Samuels, H. H., and Thompson, E. B., 1969. Control of specific gene expression in higher organisms. Science, 166: 1474–1480. (At the translational level.)

QUESTIONS AND PROBLEMS

1. What evidence would you accept as an indication that the RNA surrounding a puff in a salivary gland chromosome is not double-stranded?

2. How would you show that the RNA associated with a puff is a transcript of the puff DNA rather than an accumulation of RNA synthesized elsewhere?

3. Why might basic proteins be necessary for the regulation of transcription of human DNA but not of phage DNA?

4. Give one advantage of the inhibition of translation during mitosis.

5. How do you suppose that ribosomes inhibited from functioning during mitosis become uninhibited?

6. D. M. Fambrough and J. Bonner have found that the histones of pea buds and calf thymus are strikingly similar. What does this result suggest about
   a. the histones in all organisms?
   b. the number of genes coding for histones?
   c. the evolutionary origin of histones?
   d. the functioning of histones in different organisms?

7. Compare the relative importance of regulation of gene action at the transcriptional and translational level in procaryotes and eucaryotes.

8. What regulatory role can you envision for redundant gene sequences?

9. In bacteria, where no true histone binds to DNA, repressors are proteins working directly on promoter or operator DNA. What bearing does this finding have on the hypothesis that nonhistone proteins are regulatory in higher organisms?

10. Spermine is a tetramine that binds to duplex DNA. How can you account for the DNA in the complex being less readily heat-denatured and scissioned?

11. In yeast, histidine biosynthesis involves three closely linked genes. How would you proceed to test the idea that these genes are translated into a tripolypeptide which is cleaved to produce separate enzymatic activities?

12. What is the function of a nucleus (such as in duck erythrocyte) whose DNA seems to be almost completely complexed with histone?

13. What interpretation can you give to the observation of H. Busch that many kinds of tumors show a high synthesis rate of lysine-rich histone?

14. Discuss the genetic and environmental factors which influence the puffing pattern in the polynemic chromosomes of larval Diptera.

15. Can you explain why a particular DNase degrades clumped but not diffuse chromatin?

16. How can you explain that in animal sperm the chromosomes are inactive even when they contain deoxyribonucleoprotamines in place of deoxyribonucleohistones?

17. What questions are raised by the finding that nuclear chromosomes are, whereas mitochondrial and chloroplast chromosomes are not, complexed with histones?

Chapter 28

Gene-Action Regulation— Position Effects in Eucaryotes

We found in Chapter 26 that gene expression, that is, phenotype, in procaryotes may depend upon the relative positions of genes. Two different kinds of *position effect* were mentioned: (1) Folding of the *E. coli* chromosome apparently brings metabolically related genes at widely separated loci near each other so that their gene products can interact in a manner that would not otherwise be possible; (2) the functioning of structural genes in an operon depends upon the nearby promoter and operator genes. In this chapter we will consider position effects in higher organisms, their molecular basis, and their role in the regulation of gene action.

28.1   In a position effect the functioning (not the primary structure) of a gene is changed by its gene neighbors.

Chromosomal rearrangements in *Drosophila* often give rise to phenotypic effects which are expressed as mosaic or variegated characteristics. For example, the gene w^+ produces dull-red eye color when in its normal location in region "3C2" of the X chromosome, near the tip of the left arm. When a paracentric inversion brings this gene near the centromere, a mottled eye color (white with dull-red speckles) results. It might be argued that the mottled eye color is caused by a change in the base sequence of the w^+ gene. Several observations, however, indicate that the primary structure of the w^+ gene is not changed. First, the relocated gene resumes its original function (to produce dull-red eye color) when placed by another inversion near its former gene neighbors in the chromosome. Second, a normal w^+ gene inserted by means of crossing over in the place of the "mottled" allele likewise becomes "mottled." Consequently, the change in phenotype brought about by the inversion seems to be the result of a position effect, in which the functioning of the w^+ gene is modified by its new linear gene neighbors.

Position effect may be one of the phenotypic consequences of mutations involving structural rearrangements, even though not a mutation itself. Since genes located some distance from a point of breakage in a rearrangement sometimes show position effects, position effect can spread somehow along the chromosome and affect the functioning of a gene whose immediate linear neighbors have not been switched. This *spreading effect* is further reason for dismissing explanations of position effect based solely upon breakage or other mutational changes.

Position effects due to structural changes might be particularly common in eucaryotic species whose chromosomes or chromosome parts take on special positions in the nucleus relative to each other. That *Drosophila* chromosomes show somatic pairing during mitosis and somatic synapsis in the interphase nuclei of larval salivary gland and other giant cells suggests that at the time of gene action different chromosomes and their parts are arranged so that the products of gene action may be formed or used in particular sequences. Owing to the presence of heterozygous reciprocal translocations in *Oenothera* (Chapter 35), chromosomal parts show a very orderly arrangement in the circle of 14 chromosomes formed during meiosis. Here also, a new arrangement of chromosomal parts might disturb functional sequences and produce position effects. As a matter of fact, position effect is known to occur in *Oenothera*, maize (Section 28.6 and Chapter 29), yeast, *Neurospora*, and in mice and men (Chapter 29). (R)

28.2   Since euchromatic and constitutive heterochromatic chromosome segments seem to differ in gene content, as well as in gene activity, their rearrangement by breakage and reunion may result in a position effect.

We have already noted that euchromatin and constitutive heterochromatin differ in gene activity, the latter being transcriptionally inactive presumably because it is clumped. Euchromatin and constitutive heterochromatin also seem to differ in gene content—constitutive heterochromatin appearing to contain more redundant DNA sequences than euchromatin. This is supported by finding that mouse satellite DNA is located near the centromeres, probably in heterochromatin. Similarly, in *Drosophila*, rapidly reannealing DNA is found in the chromocenter, which is almost entirely heterochromatic, although some is also found in euchromatic regions (which may contain short heterochromatic regions, as noted in Section 24.5). Since all the constitutive heterochromatic regions in *Drosophila* polynemic chromosomes—long regions adjacent to all centromeres, shorter regions located at the ends of all chromosomes, and short regions interspersed among the largely euchromatic arms—tend to synapse together at the chromocenter, all may have similar DNA base sequences.

Such apparent differences in gene action and content leads us to expect that the wild-type arrangement of euchromatic and heterochromatic segments within a chromosome offers some advantage to the cell. It would not be surprising, therefore, if a shuffling of euchromatic and heterochromatic segments by breakage and reunion were to give rise to position effects. For instance, a change in coiling caused by new gene neighbors might affect the ability of a gene to act as template for transcription and might be detectable cytologically.

28.3   When a segment of euchromatin is moved near to constitutive heterochromatin, it beomes heterochromatized, and vice versa. Such cytological changes are correlated with changes in gene action.

The degree of eye-color mosaicism in *Drosophila* can be correlated with the cytological appearance of the 3C2 region of the X chromosome in larval salivary cells. In wild-type individuals this region is euchromatic. In two mutant strains which have a mosaic eye color (owing to colorless ommatidia in a background of pigmented ommatidia), the 3C2 region (containing w^+) is inserted in heterochromatin or much closer to it than before, and sometimes appears heterochromatic. *Heterochromatized* euchromatin is called *facultative heterochromatin*.[1] The frequency of heterochromatization differs in the two mutant strains: the 3C2 region of one strain, located near the heterochromatin of chromosome IV, is much more often heterochromatized (and has many more colorless ommatidia) than the one located in the heterochromatin of an X chromosome. It seems also that not only the location of the euchromatic segment but its size is of some importance, for the smaller the segment, the greater the frequency of heterochromatization. These observations suggest that heterochromatization is associated with limited template availability caused by modifying the coiling of DNA.

In like manner, rearrangements in which a heterochromatic segment is inserted into a euchromatic region result in the *euchromatization* of the inserted fragment.

Note that the correlation found above is between heterochromatization in the *larval salivary glands* and gene-action mosaicism in the *pupal ommatidial cells*. This result suggests that the arrangement of genes in a chromosome is adaptive and has been

---

[1] Portions of nonrearranged polynemic and lampbrush chromosomes that are found in bands and in the main axis, respectively, may be considered to be facultatively heterochromatic if, by becoming relatively unwound at another time, they are euchromatic and form either puffs or interbands and loops.

selected on an organismal basis; a chromosome rearrangement of the type involved in our present discussion disturbs the adaptive arrangement and results in heterochromatization in many tissues. Eu- and heterochromatic states cannot be used as automatically indicating gene action or inaction, however; they can be used only as indicating potential action or inaction, since regulation of gene action can also occur at various other places in the transcription–translation pathway (discussed previously in Chapter 27). (R)

28.4 The frequency of heterochromatization of a chromosomal segment depends upon its parental derivation as well as the other chromosomes present.

The paracentric inversion *In sc*^{8} of the *Drosophila* X chromosome places the normally euchromatic region containing the *y* (yellow body color) and *ac* (achaete bristles) loci next to a normally heterochromatic region. In relatively few males (16 per cent) both loci become heterochromatic; whereas in homozygous females both loci are heterochromatic 39 per cent of the time. When this *sc*^{8} inversion is made heterozygous so that it has a noninverted homolog, a significant difference in heterochromatization can be seen in the nuclei of larval salivary gland cells, depending on which parent contributed the inverted chromosome. Both loci in the inverted chromosome are heterochromatized in only 20 per cent of the nuclei when maternally derived, but in 71 per cent of the nuclei when paternally derived. The meiotic events involving the *sc*^{8} chromosome in one generation apparently affect its potential for gene activity in the next generation.

The frequency of heterochromatization of a chromosomal segment also depends upon the other chromosomes present in the cell. Heterochromatization (and thus variegation of a trait) is reduced in *Drosophila*, for example, if an extra Y (or another heterochromatin-rich) chromosome is added to the genotype by breeding. The mechanism for this suppression of position effect is not yet clear.

As seen above, heterochromatization and euchromatization are reversible. The level of potential activity for a particular segment of chromatin, however, tends to remain fairly constant for several cell generations. (R)

28.5 Some position effects resulting from crossing over are probably not due to a change in chromatization but rather to a change in gene action after transcription.

The preceding sections describe position effects due to a shift in the relative positions of euchromatic and heterochromatic segments. Such position effects seem to involve a change in transcription capacity brought about by the action of a gene's linear neighbors. Another kind of position effect in *Drosophila* involves the arrangement of alleles at two closely linked loci, for example, the X-limited loci for eye color *apr* (apricot) and *w* (white). A genotype of *apr*$^+$ *w*/*apr w*$^+$ yields pale apricot eye color; whereas one of *apr*$^+$ *w*$^+$/*apr w* obtained from the first genotype by crossing over yields

Cis	Trans
A B	A b
a b	a B

Figure 28-1 *Cis* and *trans* positions for dihybrid, linked genes.

dull-red (wild-type) eye color. Usually the phenotype of a dihybrid is the same as the wild type whether the two + alleles are in the same chromosome (*cis position*) or in different homologs (*trans position*) (Figure 28-1). For the *apr* and *w* loci, however, we see that the *cis* and *trans* dihybrids are phenotypically different.[2]

There is no reason to expect that this position effect is related to a change in chromatization, since both loci are part of a euchromatic segment. One explanation for the position effect is that the *apr* and *w* loci are transcribed in the same mRNA (contrary to the situation described for mammals in Section 27.5) and code for two polypeptides which together form a unit of functional protein. The two polypeptides might be joined during or directly after translation. One of the two proteins made from the *cis* dihybrid thus would be completely functional since the messenger transcribed from the DNA of one homolog contains correct information for both polypeptide chains. Proteins specified by either homolog of the *trans* dihybrid would each have one defective polypeptide chain and so be less functional than the normal protein.

A position effect might also result when the two different polypeptide subunits are not coded in the same mRNA. As before, the two subunits must be combined to form functional protein. If translation occurs at the site of transcription, the subunits specified by the functional genes in the *cis* position, being closer to each other than

---

[2] The following is a detailed account of a procedure for detecting position effects resulting from crossing over. *Drosophila* females that carry an attached-X chromosome with *y apr*⁺ *w spl* on one arm and *y*⁺ *apr w*⁺ *spl*⁺ on the other are bred. Note that the use of attached-X's permits the recovery of two of the four strands involved in each crossing over (see the Section 17.3 footnote). The attached-X genetic system sometimes yields both complementary crossover types in the same gamete. Figure 28-2 (left side) shows schematically a portion of this attached-X as it would appear in the tetrad stage at the time of the crossing over and indicates the standard genetic map location of the *y* and *spl* markers. When a female with pale (dilute) apricot eye color and this chromosome is crossed with a *Bar*-containing male, *Bar* being X-limited, the non-Bar F₁ daughters (who carry a paternally derived Y) are usually noncrossovers and have pale apricot-colored eyes like their mother. Crossovers between the region containing the white locus and the centromere produce either white or apricot daughters.

If *apr*⁺ lay to the left of *w*⁺ (as shown in the left portion of the figure), a rare crossing over between these loci would produce the crossover attached-X shown at the right of the figure. As a result, the two mutants would be in the *cis* position.

When large numbers of daughters from the attached-X females are examined, several are found to have dull-red eyes. It is essential to determine whether these flies are mutant or the result of a change from the *trans* to the *cis* form. To do this we detach—that is, separate the arms of—the attached-X's in the dull-red-eyed exceptional flies (by collecting the products of the occasional crossing over that occurs between the attached-X and the Y in the heterochromatic regions near their centromeres) and determine the genes carried in each detached arm. The finding that one arm can always be represented as *y apr*⁺*w*⁺*spl*⁺ and the other as *y*⁺*apr w spl* offers strong support for the view that the dull-red exceptional females were *cis* heterozygotes, and that *apr* lies to the left of *w* on the X chromosome, as shown in the figure. (It is instructive to work out the arrangement of the markers after crossing over between *apr* and *w* on the assumption that *apr* is to the right of *w*.)

Proof that the exceptional dull-red females result from position effect rather than mutation is obtained by mating these exceptional females and occasionally obtaining daughters with pale apricot eye color. In these new exceptional daughters the original gene arrangement is found restored by crossing over.

The phenotypic difference between pale apricot and dull red is undoubtedly the result of position effect, since the only difference between the *cis* and *trans* conditions is in the arrangement of the genetic material.

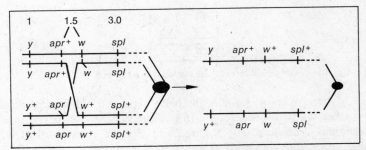

Figure 28-2 Crossing over between the *apricot* and *white* loci in attached-X chromosomes of *D. melanogaster*.

the ones in *trans*, would be more likely to interact and form functional protein. Such *cis-trans position effects*, therefore, seem to be due to a difference in gene action after transcription. Other *cis-trans* position effects which also involve two closely linked genes affecting the same phenotypic trait (see Section S28.5a) can also be explained in this manner.

A position effect can also result from crossing over between repeated, comparitively long, euchromatic chromosome regions which have synapsed unevenly or obliquely. This is the situation in the first proved case of position effect, involving the *Bar* locus in *Drosophila*, which is described in Section S28.5b. One cannot readily decide whether such a position effect is due to a change at the transcriptional or posttranscriptional levels, however, since the crossing over that yields the position effect also changes the sequence of the loci involved.

28.6 In maize the gene *Activator* (which is similar to a regulator gene) controls the functioning of the gene *Dissociation* (which is similar to an operator gene). The presence of *Dissociation* can suppress the functioning of adjacent genes.

The triploid endosperm (Figure 15-8) in maize kernels can be white, colored, or white with colored speckles. The white phenotype sometimes results from the suppression of a normal allele for color by the closely linked gene called *Dissociation* (*Ds*), which also causes chromosome breakage in regions near it. If *Ds* remains closely linked to the gene for color, the kernel will be white. If, however, *Ds* dissociates (that is, changes its position) before the kernel forms, the kernel and subsequent generations of plants will be completely colored. If *Ds* moves during kernel formation, the kernel will have colored dots or sectors on a white background. Large colored specks are due to the movement of *Ds* early in development; small ones are the result of shifting later in development, when relatively few successive cell divisions take place. We should note that the relocation of *Ds* by means of breakage is a genetic recombination and that the change in color is a phenotypic effect which depends upon the arrangement, or relative position, of genes. In other words, it is a position effect—a *Ds* gene near the gene for color prevents the latter from functioning; its absence permits the gene to function.

Ds can occur at many positions in the genome. At its various positions *Ds* often suppresses the phenotypic effect of a gene (not necessarily for color) located near it.

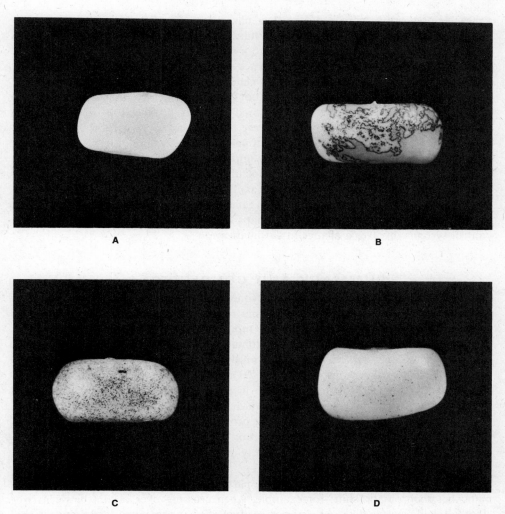

Figure 28-3 Effect of *Activator* on the action of *Dissociation*. (A) No *Ac* is present. The kernel is colorless due to the continued presence of *Ds*, which inhibits the action of a nearby pigment-producing gene. (B) One *Ac* gene is present. Breaks at *Ds* occur early in kernel development, leading to large colored sectors. (C) Two *Ac* genes are present. Time of *Ds* action is delayed, producing smaller sectors which appear as specks. (D) Three *Ac* genes are present. *Ds* action is so delayed that relatively few and tiny specks are produced. (Courtesy of B. McClintock and the Cold Spring Harbor Laboratory of Quantitative Biology.)

As long as *Ds* remains in that position, the position effect produces a phenotype which often resembles that produced by a mutation of the gene. When *Ds* is moved from this locus, the suppressed gene is again functional. *Ds* can be transferred (that is, undergo *transposition*) from one chromosomal position to another as a result of breakage or a mechanism which may involve contact with the locus to which *Ds* is relocated. It is possible to increase the number of *Ds* factors present in the endosperm by appropriate crosses. As the number of *Ds* genes in a given region of a chromosome increases, the region breaks with greater frequency.

The ability of *Ds* to cause chromosomal breakage is controlled by *Activator* (*Ac*) genes. *Ac* does not have to be in the same chromosome as *Ds* and, in fact, usually is not. By suitable crosses, kernels can be obtained whose endosperm contains one, two, or three *Ac* genes (or none) in addition to a single *Ds* gene located near a pigment-producing gene (Figure 28-3). In the absence of *Ac*, no specks are produced and the kernel is completely white. Hence, the *Ds* gene must not have moved. It appears that *Ds* cannot cause chromosomal breakage (nor can it be relocated in other ways) in the absence of *Ac*. In the presence of *Ac* colored spots are produced. Moreover, as the dosage of *Ac* increases from one to three, the colored spots become smaller and smaller. Thus, *Ac* also acts to delay the time at which *Ds* is relocated. *Ac* seems to be acting as a regulator gene, and *Ds* is comparable to an operator gene. Genes like *Ac* and *Ds* may be important in cyclical metabolic processes as well as in embryonic development and cellular differentiation, as discussed in more detail in Chapter 29. It should be noted that both *Ac* and *Ds* genes in maize undergo transposition and seem to be heterochromatic regions. Perhaps the position effect in such two-element control systems involves a change in chromatization.

SUMMARY AND CONCLUSIONS

Position effects can be detected in eucaryotes by arranging the same nuclear genetic material in different ways via chromosomal rearrangements (involving breakage or transposition) or crossing over. When the repositioning of parts changes the relative positions of euchromatin and heterochromatin (as occurs in certain paracentric inversions and other structural changes produced by breakage in *Drosophila* and, apparently, in transpositions of *Ac* and *Ds* in *Zea*), the position effect is readily attributed to a change in chromatization which presumably modifies the availability of the template for transcription. As shown in *Drosophila*, the change in chromatization associated with such a position effect probably occurs in many different tissues of the individual; although the chromatization change and its associated phenotypic effect are persistent, they can be coordinately modified by parental derivation and the presence of other chromosomes.

When the repositioning of chromosome parts does not seem to involve a euchromatic–heterochromatic shift, for example, when crossing over occurs between two closely linked genes, a detected *cis-trans* position effect is attributed to a change in the nature or fate of the transcripts or the polyeptides they code.

SPECIFIC SECTION REFERENCES

28.1   Baker, W. K. 1968. Position-effect variegation. Adv. Genet., 14: 133–169.

Giles, N. H., Case, M. E., Partridge, C. W. H., and Ahmed, S. L. 1967. A gene cluster in *Neurospora crassa* coding for an aggregate of five aromatic synthetic enzymes. Proc. Nat. Acad. Sci., U.S., 58: 1453–1460. (Position effect is involved.)

Tauro, P., Halverson, H. O., and Epstein, R. L. 1968. Time of gene expression in relation to centromere distance during the cell cycle of *Saccharomyces cereviseae*. Proc. Nat. Acad. Sci., U.S., 59: 277–284. (The time of enzyme synthesis is related to gene position in the yeast chromosome.)

28.2   Jones, K. W. 1970. Chromosomal and nuclear location of mouse satellite DNA in individual cells. Nature, Lond., 225: 912–915.

Lindsley, D. L. 1965. Chromosome function at the supragenic level. Nat. Cancer Inst. Monogr., 18: 275–290.

Rae, P. M. M. 1970. Chromosomal distribution of rapidly reannealing DNA in *Drosophila melanogaster* Proc. Nat. Acad. Sci., U.S., 67: 1018–1025.

Yunis, J. J., and Yasmineh, W. G. 1971. Heterochromatin, satellite DNA, and cell function. Science, 174: 1200–1209. (Constitutive heterochromatin.)

28.4 Prokofyeva-Belgovskaya, A. A. 1947. Heterochromatization as a change of chromosome cycle. J. Genet., 48: 80–98. (Studied in *Drosophila*.)

28.5 Lewis, E. B. 1952. The pseudoallelism of white and apricot in *Drosophila melanogaster*. Proc. Nat. Acad. Sci., U.S., 38: 953–961.

28.6 McClintock, B. 1961. Some parallels between gene control systems in maize and bacteria. Amer. Nat., 95: 265–277.

SUPPLEMENTARY SECTIONS

S28.5a   *Cis–trans* position effects also occur via crossing over between other pseudoalleles in *Drosophila*.

To detect a *cis–trans* position effect it is necessary to separate two very closely linked loci. When the genes making up the "white multiple allelic series" (Section S16.1b) are investigated more closely, some prove to be allelic to *w* and others to *apr*. Some, however, are allelic to neither, and appropriate crossing-over studies show that the "white region" on the X is a nest of five (perhaps more), closely linked but separate, linearly arranged loci with similar phenotypic effects.

Other regions in the *Drosophila* genome are now known where two or more genic alternatives —previously considered allelic—prove to be *pseudoallelic*, that is, prove to be nonallelic (but closely linked) when subjected to the *cis–trans* test. In addition to pseudoallelism in *Aspergillus*, other microorganisms, and maize, examples of pseudoallelism include cases involving color in cotton and lack of tails in mice.

Another case of pseudoallelism in *Drosophila* involves nonalleles whose functions differ somewhat more than *apr* and *w*. The normal, wild-type fly (Figure 28-4A) has small club-shaped *balancers* (*halteres*) located on the posterior part of the thorax. One of the pseudoalleles, *bithorax* (*bx*), converts the haltere into a large wing-like structure (Figure 28-4B); another, called *postbithorax* (*pbx*), appears to do much the same thing (Figure 28-4C). But close examination reveals that these two recessive pseudoalleles really have different

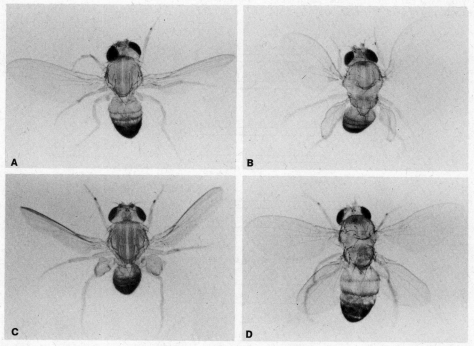

Figure 28-4   *Drosophila melanogaster* males: normal (A), bithorax (B), postbithorax (C), and bithorax postbithorax (D). (Courtesy of E. B. Lewis.)

functions. Bithorax converts the front portion and postbithorax the hind portion of the haltere into a wing-like structure. Flies homozygous for both mutants demonstrate these changes in a fully developed second pair of wings (Figure 28-4D).

What are the *cis–trans* effects for *bx* and *pbx*? The *cis* form (bx^+ pbx^+/bx pbx) has normal balancers, whereas the *trans* form (bx pbx^+/bx^+ pbx) shows a slight postbithorax effect, providing another example of *cis-trans* position effect and demonstrating the nonallelism of these genes. The map distance between these loci is 0.02.

These examples of pseudoallelism apparently involve separate but closely linked structural genes; they do not seem to involve the intragenic recombination of the type that occurs within the *A* or *B* gene of the *rII* region of ϕT4. The possibility exists, however, that recombination does occur within as well as between structural genes in *Drosophila*, although mechanisms other than crossing over may also be involved.

Consider the morphology of *Drosophila* chromosome regions which contain pseudoalleles. The white series is associated with a double band (*doublet*) in the salivary gland chromosome; *apr* may be in one band, *w* in the other. The vermilion series is associated with another doublet in the X chromosome, whereas the bithorax series (composed of five separate pseudoallelic loci) is connected with two doublets. (This last fact demonstrates what is proved by other data—that a band may contain more than a single gene.) The great number of doublets in salivary chromosomes suggests that genes located in these regions are pseudoallelic or redundant.

The origin of adjacent loci with similar types of action can be accounted for in several ways. One explanation is that during the course of evolution, adjacent genes producing different effects mutated to alleles which performed similar, presumably advantageous, functions. A second explanation might be that rearrangements brought together widely separated nonalleles with similar functions. Although both of these explanations may apply to some of the cases found, it seems more likely that most adjacent and similar genes arose as duplications that occurred one or more times (as in the bithorax case) in the ways described in Chapter 18. After duplication linearly adjacent genes—originally identical—would have become somewhat different from each other functionally by mutation, thereby becoming pseudoalleles.

Chovnick, A. 1966. Genetic organization in higher organisms. Proc. Roy. Soc., London, B164: 198–208.

Green, M. M. 1963. Pseudoalleles and recombination in *Drosophila*. In *Methodology in basic genetics*, Burdette, W. J. (Editor), pp. 279–290.

Lewis, E. B. 1963. Genes and developmental pathways. Amer. Zool., 3: 33–56.

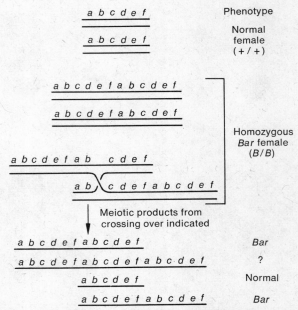

Figure 28-5 Diagrammatic representation of the normal and the *Bar* region of the X chromosome and the consequences of crossing over after oblique synapsis.

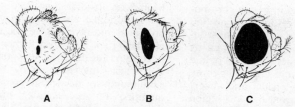

Figure 28-6   Compound eye of *Drosophila*. Left: ultrabar; center: bar; right: normal.

Sederoff, R. 1967. Rare pseudoallelic crossover between two phenotypically identical alleles at a restricted sublocus of dumpy in *Drosophila melanogaster*. Nature, Lond., 216: 1348–1349.

Welshons, W. J. 1965. Analysis of a gene in *Drosophila*. Science, 150: 1122–1129. (Pseudoallelism at the *Notch* locus.)

S28.5b   The *Bar* locus in *Drosophila* produces a position effect by means of crossing over.

An X-limited mutant in *Drosophila, Bar (B)*, reduces the number of facets (ommatidia) in the compound eyes, thereby narrowing the normally ovoid eye to a slit. When the normal (wild type) and the *Bar*-containing chromosomes are studied in nuclei of larval salivary glands, about seven successive bands in the wild-type chromosome are found duplicated in tandem in the *Bar* chromosome. Let us designate such a single region as abcdef. Consequently, a wild-type female contains abcdef/abcdef and a homozygous *Bar* female abcdef abcdef/abcdef abcdef. In wild-type (+/+) females, homologous letters (parts) of the two homologs synapse and crossing over takes place between corresponding letters. In homozygous *Bar (B/B)* females, proper synapsis and normal crossing over can also occur, but in this case a different sequence of events can cause synapsis to

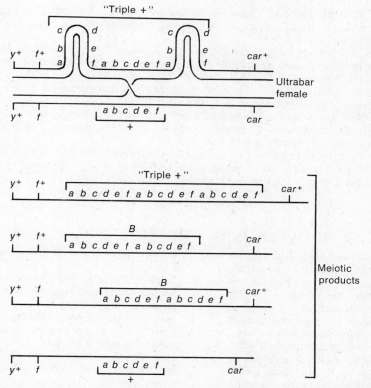

Figure 28-7   Production of *Bar* chromosomes by crossing over in ultrabar females.

occur incorrectly—the left region in one chromosome pairing with the right region of the second (Figure 28-5), leaving the other two regions unsynapsed. If this *oblique synapsis* is followed by normal crossing over anywhere in the paired region (as shown between b and c in the figure), the crossover strands will be abcdef and abcdef abcdef abcdef. The former strand has this region only once—and will, therefore, be wild type (+) —whereas the latter has this region three times. Such crossovers produced after oblique synapsis can be detected in the following way.

The B/B female is made dihybrid for genes near and on either side of B—near enough (less than 10 crossover units apart) to avoid double crossovers between them. On the X chromosome linkage map *Bar* is located at 57.0; *forked bristles* (*f*) at 56.7; and *carnation eye color* (*car*) at 62.5. Accordingly, the cross made is $f + car/Y$ ♂ by $f^+ B car/f B car^+$ ♀. About 1 daughter in 2000 is ovoid-eyed and carries a crossover between *f* and *car*; a similar precentage of crossover daughters have very narrow eyes, called *ultrabar* (Figure 28-6). The two types of exceptional flies are equally frequent, as would be expected of the reciprocal products of the hypothesized crossing over, and are much more frequent than mutations.

Moreover, ultrabar females contain a triple region in one X and a single region in the other X, as predicted and revealed by examining the salivary glands of their F_1. Any argument that the ultrabar phenotype results from a mutation—not a position effect—that is somehow dependent upon a simultaneously occurring crossing over is disqualified by occasionally obtaining perfectly typical *Bar* chromosomes in the progeny of females carrying both exceptional types of X. These *Bar* chromosomes prove to be the product of a crossing over between the single region of one chromosome and the middle region of the triple-dose homolog (Figure 28-7). We conclude, therefore, that four regions aligned in different ways by crossing over produce different phenotypes.

From a *B* (double-region) chromosome, it is also possible to obtain a few + (single-region) or *Ultrabar* (triple-region) chromosomes that are nonrecombinant for bordering markers. This unusual circumstance is brought about by an intrachromosomal exchange within the double loop that is formed when the two members of a tandemly duplicated region synapse with each other. Similarly, intrachromosomal exchange within an *Ultrabar* chromosome can yield + and *B* chromosomes.

Bridges, C. B. 1936. The Bar "gene" a duplication. Science, 83: 210–211. Reprinted in *Classic papers in gensetis*, Peters, J. A. (Editor), Englewood Cliffs, N.J.,: Prentice-Hall, Inc., 1959, pp. 163–166.

Muller, H. J., Prokofyeva-Belgovskaya, A. A., and Kossikov, K. V. 1936. Unequal crossing over in the Bar mutant as a result of duplication of a minute chromosome section. C. R. (Dokl.) Acad. Sci., U.R.S.S., N.S., 1(10): 87–88.

Peterson H. M., and Laughnan, J. R. 1963. Intrachromosomal exchanges at the Bar locus in *Drosophila*. Proc. Nat. Acad. Sci., U.S., 50: 126–133.

Schalet, A. 1969. Exchanges at the bobbed locus of *Drosophila melanogaster*. Genetics, 63: 133–153. (The duplication–deficiency products of oblique synapsis and crossing over furnish a source of new *bobbed* alleles.)

Sturtevant, A. H. 1925. The effects of unequal crossing over at the Bar locus in *Drosophila*. Genetics, 10: 117–147. Reprinted in *Classic papers in genetics*, Peters, J. A. (Editor), Englewood Cliffs, N.J.,: Prentice-Hall, Inc., 1959, pp. 124–148.

QUESTIONS AND PROBLEMS

1. If a previously unknown phenotype appears at the same time as a qualitative or quantitative change in the genetic material, can you determine whether the effect is due to mutation or to position effect? Explain.

2. Would you expect to find position effects in most sexually reproducing organisms? Why?

3. Some of the chromosomal rearrangements induced in *Drosophila* by ionizing radiations have the same, or nearly the same, points of breakage, and many nearly identical rearrangements are associated with the occurrence of the same phenotypic change. Explain.

4. What is the hypothesized role of a change in chromatization in the production of position effects?

5. Should pseudoalleles be considered subgenes (parts of one gene) rather than separate, nonallelic genes? Explain.

6. Does position effect require pseudoallelism for its detection? Explain. Is the reverse true? Explain.

7. What genotypic steps are required to prove

that a region shows a *cis–trans* position effect? Explain.

8. List evidences that position effects are due to changes in gene action not in gene primary structure.

9. What crosses would you make to test whether two recessive mutants in *Drosophila*, apparently alleles of the X-limited gene v^+ (normal allele of vermilion eye color), are pseudoalleles?

10. Using appropriate genetic markers, draw a tetrad configuration which would permit you to identify strands which have undergone intrachromosomal exchange in the *Bar* region of the X chromosome of *Drosophila melanogaster*.

11. How may the following be related—duplication, redundancy, and pseudoallelism?

12. Can position effect occur in haploids? Why?

13. Does the activity of *Dissociation* provide evidence for the genetic control of mutability? Explain.

14. What characteristics of *Dissociation* resemble those of the episome F?

Chapter 29

Gene-Action Regulation— Control Systems in Eucaryotes

The last section of Chapter 28 described how gene expression in maize sometimes involves two different control elements. The present chapter deals first with additional examples of gene-action control systems in maize before discussing some in man, mouse, and *Drosophila*.

29.1 Several different control systems for gene expression in maize have common characteristics.

Before describing some of the specific features of different systems that regulate gene action in maize, it is desirable to list and comment briefly upon some of the general features of such control systems:

1. The genetic units responsible for the regulation of structural gene action are called *controlling elements*. Controlling elements are transposable.

2. Gene expression may involve one or more than one controlling element. There are two different controlling elements in the *Ac-Ds* system. Control systems may involve more than two controlling elements (for example, 3 *Ac* may be present with 1 *Ds*, as in Figure 28-7D).

3. At least one of the controlling elements (called the *responding gene* in a two or more element control system) is always present near or within the structural gene whose expression is controlled by the system. This gene-action control is, therefore, a position effect. In the *Ac-Ds* system, *Ds* is the responding gene.

4. Controlling elements that are not

at the locus they help regulate are called *signaling genes*. *Ac* is the signaling gene in the *Ac-Ds* system.

5. The action of the structural gene is controlled by the neighbor controlling gene, whose action in turn is controlled by the action of one or more signaling genes if these are part of the control system. For example, color gene *C* has its action suppressed continuously by *Ds*; when *Ds* responds to a signal sent by *Ac*, the suppression of *C* stops.

6. Control systems can affect structural gene action in the following respects: (a) time of action, (b) intensity or degree of action, and (c) pattern of distribution of products of gene action. All these effects (some were mentioned in Section 28.6) are discussed in detail in Sections 29.2 through 29.4.

7. Each system of controlling elements is essentially autonomous, the elements in different systems not influencing each other's functioning. If, for example, one

structural gene is under the control of one system and its allele is under the control of another system—the two systems producing different patterns of gene activity— the phenotype will show both patterns superimposed on each other. This autonomy is illustrated in Section 29.5.

8. Both types of controlling elements can undergo a variety of modifications, each of which alters the expression of the structural gene or a given chromosome region. These modifications are discussed in Section 29.2.

9. Signaling and responding elements have similar properties, suggesting that they have a common origin (discussed in Section 29.3).

10. The modifications that controlling elements undergo are regulated by the control system itself (discussed in Sections 29.2 through 29.5).

11. Controlling elements are normal components of the maize genome. They do not seem to be infective or, unlike episomes, to exist free as separate chromosomes.

The signaling elements of some known control systems are listed in Figure 29-1 together with some of the structural genes they regulate. In the case of the transposable, controlling element *Dotted* (*Dt*), the higher its dosage, the larger is the number of anthocyanin dots in the aleurone layer of the kernel due to the derepression of gene A_1. Control systems using the two other signaling genes are discussed in the next few sections. It should be pointed out that although signaling and responding control elements are similar to regulator and operator genes, they may not be truly homologous with them. A controlling element that mediates transpositions has been discovered in *Drosophila*. (R)

29.2 Both of the controlling elements of the *Ac–Ds* system can change the effects they produce in a given chromosome region.

As indicated in Section 29.1 item 8, both *Ds* and *Ac* exist in several different alternative states.

The *Ds* first isolated caused chromosome breakages to occur near its locus in

Chromosome	Locus	Control by signaling gene		
		Ac	Dt	Spm
1	P	✓		
	Bz_2	✓		
3	A_1	✓	✓	✓
4	C_2			✓
5	A_2	✓		✓
	Pr			✓
9	C_1	✓		✓
	Sh_1	✓		
	Bz_1	✓		
	Wx	✓		✓

Figure 29-1   Some of the loci in maize whose action is regulated by different control systems —identified by their signaling genes.

response to signals from *Ac* (Section 28.6). Subsequently, changes occurred in *Ds* which either reduced or eliminated this breakage response to *Ac*. Even when *Ds* remains at a locus, however, it can change the level of expression of the structural gene it controls. Both types of changed effects of *Ds* seem to follow signals received from *Ac*. The complete or partial removal of *Ds* releases the structural gene from control by the *Ac-Ds* system and often changes the phenotypic effect of the structural gene.

Ac has three actions: (1) control of the responses of *Ds* (including its relocation or transposition), (2) control of transpositions of itself, as well as other *Ac*, and (3) control of structural genes close to *Ac* (this seems to involve sometimes a one-element control system). Different forms of *Ac* can affect action type 1 by changing the time for response, the effect of increasing doses of *Ac*, as well as the number of cells in a tissue responding at any one time. An alternative form of *Ac* affects action type 2 in that it is unable to induce transpositions of itself or another controlling element, although such an *inactive Ac* is still able to respond to *active Ac* located elsewhere. Both active and inactive *Ac* can influence the functioning of structural genes they are near (action type 3); the removal of *Ac* releases the structural gene from the *Ac* control system, although the released gene may then produce any one of various degrees of phenotypic effect.

29.3   Control systems that apparently have *Ac* as the single controlling element can give rise to two-element control systems.

Inactive *Ac* seems to possess many of the properties of *Ds*: (1) both seem to be composed of heterochromatin; (2) both can influence the functioning of a nearby structural gene; (3) neither can cause transposition of itself or another controlling element; (4) neither has an influence on the effect of increasing doses of active Ac; (5) both can be transposed by an active Ac; and (6) both can produce a variety of expressions of the structural gene they release by their complete or partial removal. One may expect, therefore, that active Ac also contains many of the properties of Ds and that one-element control systems occur in maize. One may also expect that if active Ac were duplicated, one of the elements might act, with or without modification, as a Ds-like element to the other, Ac, element. (When cells replicate their chromosomes and undergo division, a daughter cell may have two Ac's if the single parental Ac either duplicates twice or duplicates once and transposition puts both copies in the same daughter cell.) Support for these expectations has been obtained from studies of the regulation of gene action by the Ac system at the P (pericarp color) and Bz (bronze anthocyanin) loci, discussed in detail in Section S29.3.

29.4   The two-element *Suppressor-mutator* control system in maize provides a mechanism for producing many different patterns of gene expression.

The functioning of the structural gene A_1 in maize (anthocyanin pigment production in the plant and aleurone layer of the kernel) has been found to come under the regulation of a two-element control system. The responding element inserted at the A_1 locus determines the functional *state of the structural gene*, this sometimes being different degrees of suppression of anthocyanin formation. The top row of kernels in Figure 29-2 show some of the different states of A_1 in the presence of the responding gene only. Note that the pigmentation within a kernel is uniform, since in the absence of the signaling element the responding element cannot transpose. All the uniformly more pigmented kernels in the left-hand ear of maize in Figure 29-3 have one state of the gene and all the uniformly less pigmented kernels in the right-hand ear have another.

The phenotypic variability of plants and their kernels with respect to anthocyanin production is increased by the presence of the signaling element, *Suppressor-mutator*, *Spm*. This controlling element has two components. *Component-1* is the *Suppressor*,

Figure 29-2   Different states of A_1 due to the presence of a nearby responding gene. Top row: kernels produced in the absence of the signaling gene, *Spm*. Bottom row: corresponding kernels produced in the presence of one *Spm*. (Courtesy of B. McClintock, 1965. Brookhaven Sympos. Biol., 18: 172.)

Figure 29-3 Distinctiveness of the state of a locus whose gene is under the control of the *Spm* system. All kernels on the right-hand ear have one state and all on the left-hand ear have another. The variegated kernels on each ear have a fully active *Spm* element, whereas the uniformly pale-pigmented kernels lack this element. (Courtesy of B. McClintock, 1967. Develop. Biol., Suppl. 1: 93.)

which usually signals the responding gene to suppress the production of anthocyanin still more. *Component-2* is the *mutator*, which signals the responding gene to mutate—probably to transpose—hence permitting no-longer-controlled A_1 to produce anthocyanin in streaks or speckles of darker pigmentation. Each of the kernels in the lower row of Figure 29-2 has one *Spm* and a different state corresponding to that of the kernel above it. All (and only) the speckled kernels in both ears of Figure 29-3 carry standard *Spm*. The suppressive action of component-1 is especially clear in the left-hand ear—the pigmentation of the background in the speckled kernels being lighter than the coloration in the nonspeckled kernels. It is found that component-2 cannot function unless component-1 has functioned previously.

The different forms of the responding gene, which produce different states of the structural gene, are the result of responses to the signaling gene. The responding gene may change by losing its response to component-2, but retain its response to component-1.

The *Spm* element can further modify phenotypic expression by itself undergoing controlled types of change. Some of these changes eliminate the suppressive response (and hence the mutational response also); others reduce or eliminate only the mutational response. Changes that affect either or both components of *Spm* are retained for a limited period—subsequently returning to the original type of action. Thus, both components 1 and 2 undergo *cycles of activity*.

29.5 The action of some structural genes in maize is regulated by setting–erasure–setting cycles induced by controlling elements.

It has already been stated that the form of effect that the responding gene has upon the structural gene is determined by the response this controlling gene makes to the signaling gene. After the responding gene reacts, the signaling gene may be removed (for example, by segregation during meiosis). Since the locus retains its state, nevertheless, we conclude that the signal presets the action of the responding gene and the future state of the structural gene. If, subsequently, a different form of signaling gene is introduced, the new signal can produce a change of state, that is, the old setting can be erased and a new setting established. In the *Spm* system, setting requires the presence of an active component-1. Since changes in this component are cyclical so are the setting and erasure of the functional state of a locus within and between plant generations.

The preceding illustrates how a large variety of phenotypic responses can be produced at different times in development by the *Spm* control system via modifications (some cyclical, others not) of either the responding or signaling genes, or both. Recall from Section 29.1, item 7, moreover, that kernels containing *Spm* and two different states of A_1 have two different pigmentation patterns superimposed (Figure 29-4). *Spm*, according to B. McClintock (1963), " serves as a model of the mode of operation of one type of superregulatory mechanism. Such a system can activate or inactivate particular genes in some cells early in development, and activate or inactivate other genes later in development. It can turn on the action of some genes at the same time that it turns off the action of others. It can adjust the level of activity·of a particular gene in different parts of an organism. . . ."

Although the role of controlling genes has not been so clearly established as in

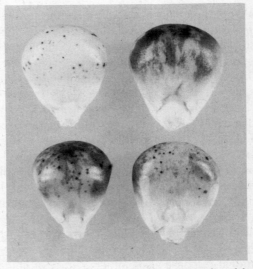

Figure 29-4   Upper row: Pigment type and distribution produced by each of two states of A_1. Lower row: Overlapping of pigment types and distributions when both these states are present as alleles. All four kernels have a fully active *Spm* element. (Courtesy of B. McClintock, 1967. Develop. Biol., Suppl. 1: 94.)

maize, there are other examples of setting and erasure in the control of gene action in other organisms. We have already discussed in Section 28.4 how, in *Drosophila*, the derivation of a particular chromosome as well as the nature of the other chromosomes present can set and erase the type of chromatization a segment of the particular chromosome undergoes. Other probable examples of setting and erasure of gene action can be found in *Drosophila* (for example, see Section 30.9), *Sciara*, and plants showing variegation. (R)

29.6   The level of action of a structural gene in one region of a chromosome can be changed depending upon the nature of this region in the homologous chromosome.

The R^r allele in chromosome 10 of maize ordinarily results in the production of the full amount of anthocyanin pigment in the aleurone and certain vegetative parts of the plant. When, however, a hybrid is formed composed of R^r and certain alleles—for example R^{st}—the R^r allele in the next and subsequent generations has a reduced capacity for anthocyanin production. Such a multigenerational change in functioning in R^r is called *paramutation*, which is produced by a *paramutagenic* gene (such as R^{st}) in a paramutable allele (such as R^r). It appears, therefore, that paramutagenic genes are involved in setting lower the gene action capacity of paramutable alleles in their homologs. Paramutagenic alleles can mutate causing paramutagenicity to be unchanged, changed in varying degrees, or lost completely. Paramutation apparently takes place in vegetative cells during plant growth.

When observed in subsequent generations, a paramutated R^r kept in homozygous condition is found to revert about halfway toward full anthocyanin production. When paramutated R^r is heterozygous either with r (which can produce no anthocyanin) or a deficiency of the R^r region, the reversion toward full anthocyanin production occurs nevertheless. Thus, although the reduction in pigment producing capacity of R^r is the result of paramutation, the enhancement (resetting of the control) is spontaneous.

The following model seems consistent with the experimental evidence regarding paramutation. The R^r region is assumed to be composed of (1) a structural gene needed for anthocyanin production, plus (2) a heterochromatic segment closely associated with the structural gene. The heterochromatic segment is a repressor segment since it is assumed to consist of a variable number of repeats of a common unit, the *metamere*, the repression of R^r being proportional to the number of metameres. Paramutable alleles are assumed to contain at least one metamere; other, nonparamutable alleles have none. Repression, and hence control of gene action, can be visualized as being caused by the condensation (clumping or coiling) of the repressor segment being carried over into the adjacent structural gene.

Paramutation then is assumed to be an increase in the number of metameres. Paramutagenic alleles like R^{st} can be thought to involve a chromosome region which affects nuclear metabolism in such a way that the metameres of R^r in the homolog are overcopied (amplified). When, however, paramutated R^r is homozygous or is present with r or a deficiency for R^r, conditions favor the underreplication of metameres, and partial reversion to full anthocyanin-forming capacity occurs.

Paramutation also occurs at the *B* locus in maize. Events very much like paramutation occur in at least several other organisms. For example, the segregation-distortion phenomenon (Section S25.4) in *Drosophila* may involve paramutational events. (R)

29.7 Many X-limited genes produce the same phenotypic effect whether in single or double dose, thus showing dosage compensation.

In diploid organisms with heteromorphic X and Y sex chromosomes, X-limited genes not involved in sex determination or differentiation occur in single dose in one sex and in double dose in the other. It would seem advantageous for the organism to control these genes so that their level of activity is equal in both sexes. One method of regulation, called *dosage compensation*, is apparent in studies of the enzyme glucose-6-phosphate dehydrogenase (G-6-PD), which is coded in human beings by an X-limited gene. Red blood corpuscles from males and from females have the same amount of G-6-PD activity, even though the female has twice the dose of the allele that the male has. Similarly, in *Drosophila*, *apr/Y* males and *apr/apr* females produce the same amount of eye pigment. Many other X-limited loci in man and in *Drosophila* also show dosage compensation.

29.8 Dosage compensation in man is effected by permitting the expression of only one allele in the two-dose condition.

In females heterozygous for a mutant gene which codes for defective G-6-PD, some red blood corpuscles have complete G-6-PD activity and others no activity at all; no corpuscles of intermediate activity are found. It appears that some of these red blood corpuscles are derived from cells in which the normal gene is nonfunctional, and the defective locus functional; others come from cells in which the mutant gene is nonfunctional and the normal locus functional. We conclude, therefore, that in a diploid female only one of the two G-6-PD alleles (sometimes the maternally derived, sometimes the paternally derived allele) is expressed in a given cell. Since the female heterozygote has some corpuscles with G-6-PD activity and some without, such an individual can be considered a *functional* (or *phenotypic*) *mosaic* for the G-6-PD locus. At least six other X-limited genes give rise to functional mosaicism in human beings, so it appears that dosage compensation is accomplished by completely suppressing the action of one of two alleles present. Since most of the nuclear DNA of eucaryotes is normally transcriptionally inactive, one may also think of dosage compensation in man as being the consequence of activating only one of two alleles present. (R)

29.9 In man, clumped sex chromatin is cytological evidence for a mechanism of dosage compensation that probably involves controlling transcription.

Many of the somatic diploid interphase nuclei of human females have a large clump of chromatin which touches the nuclear membrane. These heterochromatic clumps are not found in males. This facultative heterochromatin, called *sex chromatin* or the *Barr body* (after its discoverer), first appears at about the twelfth day of human development. The number of Barr bodies found depends on the balance between the number of X chromosomes and the number of sets of autosomes: One X chromosome is balanced by two sets of autosomes; and each X in excess of this balance clumps.[1]

These cytological observations, which show that the X chromosomes are differentially affected, suggest a mechanism for dosage compensation in man and other mammals. In those organisms that contain a Barr body, that is, an X chromosome clumped during interphase, all the inactive loci are in the same homolog. The clumping apparently prevents these genes from being transcribed to RNA. This conclusion is supported by the finding that in female fibroblasts uridine incorporation into the Barr body region is only 18 % of the amount incorporated in a similar volume of non-Barr body chromosomal region. Since dosage compensation appears to affect a large segment of the X, if not the whole chromosome, we can consider it to regulate gene activity at a "multigenic" level. (R)

29.10 Dosage compensation in mammals seems to involve a coordinated group of position effects.

Although mice (unlike most other mammals) have no Barr bodies, one of the female's X chromosomes is facultatively heterochromatic—condensing precociously in mitosis. When loci in the mouse X are heterozygous, a phenotypic mosaic is produced (for all loci tested but one)—as we might expect according to the preceding discussion. It thus appears that one X chromosome of the female is largely inactive in interphase.

Female mice heterozygous for a reciprocal translocation between an X chromosome and an autosome have been useful in studying dosage compensation. These females are often phenotypic mosaics for autosomal loci when the translocated autosome carries a particular normal allele, and its nontranslocated homolog carries the mutant allele (Figure 29-5). (We should note that this variegation by rearrangement is a position effect.) In such reciprocal translocation heterozygotes, the normal trait is more often expressed when the distance between the locus of the normal allele and its attachment to the X is increased. In other words, the normal gene is more often inactivated the closer the attachment point is to the X. A translocated autosomal locus very far away from the X attachment point may not be inactivated at all. These results indicate that the heterochromatization of one region of the X can, apparently, spread some distance to neighboring (X, or, if linked by translocation, autosomal) loci which are inactivated by the heterochromatization. We have already noted such effects in *Drosophila* (Section 28.3) and suggested they also occur in *Zea* (Section 29.6).

In one reciprocal translocation with the X, no variegation resulted even though another one broken at almost the identical autosomal position did yield variegation. Perhaps this failure was due to the union of the autosomal segment with an X segment incapable of inactivating its neighbor. The X locus normally adjacent to this segment should also be unsuppressed and not show dosage compensation. One such locus was mentioned earlier in this section. The translocation studies suggest therefore that

[1] The maximum number of Barr bodies in individuals with an abnormal number of sex chromosomes is, therefore, 0 in X0 individuals, 1 in XXY and XXYY, 2 in XXX and XXXY, and 3 in XXXX. Cells with fewer than the maximum number may have extralarge Barr bodies formed by the fusion of single Barr bodies. Tetraploid cells (four sets of A + 4X) of a female have two Barr bodies.

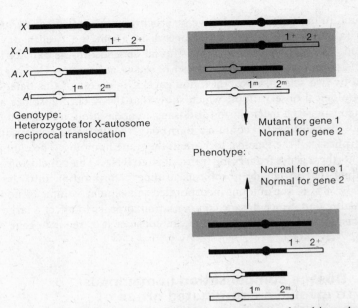

Figure 29-5   Position effect in the mouse. The X chromosome enclosed in a shaded area is heterochromatized. Phenotypes refer to autosomal markers indicated.

dosage compensation in mammals is essentially a coordinated group of position effects.

The above results suggest that not all loci on X chromosomes are dosage compensated for by repression (or activation) of one allele in the usual two-dose condition in the mouse. Certainly the genes regulating intrachromosome replication must be functional in all X chromosomes present. This is true, also, in man, where the fact that XX differs from X0 phenotypically as does XXY from XY supports the view that not all X loci are dosage compensated by the single active locus mechanism. The results obtained with X and Y isochromosomes (Section 23.8) suggest the hypothesis that it is mainly the genes in X^L which are inactive in one X of the human female. Genes in X^S are, on this view, functional when in double dose either in the female or in the male (whose Y^L seems to carry alleles of genes in the X^S)—hemizygosity for these genes

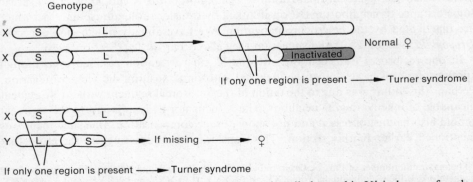

Figure 29-6   Hypothesis of inactivation of genes primarily located in X^L in human females. L, long arm; S, short arm of the sex chromosome.

(in a female missing X^S or in a male missing Y^L) producing Turner's syndrome (Figure 29-6). (R)

29.11   In mammals, groups of genes are permanently prevented from functioning as the result of dosage compensation.

In mice and in human beings the inactivation of (part of) one X occurs in somatic cells a little over a week after fertilization and seems to affect each normal X with equal probability. (X's with deletions are, however, preferentially included in Barr bodies.) This inactivation does not occur in the germ line. For example, one of the two X's in an adult female rat is heterochromatic in somatic tissues, whereas both X's stain similarly in the oocyte.

As noted earlier, the position effects in *Drosophila* involving changes in chromatization and the setting of gene action controls in maize are sometimes reversible. In human beings, mice, and other mammals, the phenotypic mosaicism due to dosage compensation also involves changes in chromatization and, apparently, position effects. But in these organisms the position effect appears to be a permanent alteration in gene function. That is, once a chromosome segment is inactivated (as in a Barr body) all descendent cells are similarly inactivated, despite the intervening mitoses. The result is a phenotypically uniform patch of tissue—not patches within patches.

We should keep in mind, however, that even genes that are permanently turned off must be replicated once each mitotic cycle. Barr body chromosomes replicate last in interphase—indicating that before this time the clumped condition prevents the synthesis both of RNA and DNA. A gene can apparently exist in two replicating forms, active or inactive with respect to transcription, and one form will persist despite intervening nuclear divisions until specific conversion to the other. For some maize genes, it is found that a given state during gametogenesis is continued in the zygote. In the endosperm, for example, one maternally derived gene has been found to be phenotypically active, whereas its paternally derived allele is inactive. Similarly, in female kangaroos it is the paternal X which is inactive in somatic cells. (R)

29.12   The mechanism of dosage compensation in *Drosophila* appears to be different from that in mammals; genes in the two-dose condition are apparently suppressed equally.

We have already mentioned that *Drosophila*, just like man, has many X-linked loci that show dosage compensation.[2] Contrary to the situation in mammals, however, the alleles in both X chromosomes of the *Drosophila* female are apparently equally

---

[2] Dosage compensation in *Drosophila* applies not only to hypomorphic mutants like *apricot* (*apr*) but also to their wild-type alleles. Other X-limited chromosome loci in *D. melanogaster* showing dosage compensation are *y, ac, sc, sn, g, f, B, 6 PGD* (*6 phosphogluconate dehydrogenase*), *G6PD* (*glucose-6-phosphate dehydrogenase*), and *XDH* (*xanthine dehydrogenase*). Only partially compensated for, however, is *fa* (*facet*), females showing somewhat more effect than males. *Hw* (*hairy wing*), *w^e* (*eosin*), *w^i* (*ivory*), and *Fl^M* (*Female lethal^Margulies*) show no compensation, nor do any Y-limited or autosomal genes, nor *bb* which has a locus in both the X and the Y chromosome and, therefore, is usually present in paired condition in both males and females.

functional. We conclude this since (1) the somatically synapsed polynemic X's in the nuclei of female larval salivary glands and other tissues appear identical; (2) although the single polynemic X of the male and the paired polynemic X's of the female in salivary gland cells have the expected DNA ratio of 1 : 2, cells with the single X seem to contain just about as much RNA and protein as those with the double X; and (3) heterozygotes for an X-limited locus coding for an enzyme composed of two polypeptide chains synthesize hybrid molecules.

Females having *apr* in triple dose (the extra *apr* locus is carried in another chromosome) have darker apricot eyes than *apr*/*apr* females, demonstrating the direction of dosage compensation—suppression of eye-pigment formation in the *apr*/*apr* female to the level produced by one *apr* locus present in the X chromosome of a male. Males carrying an extra *apr* locus have apricot eyes even darker than those of females with triple *apr*. Similar results are observed when the dosage of the X-limited gene for 6 phosphogluconate dehydrogenase, *6 PGD*, is varied and enzyme activity is scored. Dosage compensation in *Drosophila* thus seems to involve the equal suppression of genes in the two-dose condition. The comparative lack of suppression of single dosage X-limited genes in the male may be correlated with the finding that the X of males completes its replication in larval salivary gland cells faster than either the autosomes or the female X's. Dosage compensation does not depend, however, upon sex phenotype.[3]

When short segments from any part of the X except the *apr* region are added to the genotype of an *apr*/*apr* female, the eye color usually becomes lighter. These segments apparently contain genes which, on the average, suppress the activity of the *apr* gene and thus bring about dosage compensation. Hence, they are called *dosage compensator genes*.[4] (Note that the *Drosophila* female has twice the number of these genes as the male.) Perhaps the mRNA's (or the protein products) of the dosage compensator genes interact with RNA transcripts of genes to be compensated; or they could act directly upon these genes by interfering with their transcription to RNA. Evidence has been obtained consistent with the latter possibility. (R)

SUMMARY AND CONCLUSIONS

It was found earlier, in the case of the position effects in procaryotes (Chapter 26) and eucaryotes (Chapter 28), that the action of a structural gene is often regulated by linearly adjacent genes. The same situation occurs in several systems for the

---

[3] Since X0 and XY males and XX, XXY, and XXYY females—all pure for *apr*—have the same eye color, the Y chromosome cannot be responsible for dosage compensation. In addition, males with or without a Y chromosome that are $X^{apr}X^{apr}$, having been genetically transformed from females by the autosomal mutant *tra* in homozygous condition (see Section 23.2), have the same eye color as $X^{apr}Y$ males. If maleness as such prevents the suppression of gene action leading to dosage compensation, the transformed-from-female male with a double dose of *apr* should (but does not) have a darker apricot eye than a male with a single dose of *apr*. Thus, dosage compensation is not dependent upon male or female phenotype.

[4] X-limited loci or alleles without dosage compensation may be so new in terms of evolution that dosage compensator genes may not yet have had an opportunity to become established. Supporting this view is evidence that *eosin* (w^e) and *ivory* (w^i), which do not show dosage compensation, are nonallelic to *apr* and, therefore, may be mutants of a more recently evolved locus. Additional support comes from the study of mutants in the X chromosome of *D. pseudoobscura*, which is V-shaped with one arm homologous to the X, the other to the left arm of chromosome III of *D. melanogaster*. More mutants show the same degree of phenotypic effect in both males and females (probably representing dosage compensation) in the arm homologous to the *melanogaster* X than in the arm homologous to the *melanogaster* III L.

regulation of gene action in eucaryotes discussed in the present chapter. Thus, controlling elements and metameres in maize and dosage-compensating regions of the X chromosome in mice all regulate the functioning of adjacent genes.

We also saw earlier that regulatory genetic material can itself be regulated by genetic material located elsewhere—in procaryotes, regulatory genes such as promoters and operators are regulated by (often nearby) genes coding for positive and negative control factors such as sigmas and repressors; in eucaryotes, heterochromatization of a chromosome region is modified by the addition of heterochromatin elsewhere in the nucleus. The same situation is found or implied in several of the control systems discussed in this chapter. For example, responding genes respond to signaling genes in systems that use controlling elements; metamere replication is postulated to be regulated by the nature of the corresponding region in the homolog in cases of paramutation; and the formation of Barr bodies depends upon the number of other X's and of autosomal sets present.

Gene-action control in eucaryotes is either cyclical (for example, involving controlling elements or paramutation in maize, and heterochromatization in *Drosophila*) and occurs in both somatic and germinal tissue, or noncyclical (for example, dosage compensation in mammals and insects) and apparently occurs in somatic tissue only.

In maize, transpositions and other recombinations lead to an increase in the number of controlling elements; mutation of these elements can produce a variety of alleles, some of which are nontransposable or have other changes in signaling or responding properties. The result is the occurrence of a variety of control systems whose delicate control of structural gene action seems able to produce a large variety of phenotypes from a given maize genotype.

Dosage compensation occurs in organisms with heteromorphic sex homologs which contain loci, coding for non-sex-related functions, that are paired in one sex but not the other. Such gene-action regulation is accomplished either by suppressing (or activating) the functioning of one member of each pair involved via a coordinated group of position effects, as occurs in mammals, or by suppressing the functioning of both members of each gene pair involved, as occurs in *Drosophila*.

All the gene-action control systems discussed in eucaryotes, with the probable exception of *cis-trans* position effects, may involve control of the transcription of structural genes. Thus, for example, controlling elements and metameres in maize seem to involve heterochromatic regions, and Barr bodies are heterochromatin—heterochromatization preventing transcription. Even though a start has been made in understanding the molecular mechanism of heterochromatization (Chapter 27), the detailed molecular mechanisms for various other aspects of specific gene-action control systems in eucaryotes are completely unknown.

GENERAL REFERENCES

Barr, M. L. 1959. Sex chromatin and phenotype in man. Science, 130: 679–685.

Lyon, M. F. 1961. Gene action in the X-chromosome of the mouse (*Mus musculus* L.) Nature, Lond., 190: 372–373. Reprinted in *Papers on regulation of gene activity during development*, Loomis, W. M., Jr. (Editor), New York: Harper & Row, Inc., 1970, pp. 181–183. (The original presentation of the single-active-X hypothesis.)

McClintock, B. 1965. The control of gene action in maize. Brookhaven Sympos. Biol., 18: 162–184.

McClintock, B. 1968. Genetic systems regulating gene expression during development. Develop. Biol., Suppl. 1 (1967): 84–112. (In maize.)

Muller, H. J. 1950. Evidence of the precision of genetic adaptation. *The Harvey lectures* (1947–1948), Ser. 43: 165–229, Springfield, Ill.: Charles C Thomas. Excerpted in *Studies in genetics*, Muller, H. J., Bloomington, Ind.: Indiana University Press, 1962, pp. 152–171. (Dosage compensation in *Drosophila*.)

SPECIFIC SECTION REFERENCES

29.1   Green, M. M. 1969. Controlling element mediated transpositions of the *white* gene in *Drosophila melanogaster*. Genetics, 61: 429–441.

Nelson, O. E. 1969. The *waxy* locus in maize. II. The location of the controlling element alleles. Genetics, 60: 507–524.

Peterson, P. A. 1970. Controlling elements and mutable loci in maize: their relationship to bacterial episomes. Genetics, 41: 33–56.

29.5   Becker, H. J. 1966. Genetic and variegation mosaics in the eye of *Drosophila*. In *Current topics in developmental biology*, Vol. 1: Chap. 6, 155–171. (Gene action at one stage is set earlier.)

Crouse, H. V. 1966. An inducible change in state of the chromosomes of Sciara: its effects on the genetic components of the X. Chromosoma, 18: 230–253.

McClintock, B. 1963. Further studies of gene-control systems in maize. Carnegie Inst. Wash. Yearb., 62 (1962–1963): 486–493.

Stern, C. 1968. *Genetic mosaics and other essays*. Cambridge, Mass.: Harvard University Press. (The genetics of patterns and prepatterns.)

29.6   Brink, R. A., Styles, E. D., and Axtell, J. D. 1968. Paramutation: directed genetic change. Science, 159: 161–170.

Coe, E. H., Jr. 1966. The properties, origin, and mechanism of conversion-type inheritance at the *B* locus in maize. Genetics, 53: 1035–1063. (A case of paramutation that seems to involve a transposable controlling element.)

29.8   Beutler, E., Yeh, M., and Fairbanks, V. F. 1962. The normal human female as a mosaic of X-chromosome activity; studies using the gene for G-6-PD-deficiency as a marker. Proc. Nat. Acad. Sci., U.S., 48: 9–16.

Davidson, R. G., Nitowsky, H. M., and Childs, B. 1963. Demonstration of two populations of cells in the human female heterozygous for glucose-6-phosphate dehydrogenase variants. Proc. Nat. Acad. Sci., U.S., 50: 481–485. Reprinted in *Papers on regulation of gene activity during development*, Loomis, W. M., Jr. (Editor), New York: Harper & Row, Inc., 1970, pp. 184–188.

Human genetics. Cold Spring Harbor Sympos. Quant. Biol., 29. 1965.

29.9   Lyon, M. F. 1962. Sex chromatin and gene action in the mammalian X-chromosome. Amer. J. Hum. Genet., 14: 135–148.

Moore, K. L. (Editor) 1966. *The sex chromatin*. Philadelphia: W. B. Saunders Company.

29.10   Cattanach, B. M., and Perez, J. N. 1970. Parental influence on X-autosome translocation-induced variegation in the mouse. Genet. Res., Camb., 15: 43–53. (See also Section 28.4.)

Russell, L. B. 1963. Mammalian X-chromosome action: inactivation limited in spread and in region of origin. Science, 140: 976–978.

Russell, L. B. 1964. Genetic and functional mosaicism in the mouse. In *The role of chromosomes in development*, Locke, M. (Editor), New York: Academic Press, Inc., pp. 153–181.

29.11   Gandini, E., Gartler, S. M., Angioni, G., Argiolas, N., and Dell'Acqua, G. 1968. Developmental implications of multiple tissue studies in glucose-6-phosphate dehydrogenase-deficient heterozygotes. Proc. Nat. Acad. Sci., U.S., 61: 945–948. Reprinted in *Papers on regulation of gene activity during development*, Loomis, W. M., Jr. (Editor), New York: Harper & Row, Inc., 1970, pp. 197–200. (Evidence that X-chromosome turnoff occurs at the eight-blood-cell stage.)

Grumbach, M. M., Morishima, A., and Taylor, J. H. 1963. Human sex chromosome abnormalities in relation to DNA replication and heterochromatinization. Proc. Nat Acad. Sci., U.S., 49: 581–589.

Schwartz, D. 1965. Regulation of gene action in maize. *Genetics today* (Proc. XI intern. Congr. Genet., The Hague, 1963), 2: 131–135. (Some maternally contributed genes function in the endosperm while paternally contributed alleles do not.)

29.12 Korge, G. 1970. Dosage compensation and effect for RNA synthesis in chromosome puffs of *Drosophila melanogaster*. Nature, Lond., 255: 386–388.

Seecof, R. L., Kaplan, W. D., and Futch, D. G. 1969. Dosage compensation for enzyme activities in *Drosophila melanogaster*. Proc. Nat. Acad. Sci., U.S., 62: 528–535.

Smith, P. D., and Lucchesi, J. C. 1969. The role of sexuality in dosage compensation in *Drosophila*. Genetics, 61: 607–618.

Stern, C. 1960. Dosage compensation—development of a concept and new facts. Canad. J. Genet. Cytol., 2: 105–118.

SUPPLEMENTARY SECTION

S29.3 Systems composed of one to several *Ac* controlling elements can regulate the action of the *Pericarp color (P)* and other loci in maize.

The pericarp of a maize kernel encloses the seed containing the embryo (Figure 15-8). Although embryo tissue is formed by the offspring generation, the pericarp is diploid tissue formed by the parental generation. Some pure-line plants are completely red and produce completely red pericarps. These are homozygous for P^r. Other plants that breed true for colorless pericarp are homozygous for the recessive P^w; still other plants are striped with red, and striping appears also in the pericarp. Plants that show medium variegation of red (therefore called *medium variegated*) are produced experimentally by backcrossing medium variegateds to a strain with colorless pericarp. Such medium variegateds are genotypically P^w/P^r Ac; having P^w in one homolog and Ac

located in or near P^r in the other homolog. Apparently the Ac sometimes permits P^r to be functional, thereby producing the medium variegation. In this case the Ac seems to act as a one-element control system for the expression of P^r. (In the original studies the controlling element was described as a *Modulator of P* action and was given the genetic symbol *Mp*.)

Medium variegated plants produce kernels of the type shown in Figure 29-7. In a random

Figure 29-8   Ears from maize plants grown from full red, light variegated, and medium variegated kernels. Left: light variegated progeny ear from a light variegated kernel. Right: full red progeny ear from full red kernel. Middle: medium variegated progeny ear from a medium variegated kernel. (Courtesy of R. A. Brink.)

Figure 29-7   Random sample of kernels from a medium variegated pericarp maize ear. (Courtesy of R. A. Brink.)

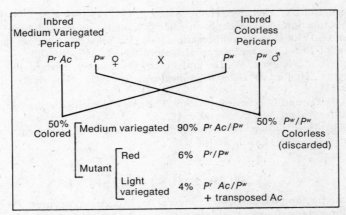

Figure 29-9   Results of test crossing medium-variegated pericarp with colorless pericarp.

sample of kernels, about 6 per cent have full red color. Medium variegated individuals produce not only red but also light variegated progeny (and kernels). The parental type and the two variant types of ears can be seen in Figure 29-8. The *light variegated kernels* (*lights*) have about half as many colored sectors as the *medium variegated kernels* (*mediums*).

The results of test-crossing mediums are shown in Figure 29-9. As expected, half the offspring are nonred (P^w/P^w). Of the remaining half with various degrees of red, 90 per cent are mediums ($P^r Ac/P^w$); about 6 per cent are full red (reds); and 4 per cent are lights. The similar frequency of the exceptional reds and lights suggests that the two types of variant may somehow be related in origin.

Occasionally, medium ears show the two variants, light and red, as twin patches of kernels (Figure 29-10). This situation suggests that reds and lights are not merely related to one another in origin but are complementary. In other words, in the process of being formed, one has gained something the other has lost. The reds produced by mediums behave in crosses with P^w/P^w as though they are genotypically P^r/P^w, that is, as though they have lost Ac by transposition; accordingly, it is hypothesized that lights are $P^r Ac/P^w$ which have gained another Ac by transposition. Thus, lights presumably contain a two-element control system, both controlling elements being Ac; the Ac at the P^r locus behaving like a responding gene to the signals of a second Ac located elsewhere.

On this hypothesis consider the results obtained when certain lights ($P^r Ac/P^w$ plus transposed Ac) are test crossed by $P^w P^w$. Half the offspring are nonred ($P^w P^w$); the other half are colored—about half of them lights (genetically similar to the light parent), half mediums (similar to the light parent

but lacking the transposed Ac) with a few reds (cases where Ac is transposed from $P^r Ac$, leaving P^r alone).

One possible outcome of transposing Ac away from $P^r Ac$ is illustrated in Figure 29-11, where the medium parent cell chromosomes ($P^r Ac$ and P^w) are shown already divided, but daughter

Figure 29-10   Twin patches of mutant kernels, full red and light variegated, in a medium variegated pericarp maize ear. The right and left ears of Figure 29-8 were grown from twin mutant red and light kernels in an otherwise medium ear. (Courtesy of R. A. Brink.)

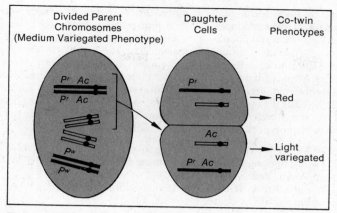

Figure 29-11   Transposition of *Ac* and the origin of twin sectors.

strands are still connected at the centromere. Normal division would have produced two daughter cells—each carrying *P^r Ac/P^w*, each giving rise to medium sectors. But, if as a result of two or more breaks or some other mutational mechanism, the *Ac* in one daughter strand is transposed into a nonhomologous chromosome (hollow bar), the daughter cell which receives the transposed *Ac* may be the one carrying *P^r Ac*, while the other daughter cell carries only *P^r*. Thereafter, normal mitosis of the cell containing *P^r* alone will produce reds; and mitosis of the sister cell will produce lights. These cells will then become adjacent mutant patches in a medium background (Figure 29-10).

Other properties of *Ac* have been discovered relative to the *P* locus. *Ac* may become fixed at the *P^r* locus so that a medium becomes a stable nonred form. Transposed *Ac* may occupy a variety of sites—linked and no longer linked to chromosome 1. In 57 of 87 cases, transposed *Ac* was found still linked to chromosome 1, the allele having moved less than 50 crossover units from *P^r*. In the remaining 30 cases *Ac* was found transposed to one of five different nonhomologous chromosomes. Of the 57 cases where transposed *Ac* was still linked to chromosome 1, 37 showed *Ac* within 5 crossover units of *P^r*; 10 showed *Ac* within 5 to 15 units; and the remainder showed *Ac* to be farther away. Hence, *Ac* tends to move from the *P* locus by short rather than by long jumps. This situation suggests that contact between old and new sites may be required for shifts and transpositions of *Ac*.

Reds sometimes revert to variegated. In such cases an *Ac* is found transposed near *P^r*. The frequency of such reversions from red to variegated can be studied after introducing an *Ac* locus various distances from *P^r* in a *P^r*-containing chromosome. As shown in Figure 29-12, the

closer to *P^r* the introduced *Ac* is, the greater is the frequency of reversions. In summary, medium mutates to red by loss of *Ac* from its position near the *P^r* locus. In this process, complementary lights may be produced possessing an extra *Ac*—a transposed *Ac*. The medium type is reconstituted by the return of a transposed *Ac* near the *P^r* locus. It should be recognized that changes in phenotype involving reds, mediums, lights, and nonreds are not mutations at the *P* locus. These changes are, however, the phenotypic consequences of mutations involving the transposition of *Ac*.

The relative frequency with which *Ac* transposes away from *P^r* is 100 in the absence of an additional *Ac*, about 60 in the presence of one additional *Ac*, and about 5 in the presence of two additional *Ac*'s. Thus, the transposition of *Ac* from *P^r Ac* is controlled by the presence of additional *Ac*'s. Note that both types of responding genes—*Ac* in the present case, and *Ds* in the previous one (Section 28.8)—transpose less often as the number of signaling *Ac*'s increase.

Per Cent Recombination *P^r Ac*	Variegated Sectors per 1,000 Kernels
2.6	15
4.3	11
7.6	8
12.0	3
42.0	0.2

Figure 29-12   Effect of distance of *Ac* from *P^r* upon transposition rate of *Ac* to *P^r*.

Transposition of *Ac* to another locus may change the phenotype the recipient locus produces. For example, a "mutation" to the waxy phenotype was observed in a particular medium variegated individual whose chromosome 9 carried the *Wx* allele for the starchy phenotype. The waxy phenotype was unstable and frequently "mutated" back to starchy. Tests showed that *Ac* had been transposed to the starchy locus, which then produced the waxy phenotype; further-more, the reversions to starchy were the result of *Ac*'s transposition away from this locus.

Other studies of the gene for bronze color in maize, *Bz₁*, show that it—like *Pʳ* and *Wx*—is sometimes under the control of a single *Ac* element. Occasionally, however, this one-element control system becomes a two-element, apparently two-*Ac*, system which is identified when transposition removes a signaling-*Ac* but leaves behind a responding gene.

Brink, R. A. 1954. Very light variegated pericarp in maize. Genetics, 39: 724–740.

McClintock, B. 1962. Topographical relations between elements of control systems in maize. Carnegie Inst. Wash. Yearb., 61: 448–461.

van Schaik, N. W., and Brink, R. A. 1959. Transpositions of *Modulator*, a modifier of the variegated pericarp allele in maize. Genetics, 44: 725–738.

QUESTIONS AND PROBLEMS

1. Could you detect the transposition of *Ac* to a locus near *Pʷ*? Explain.

2. Why does a light variegated individual of maize, with a transposed *Ac* on the same chromosome as *Pʳ*, produce among the F₁ offspring more than one fourth lights and less than one fourth mediums when this individual is backcrossed to nonred (*Pʷ Pʷ*)?

3. Could genes similar to *Activator* be the cause of relatively rare "mutants" of amorphic, hypomorphic, and neomorphic types? Upon what do you base your opinion?

4. Is paramutation a normal mechanism for controlling gene action? Explain.

5. Compare the mechanisms for controlling gene action in maize and *E. coli*.

6. How do you account for the finding that radiation-induced structural changes in chromosomes involve heterochromatic regions more frequently than euchromatic regions?

7. Construct a formula for the maximum number of Barr bodies in a cell nucleus in terms of *x*, the number of X chromosomes, and *a*, the number of sets of autosomes.

8. How can you explain that not all nuclei in a somatic tissue of a human female contain a Barr body?

9. Compare human males and females with respect to functional X loci.

10. What evidence can you give that chromosomal rearrangements can produce position effects on genes some distance from the breakage point?

11. How do you know that the Y chromosome is not responsible for dosage compensation in man or *Drosophila*?

12. Are you justified in considering an individual a mutant if it has the same phenotype as a known mutant? Explain.

13. Do you expect the gene *bobbed* (*bb*), which has a locus in both the X and Y chromosomes of *Drosophila*, to show dosage compensation? Why?

14. Are all the loci in one X of a human female inactivated during all interphases? Explain.

15. How do you know it is the heterochromatic X that is inactivated in the normal human female?

16. What eye color do you expect in *Drosophila* females that have the *apr* region deleted in one X and a single *apr* present in the other?

17. How much G-6-PD activity do you expect in cells that are X0, XX, XXXY, or XXXX in an otherwise diploid organism? Explain.

18. How can you explain the phenotype of a woman who is red–green colorblind in only one eye?

19. A mule contains two distinguishable X's derived from the paternal donkey and maternal horse. A study of late replicating chromosomes in mule cells shows that half are the paternal and half the maternal X's. What conclusions can you draw from this result?

Chapter 30

Gene-Action Regulation—
General Development and
Differentiation

An understanding of the mechanisms of cell differentiation and development is one of the most important goals of biology. A fundamental question to be answered is how cells derived from the same cell develop to perform different functions. For instance, brain cells, kidney cells, and muscle cells in an organism are functionally very different from each other, even though all are derived from the same zygote. Another basic question is how the different kinds of cells in an organism are coordinated. In this chapter we will discuss the general ways that development and differentiation and their regulation depend upon genetic information.

30.1 The growth and differentiation of cells can be modified by exposure to extrinsic nucleic acid information.

Nucleic acid information added to an organism via (1) extrinsic m and t RNA's, (2) viruses, (3) symbionts and parasites can affect its growth and differentiation.

Extrinsic mRNA's and tRNA's

Developmental changes can be induced in a growing cell by the introduction of extrinsic RNA. For example, mouse ascites tumor cells ordinarily do not produce serum albumin *in vitro*, but can do so after exposure to RNA from the liver of a normal mouse or calf. In several strains of cancer cells RNA introduced into the cell seems to function as mRNA for at least an hour. The enzymes synthesized (for example, tryptophan pyrrolase and glucose-6-phosphatase) apparently have much the same activity as the enzymes produced by the RNA-donor cell. Certain mammalian cells *in vitro* will take up RNA made (in response to an antigen[1]) by other cells and synthesize specific proteins (antibodies[1]).

Mammalian cells will take up *E. coli* tRNA, 20 per cent of which will still be functional.

Viruses

In a sense, viruses regulate the growth and differentiation of hosts by taking over their metabolic machinery. As we saw earlier, ϕT4 utilizes host materials for synthesis

---

[1] Defined in Section S16.1a as well as Section 32.6.

of its own DNA and protein.[2] Temperate phages and various episomes can modify cellular growth and differentiation by turning host genes on or off. The cancer-inducing viruses polyoma and SV40 are able permanently to alter properties of mouse fibroblast cells grown in tissue culture. Some of the characteristics acquired by the virus-infected cells appear to involve latent properties of the cell. For example, polyoma virus causes a marked increase in the synthesis of host DNA and enzymes involved in its synthesis; and certain virus-infected cells regain their ability to synthesize collagen, a protein whose production has been suppressed in the uninfected cells.

In some cases the genetic background normally seems to include a viral component which affects differentiation. For example, all King Edward VII potatoes carry the paracrinkle virus without any detectable pathological lesions, although plants freed of the virus look different from infecteds and give a higher yield. In inbred mice the occurrence of certain skeletal abnormalities seems to involve the presence of virus.

Symbionts and Parasites

Well-adapted symbiotic microorganisms may become part of their host's genetic system and determine host traits. Kappa (see Section S19.2), for example, is a symbiotic microorganism whose presence can make its host, *Paramecium*, a killer of kappa-free *Paramecium*. Like kappa, the rickettsial organism causing Rocky Mountain spotted fever is visible and transmitted through the cytoplasm of carrier cells. These *rickettsiae*, as well as the DNA virus *sigma* which causes sensitivity to CO_2 gas in *Drosophila* and a spirochaete that is transmitted through the *Drosophila* egg and causes the death of almost all developing males, also determine traits of their hosts. Parasitic protozoa, microsporidians, and wasps are known to affect the structure and activities of their host's chromosomes.

Whenever infection by nucleic acids or organisms such as those mentioned above occurs at a nonrandom time in differentiation and development, we may expect the addition of extrinsic nucleic acid information to produce changes in these processes. (R)

30.2   Some development and differentiation is associated with changes in the quality and quantity of intrinsic genetic material.

We noted in the last section how extrinsic DNA information or its transcripts can affect the differentiation and development of the host. Some changes which occur in the amount of DNA intrinsic to the organism are also correlated with differentiation and development. We have already mentioned in Section 24.9 several examples of changes in the *quality of DNA information* present when parts of chromosomes and whole chromosomes are lost from a nucleus. Such losses are associated with the differentiation which occurs in different cells of the somatic line or the germ line, or which occurs between these two lines.[3]

---

[2] In poxvirus infection, viral DNA attaches to the chromosomes of the host; host DNA is lost, some entering the cytoplasm to be used in viral DNA replication.

[3] It may be noted that nuclear DNA in the cytoplasm may serve as raw material for the synthesis of new DNA in the nucleus or other organelles. This function may be the fate of the DNA lost as mentioned above. Other DNA may be supplied by sperm which enter an egg but do not fertilize it, since only one sperm per egg is used in fertilization. It is conceivable that such DNA may also be transcribed or act directly as a messenger in protein synthesis.

Development can also involve changes in *quantity of DNA information* via gain or loss in the number of replicas present either in whole or parts of nuclear genomes. The whole genome type of change is illustrated by the gametophyte generation being haploid, and the sporophyte generation diploid—as in maize; by polynemy—as occurs in many different dipteran larval tissues; and by polyploidy—as occurs in human liver cells.

Quantitative changes in parts of genomes occur during chromosome replication and in amplification (Sections 24.10 and 24.11) followed in some cases by deamplification (as when the extra nucleolar DNA of amphibian and certain dipteran oocytes is lost). Once DNA is amplified it is, of course, redundant. How amplified DNA is related to the large amounts of complete and partially redundant DNA's found in eucaryotes (described in Section 8.5) is presently unknown. The possible functions in development and differentiation of a small fraction of routinely present completely redundant genes —those for rRNA—and partially redundant genes—those for tRNA (see Section 8.4) are discussed in Sections 30.6 and 30.7, respectively; how the bulk of reiterated DNA functions in these processes is speculated on in the footnote to Section 30.7.

Finally, changes at least in quantity of DNA information are certainly involved in the differentiation and development of those features of cells associated with mito- chondria and chloroplasts.

30.3   The largest portion of differentiation and development seems to occur in cells containing the same qualitative set of genetic information.

Even if some cells develop and differentiate by changing their DNA genetic informa- tion qualitatively and others do so by changing this storehouse of information quantitatively, the following evidence offers convincing support for the view that most differentiation and development in multicellular organisms occurs in cells that carry the same qualitative set of genetic information.

1. Chromosome number and gross morphology remain the same throughout the lifetime of most cells, despite any differentiation that occurs. Evidence for this comes from the relative constancy of DNA content per nucleus of a nondividing differentiating cell, the constancy of Barr bodies, nucleoli, and appearance of chromosomes when these are visible during interphase.

2. Repeated mitotic divisions produce cells of diverse tissues all having the same number and kind of chromosomes.

3. Natural or induced gross structural changes in chromosomes are repeated in all progeny chromosomes regardless of type of cell differentiated.

4. Fine-structural features of chromosomes are repeated in all nuclei derived from a common ancestor. Thus, the sequence of bands in all polynemic tissues is the same regardless of tissue type, taking into account the fact that certain bands puff and unpuff in tissue-specific sequences.

5. Specific chromosomal regions known to be functional in certain tissues are also present in other tissues. Thus, for example, the loci for *yellow* body color, *white* eyes, and *Bar* eyes in the X chromosome of *Drosophila* are also present in the

larval salivary gland X chromosome (as discussed in Chapter 28).

6. Nuclei destined to differentiate in different ways, or that have already differentiated, retain the total scope of information that was present in a zygote. This is illustrated by the capacity for monozygotic twinning (Chapter 22); by a nucleus from a differentiated intestinal cell of *Xenopus* tadpole being able to direct a complete development when transplanted into an enucleated egg of the same species; and by a single phloem cell obtained from the root of a carrot dividing and differentiating into a complete plant.

7. All the DNA sequences in one type of differentiated cell are present in all other types. Evidence for this comes from experiments involving annealing of DNA, which in most studies of eucaryotes detects the presence of families of DNA sequences, each family being composed of partially redundant DNA[4] (see Section 8.5). (R)

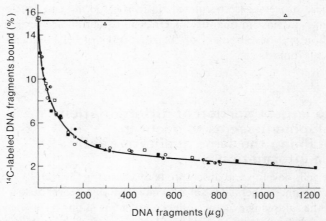

Figure 30-1   Competition by unlabeled DNA fragments in the reaction of labeled DNA fragments with DNA agar. One microgram of ^{14}C-labeled DNA fragments (2,500 counts/min/μg) from mouse L cells was incubated with 0.50 g of agar containing 60 μg of mouse embryo DNA in the presence of varying quantities of unlabeled DNA fragments from various mouse tissues, from mouse L cells, or from *B. subtilis*. The percentage of ^{14}C-labeled DNA fragments bound is plotted against the amount of unlabeled DNA present. Open circle, mouse L cell; filled circle, embryo; open square, brain; filled square, kidney; circle, open left, filled right, thymus; circle, filled left, open right, spleen; filled triangle, liver; open triangle, *B. subtilis*. (Courtesy of B. J. McCarthy and B. H. Hoyer, 1964. Proc. Nat. Acad. Sci., U.S., 52: 918.)

[4] In one study, mouse embryo DNA is isolated and, by heating followed by quick cooling, is trapped on agar in single-stranded condition. Single-stranded DNA fragments, labeled with ^{14}C, are obtained from tissue-cultured mouse L cells (derived from connective tissue), whereas similar but unlabeled fragments are obtained from various other mouse tissues, the whole embryo, and from *B. subtilis*. The amount of the labeled DNA that binds to the DNA in the agar is measured in the presence of increasing amounts of the same and another source of unlabeled DNA (Figure 30-1). The top curve in the figure shows that the labeled DNA can anneal to the trapped embryo DNA, and that *B. subtilis* contains no similar families of DNA sequences since it provides no competition—the amount of labeled DNA annealed is unchanged regardless of increasing concentration of added bacterial DNA.

The unlabeled mouse enbryo DNA, however, does compete with the labeled DNA, showing, as expected, that when competition is expected it is obtained (Figure 30-1, lower curve). What is especially noteworthy is that all the other tissues tested—kidney, thymus, spleen, and liver—have competitive abilities that are indistinguishable from that of the whole enbryo. We conclude, therefore, that the same families of DNA sequences are present in the mouse in all undifferentiated and differentiated tissues and at all stages of development.

30.4   About 10 percent of the genes in a nucleus are transcribed at any given time.

Almost all the genes in *E. coli* are transcribed in the log growth phase; about 60 per cent of the genes in *B. cereus* are transcribed under similar conditions. In eucaryotes, however, taking puffs as an index of transcription, only about 20 per cent of genes in a cell with polynemic chromosomes are ever active in the lifetime of the cell (Section 27.3); and taking the loops of lampbrush chromosomes as an index of transcribing regions, only about 5 percent are active since this is the percentage of all the lampbrush DNA in loops.

Various kinds of studies have been made of the portion of the DNA templates being used in the synthesis of complementary RNA. The results of one such type of study are summarized in Figure 27-5, last column. All these studies are consistent in showing that 10 to 20 per cent, or less, of the DNA is template-active in various embryonic or differentiated tissues. This conclusion seems to hold both for nonrepeated and repeated DNA sequences. (R)

30.5   The development and differentiation of a cell is linked to the differential transcription of its genetic information.

In both unicellular and multicellular organisms, the genetic material is differentially transcribed to RNA during various stages of differentiation and development. For example, RNA–DNA hybridization studies of *B. subtilis* show that the mRNA's from three different growth phases are derived from distinctly different groups of loci. Apparently, different parts of the genome are transcribed at different times in the bacterial growth cycle. This conclusion is further supported by finding changes in template specificity of DNA-dependent RNA polymerase during sporulation of *B. subtilis* (see also the footnote to Section 26.1).

Differential transcription is indicated during the differentiation of tissue cells in multicellular organisms by different regions in a polynemic chromosome puffing at different times. Furthermore, the pattern of puffing during differentiation varies from tissue to tissue. RNA–DNA hybridization experiments also indicate that the spectrum of active genes changes during differentiation of a tissue.

Cells that have completed differentiation also show differential transcription. In this case, although only 10 per cent or so of the genes are being transcribed, it is not the same 10 per cent in different tissues. For example, in various somatic cells of the mouse large differences are found among radioactively labeled RNA molecules isolated from different organs,[5] even though the cells contain the same DNA information. In different differentiated cells, therefore, different DNA information is being read.[6]

---

[5] It should be noted that, just as DNA–DNA hybridization experiments with eucaryotes usually detect the occurrence of families of partially redundant genes, so eucaryotic RNA–DNA hybridization studies detect transcription mainly involving such families.

[6] Certain features of metabolism are performed by all or almost all cells of a multicellular organism. Insofar as these "housekeeping" functions depend upon protein, these cells would seem to have a common portion of their genetic information functional at one time or another, or continuously. Although large groups of these housekeeping genes have not been identified (some may be located in mitochondria) they must comprise only a portion of those functioning at any time, the remainder being active in growth and differentiation. The possibility is not excluded that different but approximately functionally equivalent housekeeping genes are active in different tissues or at different stages of development.

Whereas the above results amply demonstrate a general relationship between differential transcription and differentiation and development, the details in specific situations in eucaryotes will be described in Chapters 31 and 32. (R)

30.6   Redundancy of rDNA is necessary for normal differentiation and development.

That only about 10 per cent of the genes in a eucaryote are active regardless of cell type or state of differentiation suggests that in the course of evolution structural and functional specializations were distributed among different cells, at least in part, because it was most adaptive for such a fraction of all genes to be functional in any given cell. Similarly, the number of redundant genes for rRNA in an ordinary somatic cell must be part of this adaptive adjustment. Thus, on the average, the 10 per cent of active genes in *Xenopus* require the functioning of 450 genes for rRNA to provide sufficient ribosomes for translation. Under extraordinary circumstances, however, as in the amphibian oocyte, the standard amount of redundancy is inadequate (see Section 31.1) and amplification occurs (followed by deamplification in subsequent development). The intrinsic amount of rDNA redundancy (and rDNA amplification) is expected to be determined, of course, by genes that are subject to evolutionary pressures (see Chapter 34).

The balanced relationship between genome transcription and translation involves more than the redundancy of genes for rRNA only. The genes for other ribosomal components must also be in appropriate numbers. The genes for 5s RNA in *Xenopus* are also apparently present in sufficient redundant copies; the genes for ribosomal proteins may or may not be redundant, however, since each of their mRNA's may be translated a large number of times. In any event, the production of all ribosomal components must be coordinately controlled during development and differentiation. Evidence for this has been obtained in *Xenopus*, where synthesis of 5s rRNA is coordinated with the synthesis of 28s and 18s rRNA, and the synthesis of ribosomal protein is coordinate with that for the three types of rRNA. (R)

30.7   The partial redundancy of tRNA's may be involved in differential translation during and after development and differentiation.

Most proteins contain most amino acids. Nevertheless, it is possible to regulate the production of specific proteins at the translation level, if the same amino acids are coded by different codons in different proteins and the corresponding tRNA's have a differential availability at different times. That the degeneracy in mRNA codons is used to regulate gene action at the translation level via partially redundant tRNA's is supported in studies of sea urchins. Here one finds multiple forms of Lys tRNA whose distribution during early embryogenesis suggests that these tRNA's are involved in the regulation of protein synthesis. Moreover, other data indicate that aminoacyl-tRNA synthetases change both qualitatively and quantitatively during embryonic development.

Other studies with mammalian cells indicate that differentiated cells also differ in their aminoacyl-tRNA's. Of all the aminoacyl-tRNA's in mammalian cells from different sources, Tyr-tRNA is the most variable when studied chromatographically. The Tyr-tRNA of fibroblasts is different from that of white blood cells, epithelial cells, and most differentiated tissues and organs. The Leu-tRNA's in soybean seedlings are different in the cotyledon and hypocotyl. In the rabbit different tissues have different Ala-tRNA synthetases for two different Ala tRNA's; an organ-specific Leu-tRNA synthetase has been found in the soybean seedling. Such alterations accompanying differentiation are consistent with the hypothesis that partially redundant tRNA's may be involved in the regulation of gene action via differential translation.[7] (R)

30.8 RNA's of different longevities have various significant roles in the translational control of differentiation and development.

The regulation of gene action in differentiation and development can occur at various steps in the sequence of events starting after transcription and ending with the release of polypeptides from ribosomes (Chapters 26 and 27). We discussed tRNA's role in this connection in the last section. Certain findings with the giant, unicellular, green alga *Acetabularia* are of interest in this regard. The RNA of *Acetabularia* is translated *in vitro* using translation machinery obtained from *E. coli*; the translatable amount decreases, however, as differentiation of the alga proceeds. It is possible that the base sequence on mRNA that signals attachment to ribosomal subunits changes during *Acetabularia* differentiation.

Our primary consideration in this section is the variability in the longevity of RNA and the bearing this has on differentiation and development.

Long-lived RNA's

The RNA's stored in seeds are responsible for postgermination protein synthesis. This is so because during germination no RNA is synthesized and actinomycin D exposure does not change the profile of polysomes. Some of these stockpiled mRNA's must be able to persist for years, for example those in ancient lotus seeds, which can still germinate after 1,700 years. Degradation of such RNA must depend upon the occurrence of a subsequent stage of development. A similar stockpiling of RNA other than rRNA occurs during oogenesis in Amphibia (see Section 31.1). Long-lived RNA is absent from bacteria.

---

[7] As mentioned earlier, only a minor portion of the redundancy in eucaryotic DNA is accounted for by rDNA and *tDNA*. The remaining completely and partially redundant DNA may have a role in differential translation also and, perhaps, in differential transcription. There are several ways to imagine such functioning.

If, for example, holoenzymes of RNA polymerase must pass over redundant DNA sequences before getting to more typical protein-coding ones, a redundant sequence can function as a timing device—the longer the redundancy, the later the protein-coding transcription will occur. If the RNA polymerase transcribes the redundant portion, the protein-coding portion of mRNA could be preceded by an mRNA redundancy that is not translated. Such an untranslated nucleotide sequence is found at the 5′ end of φR17's RNA. If pieces of the redundancy were removed by exonuclease starting at the 5′ end, the longer the redundant end of mRNA, the more copies of the subsequently coded protein would be made. The longevity of different RNA's is discussed in the next section.

Moderately long-lived RNA's

These RNA's can be stored for hours to days; they are protected from decay possibly by polysomes, single ribosomes, or ribosomal-like structures perhaps in association with proteins and membranes (see also Section 27.14). Examples of RNA's of this class include the template RNA for synthesizing feather keratin which appears in the developing chick 2 days before it is translated; and the RNA, whose translation produces lens protein in the developing chick, which is stored temporarily in inactive polysomes. A well-studied mRNA of this type is that for hemoglobin, which survives for a minimum of about 24 hours, as readily shown by the continuation of hemoglobin synthesis even after the loss of the nucleus from reticulocytes. Experiments using actinomycin D show that hemoglobin-coding RNA is present at the midprimitive streak stage of chick development and persists (untranslated) many hours later until the 7- to 8-somite stage. Moderately long-lived RNA is widespread, occurring in procaryotes as well as in eucaryotes whose nuclei (1) continue to divide, (2) persist without dividing, and (3) are lost.

Short-lived RNA's

In bacteria, although some RNA's are moderately long-lived, studies of RNA's in general show that most are short-lived, having a half life of 2 to 5 minutes (Section 6.9). Specific messengers that have been studied also fall in the short-lived range—for example, that for β-galactosidase in *E. coli* and for histidase in *B. subtilis*.

In eucaryotes most of the RNA has a half-life of about 2 hours. Although this RNA is short-lived, its half-life is 20 to 60 times longer than that for procaryotes. The specific template for δ-aminolevulinic acid in rat liver has a half-life of 40 to 70 minutes.

RNA's with widely different half-lives coexist in the same cell. In rat liver, for example, the half-lives of the templates for three enzymes are 18 to 24 hours, 6 to 8 hours, and 3 hours.

The longevity, distribution, and translational products of these three classes of RNA's suggests that they perform different general functions in the control or regulation of differentiation and development. Long-lived RNA functions as the storehouse of information needed to quickly support a large bulk of protoplasm (as in seeds and amphibian oocytes) after initiation of active metabolism following a period of quiescence. Moderately long-lived RNA functions to serve smaller packages of protoplasm that initiate active metabolism (spore germination) after a protected quiescent period and to support the synthesis of special substances (for example, keratin, hemoglobin, and lens protein) characterizing differentiated cells. Short-lived RNA's occur in cells that are or are not differentiated and are used to make products needed for short periods in response to a changing environment (for example, enzymes for nutrition, growth, and division). The shorter the lifetime of an RNA, the more quickly the cell can obtain a response to repressing the transcription of that RNA; in other words, the shorter the RNA half-life, the greater is the *immediacy* in the control of the gene products. (R)

30.9   The reversibility of differentiation is illustrated in the phenomenon of transdetermination.

Differentiation associated with the qualitative loss of intrinsic genetic material is, of course, irreversible, barring the subsequent gain of such information by infection.

Differentiation associated with no qualitative change in nucleic acid information should be, in principle, reversible spontaneously or, with the proper techniques, experimentally. Some well-known examples of dedifferentiation and redifferentiation include

1. Pigment cells can become neural retina cells during regeneration of the newt eye.
2. Blood lymphocytes can be experimentally transformed first into phagocytic macrophages, then into collagen-secreting fibroblasts.

3. Differentiated intestinal cells of *Xenopus* have totipotent nuclei, that is, they can dedifferentiate after nuclear transplantation and then, after mitosis, redifferentiate nuclei of all cell types (see Section 30.3).

Even before a cell differentiates into a particular cell type, it is often determined to have that particular destiny. Experiments with *Drosophila* show that larval cells determined to have one fate in the pupa and adult can be changed to have another; that is, cells destined to differentiate one way can be made to differentiate another way —they can undergo *transdetermination*. The transdetermination of clusters of dividing larval cells (*anlage* or *imaginal discs*) transplanted into other larvae is accomplished by first transplanting them from adult to adult for many generations.[8] The transdetermined state, which is similar in stability to the original state, can undergo further transdeterminations, sometimes to the original state.

The results of the transplantation and other studies with *Drosophila* suggest that all the genetic information to develop into any differentiated adult somatic cell is possessed by all anlage cells. Determination seems to involve the activation of a previously repressed portion of the genome, this activation being irreversible under the normal circumstances of environment, growth, and division. Under the new circumstances of unrestricted growth and division which occurs for anlage cells transplanted into the adult, however, a shift might occur in the substances regulating

---

[8] In *Drosophila* anlage cells are determined in the larval stage to respond later (possibly to ecdysone) in the pupal stage by differentiating into a specific organ of the adult stage. Thus, for example, the right wing of the adult differentiates in the pupa from a particular anlage determined in the larva. A piece of an anlage can be experimentally transplanted from one larva to another; when the host larva pupates this piece differentiates *autotypically*, that is, as expected from its original determination. single or groups of cells from any one anlage can also be transplanted into the body cavity of the adult, where, having bypassed the pupal stage, the cells grow and divide without limit. Groups of such cells can be transplanted back into larvae; when this is done three types of outcome are later observed in the pupae:

1. Differentiation occurs autotypically even though transfers from adult to adult have been made over numerous generations.
2. After several to many generations in which transplants made from adult to adult test autotypically in pupae, differentiation sometimes suddenly occurs *allotypically*, producing organs that in normal development come from different anlage. Such cells have undergone transdetermination, and repeated samples of such cells cultured in adults over many generations show that the transdetermined state is similar in stability to the original determined state. Some transdeterminations eventually revert to the original type of determination, some progress to still different types.
3. After a period of autotypic (or allotypic) differentiation, a few sublines occur in the adult-to-adult transplants which when tested in pupae produce somewhat abnormal differentiation. These abnormalities continue indefinitely, never reverting to normality in future transplants. In a few sublines the ability for differentiation seems to be lost since test pieces in pupae never produce differentiated structures. The relative permanence of lines showing abnormal or no differentiation suggests that these rare exceptions are due to mutations.

activation of some genes and/or the repression of others. This shift would make a different set of genes more or less stably operational, producing transdetermination when the cells are subsequently implanted into larvae. Although the present explanation is only hypothesis, future studies on the molecular basis of determination should be of considerable interest in helping us understand development and differentiation in general. (R)

30.10 The information or instructions for the assemblage of organelles may be self-contained or specifically contributed by the genotype.

Growth and division of undifferentiated cells require the additional formation of various membranes—cell, endoplasmic, and nuclear; growth, development, and differentiation also involve the formation of organelles—neurofibrils, myofibrils, centrosomes, lysosomes, mitochondria, plastids, vacuoles, ribosomes, etc. It is generally agreed that via RNA the genetic material of the cell codes directly for the proteins and any nucleic acids included in these structures, and codes indirectly for other components that may be incorporated by specifying the enzymes which control the production or availability of such components.

The information for assemblage of certain macromolecules is clearly self-contained under ordinary biological conditions. For example, the three-dimensional form of proteins seems to be derived directly from the step-by-step buildup of this conformation as dictated by the interaction of the amino acids as these are added onto the polypeptide chain during its synthesis. Even after synthesis is completed, simple proteins such as RNase can spontaneously renature after being heat denatured.

Simple nucleoproteins can also self-assembly *in vitro* from their nucleic acid and protein components. Thus, tobacco mosaic virus (Section 1.2) can be reconstituted *in vitro* by TMV protein monomers joining to TMV RNA under appropriate experimental conditions.

The 30s subunit of the 50s ribosome of *E. coli* can also self-assemble *in vitro*, even though it is a relatively complex nucleoprotein.[9] This means that all the information needed to self-assemble into a functional subunit is contained in the components themselves. That information is involved is shown by the fact that these components are specific for each other—the RNA of *E. coli* cannot be replaced by that of another species nor further degraded yet remain functional.

More than 40 genes in the chromosome of phage T4 are known to be required for the formation of the head, tail, and tail fibers (Figure 10-5). Each of these three components contains different proteins and is constructed by pieces being added on successively in a self-assembly-line manner. Completed heads can also join to tails spontaneously (this apparently does not require covalent bond formation; hence no enzyme is necessary). The last stage, however, the joining of tail fibers to a mature head–tail combination, may require an enzyme. If so, DNA information other than for the physical components is necessary for the morphogenesis of a cellular in-

---

[9] Thus, if the nucleoprotein of the 30s subunit is separated into its 16s and protein portions (19 to 20 different protein molecules) the 30s subunit can be reconstituted upon mixing the two together. The self-assembly is accomplished in three steps: (a) rapid binding of some of the proteins to the RNA, (b) a slow heat-requiring structural rearrangement of this intermediate, (c) rapid binding of the rest of the proteins.

clusion as complex as a phage. It seems likely that similarly complex or more complex organelles require genes catalyzing assemblage of components. (R)

30.11   Studies of morphological differentiation in protozoa reveal the importance of localized areas in the cell cortex, their self-reproducing organization, and their interactions with the genetic material and other aspects of the metabolism of other parts.

Various studies of *Paramecium* and other protozoa reveal that (1) different experimentally made modifications of the *cell cortex*—the outermost layer of protoplasm—are perpetuated during cell reproduction, and (2) certain perpetuated cortical structures, initially absent but produced experimentally, do not arise *de novo*.[10] Such results show that the cortex of unicellular eucaryotes is differentiated into localized areas whose organization is self-reproducing. (How this self-perpetuating organization is related to the DNA content of these localized areas is as yet unknown.) The cortex is not completely autonomous, however, since some nuclear genes are known to determine visible cortical structures or their morphogenesis. Clearly then, the nature and action of the cortex is dependent not only upon its own composition but upon nuclear genes and their products as well as metabolism in general. At present, the mode of operation of the cortex can only be described in general, largely speculative, terms. It remains to be seen, moreover, to what extent the cortex has a role in cell differentiation in multicellular eucaryotes. "The much more difficult task for the future is to define and specify in molecular terms the decisive structures, gradients, and inductor-response systems and to reveal how specific absorption, orientation, and activation of migratory molecules leads to visible morphogenesis and genetic stability of cell organization" (T. M. Sonneborn, 1963). (R)

SUMMARY AND CONCLUSIONS

Although some features of growth, development, and differentiation of cells are naturally or artificially modified by exposure to extrinsic m and t RNA's and to the

---

[10] Although *Paramecium* is normally a single animal, or *singlet*, double animals, or *doublets*, occur. Singlets and doublets reproduce true to type through numerous fissions (see Section S19.2). A doublet can also conjugate with two singlets and each singlet exconjugant regularly produces singlet clones and the doublet exconjugant, a doublet clone. The singlet–doublet difference cannot be due to micronuclear genes since exconjugants are identical in this respect. This same phenotypic result is obtained even when a cytoplasmic bridge lasts long enough to permit an extensive exchange of cytoplasm between conjugants. Consequently, the difference between doublet and singlet does not have a basis in any cytoplasmic component free to migrate. Other evidence seems to exclude the macronucleus from being involved. The only portion of the cell unaccounted for then is the immobile 0.5-μ-thick outer layer of ectoplasm, the cortex.

In one experiment, after cytoplasmic bridge formation between a singlet and doublet, a rare free singlet exconjugant was found bearing a conspicuous extra piece of cortex. The doublet exconjugant, on the other hand, showed a corresponding nick in its cortex. The extra piece in the singlet later flattened out and, after fission, one of the two daughter cells gave rise to a clone phenotypically intermediate between singlets and doublets. This natural grafting of only a small piece of a paramecium's oral segment gave rise to a strain having a complete extra oral segment including an extra vestibule, mouth, and gullet. Thus, a small additional piece of cortex gave rise to cortical changes of greater degree which were stably established in a strain.

nucleic acids of viruses, symbionts, and parasites, while other features are normally associated with changes in the quality and quantity of intrinsic genetic material, most aspects of these processes seem to result from the differential transcription and translation of a given qualitative set of information.

We have already discussed in earlier chapters several mechanisms that can be used to attain such a differential transcription. Differential transcription is indicated in the present chapter by different nuclei transcribing different portions (about 10 per cent) of their genomes at any given time. The translation of the transcripts of even this minor fraction of all genes requires the coordinate functioning of sufficiently redundant rDNA and (5s DNA) and other genes for ribosomal components. The translation mechanism also has many components whose control can result in differential translation during and after development and differentiation. Only a few features are discussed here: the presence of different tRNA's or aminoacyl-tRNA synthetases in different amounts at different times, and the different longevities of different mRNA's.

Additional understanding of the genetic basis and molecular mechanisms of development and differentiation is expected from studies of (1) experimental dedifferentiation and redifferentiation (as illustrated by transdetermination in *Drosophila*), (2) the assemblage of components in the formation of organelles, and (3) the coordination between genetic material (nuclear and nonnuclear) and highly organized nongenetic material (such as of organelles and membranes) in the production of perpetuated phenotypic features (as found in the cell cortex of *Paramecium*).

GENERAL REFERENCES

Bell, E. 1967. *Molecular and cellular aspects of development*, revised edition. New York: Harper & Row, Inc.
Bonner, J. 1965. *The molecular biology of development*. New York: Oxford University Press, Inc.
Davidson, E. H. 1968. *Genetic activity in early development*. New York: Academic Press, Inc.
Genetic control of differentiation. 1965. Brookhaven Sympos. Biol., No. 18.

SPECIFIC SECTION REFERENCES

30.1   Da Cunha, A. B., Morgante, J. S., Pavan, C., and Garrido, M. C. 1968. Studies on cytology and differentiation in Sciaridae. I. Chromosome changes induced by a gregarine in *Trichosia sp.* (Diptera, Sciaridae). Caryologia, 21 (No. 3): 271–282.
Eckhart, W. 1969. Cell transformation by polyoma virus and SV40. Nature, Lond., 224: 1069–1071.
Grüneberg, H. 1970. Is there a viral component in the genetic background? Nature, Lond., 225: 39–41.
Herrera, F., Adamson, R. H., and Gallo, R. C. 1970. Uptake of transfer ribonucleic acid by normal and leukemic cells. Proc. Nat. Acad. Sci., U.S., 67: 1943–1950.
Lust, G. 1966. Effect of infection on protein and nucleic acid synthesis in mammalian organs and tissues. Fed. Proc., 25: 1688–1694.
Sanyal, S., and Niu, M. C. 1966. Effect of RNA on the developmental potentiality of the posterior primitive streak of the chick blastoderm. Proc. Nat. Acad. Sci., U.S., 55: 743–750.
Sjolund, R. D., and Shih, C. Y. 1970. Viruslike particles in nuclei of cultured plant cells which have lost the ability to differentiate. Proc. Nat. Acad. Sci., U.S., 66: 25–31.
Walen, K. H. 1971. Nuclear involvement in poxvirus infection. Proc. Nat. Acad. Sci., U.S., 68: 165–168.

30.3   Gurdon, J. B. 1968. Transplanted nuclei and cell differentiation. Scient. Amer., 219 (No. 6): 24–35, 144.

Laskey, R. A., and Gurdon, J. B. 1970. Genetic content of adult somatic cells tested by nuclear transplantation from cultured cells. Nature, Lond., 228: 1332–1334. (Adult somatic cells of frog seem to have full developmental potential.)

30.4   Gelderman, A. H., Rake, A. V., and Britten, R. J. 1971. Transcription of nonrepeated DNA in neonatal and fetal mice. Proc. Nat. Acad. Sci., U.S., 68: 172–176. (About 70 per cent of newly made RNA in fetus is from nonrepeated DNA; the newborn mouse has RNA from 12 per cent of nonrepeated DNA sequences.)

30.5   Doi, R. H., and Igarashi, R. T. 1964. Genetic transcription during morphogenesis. Proc. Nat. Acad. Sci., U.S., 52: 755–762.

McCarthy, B. J., and Hoyer, B. H. 1964. Identity of DNA and diversity of messenger RNA molecules in normal mouse tissues. Proc. Nat. Acad. Sci., U.S., 52: 915–922.

Newell, P. C., and Sussman, M. 1970. Regulation of enzyme synthesis by slime mold cell assemblies embarked upon alternative developmental programs. J. Mol. Biol., 49: 627–637. (Control seems to be at the transcriptional level.)

Sueoka, N., and Armstrong, R. L. 1968. Phase transitions in ribonucleic acid synthesis during germination of *Bacillus subtilis* spores. Proc. Nat. Acad. Sci., U.S., 59: 153–160. (Cell differentiation from dormant to metabolically active condition.)

Whiteley, A. H., McCarthy, B. J., and Whiteley, H. R. 1966. Changing populations of messenger RNA during sea urchin development. Proc. Nat. Acad. Sci., U.S., 55: 519–525.

30.6   Brown, D. D., Dawid, I. B., and Reeder, R. 1969. Ribosomal RNA and its genes during oogenesis and development. Carneg. Inst. Wash. Yearb., 67: 401–404.

Hallberg, R. L. 1969. Synthesis of ribosomal proteins in *Xenopus laevis* embryos. Carneg. Inst. Wash. Yearb., 67: 409–413.

30.7   Adams, J. M., and Cory, S. 1970. Untranslated nucleotide sequences at the 5′-end of R17 bacteriophage RNA. Nature, Lond., 227: 570–574. (The first 74 nucleotides are not translated *in vivo*.)

Ceccarini, C., Maggio, R., and Barbata, G. 1967. Aminoacyl-sRNA synthetases as possible regulators of protein synthesis in the embryo of the sea urchin *Paracentrotus lividus*. Proc. Nat. Acad. Sci., U.S., 58: 2235–2239.

Gaskill, P., and Kabat, D. 1971. Unexpectedly large size of globin messenger ribonucleic acid. Proc. Nat. Acad. Sci., U.S., 68: 72-75. (In rabbit reticulocytes, a 9s mRNA coding for globin contains about 650 nucleotides, about 200 more than needed to code for the 141–146 amino acids in a globin chain.)

Ilan, J. 1970. The role of tRNA in translational control of specific mRNA during insect morphogenesis. Cold Spring Harbor Sympos. Quant. Biol., 34: 787–791.

Kanabus, J., and Cherry, J. H. 1971. Isolation of an organ-specific leucyl-tRNA synthetase from soybean seedlings. Proc. Nat. Acad. Sci., U.S., 68: 873–876.

Philipson, L., Wall, R., Glickman, G., and Darnell, J. E. 1971. Addition of polyadenylate sequences to virus-specific RNA during adenovirus replication. Proc. Nat. Acad. Sci., U.S., 68: 2806–2809. (Posttranscriptional addition of poly A to mRNA of a DNA virus.)

Sussman, M. 1970. Model for quantitative and qualitative control of mRNA translation in eukaryotes. Nature, Lond., 225: 1245–1246. (Hypothesis that one set of a series of redundant base sequences at the 5′ end of mRNA is removed each time mRNA is translated.)

Thomas, C. A. 1970. The theory of the master gene. In *Neurosciences II: a study program*, New York: Rockefeller University Press, pp. 973–998. (The role of gene redundancy.)

30.8   Farber, F. E., Cape, M., Decroly, M., and Brachet, J. 1968. The *in vitro* translation of *Acetabularia mediterranea* RNA. Proc. Nat. Acad. Sci., U.S., 61: 843–846.

Kafatos, F. C., and Reich, J. 1968. Stability of differentiation-specific and nonspecific messenger RNA in insect cells. Proc. Nat. Acad. Sci., U.S., 60: 1458–1465.

Wilt, F. H. 1965. Regulation of the initiation of chick embryo hemoglobin synthesis. J. Mol. Biol., 12: 331–341. Reprinted in *Papers on regulation of gene activity during development*, Loomis, W. F., Jr. (Editor), New York: Harper & Row, Inc., 1970, pp. 385–395.

Yaffe, D. 1968. Retention of differentiation potentialities during prolonged cultivation of myogenic cells. Proc. Nat. Acad. Sci., U.S., 61: 477–483. (Proteins made using stable mRNA.)

30.9   Hadorn, E. 1968. Transdetermination in cells. Scient. Amer., 219 (No. 5): 110–120, 172.

Hadorn, E., Gsell, R., and Schultz, J. 1970. Stability of a position effect variegation in normal and transdetermined larval blastemas from *Drosophila melanogaster*. Proc. Nat. Acad. Sci., U.S., 65: 633–637. (Variegation and transdetermination are separately controlled.)

30.10 Nomura, M. 1969. Ribosomes. Scient. Amer., 221 (No. 4): 28–35, 148.

Nomura, M., and Erdmann, V. A. 1970. Reconstitution of 50s ribosomal subunits from dissociated molecular components. Nature, Lond., 288: 744–748. (The dissociated RNA and protein components will reassociate at high temperatures.)

Wood, W. B., and Edgar, R. S. 1967. Building a bacterial virus. Scient. Amer., 217 (No. 1): 60–74, 134.

30.11 Miller, P. L. (Editor). 1970. *Control of organelle development*. Sympos. Soc. Exp. Biol., Vol. 24. New York: Academic Press, Inc.

Sonneborn, T. M. 1963. Does preformed cell structure play an essential role in cell heredity? In *The nature of biological diversity*, Allen, J. M. (Editor), New York: McGraw-Hill Book Company, Chap. 7, 165–221.

Sonneborn, T. M. 1970. Gene action in development. Proc. Roy. Soc. Lond., B176: 347–366. (The assembly of genic products into organized structures and the control of such assembly is discussed mainly with regard to cortical structures of *Paramecium*.)

QUESTIONS AND PROBLEMS

1. Criticize the following definitions of differentiation and development.
   a. *Differentiation* refers to all cyclical and directional changes in an organism which occur at the cell, tissue, organ, and organismal levels as observed from the biochemical and biophysical levels through the level of gross anatomy.
   b. *Development* refers to a description of the life history of an organism as observed from the same levels as is differentiation.
2. In what way does the genotype itself differentiate during a human life cycle?
3. Give experimental evidence that development of a mammal is not the result of the organism's genetic information alone.
4. Describe how you suppose actinomycin was used during chick development to show (Section 30.8) that template RNA for hemoglobin is present at the midprimitive streak stage even though hemoglobin is not synthesized until the 7- to 8-somite stage.
5. In what way does the research in *Drosophila* on transdetermination have bearing on the problem of the cause and cure of cancer?
6. How can you prove that the anlage, which differentiate in the pupa, are ordinarily determined in the larva?
7. What is "vitalism" and "mechanism" in

biology? What bearing has Section 30.10 in this regard?
8. How can you explain the finding that the nucleolus occupies roughly the same proportion of the nuclear volume in polynemic cells of larval *Drosophila* (1) in a given type of tissue cell regardless of amount of polynemy, and (2) in cells of different tissues?
9. How can you use *Xenopus* embryos and oocytes that are anucleolate homozygotes, normal homozygotes, and heterozygotes to test whether the three types of rRNA are synthesized coordinately?
10. In what ways are each of the following related to differentiation and development?
    1. Amount of genetic material in different cells of an organism.
    2. Differential transcription.
    3. Differential persistence of mRNA.
    4. Differential translation.
11. Differentiate between redundancy and amplification.
12. Give three examples of "reiterated" DNA in particular organisms. In each case state the known or suspected function of such DNA.
13. Suggest an explanation for the dedifferentiation which chondrocytes in vertebral cartilage undergo when grown *in vitro*.

Chapter 31

Gene-Action Regulation— During Development and Differentiation

Chapter 30 dealt with the genetic mechanisms employed by procaryotic and eucaryotic organisms to accomplish general development and differentiation. This chapter, dealing with eucaryotes only, describes first how these genetic mechanisms are applied or modified during specific early developmental stages and, subsequently, considers the general genetic mechanisms involved in hormonal action and in the programming of aging and death. Some new general mechanisms for gene-action regulation in eucaryotes are also presented.

31.1 Certain genetic mechanisms generally employed in development and differentiation are illustrated in the oocyte–ovum–early embryogenesis period in Amphibia.

The period in development from the early oocyte through the early embryo is of special interest since it is one that employs in an integrated manner many of the particular genetic regulatory mechanisms previously described one at a time. Our discussion of this period will deal mainly with Amphibia. Special differences and features in sea urchins, insects, and other organisms will be noted in the next few sections.

During prophase I of meiosis in Amphibia, probably near pachynema, amplification occurs of rDNA. Whereas only about 0.11 per cent of an ordinary genome is rDNA, the total nucleolar DNA after amplification is about $2\frac{1}{2}$ times the total DNA content of the ordinary nucleus. When the chromosomes subsequently assume the lampbrush configuration, 1.1×10^{12} rRNA molecules are synthesized and accumulated without turnover in *Xenopus*. Since it would take an ordinary cell of this organism 1.7×10^5 days to synthesize this amount of rRNA, the advantage of amplification (which permits this to occur 1 to 2×10^2 days—a period actually consistent with the length of the lampbrush stage) is obvious.

rRNA is not the only RNA synthesized in the lampbrush stage. About 2 per cent is informational, template-active, RNA transcribed from roughly 3 per cent of the genome. (Recall that most of the DNA template in eucaryotes is repressed.) This informational RNA is unusual in that, like rRNA, it shows no turnover and stops being synthesized after the lampbrush stage.

The locus and utilization of RNA's accumulated in the oocyte is suggested by studies of the amounts of RNA and protein in the lampbrush chromosome relative to that in liver chromosomes (taken to represent typical somatic chromosomes.) The RNA/DNA ratio (about 9) in lampbrush chromosomes is nearly 150 times the ratio found in liver chromosomes; and the protein/DNA ratio (over 550) in lampbrush chromosomes is about 200 times the ratio found in liver chromosomes. These results indicate that the products both of transcription and of translation (known from other evidence to occur in the loops of lampbrush chromosomes) accumulate on the oocyte chromosome.

At least 65 per cent of the informational RNA transcribed from families of partially redundant genes in the immature oocyte is still present in the mature oocyte. A portion of this long-lived template RNA may be translated during the last months of oocyte development. The large portion of oocyte informational RNA still present at fertilization represents maternal messengers to be used at least in part for cleavage and blastulation, including the coding for specific housekeeping proteins such as those needed for mitosis and glycolysis. About 25 per cent of the maternally inherited messenger RNA is lost by mid to late blastula.

The oocyte nucleus may also store proteins needed for early embryonic development. This possibility is supported by finding in axolotl (a kind of salamander) that the oocyte nucleus contains a high-molecular-weight substance, apparently protein, that is released to the cytoplasm of eggs where it must be stored in order to later complete gastrulation.

The preceding three paragraphs have indicated that, during oogenesis, RNA and protein products of maternal gene action are synthesized and are stored and released at specific times and places. Control of the availability of the products of gene action as well as of gene action itself seems to be the basis of the *localization* in the cytoplasm of a variety of metabolic substances which in turn influence which portion of the genome becomes expressed, permitting further development and differentiation.

Mature oocytes are transcriptionally inactive. In the sea urchin, protein synthesis does not occur in the unfertilized egg, even though maternal mRNA and ribosomes are present (see also Section 27.14). Evidence indicates that proteins complexed with these ribosomes prevent translation of the bound messenger. After fertilization or parthenogenesis, proteases (probably converted from an inactive to an active form) digest the protein from the mRNA–ribosome complex and thus permit translation. Polypeptide chain initiation seems to be stepped up upon fertilization.

Such translational activity, the release of stored gene products, and the presence of other localized morphogenetic substances soon differentially activates the developing individual's own genetic material, so that the destiny of the individual gradually comes under the control of its own genotype. Thus, in Amphibia, some informational RNA is made starting at cleavage, tRNA starting at mid-to-late blastula, and rRNA starting near the beginning of gastrulation, about the time at which nucleoli first appear. Newly synthesized rRNA is not incorporated into ribosomes, however, until later (after the tail bud is formed), when yolk utilization starts, and the embryo is some 30,000 cells. Evidence indicates that at least some new informational RNA is not translated immediately but, like rRNA, is stored for later use (recall hemoglobin synthesis in the chick embryo), in this instance by forming some kind of inactivating complex with ribosomes or ribosome-like particles (thereby comprising *informosomes*). Such embryonic gene action is regulated at the level of translation just as maternal mRNA is in the sea urchin.[1]

---

[1] In early *Ascaris* development, for another example, new informational RNA is associated with stable polysomal structures, is resistant to RNase, and is not template-active. Treatment with trypsin, however, renders this RNA RNase-sensitive and template-active. By blastulation some, perhaps all, new RNA is RNase-sensitive and template-active.

In summary, then, we see that the unfertilized egg carries a store of suppressed maternal informational RNA which becomes functional after fertilization. Embryonic informational RNA is then synthesized, and stored in nonfunctional condition until a subsequent stage when it becomes functional. (R)

31.2   Oocytes receive the products of gene action of other cells.

When, in amphibians and echinoderms, the embryo plus abundant nutrient is a separate developing unit, the oocyte stage anticipates by preparing a stockpile of informational RNA and translational equipment, and the assumption of developmental responsibility by the embryonic genotype is delayed. In mammals, on the other hand, where the embryo plus limited nutrient is not separate from the mother, control by the embryonic genome occurs earlier—embryonic informational RNA appearing as early as before the first cleavage division and new rRNA at the 4 to 8-cell stage. Eggs of the first type also occur in the lamprey, in nematodes, mollusks, and insects. These organisms possess *nurse cells*, which are characteristically joined to the oocyte via cytoplasmic bridges through which whole mitochondria, polysomes, and other pre-formed materials (including DNA) can pass from the nurse cells into the oocyte (Figure 31-1). The presence of nurse cells is often correlated with the absence of both lampbrush chromosomes and a prolonged prophase I.

Almost all oocytes (with their nurse cells if present) are surrounded by a layer of

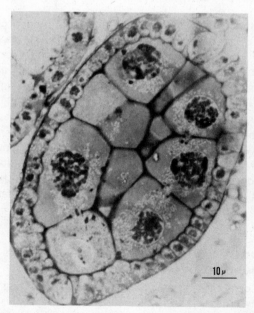

10 µ

Figure 31-1   Photomicrograph of a section through a *Drosophila* egg chamber. At this stage a single layer of cuboidal follicle cells surrounds the oocyte, which occupies a position at the lower left corner of the chamber, and the 15 nurse cells, 9 of which are evident in this section. Three ring canals are evident, one connecting the oocyte with a nurse cell and two inter-connecting three nurse cells. Note the particulate material which appears to have been fixed during its passage through the ring canals. (Courtesy of E. H. Brown and R. C. King, 1964. Growth, 28: 41–81, Fig. 3.)

follicle cells (Figure 31-1). These cells are active in protein and RNA synthesis, and proteins made in them or elsewhere are transported from them into the oocyte. In some cases there is no cytoplasmic continuity between follicle cells and the oocyte; when there is, follicular cytoplasm flows into the oocyte. In the snail *Helix* the oocyte phagocytizes entire follicle cells. It seems, therefore, that the oocyte always obtains synthetic products from other cells, whether or not additional products are provided by nurse cells or by synthesis involving a lampbrush stage. (R)

31.3   Chromatin which is functionally or physically eliminated either somatically or in the male seems to have a prior function, and to be present and functional during at least part of oogenesis.

How the need for gene product for the growth of oocytes is solved has been discussed in previous sections. We are concerned now with how this need is correlated with the functional or physical elimination of chromatin that occurs in various species.

Functional inactivation of chromosomes or chromosome parts occurs via heterochromatization during interphase. It is noteworthy that the Barr body of the somatic tissues of the female rat is absent, however, in the oocyte. Moreover, in coccids, one entire genome of the two present in an egg may be heterochromatized; such eggs produce only males. This suggests, therefore, that oogenesis always functionally utilizes portions of the genotype which are inactivated in the somatic line or in the male germ line.

Physical elimination of whole chromosomes or parts of them occurs both germinally and somatically. Note that all transcriptional activity during oogenesis occurs prior to the chromosomal elimination involved in polar body formation; and that the chromosome elimination in the germ line of *Sciara* occurs only after the completion of the oogonial divisions. Chromosome diminution occurs in the somatic line of *Ascaris lumbricoides*. In this species, fertilization occurs while the oocyte is undergoing meiosis. It requires the next 50 to 60 hours for this meiotic process to be completed and to form the haploid female pronucleus. Active template and rRNA synthesis occurs directly after fertilization, however, using the DNA templates of the male pronucleus. This RNA is apparently used in postcleavage development. Since chromosome diminution occurs in the somatic line during cleavage, the earlier transcriptional activity seems to take advantage of the presence of a complete paternal genome. (R)

31.4   Eggs contain large amounts of cytoplasmic genetic DNA.

It is common for eggs of multicellular eucaryotes to contain hundreds of times more DNA in their cytoplasm than in their nucleus. The cytoplasmic DNA is mostly mitochondrial DNA, although some may be associated with the DNA of yolk platelets. The stockpiling of such DNA's in the oocyte assures that cleaving cells will have adequate DNA's of these types even if little or no cytoplasmic DNA synthesis occurs during early development. Since an adequate supply of cytoplasmic DNA information for transcription and translation in early development has been provided, the entire DNA synthesizing capacity of the egg can be concentrated in the nucleus, and mitosis and cleavage can occur with minimal delay. (R)

31.5   The transcription of nuclear DNA depends upon cytoplasmic factors.

We have already indicated how, in general, cell differentiation and development depend upon cytoplasmic factors (Chapter 19 and Sections 24.4, 30.11, and 31.1). Note that nuclear histones are synthesized in the cytoplasm (see footnote 5 in Section 27.12). Studies of the types of RNA synthesized by transplanted nuclei reveal that the synthesis of RNA by a nucleus is subject to control by cytoplasmic factors. Thus, a single nucleus from the neurula stage of *Xenopus* development, which is synthesizing informational, t, and r RNA's, can be transplanted into an enucleated *Xenopus* egg, which is synthesizing no RNA. Within 1 hour of transplantation into the egg cytoplasm all detectable RNA synthesis is halted in the transplanted nucleus. (When this cell later undergoes development, however, t and r RNA's are synthesized at their normal times in embryogeny.) Similarly, when adult amphibian brain nuclei, which are synthesizing RNA, are transplanted into nucleated, parthenogenetically activated eggs of the same species, which are synthesizing no RNA, within 1 to 2 hours the transplanted nuclei stop RNA synthesis (see Section 24.4 for the effects of such transplantations on DNA synthesis.)

Reciprocally, activation of an essentially nontranscribing nucleus can apparently be induced by the cytoplasm of an actively transcribing cell, as indicated by the following: (1) When a nucleated erythrocyte of a hen, which has clumped chromatin, fuses with a cell of the HeLa tissue culture, the erythrocyte nucleus swells and the chromatin becomes less clumped and capable of RNA synthesis, and (2) when midblastula nuclei, which are inactive in RNA synthesis, are transplanted into nucleated, growing, RNA-synthesizing oocytes, the transplanted nuclei start synthesizing RNA. (R)

31.6   Hormones regulate gene action by affecting transcription and translation.

Although some hormones are proteins, many others are steroids or derivatives of a single amino acid (see Figure 31-2)—small molecules in comparison to proteins or nucleic acids. Since hormones act at low concentration, their metabolic effect must somehow be magnified. This metabolic effect often seems to be on the synthesis of RNA and protein. Usually hormones stimulate RNA synthesis; for example in uterine tissue by estrogens, in the prostate gland by testosterone, in plant buds by a flowering hormone, and in larval polynemic chromosomes by insect hormones (see Section 27.3). Some hormones decrease RNA synthesis, however; for example hydrocortisone in cultured osteocytes and thyroxine in anuran tail skin. It is possible that some hormones

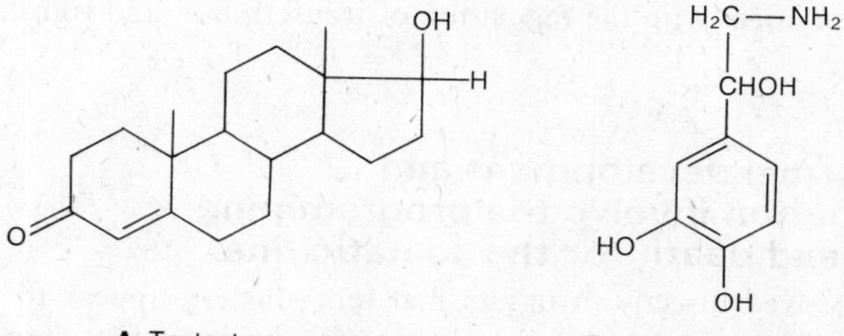

A. Testosterone   **B.** Norepinephrine

Figure 31-2   Structural formulas of a hormone of steroid (A) and amino acid–derivative (B) types.

act to repress gene action and their antagonistic hormones to derepress gene action.

Experiments involving a variety of hormones have indicated several ways, listed below, in which they may act at the molecular level.

1. The flowering hormone, which stimulates protein and mRNA synthesis in plant buds, is found to lower the ratio of histone to DNA. Perhaps this hormone enables the DNA to be used as template by causing the removal of histone. Similarly, estrogen causes an increase in RNA and total protein but decreases the histone content of chromatin; the binding of the hormone to chromatin also increases *in vivo*.

2. Hormones such as glucagon and insulin (but not hydrocortisone or adrenocorticotrophic hormone) cause an increase in the phosphorylation of histone in rat liver.

3. In several cases RNA increase in the target cell requires the combination of a hormone with protein. When an auxin–protein complex is added to isolated chromatin or isolated nuclei of target cells, an increase in transcription is observed, whereas no change in transcription occurs when pure auxin is used.

4. Several other types of hormone are known to change the melting profile of isolated mammalian DNA (but not bacterial DNA) in a manner which indicates that they promote strand separation of specific segments of DNA; hence, they also may promote the use of DNA as a template.

5. Some hormones may affect regulator genes or their products; for example, androgens appear to cause a differential transcription to RNA which could be explained in these terms. The differential transcription effect of the androgen testosterone is indicated by finding that the hormone-induced transcripts are rich in G and C, as if they were transcripts of DNA in the nucleolus organizer region.

6. Cytokinin, a natural plant hormone, can influence the acylation of a specific tRNA. Regulation of gene action at the level of translation is possible therefore. This is further supported by studies that show the synthesis of amylase is stimulated by epinephrine treatment of slices of rat parotid gland in the absence of RNA synthesis.

7. A study of the effect of gibberellic acid and abscisic acid on early germination in wheat embryos suggests that they affect development at the translation level.

As expected from the large effect which small quantities of hormones have on differentiation and development, the preceding indicates that many hormones may act more or less directly on the regulation of transcription and translation. (R)

31.7 Normal development and differentiation involve the programming of aging and death for the somatic line.

The cells involved directly in organismal reproduction appear to be immortal—present-day people, mice, insects, and bacteria being direct descendants of an unbroken ancestral reproductive chain. When, however, a separate line is established of somatic plasm (as is involved in macronuclear formation and function in ciliate protozoa, for example) or somatic cells, several lines of evidence show that the soma is not immortal.

1. Paramecium cannot indefinitely reproduce by fission unless, on occasion, *autogamy* occurs. In this process diploid micronuclei undergo meiosis and all products but one disintegrate; the surviving haploid micronucleus divides mitotically and the two products fuse to form a completely homozygous diploid micronucleus; this, in turn, divides to produce a new (somatic) macronucleus that replaces the old one, which has meanwhile disintegrated. Autogamy, which replaces somatic plasm, rejuvenates *Paramecium.*

2. Somatic tissue and organ death is normally programmed (review Section 24.9) during developmental or immature stages in a variety of organisms.

3. Aging and death are also normally programmed in somatic cells of the adult stage, as indicated from the following evidence.

Despite the increase in average life expectancy in man due to advances in nutrition and medicine, there is little evidence for a significant change in *life span*, the typical upper limit still being 70 to 80 years. In other words, somatic death seems to be an intrinsic feature of organisms. The limitation in life span is associated with *aging*, which in man seems to involve a decreased efficiency of the muscular and nervous systems, loss of flexibility of collagen, and a decreased frequency of cell division.

Although cancerous cells can apparently divide indefinitely in cell culture, normal fibroblasts obtained from human embryos can be subcultured after the culture has doubled its size only 50 ± 10 times before subculturing fails. The number of doublings possible decreases with age of the fibroblast, being 30 ± 10 times from donors over 20. Shorter-lived species have a smaller capacity for fibroblast division in cell culture —embryos of chicken, rat, mouse, and hamster have a doubling number of about 15, this number being considerably smaller for fibroblasts obtained from the adult forms.

That the restricted life span for subculturing a normal somatic cell culture is programmed intrinsically is demonstrated by the following experiment. Fibroblasts without Barr bodies (originally isolated from males) that have doubled about 40 times are cultured together with fibroblasts with Barr bodies (isolated from females) that have doubled only about 10 times. After 25 more doublings only cells with Barr bodies are present in the subcultures. Apparently the more divisions a somatic cell undergoes, the greater the chance it will fail to divide—this chance becoming 100 per cent by the 45th to 50th doubling generation. It should be noted that as a fibroblast culture nears extinction, an increase is observed in gross chromosomal abnormalities.

The intrinsic programming that produces somatic cell aging and death must more or less directly involve the genetic material. Thus, involvement can conceivably occur directly, at the level of DNA, due to mutations which make defective templates in the genes concerned with (1) enzymes for replication, transcription, or translation; (2) structural proteins and nucleic acids needed for these processes; (3) the repair of damaged templates; and (4) substances that regulate gene action. The program may also involve genetic material indirectly, via changes not in DNA templates, but in their products—changes in the rate of destruction of defective parts (including proteins) or their replacement in the cell. In other words, the change in programming may be due to changes in the chemistry of the genes themselves, the spectrum of genes that are functional, or gene products that are limited in supply or replacement. At present we cannot assess more specifically just where and how the genetic material is involved in programming somatic cell aging and death. (R)

SUMMARY AND CONCLUSIONS

Many of the mechanisms for differential transcription and translation described in earlier chapters are illustrated in the regulation of gene action in eucaryotes during the developmental period from oocyte to early embryo. Specific features of gene-action regulation in Amphibia during this developmental period include (1) during oocyte maturation, the receipt of the products of gene action of follicle cells, the amplification and transcription of rDNA, and the stockpiling and localization of cytoplasmic DNA, maternal proteins, and mRNA's; (2) during fertilized egg development, the selective use and decay of maternal proteins and mRNA's; and (3) during embryonic development, the differential transcription of genetic material as development progresses until the new organism is controlled by its own genotype. Other special features of gene-action regulation that other organisms have in this developmental period include the use of nurse cells and the production of suitably long-lived mRNA transcripts from genetic material which is subsequently functionally or physically eliminated.

Other general mechanisms for the regulation of gene action in development and differentiation of eucaryotes are presented or discussed in detail for the first time: (1) nuclear gene transcription depends upon cytoplasmic factors (which may, in turn, depend upon nuclear or extranuclear genetic material), (2) nuclear gene transcription and translation in certain cells are often regulated by hormones produced by other cells, and (3) aging and death of the somatic line seem to be normally programmed, genetically determined events.

GENERAL REFERENCES

Ebert, J., and Sussex, I. M. 1970. *Interacting systems in development*, second edition. New York: Holt, Rinehart and Winston, Inc.

Loomis, W. F., Jr. (Editor), 1970. *Papers on the regulation of gene activity during development*. New York: Harper & Row, Inc.

SPECIFIC SECTION REFERENCES

31.1 Brown, D. D., and Dawid, I. B. 1969. Developmental genetics. Ann. Rev. Genet., 3: 127–154.

Kedes, L. H., Hogan, B., Cognetti, G., Selvig, S., Yanover, P., and Gross, P. R. 1970. Regulation of translation and transcription of messenger RNA during early embryonic development. Cold Spring Harbor Sympos. Quant. Biol., 34: 717–723.

MacKintosch, F. R., and Bell, E. 1969. Regulation of protein synthesis in sea urchin eggs. J. Mol. Biol., 41: 365–380.

31.2 Dapples, C. C., and King, R. C. 1970. The development of the nucleolus of the ovarian nurse cell of *Drosophila melanogaster*. Z. Zellforsch., 103: 34–47. (Ribosomes stored in *Drosophila* ooplasm are derived almost exclusively from the nurse cell.)

31.3 Brown, S. W. 1969. Developmental control of heterochromatization in coccids. Genetics, 61 (Suppl. 1/2): 191–198.

31.4 Baltus, E., Hanocq-Quertier, J., and Brachet, J. 1968. Isolation of deoxyribonucleic acid from the yolk platelets of *Xenopus laevis* oocyte. Proc. Nat. Acad. Sci., U.S., 61: 469–476.

Dawid, I. B. 1966. Evidence for the mitochondrial origin of frog egg cytoplasmic DNA. Proc. Nat. Acad. Sci., U.S., 56: 269–276.

31.5 Gurdon, J. B. 1968. Transplanted nuclei and cell differentiation. Scient. Amer., 219 (No. 6): 24–35, 144.

Gurdon, J. B., and Woodland, H. R. 1968. The cytoplasmic control of nuclear activity in animal development. Biol. Rev., Camb., 43 (No. 2): 233–267.

Harris, H. 1968. *Nucleus and cytoplasm.* Oxford: Clarendon Press. (Cell-fusion experiments as a means of studying gene control mechanisms.)

31.6 Chen, D., and Osborne, D. J. 1970. Hormones in the translational control of early germination in wheat embryos. Nature, Lond., 226: 1157–1160.

Chin, R.-C., and Kidson, C. 1971. Selective associations of hormonal steroids with aminoacyl transfer RNA's and control of protein synthesis. Proc. Nat. Acad. Sci., U.S., 68: 2448–2452. (*In vitro*, specific hormones bind to specific aminoacyl-tRNA's.)

De Angelo, A. B., and Gorski, J. 1970. Role of RNA synthesis in the estrogen induction of a specific uterine protein. Proc. Nat. Acad. Sci., U.S., 66: 693–700.

Gelehrter, T. D., and Tomkins, G. M. 1970. Posttranscriptional control of tyrosine aminotransferase synthesis by insulin. Proc. Nat. Acad. Sci., U.S., 66: 390–397. (Stimulation of enzyme synthesis involves no increase in RNA synthesis.)

Grand, R. J., and Gross, P. R. 1970. Translation-level control of amylase and protein synthesis by epinephrine. Proc. Nat. Acad. Sci., U.S., 65: 1081–1088.

Langan, T. A. 1969. Phosphorylation of liver histone following the administration of glucagon and insulin. Proc. Nat. Acad. Sci., U.S., 64: 1276–1283.

Matthysse, A. G., and Phillips, C. 1969. A protein intermediary in the action of a hormone with the genome. Proc. Nat. Acad. Sci., U.S., 63: 897–903.

Morgan, C. R., and Bonner, J. 1970. Template activity of liver chromatin increased by *in vivo* administration of insulin. Proc. Nat. Acad. Sci., U.S., 65: 1077–1080. (Insulin derepresses genetic material repressed in the absence of insulin.)

Shelton, K. R., and Allfrey, V. G. 1970. Selective synthesis of a nuclear acidic protein in liver cells stimulated by cortisol. Nature, Lond., 228: 132–134. (Acidic protein synthesis in nucleus stimulated by steroid hormone.)

31.7 Eyring, H., and Stover, B. J. 1970. The dynamics of life, II. The steady-state theory of mutation rates. Proc. Nat. Acad. Sci., U.S., 66: 441–444. (The nature of cellular alterations that lead to nonsurvival.)

Hayflick, L. 1968. Human cells and aging. Scient. Amer., 218 (No. 3): 32–37, 150.

Lewis, C. M., and Holliday, R. 1970. Mistranslation and ageing in *Neurospora.* Nature, Lond., 228: 877–880. (Aging may involve mistranslation which will also result in defective DNA and RNA polymerases and hence an increased number of mutations.)

Webster, D. A., and Gross, J. 1970. Studies on possible mechanisms of programmed cell death in the chick embryo. Develop. Biol., 22: 157–184.

QUESTIONS AND PROBLEMS

1. In what general or specific ways do genetic factors affect developmental pathways?

2. What do you suppose happens to radioactively labeled DNA taken in by mammalian cells in tissue culture? How would you test your hypothesis?

3. Tell how the following may be used by the cell:
   a. DNA excised in the repair of dimer formation and single-strand breaks;
   b. nonintegrated DNA transferred in transformation, conjugation, or transduction.

4. What general conclusions about genes and development are supported by the following observations of K. Marushige and H. Ozaki, working with sea urchin embryos?
   a. Chromatin isolated from a later stage (pluteus) has twice the template activity for DNA-dependent RNA synthesis *in vitro* as chromatin isolated from an earlier stage (blastula).
   b. Removal of chromosomal proteins increases this template activity of the DNA and abolishes the difference in template activity between blastula and pluteus chromatin.
   c. They obtained results indicating that pluteus chromatin has twice the number of sites for binding DNA-dependent RNA polymerase as blastula chromatin.

5. Although the administration of hydrocortisone *in vivo* causes isolated rat liver chromatin to have an increased template activity for RNA synthesis *in vitro*, M. E. Dahmus

found that the administration of hydrocortisone directly to liver chromatin isolated from untreated rats had no such effect on template activity. What can you conclude from these results about the mechanism of action of this hormone?

6. Axolotls whose female parent have o/o genotype cannot, whereas those with o^+/o^+ or o^+/o can, complete gastrulation. Making use of an egg-injection technique, describe how you would study the molecular basis of this maternal influence.

7. What do you think of the (rephrased) view of E. H. Davidson that "were the storage in the egg cytoplasm of molecules whose function is the selective specification of embryo gene activity understood in molecular terms, such a mechanism would go far to explain the initial set of mysteries facing the developmental biologist, viz., the onset of embryo genome control and the appearance of the first patterns of embryonic differentiation."

8. Discuss the statement that early development at least through cleavage is independent of embryo gene action. How could you test this statement experimentally?

9. After consulting embryology textbooks, make a report on the formation and role of pole plasm and pole cells in the determination of the germ line. In what way is your report of genetic interest?

10. What genetic adaptations are associated with the accumulation of large amounts of gene product in the maturing oocyte?

11. How many hormones function at the molecular level of the gene to influence differentiation and development?

12. Define maternal effect. Give an example at the molecular level.

13. In the snail *Limnea peregra*, self-fertilization of pure-line individuals whose shell coils to the right, dextrally, or to the left, sinistrally, produces progeny all of which coil as their parents. A cross of dextral ♀ by sinistral ♂ yields all dextral F_1 which, when self-fertilized, yield all dextral progeny in F_2. After self-fertilization, however, $\frac{3}{4}$ of the F_2 give rise to dextral F_3 and $\frac{1}{4}$ of the F_2 to sinistral F_3. The reciprocal cross, dextral ♂ by sinistral ♀, yields all sinistral F_1. The F_1 produces F_2 and F_3 phenotypically the same as the reciprocal cross. Give a genetic explanation for these results. Are cytoplasmic genes involved? Explain.

14. T. Yamada has found that isolated prospective ectoderm gives rise only to epidermal cells when cultured *in vitro* in standard medium, but forms mesodermal tissues if a protein fraction from bone marrow is added to the medium. To what can you attribute these results?

15. An enucleated egg of one species of Amphibia can be fertilized by sperm of another species. How can you explain molecularly and genetically (1) that early development occurs, and (2) that death typically occurs before gastrulation.

16. Justify the statement that cell differentiation depends upon nucleocytoplasmic interaction.

Chapter 32

Gene-Action Regulation— Differentiation in Specific Tissues

In many tissues differentiation involves the production of unique proteins. These proteins are often required either in large quantities (as in muscle tissue and red blood corpuscles) or in large variety (as in the white blood cells that make antibodies, and perhaps in nerve tissue). Each former type of protein serves intrinsic metabolic needs independently of changes in the external environment. The latter type of protein is produced in response to stimuli originating in the external environment, the specific protein response involving the storage of information (immunological memory or neurological memory). This chapter considers the genetic bases for hemoglobin, antibodies, learning and memory, and cancer.

32.1   Hemoglobin is a tetrameric protein composed of two different dimers. Normal adults synthesize hemoglobin A and hemoglobin A$_2$.

Human hemoglobin is a protein composed of two different dimers, each dimer always consisting of identical polypeptide chains. These four chains, arranged approximately in the form of a tetrahedron, each contain about 140 amino acids and have a molecular weight of about 17,000. The chains are folded back on themselves and each has an iron-containing heme group that fits into a pocket on the strand's outer surface.

Hemoglobin isolated from normal adults is of three types: A (or A$_1$), A$_2$, and A$_3$. The A component, called *hemoglobin A (Hb-A)* makes up nearly 90 per cent of the total hemoglobin; the A$_2$ component (Hb-A$_2$) about 2.5 per cent. The rest is Hb-A$_3$, which is probably Hb-A that has become chemically altered during aging of the red blood corpuscles.

In vitro, Hb-A can dissociate into its two dimers, which can reassociate to form the Hb-A tetramer once again. If the monomers are represented as α^A and β^A, the reversible reaction can be symbolized as

$$\alpha_2^A \beta_2^A \rightleftharpoons \alpha_2^A + \beta_2^A. \qquad (R)$$

32.2   The α and β chains of Hb-A are coded at different loci. Various mutant genes cause single amino acid substitutions in these chains.

Sickle-cell anemia (Section 22.1) occurs in individuals homozygous for a gene for sickling (Figure 22-2). The red blood corpuscles of such individuals assume a sickle-like shape when deoxygenated and are destroyed by the spleen, thus leading to a serious anemia. Persons heterozygous for this mutant gene have *sickle-cell trait* but are only mildly anemic, if at all. The difference between normal and sickle cells is found in the hemoglobin they contain; the hemoglobin of the mutant homozygote differs from hemoglobin A (Figure 32-1) at only one amino acid position, number 6 in the β chain, where valine is present instead of glutamic acid. Cells heterozygous for the sickling gene produce both this abnormal type of hemoglobin, *hemoglobin S* ($\alpha_2^A \beta_2^S$), and the normal hemoglobin, A ($\alpha_2^A \beta_2^A$).

Numerous other abnormal hemoglobins have been found (Figure 32-2). In some instances the alteration in the amino acid sequence occurs in the α chain, as in hemoglobin I (which has a substitution at position 16). These single amino acid substitutions can be explained as the result of the mutation of a single base in the genetic material coding hemoglobin. The two kinds of chains are coded by different genes, since mutant genes that change the α chain produce no change in the β chain (and vice

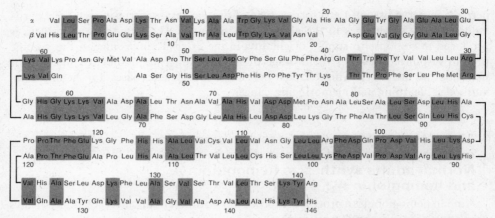

Figure 32-1   Amino acid sequences of the α and β peptide chains of Hb-A. The amino acids enclosed by shaded boxes are identical and occupy corresponding positions along the peptide chains. The amino acids are numerated sequentially from the N terminus. (Reproduced by permission of Dr. Vernon M. Ingram.)

Hb Type	Amino Acid Position	Change Involved
	β Chain	
S	6	Glu → Val
C	6	Glu → Lys
G San José	7	Glu → Gly
E	26	Glu → Lys
M Saskatoon	63	His → Tyr
Zürich	63	His → Arg
M Milwaukee-1	67	Val → Glu
O Arabia	121	Glu → Lys
D Punjab (= D Cyprus)	121	Glu → Gln
	α Chain	
I	16	Lys → Asp
G Honolulu	30	Glu → Gln
Norfolk	57	Gly → Asp
M Boston	58	His → Tyr
G Philadelphia (= G Azakuoli)	68	Asn → Lys
O Indonesia	116	Glu → Lys

Figure 32-2   Some variants of Hemoglobin A. Amino acid substitutions are already known for 49 positions in the β chain and 29 positions in the α chain.

versa) and since the genes for defects of the α and β chains segregate independently. An adult homozygous for the hemoglobin A genes ($\alpha^A \alpha^A \beta^A \beta^A$) thus produces $\alpha_2^A \beta_2^A$ tetramers. A homozygote for the sickle-cell gene ($\alpha^A \alpha^A \beta^S \beta^S$) produces $\alpha_2^A \beta_2^S$ hemoglobin, and one homozygous for hemoglobin I ($\alpha^I \alpha^I \beta^A \beta^A$) produces $\alpha_2^I \beta_2^A$. A dihybrid, $\alpha^A \alpha^I \beta^A \beta^S$, produces four types of globin: $\alpha_2^A \beta_2^A$, $\alpha_2^I \beta_2^A$, $\alpha_2^A \beta_2^S$, and $\alpha_2^I \beta_2^S$, since either product of the two different α-specifying genes can join to either product of the two different β-specifying genes.

32.3   The Hb-A$_2$ tetramer contains an α dimer and a δ dimer. The latter is coded by a gene δ, which has mutant alleles and is linked to gene β.

The Hb-A$_2$ tetramer can also be dissociated into its two dimers; one is the α_2^A dimer, and the other is called a $\delta_2^{A_2}$ dimer, which is very similar to β_2^A, differing only by 4 (or perhaps 8) of 146 amino acids.

Some individuals produce only about half the normal amount of Hb-A$_2$. In place of the missing hemoglobin is an equal amount of another kind of hemoglobin, Hb-B$_2$, which also consists of two α and two δ chains. The α chains are of the normal α^A type, but the δ chain appears to differ from the δ^{A_2} type by one amino acid: Gly $\rightarrow$ Arg at position 16.

The δ chain is specified by a gene, δ, which is allelic to neither α^A nor β^A. Persons with both Hb-A$_2$ and Hb-B$_2$, therefore, have the hybrid genotype $\delta^{A_2}\,\delta^{B_2}$ with respect to the δ genes. The δ gene has been found to be recombinationally linked to the β gene. Thus, the rare person who produces some Hb-S ($\alpha_2^A\beta_2^S$) and Hb-A and some Hb-B$_2$ ($\alpha_2^A\delta_2^{B_2}$) and Hb-A$_2$ most likely has the genotype $\dfrac{\alpha^A\ \ \ \ \beta^A\ \ \delta^{B_2}}{\alpha^A\ \ \ \ \beta^S\ \ \delta^{A_2}}$, each parent having contributed one mutant gene.

32.4   Fetal hemoglobin is $\alpha_2^A\,\gamma_2^F$. Its γ chains are coded at a fourth locus, γ.

The hemoglobin of a human fetus, *hemoglobin F*, contains two α chains identical to those in adult hemoglobin A. The other two chains in Hb-F differ from the α, β, and δ chains and are called γ chains (Figure 32-3). Normal hemoglobin F is thus $\alpha_2^A\gamma_2^F$. Homozygotes for the sickling gene make hemoglobin F, which seems to be normal.

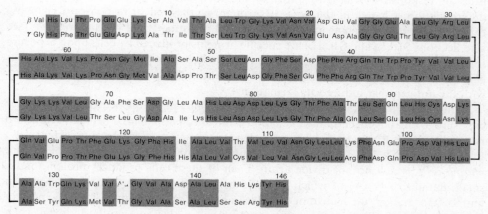

Figure 32-3   Amino acid sequence of the β peptide chain of Hb-A and of the γ peptide chain of Hb-F. The amino acids enclosed by shaded boxes are identical and occupy corresponding positions along the peptide chains. The amino acids are numerated sequentially from the N terminus. (Reproduced by permission of Dr. Vernon M. Ingram.)

Apparently, then, the gene for the mutant β chain has no effect on the γ chain. Some abnormal types of Hb-F, however, are thought to contain altered γ chains. It is likely, therefore, that a separate gene, γ^F, specifies γ^F chains.

In summary, four genes seem to be involved in the manufacture of human hemoglobin—α, β, δ, and γ—each of which codes for a different polypeptide.

32.5 The amount and type of hemoglobin synthesized during development and differentiation is regulated.

We have already noted in previous chapters that the α and β chains of hemoglobin are apparently coded in segments of one or more giant informational RNA molecules; that the RNA codons for the polypeptide chains exist in the developing embryo long before translation occurs; and that the mRNA for these polypeptides is moderately long-lived. These results plus those mentioned in the next two paragraphs suggest that the production of a given type of hemoglobin may involve regulation at both the transcriptional and translational levels.

The types of hemoglobin chains synthesized shifts during human development. Hb-A appears in the fetus as early as the twentieth week and gradually replaces Hb-F. Even at the time of birth, however, an infant has some Hb-F in its blood. This change from Hb-F to Hb-A indicates that during development the γ^F gene is turned off and gene β^A is turned on. The genetic basis for this regulating mechanism is not yet well understood.

In the frog, the tadpole has three kinds of hemoglobin and the adult four different kinds of hemoglobin. All these hemoglobins are present during metamorphosis, the switch from tadpole to adult types probably being stimulated by thyroxin. (R)

32.6 Certain cells differentiate to produce a particular antibody.

As we have just seen, several types of hemoglobin are synthesized in large quantities in response to changing intrinsic metabolic needs during development and differentiation. Change in the types of protein synthesized in response to changing extrinsic factors in the environment is illustrated in antibody synthesis. *Antibodies* (see also Sections S16.1a and S16.1b) are specific proteins produced by cells upon exposure to foreign macromolecular substances called *antigens*, which are often proteins but can also be carbohydrates or nucleic acids. The antibody is used by the cell to complex with the antigen that induced its formation.

Antibody formation in the rat involves the following sequence of events. After exposure to an antigen, certain white blood cells called *plasmablasts* begin to synthesize ribosomes and mRNA at a high rate; their endoplasmic reticulum develops extensively. Each plasmablast then undergoes about nine divisions to form a colony of mature *plasma cells*, which do not divide again. Each of these cells produces protein (and a small amount of RNA) of which 90 to 95 per cent is a single type of antibody. In antibody formation, then, an antigen causes a plasma cell to produce a specific protein almost exclusively. With rare exceptions each cell makes one antibody, even when other plasma cells in the lymph nodes are synthesizing other antibodies. Another type of white blood cell, the *lymphocyte*, produces a minor amount of antibody (Figure 32-4). (R)

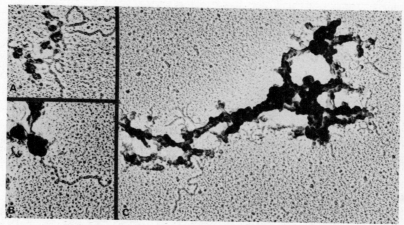

Figure 32-4 Electron micrograph of plasma membranes from diploid human lymphocytes showing associated DNA molecules. Samples were prepared according to a modification of the spreading procedure of Kleinschmidt and Zahn. DNA was not seen when membranes were treated with deoxyribonuclease. Although the function of this plasma-membrane-associated DNA is still unknown, it differs from nuclear and mitochondrial DNA in time of synthesis and physical properties and may, perhaps, be related to γG globulin production. (Courtesy of R. A. Lerner, W. Meinke, and D. A. Goldstein, 1971. Proc. Nat. Acad. Sci., U.S., 68: 1212–1216.)

32.7 The specificity of antibodies is a reflection of diversity in their primary structure.

Specific immune responses are developed most highly in mammals, where it is estimated that 10^4 to 10^6 different antibodies can be made to specifically bind a similar number of different antigens. The differences in specificity among antibodies seem to be the result of differences in antibody primary structure, that is, the number and sequence of their amino acids, rather than, say, from changes in conformation superimposed upon a common primary structure. Evidence favoring this view is included in the remaining portion of this section.

Since antibodies are globulins, they are also called *immunoglobulins*, or because of their electrophoretic mobility, *gamma* (γ) *globulins*. Gamma globulins occur in four main classes: γM, γG, γA, and γD, some of whose properties are listed in Figure 32-5. The relative heavy γM globulins are the ones made first in response to an antigen; subsequent exposures elicit the production of other, lighter classes—usually γG. All γ globulins have a basic tetrameric structure composed of two identical light chains (MW 23,000) joined to two identical μ, γ, or α heavy chains (55,000 MW for γ chains; 70,000 MW for μ chains). The light chains come in two classes, κ and λ, both types being found in all classes of γ globulin. Figure 32-6 shows a model of a γG globulin. A small amount of carbohydrate (not shown in the figure), always present and attached covalently to the heavy chains, has no known function. Since each end of the model has a combining site, each such molecule can bind two antigens or two antigenic sites.

In normal serum about 60 per cent of immunoglobulins contain the κ dimer and about 30 per cent the λ dimer. The variability in amino acid sequence among the immunoglobins of a particular class is usually so great that it is impossible to do amino

Class	S Value	M.W. $\times 10^5$	% Carbohydrate	Polypeptide Chains Light	Heavy	Molecular Formula
γ M	19	9	9.8	κ or λ	μ	$(\mu_2 \kappa_2)_5$ or $(\mu_2 \lambda_2)_5$
γ G	6.6	1.5	2.5	κ or λ	γ	$\gamma_2 \kappa_2$ or $\gamma_2 \lambda_2$
γ A	6.6	1.5	5.7	κ or λ	α	$\alpha_2 \kappa_2$ or $\alpha_2 \lambda_2$
γ D	7	—	—	—	—	—

Figure 32-5   Some properties of major classes of immunoglobulin.

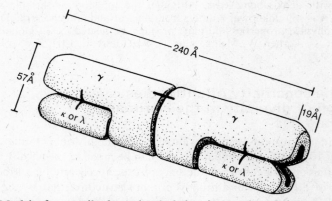

Figure 32-6   Model of an antibody molecule belonging to the γG immunoglobulin class. γ, heavy polypeptide chain; κ or λ, light polypeptide chain. The single lines drawn on the model represent interchain disulfide bonds. The darkened area at the right represents one of the two combining sites.

acid sequence analysis even when the isolated γ globulins are all of Gκ or Gλ types. As described below, it proves to be useful for such amino acid sequencing that certain cancers cause the excessive production of immunoglobulins. For example, *multiple myeloma* in man, a plasma cell cancer, causes the excessive production of γG or γA globulin; moreover, the urine frequently contains *Bence Jones protein*. Electrophoretic analysis shows that the γG (or γA) globulin produced by the malignancy is remarkably uniform, the urinary Bence Jones protein being the κ or λ light chains of the globulin class produced by the malignant cells. A given human myeloma produces but a single type of κ (or λ) chain; this chain is also sufficiently abundant in urine that its amino acid sequence can be determined from the Bence Jones protein.

The variation in γ globulin primary structure is indicated by the fact that the Bence Jones protein in each human being has a unique amino acid sequence. (It is possible to induce neoplasias in mice by injecting mineral oil; these neoplasias produce myeloma proteins and urinary Bence Jones proteins which are also unique in each mouse.)

When Bence Jones proteins of types κ and λ are analyzed after trypsin treatment they are found to have no peptides in common. All Bence Jones proteins of κ type have some (nine) peptides in common and others not in common; those of type λ also have some (eight) peptides in common and others not in common. It appears, therefore, that light chains have an amino acid sequence in different individuals that is relatively constant in certain regions and relatively variable in others. In a given molecule, these two regions are always the same type—both κ or both λ.

Kappa and λ chains are the same length. When the amino acid sequences of human κ and λ and mouse κ chains are compared, certain general features are apparent (Figure 32-7). The molecule forms two loops due to intrastrand disulfide bonds, one in the amino and one in the carboxyl halves. The amino half is more variable than the carboxyl half, however, since all the sequences determined so far have only 19 residues in common in the amino half, but have 35 residues in common in the carboxyl half of the light chain. The relative variability of the amino half is consistent with this end being the one included in the highly specific antigen-combining site, whereas the carboxyl half is the one that joins by interchain disulfide linkage to the heavy chain (refer again to Figure 32-6). The brackets in Figure 32-7 enclose 29 residues which may be homologous in the two halves of the light chain—that is, these portions may have originated by a mutational duplication.

The amino acid sequence analysis of heavy chains has been hampered by the absence of large amounts of homogeneous material. Nevertheless, results indicate that the γ chain of γG globulin also has a relatively variable portion near its amino end (probably contributing to the antigen-combining site) and a relatively constant portion near its carboxyl end. Contrary to the situation within the light chain, the same variable portion of the heavy chain can be joined to constant regions specific for μ, γ, or α chains. (R)

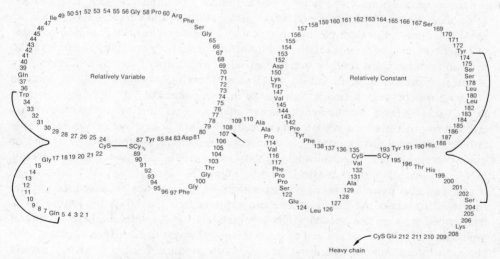

Figure 32-7   Nature and distribution of the invariant residues in human κ and λ and mouse κ chains. Amino terminus = 1; carboxyl terminus joins to heavy chain by Cys linkage. Amino half of molecule (107 residues long with one intrachain disulfide bond) is relatively variant (having only 19 residues so far invariant); carboxyl half (also 107 residues long containing one disulfide bond) is relatively constant (having 35 residues so far invariant). Bracketed areas may be homologous.

32.8 Although antibodies are coded by genetic material, the mechanism by which antigens elicit the amino acid specificity of antibodies remains unclear.

Two lines of evidence indicate that the protein portions of antibodies are coded in genetic material.

1. The γG globulins in some individuals come in two forms, as recognized from the antibodies made against γG globulins. These two alternatives prove to be due to heterozygosity for a single pair of segregating genes, the two different alleles coding for a different amino acid in the relatively constant portion of the light chain. Different alleles of another gene pair can make single amino acid substitutions in the relatively constant region of the heavy chain. Other studies support the hypothesis that although the heavy chains are each single polypeptides, each appears to contain information coded in two genes chosen from at least four nonalleles.

2. The biosynthesis of light and heavy chains involves mRNA translation on ribosomes. Polyribosomes containing 10 to 20 ribosomes seem to be making heavy chains (or heavy chain segments), whereas polyribosomes containing 4 to 8 ribosomes seem to be making light chains (or their segments).

It is clear that an antigen contains information which leaves an impression or memory on cells so that soon after exposure (and later, too) antibody that specifically binds the antigen is produced in large quantity. We do not know yet how this antigen information is accepted, imprinted, and stored in the cell, or how this information is used to specify amino acid sequence in antibody. The latter has been hypothesized to be accomplished by a variety of mechanisms, alone and in combination, which act at different levels. For example, the antigen may somehow select which of a large series of genetic sequences for the relatively variable and relatively constant portions of the light and heavy chains shall be transcribed. The large series of genetic sequences may already be present at fertilization, or some of them may be generated by somatic crossing over between a smaller number of different segments. A continuous strip of mRNA coding for a specific light or heavy chain may result from intermittent transcription (a process not as yet known to occur) in which a sequence of DNA is transcribed, sequences are skipped, and transcription continued subsequently at one or more places. In these mechanisms antibody specificity is determined at the level of DNA and transcription (see also legend to Figure 32-4).

One can also hypothesize that the specificity of an antibody is determined at the time of translation. At this level one can suppose that the DNA for antibodies is transcribed into certain special mRNA triplets (1) which, with the help of special aminoacyl-tRNA's, code for amino acids in special ways; or (2) which combine with chemical information specified by the antigen to produce deformed mRNA triplets recognized by typical aminoacyl-tRNA's. Such processes are not yet known to occur.

"It is perhaps most fair to conclude this section by saying that we at present have no idea as to how antigen plays a role in the synthesis of specific antibody" (E. A. Kabat, 1967). (R)

32.9   Learning and memory are associated with the synthesis of specific as well as nonspecific types of RNA.

Learning refers to the capacity of a system to react in a new or changed way as the result of experience. *Memory* refers to the capacity to store and subsequently retrieve learned information. The learning that occurs during a series of trials performed over a short interval is said to involve *short-term memory*. After short-term memory is evoked, a period of *consolidation* or *fixation* must follow before the learning can become part of *long-term memory*. For example, a rat is given a series of trials in which he has a choice of two kinds of behavior, one of which is followed by an electric shock. Via short-term memory the rat learns to avoid the behavior which is followed by shock, and, after a period of consolidation, retains this behaviorial tendency some days later as part of its long-term memory. Cyclical behavior in which a particular function is repeated at somewhat lengthy periodic intervals also involves long-term memory.

The following kinds of evidence indicate that RNA synthesis is intimately associated with learning and memory.

1. In Parkinson's disease, a nervous disorder, profound changes in RNA base ratios arise in nerve tissue.

2. When goldfish have a piece of polystyrene foam attached to their lower jaw, the foam tending to turn them over, they learn to adjust their behavior so that in a few hours their swimming posture is once again normal. The uracil/cytosine ratio in newly made RNA in the whole brain can be determined. Whereas this ratio is 3 : 1 in control, untrained fish, it is 6 : 1 in the trained ones, suggesting that learning involves differential transcription.

3. RNA content per cell and base ratios have also been studied in single cortical neurons of right-handed rats forced to use the left hand to obtain food. Neurons serving both sides of a single individual show an increase in RNA. Early in the learning period, however, the cortical neurons on the learning side synthesize small amounts of RNA rich in A and U; later in the learning period these neurons synthesize a relatively large amount of RNA with a base ratio like that of rRNA (rich in G and C). These results suggest that in an acute learning situation select parts of the genome are transcribed to produce specific RNA's in a first stage which may correspond to the labile period of short-term memory; a second stage, in which nonspecific, ribosomal-type RNA is formed, may constitute the period of fixation of long-term memory. In another experiment when rats are placed in a learning situation (involving balance), the amount of nuclear RNA in specific neurons and the A/U ratio increase. Sometimes learning is accompanied by an increase in the U/C ratio. The change in base ratio seems specific for the learning experiment.

4. In the California sea hare, *Aplysia californica*, giant neurons in certain ganglia produce electrical discharges with characteristic patterns and frequencies, that is, cyclically, even after removal from the organism. One particular neuron shows a burst of electrical activity at about the time of transition from dark to

light (dawn). (In about 10 per cent of preparations in which this neuron is isolated, the peak of impulse activity occurs at projected dusk rather than dawn.) A change in the sea hare's light–dark schedule for half a dozen or so cycles causes the subsequently isolated cells to have a new discharge pattern. Thus a change in prior experience can change the activity of an isolated nerve cell.

If the isolated neuron, previously trained to a light–dark schedule in the intact animal, is treated during the projected dark period with either heat pulses or an injection of actinomycin D, a phase advance (earlier expression) of the peak in discharges is obtained. This result suggests that the cyclical occurrence of impulses involves long-term memory which is dependent upon transcription. That actinomycin D causes an inhibition in the cyclical luminescence of a marine dinoflagellate, and blocks cyclical photosynthesis in nucleated but not enucleated *Acetabularia*, further supports the involvement of RNA in cyclical behavior.

The preceding discussion suggests that the experimental establishment of new behavior is intimately associated with the synthesis of RNA, which has at certain times a specific and other times a nonspecific base composition. (R)

32.10   Protein synthesis is also associated with learning and memory.

Since the previous section implicated RNA in memory and learning, it is reasonable to also expect protein synthesis to be implicated because at least a portion of informational RNA is concerned with protein synthesis. It is not surprising, therefore, that in learning experiments involving handedness of rats, the learning side of the brain cortex has four bands of protein not found in the control side. It is not yet proved, however, that these proteins are newly made. Other evidence that more directly indicates protein synthesis is associated with learning and memory is summarized next.

1. Single goldfish are placed in "shuttle boxes" and exposed to repetitive electric shock after being in the light for a given period of time. The fish can avoid shock, however, by swimming over a hurdle from the light to the dark half of the box before the end of the light period. After a series of trials the fish learns to avoid the shock (as much as 80 per cent of the time if trained over a period of days). During a series of trials undertaken over a brief period, the performance of the goldfish improves—thus demonstrating short-term memory. The goldfish must be removed from the training environment, however, to trigger the start of fixation of long-term memory. (Hence no memory is fixed during a short-term training session.) The consolidation period lasts about 1 hour. Trials in the shuttle box on subsequent days show that the goldfish has long-term memory of his previous learning.

When puromycin is injected into the cranium of goldfish immediately after training, long-term memory is completely obliterated. When the same dose is injected 1 hour after newly trained fish are returned to their home tanks, no effect is produced on long-term memory. Injection of puromycin just before training also has no effect on learning. The last two findings show that puromycin has an effect only during the period of consolidation of long-term memory (having no effect on short-term memory).

Since puromycin is mistaken for Phe-tRNA during protein synthesis, its incorporation into the polypeptide being synthesized results in the premature termination and release of the chain. We hypothesize, therefore, that short-term memory does not require protein synthesis, but that the fixation of long-term memory does. This hypothesis is supported by studies on the incorporation of labeled leucine in the brain of fish injected with puromycin or with a salt solution. Protein synthesis is greatly inhibited by the puromycin, not by the salt solution. Moreover, acetoxycycloheximide (Figure 32-8), which is known to slow down the rate of amino acid incorporation into a polypeptide, interferes with both memory and protein synthesis in the goldfish when injected intracranially alone or in combination with puromycin.

2. A mouse placed in the base of a Y maze is given a short time to select the correct arm to enter before being shocked continuously. During a training period (about 20 minutes) the level of correct responses increases and, after a period of fixation, the short-term memory becomes long-term memory. In some experiments puromycin was injected bilaterally into the temporal sites of the brain 1, 3, or more than 3 days after training. Only injections made 3 days after training blocked long-term memory. The negative effect of injections given 1 day after training, which presumably is relatively close to the period of fixation, and the positive effect of injections given 3 days after training, at a time which is presumably beyond the period of fixation, are results which differ from those expected from the goldfish experiments described above.

Also contrary to the results with goldfish is the finding that acetoxycycloheximide blocks mouse brain protein synthesis without affecting memory when large amounts are injected into the brain alone or in combination with puromycin. Consistent with the goldfish results is the lack of effect on memory of cycloheximide (which also blocks protein synthesis) injected before training.

3. Rats are placed in a long-term learning situation where they are induced to change their handedness to retrieve food. Simultaneously, protein synthesis response is studied in the CA3 nerve cells of the hippocampus, the structure functionally most important for the formation of memory. Study of three protein fractions strongly supports the view that their synthesis is specific for the learning process. For example, one brain-specific protein increases in the hippocampal nerve cells during training. When antibodies made against this protein are injected, they accumulate in hippocampal nerve cells of learning rats and prevent further increases in learning. On the other hand, neutralized antibodies have no such effect.

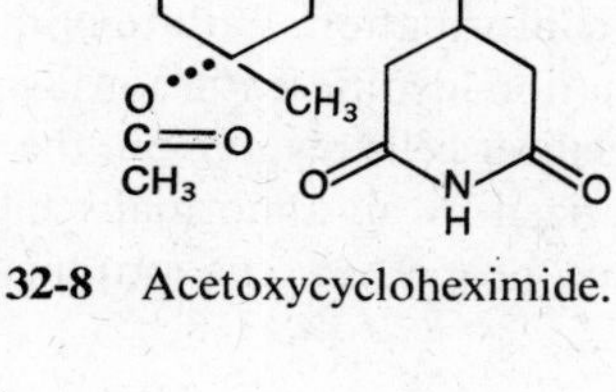

Figure 32-8   Acetoxycycloheximide.

The preceding findings lead us to conclude that (1) protein synthesis is unnecessary in short-term memory, and (2) protein synthesis of some kind is needed for the establishment of long-term memory. The inconsistencies in the effects of protein synthesis inhibition in mouse and goldfish suggest that, of the two, transcription rather than translation of RNA is more directly involved in memory and learning. (R)

32.11 New experimental studies on the physiology and cytochemistry of nerve cells should further our understanding of the role of genetics in memory and learning.

Although memory and learning are related to DNA, RNA, and protein, we do not know (1) at which level DNA is involved, (2) how behavioral changes are converted to RNA and protein changes, or (3) how these macromolecules affect neuron behavior if, indeed, they are the ones used to store and retrieve information. Some progress has already been made, fortunately, in understanding the physiology and biochemistry of the nerve cell from the DNA–RNA–protein standpoint.

Nerve tissue is composed of two kinds of cells, relatively differentiated *neurons* and the relatively undifferentiated *neuroglia* or *glial cells* that surround the neuron except at the synapses. Glia are the satellite, supportive, or connective tissue cells of nerve tissue. They are about one tenth the volume of a typical neuron; they can undergo mitosis. Some glia may be neuron precursor cells, some have nuclei with polynemic chromosomes.

Both glia and neurons are rich in ribosomal-type RNA. Certain neurons have 30 $\mu\mu$g RNA in the nucleus (neurons have small nuclei in comparison with their cytoplasmic volume) and 650 $\mu\mu$g RNA cytoplasmically. Very little RNA is present in dendrites, little or none is present in axons. The very intimate physical relationship between glia and neurons (glial membranes can penetrate neuronal cytoplasm) is paralleled by an intimate functional relationship. For example, various physiological stimuli and processes cause ribosomal-type RNA and respiratory enzyme activities to increase in the neuron and decrease in the glia. Moreover, the RNA fraction lost from the glia is quantitatively and qualitatively similar to the RNA that appears in the neuron, indicating a transport of RNA from glia to neuron. During learning, however, the RNA content increases in both glia and neurons. Such results suggest that further experimental cytochemical studies of the neuron-glia functional unit will be fruitful in helping to elucidate the role of DNA–RNA–protein in memory and learning. (R)

32.12 Abnormal differentiation, as in cancer, may be due to changes in genetic information, transcription, or translation.

We have seen in this chapter that normal differentiation requires the correct transcription and translation of a given amount of genetic information. Failure of differentiation to occur (or loss of accomplished differentiation–dedifferentiation) is clearly often due to changes in these normal components. Cancer cells result from the abnormal differentiation of normal cells and are characterized by an abnormally high rate of mitosis associated with a change in cell surface properties, the production of cancerous progeny cells, and a lesser response to the organism's mechanisms of regulation than the normal cells from which they arose.

The apparent permanency and transmissibility of a cancerous condition implies that there must be a permanent modification in gene content or action. It is not surprising, therefore, that the following can be carcinogenic: (1) exposure to mutagenic agents such as high-energy radiations and certain chemical substances, (2) various viral infections, and (3) exposure to certain nonmutagenic chemical substances. In no instance are we yet sure, however, whether a cancer is due to a mutation (say, by addition, subtraction, or relocation of genetic material), a change in transcription (by a permanent turning off or turning on of genes that are normally otherwise), or an alteration of the translational machinery (perhaps a self-perpetuating change at the level of the ribosome and aminoacyl-tRNA's). It is probable that different cancers arise by different means. Different mechanisms may be involved in initiation, promotion, and maintenance of cancer. (R)

SUMMARY AND CONCLUSIONS

This chapter deals mainly with the genetic basis for the differentiation of specific tissues concerned with hemoglobin synthesis, antibody synthesis, and learning and memory.

Red blood corpuscles differentiate to produce large quantities of a few types of globin. In man four gene pairs specify the polypeptides involved; the functioning of one locus (γ) in the fetus being replaced by that of two loci (β and δ) in the adult, the fourth locus (α) being functional at all stages. Hemoglobin synthesis apparently involves genetic controls at both the transcriptional and translational levels.

Each of certain white blood cells synthesizes large amounts of a single type of antibody. Antibodies are proteins composed of two pairs of polypeptides, the members of each dimer being identical. Although antibodies are like hemoglobins in these respects, they differ in that the antibodies produced by different cells vary greatly in primary structure. Thus, in a single individual, there is very large variety in the amino acid sequences of the relatively variable halves of both the light and heavy chains of different antibodies produced in different cells in response to an equally large variety of antigenic sites. Although antibodies are translations of transcripts, it is not yet known how the antigen elicits the antibody response and immunological memory from the genetic material.

The learning and memory which occur through the differentiation of neurons and glia involve the transcriptive synthesis of specific and nonspecific types of RNA as well as of specific types of protein. We do not know in any detail, however, how the genetic material is involved when the stimulus is converted into learning and when what is learned becomes memory.

Abnormal differentiation, as occurs in cancer cells, can be attributed to perpetuated defects in genetic content, transcription, or translation.

GENERAL REFERENCES

Burnet, F. M. 1969. *Cellular immunology.* New York: Cambridge University Press.

Davis, B. D., Dulbecco, R., Eisen, H. N., Ginsberg, H. S., and Wood, W. B., Jr. 1967. *Microbiology.* New York: Harper and Row, Inc. (See section on immunology.)

Kabat, E. A. 1968. *Structural concepts in immunology and immunochemistry.* New York: Holt, Rinehart and Winston, Inc.

Quarton, G. C., Melnechuk, T., and Schmidt, F. O. (Editors) 1967. *The neurosciences*. New York: Rockefeller University Press.

Watson, J. D. 1970. *Molecular biology of the gene*, second edition. Menlo Park, Calif.: W. A. Benjamin, Inc.

SPECIFIC SECTION REFERENCES

32.1 Baglioni, C. 1963. Correlations between genetics and chemistry of human hemoglobins. In *Molecular genetics*, Part I, Taylor, J. H. (Editor), New York: Academic Press, Inc., Chap. 9, pp. 405–475.

32.5 Baglioni, C., and Sparks, C. E. 1963. A study of hemoglobin differentiation in *Rana catesbiana*. Develop. Biol., 8: 272–285. Reprinted in *Molecular and cellular aspects of development*, Bell, E. (Editor), New York: Harper & Row, Inc., pp. 150–159.

Fantoni, A., de la Chapelle, A., and Marks, P. A. 1969. Synthesis of embryonic hemoglobins during erthyroid cell development in fetal mice. J. Biol. Chem., 244: 675–681. Reprinted in *Papers on regulation of gene activity during early development*, Loomis, W. F., Jr. (Editor), New York: Harper & Row, Inc., 1970, pp. 396–402.

Moss, B., and Ingram, V. M. 1965. The repression and induction by thyroxin of hemoglobin synthesis during amphibian metamorphosis. Proc. Nat. Acad. Sci., U.S., 54: 967–974.

Rabinovitz, M., Freedman, M. L., Fisher, J. M., and Maxwell, C. R. 1970. Translational control in hemoglobin synthesis. Cold Spring Harbor Sympos. Quant. Biol., 1969, 34: 567–578.

32.6 Nossal, G. J. V. 1964. How cells make antibodies. Scient. Amer., 211: 106–115, 154, 156.

32.7 Edelman, G. M. 1970. The structure and function of antibodies. Scient. Amer., 223 (No. 2): 34–42, 128.

Edelman, G. M., Cunningham, B. A., Gall, W. E., Gottlieb, P. D., Rutishauser, U., and Waxdel, M. J. 1969. The covalent structure of an entire γG immunoglobulin molecule. Proc. Nat. Acad. Sci., U.S., 63: 78–85.

Wang, A. C., Pink, J. R. L., Fudenberg, H. H., and Ohms, J. 1970. A variable region subclass of heavy chains common to immunoglobulins G, A, and M and characterized by an unblocked amino-terminal residue. Proc. Nat. Acad. Sci., U.S., 66: 657–663.

32.8 Gally, J. A., and Edelman, G. M. 1970. Somatic translocation of antibody genes. Nature, Lond., 227: 341–348. (Review of support for role of somatic recombination in antibody formation.)

Hood, L., and Talmage, D. W. 1970. Mechanism of antibody diversity: germ line bases for variability. Science, 168: 325–334.

Koshland, M. E., Davis, J. J., and Fujita, N. J. 1969. Evidence for multiple gene control of a single polypeptide chain: the heavy chain of rabbit immunoglobulin. Proc. Nat. Acad. Sci., U.S., 63: 1274–1281. (Three genes that control the relatively constant region seem to be nonalleles of the locus controlling the relatively variable region.)

LaVia, M. F., Vatter, A. E., Hammond, W. S. and Northrup, P. V. 1967. The nature of polysomes isolated from spleen cells of rats stimulated by antigen. Proc. Nat. Acad. Sci., U.S., 57: 79–86.

32.9 Hydén, H. 1967. Behavior, neural function, and RNA. Progr. Nucleic Acid Res. and Mol. Biol., 6: 187–218.

Shashoua, V. E. 1970. RNA metabolism in goldfish brain during acquisition of new behaviorial patterns. Proc. Nat. Acad. Sci., U.S., 65: 160–167.

Strumwasser, F. 1967. Types of information stored in single neurons. In *Invertebrate nervous systems*, Wiersma, C. A. G. (Editor), Chicago: University of Chicago Press, pp. 291–319.

32.10 Agranoff, B. W. 1967. Memory and protein synthesis. Scient. Amer., 216 (No. 6): 115–122, 156.

Flexner, L. B., Flexner, J. B., and Roberts, R. B. 1967. Memory in mice analyzed with antibiotics. Science, 155: 1377–1383.

Hydén, H., and Lange, P. W. 1970. S100 brain protein: correlation with behavior. Proc. Nat. Acad. Sci., U.S., 67: 1959–1966.

32.11 Griffith, J. S., and Mahler, H. R. 1969. DNA ticketing theory of memory. Nature, Lond., 223: 580–582. (Hypothesized use of redundant or protein-silent DNA for memory.)

32.12 Buiatti, M. 1968. The induction of tumors in the hybrid *Nicotiana glauca* × *N. langsdorffi* plants by 6-azauracil and its reversal by uracil and actinomycin D. Cancer Res., 28: 166–169. (Alteration in gene function, not mutation, may produce abnormal RNA that induces tumors.)

Craddock, V. M. 1970. Transfer RNA methylases and cancer. Nature, Lond., 228: 1264–1268. (Those in tumors differ from those in normal tissues.)

Dulbecco, R. 1967. The induction of cancer by viruses. Scient. Amer., 216 (No. 4): 28–36, 146. (Experimental cancers induced by polyoma virus and SV40.)

Gottlieb, S. K. 1969. Chromosomal abnormalities in certain human malignancies. J. Amer. Med. Assoc., 209 (No. 7): 1063–1066. (A review.)

Halpern, B. C., Halpern, R. M., Chaney, S. Q., and Smith, R. A. 1970. Reversal of malignant transformation by tumor DNA. Proc. Nat. Acad. Sci., U.S., 67: 1827–1833. (Exposure to such DNA induces tRNA methylase inhibitors in malignant cells which then show reduced malignant capacity. Removal of this DNA causes return of malignant capacity. Many tumors are associated with a rise in tRNA methylase activity.)

Huebner, R. J., and Todaro, G. J. 1969. Oncogenes of RNA tumor viruses as determinants of cancer. Proc. Nat. Acad. Sci., U.S., 64: 1087–1094. (Proposal that cancer results from the activity of permanently present viral genes.)

Levy, H. B., Law, L. W., and Rabison, A. S. 1969. Inhibition of tumor growth by polyinosinic-polycytidylic acid. Proc. Nat. Acad. Sci., U.S., 62: 357–361. (The duplex RNA stimulates the cell to produce interferon, which leads to the synthesis of modified ribosomal subunits. The modified ribosomes bind and translate cell mRNA well but part of viral RNA poorly.)

Setlow, R. B., Regan, J. D., German, J., and Carrier, W. L. 1969. Evidence that xeroderma pigmentosum cells do not perform the first step in the repair of ultraviolet damage to their DNA. Proc. Nat. Acad. Sci., U.S., 64: 1035–1041. (Pyrimidine dimers implicated in carcinogenesis.)

Watson, J. D., 1970. A geneticist's view of cancer. In *Molecular biology of the gene*, second edition, Chap. 18 pp. 588–628. Menlo Park, Calif.: W. A. Benjamin, Inc. (How studies of the genetics of viruses offer an opportunity to discover the molecular basis of carcinogenesis.)

QUESTIONS AND PROBLEMS

1. How many heme groups are present in hemoglobin A? In A_2?

2. What specific mutations in the β^A gene will give rise to its β^S allele?

3. What Hb-A_2 tetramers are found in individuals heterozygous for Hb-S? For Hb-I?

4. Why is it extremely difficult to study by means of recombination techniques the position within the hemoglobin gene of mutant loci affecting the same polypeptide chain?

5. Give two possible explanations of why hemoglobin never contains heterodimers, even in heterozygotes.

6. Write the tetrameric formulas for the hemoglobins produced in the human fetus and adult of individuals with the following genotypes:

a. $\alpha^A \alpha^A \ \beta^A \beta^A \ \delta^{A_2}\delta^{A_2} \ \gamma^F\gamma^F$
b. $\alpha^A \alpha^I \ \beta^A \beta^A \ \delta^{A_2}\delta^{A_2} \ \gamma^F\gamma^F$
c. $\alpha^A \alpha^A \ \beta^A \beta^S \ \delta^{A_2}\delta^{A_2} \ \gamma^F\gamma^F$
d. $\alpha^A \alpha^I \ \beta^A \beta^A \ \delta^{A_2}\delta^{B_2} \ \gamma^F\gamma^F$

7. A woman who produces Hb-S marries a man who produces Hb-B_2. What are their most probable genotypes? What genotypes and what kinds of hemoglobin are expected in their children?

8. What inferences can you make from the observations that the nucleus of a plasma cell is shrunken and dense, and seems to have no nucleolus? Formulate your answer in molecular terms.

9. What are the expected consequences when rabbit reticulocytes are incubated in complete nutrient medium, and then transferred to complete nutrient medium minus tryptophan? Note that the normal polysome

synthesizing hemoglobin contains six ribosomes and that Trp is located at position 14 in the α chain and at positions 15 and 37 in the β chain of rabbit hemoglobin A.

10. Are the antigens bound by a given antibody molecule always identical? Explain.

11. What are the similarities and differences between the oocyte–nurse cell pair and the neuron–glial cell pair?

12. Such DNA-containing viruses as vaccinia and pseudorabies never stimulate but often inhibit host DNA synthesis. On the basis of this observation and information given in this chapter, propose a mechanism for the molecular basis of virus-induced cancer.

13. Certain cancer-inducing DNA viruses have such a small amount of genetic material that it is difficult to determine whether or not the cancer cells contain any viral DNA. Suggest a way to detect the presence of viral genes in these cells.

14. In what way does the arrangement of the genes in the map of ϕT4D shown in Figure 10-5 suggest that viral gene action is regulated during phage development?

15. A monkey cell, tumorous because of the presence of SV40 DNA integrated in one or more nuclear chromosomes, permits the reading of "early" but not "late" SV40 genes. Fusion of this cell with an uninfected SV40 cell induces the reading of late SV40 genes. Discuss whether positive or negative control of gene action is involved in the reading of early and late SV40 genes and state specifically possible ways such gene action might be controlled.

16. Cycloheximide inhibits protein synthesis by 80s, but not 70s, ribosomes. What does this fact suggest about the location of genetic information involved in memory and learning?

PART VII

Evolution

Chapter 33

Population Genotypes and Mating Systems

In previous chapters we considered many of the characteristics of the genetic material of various types of organisms. This chapter and those remaining are concerned with the state of the genetic material as it presently exists in nature, how this state came about, and what we can expect it to be in the future. In other words, we shall be concerned with the history—the evolution—of genetic material.

33.1 Since it is not feasible to study the evolution of complete genotypes in cross-fertilizing populations, the population genetics of single loci will be considered first.

Under present natural conditions, the success or failure of genetic material is tested in organisms and involves whole genotypes. Moreover, since organisms tend to increase their numbers, all such tests involve the success or failure of the genotypes of groups of individuals of the same kind. The task of determining the history of the genotype of an organism that reproduces asexually only and has no other special mechanisms for genetic recombination is not necessarily insurmountable, for, barring new mutations, all descendants of a single individual are genetically uniform; even if mutations occur occasionally, the two or more groups of genotypically different individuals can be followed and observed for their relative success.

The situation is different, however, for individuals that reproduce sexually by cross-fertilization—all the actually or potentially interbreeding members of a kind of organism comprising a *population*. Because the number of genes in many genotypes is large, the potential number of different genotypes (generated by genetic recombination among individuals of different genotypes produced by occasionally occurring mutations) readily exceeds the number that can actually occur in a population. Thus, a population with just *two* alleles at 1, 2, 3, . . ., 100 loci would have 3^1, 3^2, 3^3, . . ., 3^{100} possible diploid genotypes,[1] the last being larger than the number of individuals in any population. Not only is it usually impossible to obtain all possible genotypes in a population, but the genotypes of one generation are shuffled by genetic recombination into different genotypes in the next generation. To understand the evolution of the genetic material of populations, at least in part, it is desirable to oversimplify the problem and study the population characteristics of only part of the genotype. We shall first consider the genotype with respect to a single locus.

33.2 If matings are random, gene frequencies can be used to determine genotypic frequencies in populations.

When only one locus having two alleles is under consideration, it is sometimes simple to describe the genotypes present in a diploid population. Suppose, for example, we find with respect to MN blood type that a population of 1,000 persons is composed (Figure 33-1) of 358 M, 484 MN, and 158 N blood types. In the absence of dominance we can assign a unique genotype for each of these phenotypes, and determine the relative frequencies of these genotypes. We can also determine (see Figure 33-1) the *gene frequency* of M, p_M, in the population as being 0.6 and of N, p_N, as being 0.4.

We can suppose that matings in this population occur without regard to the genotypes involved; that is, *random mating* occurs. This assumption is supported by finding that the expected frequencies of the nine possible types of random child-bearing mating (see Figure 33-2, for the population under consideration) are very close to those actually observed. If we assume that random mating between individuals can be represented by a random combination of gametes, we can then obtain the genotypic frequencies expected in a population with regard to MN blood type (Figure 33-3), using for both eggs and sperm the gene frequencies already determined. We

Phenotype	M	M N	N
Genotype	*M M*	*M N*	*N N*
Number (Total = 1000)	358	484	158
Frequency (Total = 1.0)	0.358	0.484	0.158

Frequency of $M = p_M = 0.358 + \frac{1}{2}(0.484) = 0.6$

Frequency of $N = p_N = 0.158 + \frac{1}{2}(0.484) = 0.4$

$$p_M + p_N = 0.6 + 0.4 = 1.0$$

Figure 33-1   Phenotypic, genotypic, and gene frequencies in a specific population.

[1] The base 3 represents the three genotypes possible at each locus, for example *A A, A a, a a.*

Genotypes ♂ ♀	Expected Frequency
M M X M M	0.358 X 0.358
X M N	0.358 X 0.484
X N N	0.358 X 0.158
M N X M M	0.484 X 0.358
X M N	0.484 X 0.484
X N N	0.484 X 0.158
N N X M M	0.158 X 0.358
X M N	0.158 X 0.484
X N N	0.158 X 0.158
Total	1.0

Figure 33-2 Expected frequencies of different matings, in the population of Figure 33-1, if random mating occurs.

Female Gametes

		0.6 M	0.4 N
Male Gametes	0.6 M	0.36 M M	0.24 M N
	0.4 N	0.24 M N	0.16 N N

Population Genotypic Frequencies

	M M	M N	N N
Expected	0.36	0.48	0.16
Actual (Fig. 33-1)	0.358	0.484	0.158

The expected gene pool

$$p_M = 0.36 + 0.24 = 0.6$$
$$p_N = 0.16 + 0.24 = 0.4$$

Figure 33-3 Gene frequencies (in the gene pool) and genotypic frequencies in a population where random union occurs between gametes.

find that the expected genotypic frequencies closely approximate those actually found in the population.

We can consider the gametes of all mating individuals to constitute a *gene pool* from which the genes of the next generation are drawn. The actual gene pool is composed of $p_M = 0.6$ and $p_N = 0.4$. Following random union of these gametes the genotypes produced are expected in turn to produce a gene pool of the same composition (Figure 33-3). Thus, the gene pool of the F_1 is identical to that of the P_1. Furthermore, the genotypes of the next (F_2) generation and all subsequent generations will remain in the same expected ratio, because the frequencies of M and N in the gene pool remain constant.

33.3 The general rule that gene frequencies and random union of gametes can be used to describe the genotypes and gene pool of cross-fertilizing populations in future generations is called the *Hardy–Weinberg principle*.

We can express the preceding analysis in more general terms by letting p_1 equal the fraction of male and female gametes in the population which carry A_1, and p_2 equal the fraction which carry A_2. For eggs, as well as for sperm, $p_1 + p_2 = 1$. Figure 33-4 gives the results of random union of these gametes. The offspring population, then, is $p_1^2\, A_1 A_1 + 2p_1 p_2\, A_1 A_2 + p_2^2\, A_2 A_2$. And, the frequency of A_1 and A_2 among the gametes produced by the offspring population is

$$A_1 = p_1^2 + p_1 p_2 = p_1(p_1 + p_2) = p_1$$
$$A_2 = p_2^2 + p_1 p_2 = p_2(p_2 + p_1) = p_2.$$

Eggs

	$p_1\ A_1$	$p_2\ A_2$
$p_1\ A_1$	$p_1^2\ A_1\ A_1$	$p_1 p_2\ A_1\ A_2$
$p_2\ A_2$	$p_1 p_2\ A_1\ A_2$	$p_2^2\ A_2\ A_2$

Sperms

Figure 33-4 Types and frequencies of genotypes produced by random union of gametes in a gene pool composed of $p_1\ A_1$ and $p_2\ A_2$.

Mating ♂ ♀	Frequency of Mating	Proportions of Offspring $A_1 A_1$	$A_1 A_2$	$A_2 A_2$
$A_1 A_1$ X $A_1 A_1$	p_1^2 X $p_1^2 = p_1^4$	p_1^4		
X $A_1 A_2$	p_1^2 X $2p_1 p_2 = 2p_1^3 p_2$	$p_1^3 p_2$	$p_1^3 p_2$	
X $A_2 A_2$	p_1^2 X $p_2^2 = p_1^2 p_2^2$		$p_1^2 p_2^2$	
$A_1 A_2$ X $A_1 A_1$	$2p_1 p_2$ X $p_1^2 = 2p_1^3 p_2$	$p_1^3 p_2$	$p_1^3 p_2$	
X $A_1 A_2$	$2p_1 p_2$ X $2p_1 p_2 = 4p_1^2 p_2^2$	$p_1^2 p_2^2$	$2p_1^2 p_2^2$	$p_1^2 p_2^2$
X $A_2 A_2$	$2p_1 p_2$ X $p_2^2 = 2p_1 p_2^3$		$p_1 p_2^3$	$p_1 p_2^3$
$A_2 A_2$ X $A_1 A_1$	p_2^2 X $p_1^2 = p_1^2 p_2^2$		$p_1^2 p_2^2$	
X $A_1 A_2$	p_2^2 X $2p_1 p_2 = 2p_1 p_2^3$		$p_1 p_2^3$	$p_1 p_2^3$
X $A_2 A_2$	p_2^2 X $p_2^2 = p_2^4$			p_2^4
Total	1.0	p_1^2	$2p_1 p_2$	p_2^2

Figure 33-5 Hardy–Weinberg frequencies of progeny genotypes derived from the random mating of parents occurring in Hardy–Weinberg frequencies.

Thus, the gene frequencies have remained the same as in the gametes of the previous generation. Likewise, all future generations will have the same gene pool and the same relative frequencies of diploid genotypes. The concept that one can use gene frequencies and random union of gametes to obtain the composition of the genotypes and the gene pool of future generations of cross-fertilizing populations is called the *Hardy–Weinberg principle*. This analytical method gives the same frequencies of genotypes in the progeny as is obtained by the more cumbersome method of calculating the frequencies of each type of random mating and the proportion of the progeny of each mating which are of the different genotypes (Figure 33-5).

When cross fertilization is random and no other factors disturb the frequencies either of genotypes or of genes in the gene pool, the Hardy–Weinberg rule shows that gene and genotypic frequencies are stabilized in one generation and are static thereafter. The value of the Hardy–Weinberg principle is not that the alleles of most genes in cross-fertilizing populations are in such an unchanging equilibrium; the value is rather in the fact that, as we shall see later, loci often closely approximate Hardy–Weinberg expectation—showing that the factors which upset the equilibrium often have small rather than drastic effects in a single generation. Moreover, it becomes possible to analyze the effects on the Hardy–Weinberg equilibrium of disequilibrating factors alone and in combination. (R)

33.4   The Hardy–Weinberg principle can be readily applied to cases of dominance.

Assuming that factors permit a precise or approximate establishment of Hardy–Weinberg equilibria, we can consider the genotypic consequences to the population of various modifications of our initial oversimplified model.

Knowing the gene frequencies, one can readily reckon the genotypic and phenotypic ratios in a population at equilibrium even when one allele is completely dominant to its alternative allele. When dominance prevents one from identifying each genotypic class phenotypically, however, it is necessary (in the absence of contrary information) to assume that mating is random in order to calculate the gene frequencies from phenotypic information. This can be done using the frequency of recessive homozygotes; this frequency is the square of the gene frequency of the recessive allele, 1 minus the recessive gene frequency being the gene frequency of the dominant allele.

The Hardy–Weinberg principle can also be readily applied to cases involving multiple allelism and X-limited single loci, as well as cases involving two or more loci (as discussed in Section S33.4).

33.5   When a gene is rare, nonrandom mating may have little effect on population genotypic frequencies.

As hinted earlier in Section 33.3, various factors can disturb either or both genotypic and gene frequencies in populations. One of these factors is *nonrandom mating*. In deriving the types and frequencies of genotypes in a population at equilibrium, we assumed that marriages were random with respect to the genotypically determined

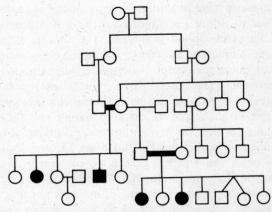

Figure 33-6 Pedigree showing the occurrence of phenylketonuria among the offspring of cousin marriages (denoted by thick marriage lines).

trait under consideration. Such a randomly mating population is said to be panmictic or to undergo *panmixis*. What happens if the different genotypes do not marry at random? Consider the disease *phenylketonuria* (Figure 33-6), which involves a type of feeblemindedness in individuals who are homozygous for a recessive gene, and who metabolize the amino acid phenylalanine to phenylpyruvic acid, which is toxic. The frequency in the gene pool of the normal gene (A) is 0.99 and of the abnormal gene (a) is 0.01. In the population at equilibrium, therefore, $A\,A$:$A\,a$:$a\,a$ individuals have frequencies of 9,801/10,000 : 198/10,000 : 1/10,000, respectively. Notice that $A\,a$ individuals are 198 times more frequent than $a\,a$, and contain 99 per cent of all a genes in the population.

$A\,A$ and $A\,a$ individuals apparently marry at random but feebleminded people do not. So panmixis does not occur with respect to this trait, and persons with different genotypes tend to be restricted in their marriages—all the available marriage partners making up a person's *reproductive isolate*. The occurrence of different reproductive isolates for normals and phenylketonurics has little effect on the relative frequencies of different genotypes in successive generations, because $a\,a$ people have so few of all the a genes present in the population. Clearly, only marriages between two $A\,a$ individuals are of consequence, since those are the major source of $a\,a$ offspring.

The example of phenylketonuria shows that when a gene is rare, nonrandom marriage may have little influence upon the diploid (heterozygous or homozygous) genotypes in which it is found in the population.

33.6 Inbreeding and assortative mating are types of nonrandom mating; they result in a population increasing the (1) average homozygosity and (2) total variance of its genotypes without changing gene frequencies.

Consider two ways in which mating can be nonrandom. The first involves *inbreeding*, the tendency for mates to be more closely related in descent than randomly chosen mates. The second departure from random mating involves *assortative mating*, the tendency for mates to be phenotypically similar (except for sex). This kind of breeding pattern is generally true in animals including human beings. Inbreeding is concerned with the mating of individuals who are genotypically similar, assortative mating with individuals phenotypically similar. To the degree that phenotypic similarities are based upon genotypic similarities, assortative mating has much the same population consequences as inbreeding.

We can see the genotypic population consequences of nonrandom matings involving nonrare genes using a simple example. Suppose a trait is the result of the contribution of two loci, A and B, each of whose A_1 or B_1 alleles adds one unit of phenotypic effect and whose A_0 or B_0 alleles adds nothing. $A_1 A_1 B_1 B_1$ has a 4 phenotype; $A_0 A_0 B_0 B_0$ has 0; the intermediate 3, 2, and 1 phenotypes having appropriate genotypes (Figure 33-7). With random mating all genotypes and phenotypes are present at Hardy–Weinberg equilibrium. Note, for example, that in a random-mating population all three genotypes for type 2 phenotypes mate with each other and with all the other genotypes present; on the contrary, however, each type 2 genotype tends to mate only with itself in an inbreeding population or to mate only within the type 2 phenotype in assortative mating. Consequently, inbreeding increases the frequency of all four completely homozygous genotypes ($A_1 A_1 B_1 B_1$, $A_1 A_1 B_0 B_0$, $A_0 A_0 B_1 B_1$, $A_0 A_0 B_0 B_0$), and assortative mating increases the frequency of the two phenotypically extreme complete homozygotes. In other words, both types of nonrandom mating increase the average homozygosity, and at the same time increase the variance (see Section 21.6), which measures the average variability of the individuals of the population relative to the mean value. The latter variability is illustrated diagrammatically in Figure 33-7, where a greater proportion of all the individuals comprising the population at equilibrium are further from the mean value in the cases of nonrandom mating than in random mating.

Outbreeding and *disassortative mating* (being the opposites of inbreeding and assortative mating, they have the opposite effects) increase average heterozygosity and reduce total variance of the population.

Phenotypes at Equilibrium

	4	3	Mean 2	1	0
Genotypes	$A_1 A_1 B_1 B_1$	$A_1 A_0 B_1 B_1$ $A_1 A_1 B_1 B_0$	$A_1 A_0 B_1 B_0$ $A_1 A_1 B_0 B_0$ $A_0 A_0 B_1 B_1$	$A_1 A_0 B_0 B_0$ $A_0 A_0 B_1 B_0$	$A_0 A_0 B_0 B_0$
Random mating	X	X	X	X	X
Inbreeding	X		X		X
Assortative mating	X				X

Figure 33-7 Effects of random and nonrandom matings upon homozygosity and variance in populations. X represents the presence of a phenotypic class. See the text for details.

33.7 The inbreeding coefficient, *f,* is the probability that an individual is homozygous at a locus because the alleles are derived from the same gene in a common ancestor; *f* can be readily calculated for pedigrees showing various degrees of inbreeding.

What is the effect of inbreeding carried out for a single generation? This can be determined by studying what happens to genes that are heterozygous in the parent generation. There are various degrees of inbreeding, the closest form being *self-fertilization*. In self-fertilization the heterozygote for a given pair of genes, *A a*, produces progeny of which one half are homozygous. In general, the decrease in heterozygosity because of self-fertilization can be expressed as follows: the chance that an offspring receives a given gene in the male gamete is $\frac{1}{2}$, and the chance that it receives the same allele in the female gamete is $\frac{1}{2}$; the chance that the offspring is a homozygote for that allele, therefore, is $\frac{1}{4}$. But there is an equal chance that the offspring becomes homozygous for the other allele, so that the total chance for homozygosis from this type of inbreeding is 50 per cent. If all members of the population are heterozygotes and self-fertilize, then in each successive generation, half of the genes that were heterozygous become homozygous.

Suppose, on the other hand, that a portion of a population mating at random has *x* per cent homozygous individuals. These homozygotes come from matings between two heterozygotes, two homozygotes, or a heterozygote and a homozygote. If the gene pool is at equilibrium, the random matings that tend to increase homozygosis are counterbalanced by others which decrease it, so that *x* per cent homozygosis remains constant generation after generation. Consider what happens in another portion of this population which happens to practice self-fertilization for one generation. Since this segment of the population already shows *x* per cent homozygosis, its offspring will also have *x* per cent homozygosis. But, if this segment is *z* per cent heterozygous, after self-fertilization the offspring will have only $\frac{1}{2}$ *z* per cent heterozygosis, and, therefore, will show a total homozygosis of *x* per cent + $\frac{1}{2}$ *z* per cent. In other words, each generation of self-fertilization makes half of all heterozygous genes homozygous, and, in a normally random-mating population, the effect of self-fertilization is to increase the random-mating frequency of homozygosis by one half the frequency of heterozygosis.

How much is homozygosity increased in *brother–sister* (*sib*) *matings* (Figure 33-8)? The chance that a particular gene in the father is present in the male sib is $\frac{1}{2}$, and the chance that the male sib's child receives this is similarly $\frac{1}{2}$; the chance for the occur-

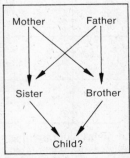

Figure 33-8 Pedigree of a brother–sister (sib) mating. See the text for the calculation of *f*.

rence of both events is $\frac{1}{4}$. The chance that the female sib receives and transmits this same gene to her child is also $\frac{1}{4}$. Therefore, the chance that the child of the sib mating receives two representatives of this same allele is $\frac{1}{4}$ times $\frac{1}{4}$, or it has $\frac{1}{16}$ chance of being homozygous for this gene. Since the child has an equal chance to become a homozygote for the other allele in his grandfather and for each of the two alleles in his grandmother, this gives him 4 times $\frac{1}{16}$ or 25 per cent chance of homozygosis. In other words, sib matings cause $\frac{1}{4}$ of the heterozygous genes to become homozygous. This chance of homozygosis from sib mating is in addition to the chance of homozygosis from mating at random.

The preceding calculation determines the probability that a child will be homozygous because the alleles received were derived from the same gene in a common ancestor. This probability of a descendant being homozygous because it received from both parents an allele present in a common ancestor, called the *inbreeding coefficient*, f, can be readily calculated for pedigrees showing various degrees of inbreeding as follows. Starting with one parent of the individual whose f is to be determined, count the number of individuals back to the common ancestor and forward to the other parent. In Figure 33-8, sister–mother–brother gives 3 as the count for one pathway. Count other possible pathways, starting with the same parent, never using the same person twice in a given pathway. In the present case, sister–father–brother provides a second pathway of 3. Assuming all common ancestors are themselves not inbred, f is obtained by taking each length of pathway as a power of $\frac{1}{2}$ and adding all the fractions together. Thus $f = (\frac{1}{2})^3 + (\frac{1}{2})^3 = \frac{1}{4}$ for a sib mating.

In pedigree 1 of Figure 33-9, the pathway C-B-A-E-D gives $(\frac{1}{2})^5 = \frac{1}{32} = f$. For the *cousin marriage* in pedigree 2, pathway E-C-B-D-F gives $(\frac{1}{2})^5 = \frac{1}{32}$ and pathway E-C-A-D-F gives $(\frac{1}{2})^5$, so that f is $\frac{1}{32} + \frac{1}{32}$, or $\frac{1}{16}$ for cousin marriage. (R)

33.8 The homozygosis that results from inbreeding occurs for detrimental (as well as beneficial) alleles.

All forms of inbreeding increase homozygosity. Let us calculate the consequence of cousin marriage upon the frequency of phenylketonuria. Its frequency of hetero-

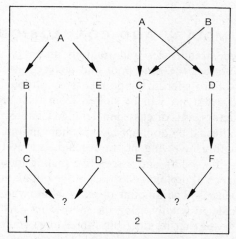

Figure 33-9   Pedigrees having different coefficients of inbreeding: $f = \frac{1}{32}$ in 1, $\frac{1}{16}$ in the cousin marriage of 2.

	Frequency from Unrelated Parents	Increase in Frequency with Cousin Marriage	Per cent Increase
Congenital Malformation	0.011	0.005	48
Stillbirths	0.025	0.006	24
Infant Deaths	0.023	0.008	34

Figure 33-10   Increased risk of genetic defect with cousin marriages. (Data from Hiroshima and Nagasaki.)

zygotes per 10,000 people is 198 (see Section 33.5). Cousin marriage reduces hetero-zygosity by $\frac{1}{16}$, or by 12 individuals, of which half are expected to be normal ($A\,A$) and half affected ($a\,a$). Since random mating produces 1 affected individual per 10,000, cousin marriages bring the total number of affected homozygotes in this population to seven (six from inbreeding, one from random breeding). Accordingly, there is a sevenfold greater chance for phenylketonuric children from cousin marriages than from marriages between unrelated parents.

Another example of how cousin marriages increase the risk of defect comes from a study which found that in a Japanese population (Figure 33-10) congenital mal-formations, stillbirths, and infant deaths were 24 to 48 per cent higher when cousins married than when parents were unrelated. Since, in some cases, defects such as these are known to be due to recessive genes in homozygous condition, these results support the view that homozygosis resulting from inbreeding can produce detrimental effects. Although inbreeding produces homozygosis and homozygosis can lead to the appearance of defects, it must not be inferred that inbreeding is disadvantageous under all circumstances. Many individuals do become homozygous for detrimental genes as a result of inbreeding, but just as many become homozygous for the normal alleles. No obvious disadvantage seems to have resulted from the brother–sister matings practiced for many generations by the Pharoahs of ancient Egypt. In fact, the success of self-fertilizing species is testimony to the general advantage of homo-zygosity at least for some types of organisms. (R)

SUMMARY AND CONCLUSIONS

On the basis of gene frequencies and random union of gametes, the Hardy–Weinberg principle describes the gene pool and genotypes for mendelian genes in successive generations of cross-fertilizing populations. Although both the population gene pool and diploid genotypes can be shifted from their static Hardy–Weinberg equilibria by various factors, as is discussed in detail in Chapter 34, neither population characteristic need be affected by dominance or by nonrandom mating involving rare genes. Nonrandom mating involving nonrare genes, however, will change diploid genotypic frequencies—inbreeding and assortative mating increasing average homo-zygosity and total variance of diploid genotypes in the population—without changing population gene frequencies. The amount of extra homozygosis that occurs due to inbreeding can be calculated readily using the inbreeding coefficient, f. It should be noted that the homozygosis that results from inbreeding occurs alike for detrimental and beneficial alleles.

GENERAL REFERENCES

Brousseau, G. E., Jr. (Editor) 1967. *Evolution.* Dubuque, Iowa: William C. Brown Company. (A book of readings.)

Crow, J. F., and Kimura, M. 1970. *An introduction to population genetics theory.* New York: Harper & Row, Inc.

Lerner, I. M. 1968. *Heredity, evolution, and society.* San Francisco: W. H. Freeman and Company, Publishers.

Li, C. C. 1955. *Population genetics.* Chicago: University of Chicago Press.

Li, C. C. 1961. *Human genetics.* New York: McGraw-Hill Book Company.

Rasmuson, M. 1961. *Genetics on the population level.* Stockholm: Svenska Bokforlaget Bonniers; London: William Heinemann Ltd.

Spiess, E. B. (Editor) 1962. *Papers on animal population genetics.* Boston: Little, Brown and Company.

SPECIFIC SECTION REFERENCES

33.3   Hardy, G. H. 1908. Mendelian proportions in a mixed population. Science, 28: 49–50. Reprinted in *Classic papers in genetics*, Peters, J. A. (Editor), Englewood Cliffs, N.J.: Prentice-Hall, Inc., 1959, pp. 60–62; in *Great experiments in biology*, Gabriel, M. L., and Fogel, S. (Editors), Englewood Cliffs, N.J.: Prentice-Hall, Inc., 1955, pp. 295–297; and in *Evolution*, Brousseau, G. E., Jr. (Editor), Dubuque, Iowa: William C. Brown Company, 1967, pp. 48–50.

Weinberg, W. 1908. Über den Nachweiss des Vererbung beim Menschen. Jahresh. Verein f. vaterl. Naturk. in Württemberg, 64: 368–382. Translated, in part, in Stern, C., 1943. The Hardy–Weinberg law. Science, 97: 137–138.

33.7   Fisher, R. A. 1965. *The theory of inbreeding,* second edition. Edinburgh: Oliver & Boyd Ltd.

Wright, S. 1921. Systems of mating. Genetics, 6: 111–178.

Wright, S. *Evolution and the genetics of populations.* 1968. Vol. 1, *Genetic and biometric*

Wilhelm Weinberg (1862–1937). [From Genetics, 47: 1 (1962).]

foundations; 1969. Vol. 2, *The theory of gene frequencies*. Chicago: University of Chicago Press.

33.8   Farrow, M. G., and Juberg, R. C. 1969. Genetics and laws prohibiting marriage in the United States. J. Amer. Med. Assoc., 209 (No. 4): 534–538.

SUPPLEMENTARY SECTION

S33.4   The Hardy–Weinberg principle can be readily applied to cases of (1) multiple allelism, (2) X-limited loci, and (3) two or more loci.

Assuming that conditions permit the precise or approximate establishment of Hardy–Weinberg equilibria, the Hardy–Weinberg principle can be readily applied under the following circumstances:

Multiple allelism.   Note that with two alleles, A_1 and A_2, at a locus the equilibrium frequency of diploid genotypes is given by $(p_1 + p_2)$ for eggs $\times$ $(p_1 + p_2)$ for sperm, or $(p_1 + p_2)^2$. With three alleles A_1, A_2, and A_3 the expression becomes $(p_1 + p_2 + p_3)^2$, which upon expansion becomes $p_1^2(A_1 A_1) + 2p_1p_2(A_1 A_2) + 2p_1p_3(A_1 A_3) + p_2^2(A_2 A_2) + 2p_2p_3(A_2 A_3) + p_3^2(A_3 A_3)$. With more alleles the expression becomes $(p_1 + p_2 + p_3 + \cdots + p_n)^2$. In this case the frequency of $A_n A_n$ zygotes is p_n^2; of $A_n A_1$ is $2p_np_1$; and of all heterozygotes for A_n, $2p_np_{1-n}$.

X-limited loci.   The Hardy–Weinberg principle was derived for paired genes, whether these are autosomal or sex-linked. When a locus is X-limited, however, human females for example will have a pair of genes and males only one representative. At Hardy–Weinberg equilibrium A_1 and A_2 alleles will occur in males with frequencies of $p_1(A_1)$ and $p_2(A_2)$, whereas females will have the genes in the same frequencies distributed in the usual paired genotypic frequencies $p_1^2(A_1 A_1) + p_1p_2(A_1 A_2) + p_2^2(A_2 A_2)$. If the gene frequencies determined from the female genotypes are not equivalent to those observed directly from the males, the population is not in equilibrium for the locus under consideration. In this case more than one generation of random mating is required to reach equilibrium.

Two or more loci.   When only one locus with two alleles A_1 and A_2 is followed, the gene pool at equilibrium is static, being composed of $p_1(A_1)$ and $p_2(A_2)$. If a second locus with two alleles B_1 and B_2 is also followed, the gene pool at equilibrium can be stated to be composed of $q_1(B_1)$ and $q_2(B_2)$. When both loci are considered simultaneously, the gametic frequencies total 1.0 and at equilibrium $= p_1q_1(A_1 B_1) + p_1q_2(A_1 B_2) + p_2q_1(A_2 B_1) + p_2q_2(A_2 B_2)$; the zygotic (diploid genotypic) ratios will also be in equilibrium. Since the A and B loci each have three different diploid genotypes, there will be 3×3 or 9 different diploid genotypes for these loci considered simultaneously, the equilibrium frequencies determined from the expansion of $(p_1q_1 + p_1q_2 + p_2q_1 + p_2q_2)^2$. For example, at equilibrium $A_1 A_1 B_1 B_1$ will occur with the frequency $p_1^2q_1^2$; and $A_1 A_2 B_1 B_1$ with the frequency $2p_1p_2q_1^2$.

Note that at equilibrium the product of the frequencies of gametes $A_1 B_1 \times A_2 B_2 = A_1 B_2 \times A_2 B_1$, that is, $p_1q_1 \times p_2q_2 = p_1q_2 \times p_2q_1$. Recall that single-paired loci reach Hardy–Weinberg equilibrium in one generation. The rapidity with which equilibrium is reached for two loci followed simultaneously depends both upon the amount of gametic disequilibrium and the linkage relationship of the loci. It will take about five generations for grossly unbalanced gametes to reach an approximate equilibrium if the loci are segregating independently; it takes longer if these loci are linked, and longer the closer they are linked. When more than two loci are considered simultaneously, it takes even longer to reach equilibrium.

QUESTIONS AND PROBLEMS

1. Assuming that the Hardy–Weinberg principle applies, what is the frequency of the gene R if its only allele R' is homozygous in the following percentages of the population: 49 per cent? 4 per cent? 25 per cent? 36 per cent?

2. In the United States about 70 per cent of the population gets a bitter taste from the drug phenylthiocarbamide (PTC). These people are called "tasters"; the remaining 30 per cent, who get no bitter taste from PTC, are called "nontasters." All marriages between nontasters produce all nontaster offspring. Every experimental result supports the view that a single pair of non-sex-linked genes determines the difference between tasters and nontasters; dominance is complete between the only two kinds of alleles that occur; penetrance of the dominant allele is complete.

   a. Which of the two alleles is the dominant one?

b. What proportion of all marriages between tasters and nontasters have no chance (barring mutation) of producing a nontaster child?

c. What proportion of all marriages occurs between two nontasters? Two tasters?

3. The proportion of $A\,A$ individuals in a large cross-breeding population is 0.09. Assuming that all genotypes with respect to this locus have the same reproductive potential, what proportion of the population should be heterozygous for A?

4. What do you suppose would happen to a population whose gene pool obeyed the Hardy–Weinberg rule for a very large number of generations? Why?

5. Can a population obey the Hardy–Weinberg rule for one gene pair but not for another? Explain.

6. Are inbreeding and assortative mating mutually exclusive departures from random mating (panmixis)? Explain.

7. Explain why the inbreeding coefficient, f, is $\frac{1}{16}$ for cousin marriages.

8. Suppose the frequencies of alleles A and a are 0.3 and 0.7, respectively, in a population obeying the Hardy–Weinberg rule:

a. What per cent of the population is composed of homozygotes with respect to these genes?

b. What would be your answer to part a after one generation of mating hybrids only with hybrids?

c. How would the conditions in part b affect the composition of the gene pool?

9. Discuss, from a genetic standpoint, the advantages and disadvantages of cousin marriages in man.

10. Two inbred strains of mice and their F_1 hybrids are tested for locomotor activity (measured for each subject in each group during three consecutive 5-minute periods) and for oxygen consumption. In both these respects the F_1 hybrid is less variable than the parental strains. Propose a genetic hypothesis to explain these results.

11. Compare the reproductive isolates of people who were marrying in 1900 with those marrying today. Which factors are the same and which are different? Is the change desirable from a biological standpoint? Explain.

12. A population gene pool is composed of 0.6 A and 0.4 a. What are the diploid genotypes and their frequencies expected at Hardy–Weinberg equilibrium?

13. Suppose amylase occurs in two alternative forms, A and B, in a *Drosophila* population at Hardy–Weinberg equilibrium. If 49 per cent of the population has only type A, what percentage of the population is expected to produce both A and B types?

14. What percentage of individuals in a population at Hardy–Weinberg equilibrium is heterozygous for B if its only allele, b, is homozygous in 0.01 per cent, 9 per cent, 16 per cent of the individuals?

15. Assume that a population gene pool at Hardy–Weinberg equilibrium contains three alleles a^1, a^2, and a^3 in the proportion 0.6, 0.3, 0.1. For each allele give the proportion of individuals expected to be

a. homozygotes.

b. heterozygotes.

16. Calculate the inbreeding coefficient for X in each of the pedigrees shown.

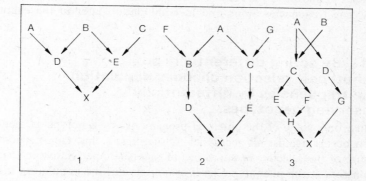

Chapter 34

Factors Affecting Population Gene Frequencies

Having decided at the start of Chapter 33 that the study of the total genotype in all individuals of a cross-fertilizing population is impossibly complex, we substituted a consideration of an oversimplified model of a population in order to discover some simple basic principles of population genetics. In the population model we used, the generations were nonoverlapping and various factors which would increase or decrease gene frequencies were assumed to play a minor or no role. This permitted us to study the effect of random and nonrandom mating systems on the genotypes found in populations.

The present chapter deals with the factors that can change gene frequencies by introducing alleles, increasing their frequency once present, as well as reducing their frequency or eliminating them. Some gene-frequency changes prove to have a chance, fortuitous basis, but others result because certain alleles make the genotype and phenotype more successful or adaptive than other alleles. The *adaptive value* or *biological fitness* of a genotype is best described in terms of its effect upon the organism's ability to produce surviving offspring, that is, upon *reproductive potential* (see Section 20.4). This potential includes the individual's capacity to reach the reproductive stage and its fertility and fecundity during this period, as well as the viability of its offspring until sexual maturity. Therefore, *fitness*, w, is usually considered to refer to survival (or viability) and reproduction (or fertility) of a genotype, being 1.0 for the most fit genotype and less, $1 - s$, for relatively less fit genotypes. The quantity, s, called the *selection coefficient*, refers to the degree, from 0 to 1, that the genotype is relatively unfit, and therefore, relatively selected against.

We shall discuss first the factors that affect fitness, considering other factors that disturb gene frequencies alone and in combination later in the chapter.

34.1 By acting differentially on phenotypes, selection changes population gene frequencies by differentially conserving genotypes.

Because only some of the potential progeny of any genotype are actually realized, selection occurs against all genotypes. (Note, again, that the selection coefficient is a measure of the selective *disadvantage* of one genotype relative to that of another.) Selection acts at the phenotypic level to conserve in the population those genotypes which provide the greatest fitness. Selection takes place at all stages in the life cycle of an individual. Since it acts to preserve whole phenotypes and not single traits, selection conserves genotypes and not single genes. Sometimes selection acts upon the phenotypes produced by single genomes in haploid species or stages; at other times—in sexually reproducing organisms—it acts upon the combined phenotypic effect of two genomes. It should be noted that what is a relatively adaptive genotype at one stage of the life cycle may be relatively ill-adaptive at another, whether or not these stages have the same or different ploidies. It is, of course, the total adaptiveness of all these separate features which determines the overall reproductive potential of an individual. Finally, it should be noted that in cross-fertilizing populations, selection favors genotypes that produce maximal fitness of the population as a whole. Because selection acts this way, it is possible that some portion of the population receives genotypes which are decidedly not advantageous. If this is so, the same genetic components are expected to be advantageous when present in other, more probable, combinations. When some genotypes are favored by selection, a Hardy–Weinberg equilibrium will not occur, and the frequency of certain alleles will increase, while that of others will decrease, in the population gene pool. (R)

34.2   The reduction in the frequency of an allele in successive generations depends upon its selection coefficient in homozygous and heterozygous condition.

Let us consider the population frequencies for single loci having two alleles (A_1 and A_2) when one allele (A_1) is at a selective disadvantage in heterozygous, homozygous, or both conditions.

Selection against a complete dominant

If A_1 produces death before maturity or sterility, no $A_1 A_1$ homozygotes occur, and A_1 heterozygotes have $s = 1$, or a fitness, $w = 0$. In this case the population removes the A_1 allele in one generation of selection giving A_2 a frequency of 1.0 in the gene pool.

If A_1 has some fitness (s is less than 1) which is the same in homozygous and heterozygous condition, A_1 will decrease in frequency in successive generations until the entire population is composed of homozygous recessive, $A_2 A_2$. Figure 34-1 curve a shows the change in gene frequency of such an A_1 allele whose $s = 0.5$. Note

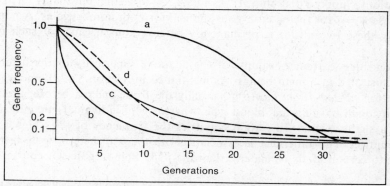

Figure 34-1   Changes in gene frequency (starting at 95 per cent) when allele A_1 is selected against in different genotypes and to different degrees. a = complete dominance; $s = 0.5$ for $A_1 A_2$. b = complete recessive; $s = 1.0$ for $A_1 A_2$. c = complete recessive; $s = 0.5$ for $A_1 A_1$. d = no dominance; $s = 0.2$ for $A_1 A_1$; $s = 0.1$ for $A_1 A_2$.

that when A_1 comprises about 95 per cent of the gene pool, there are very few homozygotes for the recessive allele and selection can increase A_2 frequency only slowly. Once the recessive allele reaches a frequency of 0.15, however, selection against the dominant allele becomes rapid in succeeding generations.

Selection against a complete recessive

If $A_1 A_1$ homozygotes have $s = 1$, meaning that this genotype is lethal or sterile, the curve showing selection against the completely recessive A_1 allele (Figure 34-1, curve b) falls sharply when A_1 is very frequent, but decreases slowly when, after 15 or so generations, the gene is less frequent.[1] Figure 34-1, curve c, shows a similar, although slower, decrease in frequency when $A_1 A_1$ is a completely recessive semilethal or semisterile whose $s = 0.5$.

Selection in the absence of dominance

If $A_1 A_1$ has $s = 0.2$ and $A_1 A_2$ has $s = 0.1$, the heterozygote $A_1 A_2$ has a fitness (0.9) exactly intermediate between that of the two homozygotes ($w = 1.0$ for $A_2 A_2$ and 0.8 for $A_1 A_1$)—that is, no dominance is involved. In this case (Figure 34-1, curve d), despite a smaller s value, the frequency of A_1 falls essentially as fast as it does for a complete recessive with $s = 0.5$ because selection is now occurring against two genotypes.

34.3   When the selective coefficient of both homozygotes is lower than that of their heterozygote, both alleles are retained in the population at equilibrium, and the heterozygote shows heterosis.

In the preceding section the frequency of A_1 is driven toward 0 because selection is occurring against it in one or more genotypes. As implied in Section 34.1, some alleles are selected against in certain combinations but are selected for in other combinations. Suppose that both $A_1 A_1$ and $A_2 A_2$ are lethal but that $A_1 A_2$ is viable. In this case $w = 1$ for the heterozygote and is 0 for both homozygotes. A population with only these two alleles is permanently heterozygous because of such *balanced lethals*.

A second, less extreme, example of the adaptive superiority of the heterozygote can be illustrated in human beings. As mentioned in Section 32-2, homozygotes for the gene for *sickle-cell anemia* ($\beta^S \beta^S$) usually die from anemia before adolescence. $\beta^A \beta^A$ individuals have normal blood type, whereas $\beta^A \beta^S$ individuals are either normal or have a slight anemia. In certain countries the frequency of β^S is higher than in other countries. This difference is associated with the $\beta^A \beta^S$ heterozygote being more resistant to certain kinds of malaria than the $\beta^A \beta^A$ homozygote. Of course, in non-

---

[1] Note in the case of phenylketonuria (Section 33.5) that even if the affected individuals ($a\,a$) did not reproduce (the mutant gene acting as a recessive lethal), only 1 per cent of the a genes present in the gene pool would be eliminated each generation. This illustrates the inefficiency of selection against homozygotes for rare recessive genes, at least insofar as lowering the frequency of such genes is concerned.

malarial countries β^S confers no antimalarial advantage, and so the fitness of the heterozygote $(1 - s)$ is lower than that of the normal homozygote (1), whereas the $\beta^S\beta^S$ individual has a fitness of zero. As expected, therefore, sickle-cell anemia is rare or absent in most of the world where certain forms of malaria are absent.

On the other hand, in certain malarial countries, even though heterozygotes may be slightly anemic, the advantage of being resistant to malaria produces a greater overall fitness than does the $\beta^A\beta^A$ genotype. Here the fitness of the heterozygote, $\beta^A\beta^S$, is maximal and therefore must be assigned the value 1, whereas that of the normal homozygote, $\beta^A\beta^A$, is $1 - s_1$. Mutant homozygotes, $\beta^S\beta^S$, have a fitness of $1 - s_2$, where $s_2 = 1$, since all $\beta^S\beta^S$ ordinarily die (even if extremely resistant to malaria). In this situation natural selection maintains both β^A and β^S in the gene pool.[2] Thus, when the heterozygote is more adaptive than either homozygote, natural selection maintains a gene such as β^S in the gene pool even though it is usually lethal when homozygous.

The greater fitness of the heterozygote over both homozygotes is an example of *hybrid vigor* or *heterosis*. In both cases of heterosis described above, the heterozygous condition of a single locus was found to be better than or "dominant over" both homozygous conditions, or to show *overdominance*. (R)

34.4 Heterosis also occurs due to the less fit genes at many loci being recessive to their alleles in the multiple heterozygote.

Heterosis can be due not only to overdominance expressed at a single locus but to dominance expressed in a heterozygote for two or more loci. The latter type of heterosis can be demonstrated by crossing two pure lines ($A\,A\,b\,b\,C\,C\,d\,d \times a\,a\,B\,B\,c\,c\,D\,D$), homozygous for different recessives that lower fitness (the recessives having lowercase letters). The genetically uniform F_1 ($A\,a\,B\,b\,C\,c\,D\,d$) are more vigorous (having dominant alleles at all four loci) than either parent (each having dominant alleles at two loci) because the dominant alleles mask the less fit recessive ones. Note in this case that the multiple heterozygote $A\,a\,B\,b\,C\,c\,D\,d$ is no more adaptive than the homozygote $A\,A\,B\,B\,C\,C\,D\,D$. The increased vigor and uniformity of heterosis have important practical applications (as discussed in Section S34.4). (R)

34.5 Heterosis can have several bases on the molecular level.

Heterosis can be produced from the effects of a single locus or multiple loci; these loci may reside inside or outside of the nucleus. Ignoring the possibility that functional genes may be involved in some cases of hybrid vigor, let us consider several ways that the products of structural gene action may produce a heterotic effect.

[2] β^S has a frequency equal to

$$\frac{1 - (1 - s_1)}{s_1 + s_2} = \frac{s_1}{s_1 + s_2}.$$

This fraction can be read as "the advantage of β^S (as shown by the advantage of $\beta^A\beta^S$ over $\beta^A\beta^A$) divided by the total disadvantage of β^A and β^S."

Separate products

The hybrid can make two proteins which when present at the same time have a better metabolic effect than either one has alone. For example, one protein may react to produce a substrate needed for the second protein to react; or the presence of both proteins can be otherwise advantageous, as in the heterozygote for the gene for sickling.

Combined products

Two proteins made by a hybrid may combine to produce a protein metabolically superior to what is made when only one of the proteins is present. Such heterotic unions may occur whenever a protein is composed of two or more polypeptides specified independently at the genetic level. For example, two alleles contribute polypeptides to a protein in the case of certain enzymes; two nonalleles contribute polypeptides in the formation of the hemoglobin or antibody molecule.

Reduced amount of single products

In the diploid, two normal alleles ordinarily produce an optimal phenotypic effect, whereas the presence of only one of these produces a near-optimal effect (see Figure 20-1 and Section 20.3). One can imagine, however, cases in which the homozygote produces too much effect, the single-dose condition producing a more optimal effect. Heterosis may occur on this basis if a suitable normal allele has not yet arisen by mutation, or if the environment has changed. This type of heterosis has been found in certain *Neurospora* whose cells contain two nuclei (see Section 15.4). When one nucleus carries the normal gene for *p*-aminobenzoic acid (pab^+) and the other the mutant allele (*pab*), growth is better than when both nuclei are pab^+ or *pab*. (R)

34.6   By having opposite effects on the same genotype under different circumstances, selection may preserve genetic polymorphism in a population.

We have seen that selection will maintain two or more alleles in a population when overdominance occurs for different genotypes containing them. When a population retains two or more genetic alternatives it is said to exhibit *genetic polymorphism*. Selection, by having opposite effects on the same genotype, can also lead to genetic polymorphism under the following circumstances:

1. If a genotype is selected against when it is frequent (because it is in competition mostly with individuals having the same genotype) and selected for when it is rare (when it is in competition mostly with other genotypes).
2. If a genotype is selected for in a particular environmental habitat and is selected against at the border of this habitat and a less favorable one.
3. If selection is in favor of a genotype in the gametic (haploid) stage and against it in the zygotic (diploid) stage. (R)

34.7 Selection may favor one phenotype or more than one; the former situation usually decreases and the latter usually increases genotypic variability.

Selection may be for one extreme phenotype (see Section 21.9), called *directional selection*, or for the intermediate or mean phenotype, called *centripetal* or *stabilizing selection*. In both cases gene frequencies change and, since unfavorable alleles tend to be lost while the favorable ones increase in frequency, the variability of the population's genotypes—the variance—decreases. When selection involves overdominance (which may occur, for example, in stabilizing selection), and gene frequencies no longer change after equilibrium is reached, genotypic variability is nevertheless again reduced since the heterozygote is favored over the homozygotes.

Other types of selection may favor more than one phenotype. Different phenotypes may be favored at different times in *cyclical selection*, which can occur when the environment is unstable. When the environment is unstable or is different in different parts of the territory occupied, the two extreme phenotypes may be selected for cyclically or simultaneously in what is called *disruptive selection*. Selection favoring more than one phenotype means that more than one genotype tends to be preserved. Thus, selection favoring two or more phenotypes tends to preserve gene variability—to increase genotypic variance. (R)

34.8 Mutation introduces genetic diversity into a population and shifts gene frequencies.

The *phenotypic diversity* that selection tests for fitness is based upon *genotypic diversity*. This genotypic diversity in turn is based upon the *genetic diversity* introduced into the population by mutation. Thus, mutation not only itself shifts gene frequencies, but provides the genotypic raw material on which selection can act to shift gene frequencies.

Nonrecurrent mutations

When a complex mutation such as a reciprocal translocation or an inversion occurs, it is unlikely that the identical mutation will occur in the population again. Such mutations are effectively unique and nonrecurrent. They originate in the population in single heterozygotes which are either lost accidentally or subjected to selection. If the mutant heterozygote is adaptively superior to the non-mutant-containing alternatives present, the frequency of the *old* alternatives will decrease somewhat as shown in Figure 34-1, curve *a*. If the mutant produces no detectable change in fitness (being *neutral*) or a reduction in fitness it will eventually be lost.

Recurrent mutations

A given point mutation, however, usually occurs repeatedly in a population at a rate that is relatively constant. If μ, the mutation rate from A_1 to A_2 is considered, it is clear that the relative increase of A_2 in the population is greater when A_1 is frequent than when it is rare. In the absence of the reverse mutation from A_2 to A_1

(and of selection against $A_1 A_2$ or $A_2 A_2$), of course, all alleles will eventually become A_2. If the reverse mutation occurs at a rate v, it will have negligible effect while the frequency of A_2 is small but will be significant when A_2 is larger. An equilibrium in the frequency A_1 and A_2 will occur in the population when the gain of A_2 (from A_1 to A_2 mutation) equals the loss of A_1 (from A_2 to A_1 mutation). If A_1 and A_2 have equilibrium frequencies p_1 and p_2, these values can be calculated from the opposing mutation rates as follows:

$$p_1 = \frac{v}{\mu + v}; \qquad p_2 = \frac{\mu}{\mu + v}.$$

If $v = 0.00002$ and $\mu = 0.00006$, $p_1 = 0.25$ and $p_2 = 0.75$.

34.9   Gene frequencies will arrive at equilibrium when the net rate of increase of an allele by mutation equals its rate of loss by selection.

We have already seen that gene frequencies can reach equilibrium in a population when a single factor operates in two opposite directions—selection against homozygotes and for heterozygotes in cases of overdominant heterosis; selection for and against the same genotype at different times or places; and mutation to and from a given allele. These and other factors which can disequilibrate gene frequency in the gene pool coexist and interact in natural populations. When two factors have opposite effects on gene frequency, an equilibrium may occur between the introduction and removal of a particular allele in the population. This equilibrium between selection and mutation is discussed next.

A gene A_2 will reach population equilibrium when the frequency with which it is gained by mutation (μ) equals its frequency of loss by selection. The latter frequency must equal the selective coefficient (s) × the frequency of the class being selected against × the fraction of its genes that are mutant. Consider this equilibrium for dominant and recessive mutants.

Dominant lethal mutant

A dominant lethal mutant A_2 causes death or sterility before maturity. It occurs only in heterozygous condition and is eliminated from the gene pool the same generation it arises. Thus, $w = 0$ and $s = 1$ for $A_1 A_2$. When A_2 is in equilibrium, $\mu = (s)\,(2p_1 p_2)(\frac{1}{2})$, $= 1(2p_1 p_2)(\frac{1}{2})$, or $\frac{1}{2}$ the frequency of affected individuals. In the absence of special medical treatment *retinoblastoma*, a type of cancer of the eye, is an example of such a dominant lethal in man.

Dominant detrimental mutant

Achondroplastic (or *chondrodystrophic*) *dwarfism* is characterized by disproportion —normal head and trunk size but shortened arms and legs. This rare, fully penetrant (see Section 22-2) disease is attributed to the presence of a gene in heterozygous condition which therefore acts as a dominant detrimental mutant. Since the frequency of such dwarfs from normal parents is 0.000084, μ from A_1 to A_2 must be 0.000042 (the reverse mutation rate can be neglected). Such dwarfs ($A_1 A_2$) are known to produce only 20 per cent as many children as normal people. Because of this $w = 0.2$ and $s = 0.8$. If the population contains A_2 in a frequency that is at equilibrium between mutation rate and selection, $\mu = (s)(2p_1p_2)(\frac{1}{2})$, or $\mu/s = (2p_1p_2)(\frac{1}{2})$. We expect, therefore, that $0.000042/0.8 = 0.0000525 = (2p_1p_2)(\frac{1}{2})$. The actual value can be obtained from $\frac{1}{2}$ the frequency of all $A_1 A_2$ in the population. Ten dwarf babies occurred in 94,075 births, or a frequency of 0.000106. (These $A_1 A_2$ dwarf children include those whose parents were normal × dwarf as well as normal × normal.) The observed value of $(2p_1p_2)(\frac{1}{2}) = 0.000106 \times \frac{1}{2} = 0.000053$; this agrees very closely with the expected value. We conclude, therefore, that in this population A_2 is in an equilibrium determined solely, or principally, by mutation and selection. Note, in this case, that the frequency of heterozygotes at equilibrium is more than twice the mutation frequency. Actually the gene frequency for dwarfism ($\frac{1}{2}$ the frequency of $A_1 A_2$) is not very much larger than the mutation frequency, demonstrating the efficiency of natural selection in eliminating such mutants from the gene pool.

Recessive lethal or detrimental mutant

If mutant A_2 is completely recessive, selection operates against the mutant only when it is homozygous. When equilibrium between mutation and selection occurs for A_2, $\mu = (s)(p_2{}^2)(1)$.

The gene for *juvenile amaurotic idiocy* (A_2) has no apparent effect when heterozygous ($A_1 A_2$); since homozygous children die, A_2 is a recessive lethal mutant. Affected individuals are found with a frequency of 1 per 100,000, or 0.00001. Since $s = 1$ for a recessive lethal, $\mu = 1(p_2{}^2)(1) = 0.00001$ assuming that the population is at equilibrium. In other words, the rate of removal of the A_2 allele in $A_2 A_2$ individuals by selection is balanced by its rate of entry into the population by mutation.

What is the frequency of A_2 in the population assuming that equilibrium has been attained? This must be $\sqrt{p_2{}^2}$, or $\sqrt{0.00001}$, or about 0.003, whereas the frequency of A_1 must be $1 - 0.0003$, or 0.997. Note from Figure 34-2 that heterozygotes (*carriers*) are 600 times more frequent than afflicted homozygotes.

We see, therefore, that at equilibrium the frequency of a recessive mutant in the gene pool can be expressed as $p_2 = \sqrt{\mu/s}$, where $s = 1$ for a recessive lethal. When the homozygous recessive mutant is detrimental without being lethal, s becomes less than 1 (but more than zero) and the frequency of the mutant in the gene pool increases. Thus, if s were $\frac{1}{4}$ instead of 1, p_2 would be twice as large.

Partially dominant mutant

Many mutants have some detrimental effect when heterozygous, and a much greater detriment when homozygous. For example, recessive lethals in *Drosophila*

	$(p_1)^2$	$2(p_1 p_2)$	$(p_2)^2$
Frequency at Equilibrium	$(0.997)^2$	$2(0.997)(0.003)$	$(0.003)^2$
	0.994	0.006	0.000,01

Figure 34-2   Juvenile amaurotic idiocy. See the text for an explanation.

have about 5 per cent detriment in heterozygous condition. In such cases selection occurs against both the heterozygote and mutant homozygote. Note in Figure 34-2 that with a typical low mutation rate most mutant genes with detrimental effect will exist in heterozygous condition. Suppose, for illustrative purposes, that the recessive lethal allele for juvenile amaurotic idiocy (Figure 34-2) has a detrimental effect in heterozygous condition of only 1 per cent; thus $s = 0.01$ for $A_1 A_2$, whereas $s = 1.0$ for $A_2 A_2$. Since there would be about 600 times as many $A_1 A_2$ as $A_2 A_2$ individuals, $(600)(0.01)$, or 6, A_2 genes would be eliminated from $A_1 A_2$ individuals for every 2 eliminated from $A_2 A_2$ persons. We see, therefore, that in establishing an equilibrium between mutation and selection, most of the elimination of detrimental alleles by selection usually occurs in the heterozygous state. (R)

34.10 Migration and random genetic drift are other factors that can change gene frequencies in populations.

Gene frequencies in populations can be changed not only by mutation and selection but by *migration* and *random genetic drift*. If the genotypes of emigrants or immigrants do not contain the same gene frequencies as the population gene pool the population gene frequencies will be changed by any differential shift in genotypes.

When, in a given situation, only one of the factors of mutation, selection, and migration continues to affect the gene pool, gene frequencies are ordinarily changed progressively, directionally. Gene frequencies can also be changed nondirectionally, that is, at random, depending upon the chance selection of which gametes and zygotes serve as the bridge between generations. The gene pool of the progeny is exactly like that of the parents only under the ideal circumstances of infinite numbers of parents, gametes, and progeny zygotes. The smaller the sample of one or more of these three factors the greater is the degree that gene frequencies will shift by chance from the parental values. The nondirectional change in gene frequency due to the variations that occur by chance in the composition of finite samples is what we have referred to above as *random genetic drift*.

We can illustrate this principle with an extreme example. Suppose a diploid population contains 0.5 A_1 and 0.5 A_2 at Hardy–Weinberg equilibrium. If only one pair of individuals is selected by chance to be the parents of the next generation (Figure 34-3), there is only a $\frac{6}{16}$ probability that the gene frequency will be unchanged. There is, however, a $\frac{1}{16}$ probability of permanently fixing gene frequency at 1.0 A_1 and 0 A_2; a $\frac{1}{16}$ chance of the opposite fixation; and $\frac{8}{16}$ chance of shifting the gene frequencies to 0.75 A_1 and 0.25 A_2 or the reverse. The same results are obtained both if only two pairs of gametes are selected by chance from an infinitely large number of parents, and if only two zygotes are selected for survival by chance from infinitely large numbers of parents and gametes. Gene frequencies can also drift if, by chance, different parents contribute unequally to the next generation. Because gene frequencies can become fixed at 1.0 and 0 due to random genetic drift, this factor operating alone tends to reduce genetic and genotypic variability in a population.

The actual number of parents assumed to contribute equally to the progeny gene pool comprises the *effective population number* (N_e). If in a population of 100 males and 100 females, only 50 of each sex mate and are fertile, the effective population number, N_e, is 100. If, however, 90 of one sex and 10 of the other mate and are fertile, $N_e = 4N_f N_m/(N_f + N_m)$, where N_f is the number of fertile females and N_m the

Parental Mating	Probability	Gene Frequency in Progeny Population	
		A_1	A_2
$A_1 A_1 \times A_1 A_1$	$\frac{1}{4} \times \frac{1}{4} = \frac{1}{16}$	1.0	0
$A_1 A_1 \times A_1 A_2$ $A_1 A_2 \times A_1 A_1$	$\left.\begin{array}{c}\frac{1}{4} \times \frac{1}{2} = \\[4pt] \frac{1}{2} \times \frac{1}{4} =\end{array}\right] \frac{4}{16}$	0.75	0.25
$A_1 A_1 \times A_2 A_2$ $A_2 A_2 \times A_1 A_1$ $A_1 A_2 \times A_1 A_2$	$\left.\begin{array}{c}\frac{1}{4} \times \frac{1}{4} = \\[4pt] \frac{1}{4} \times \frac{1}{4} = \\[4pt] \frac{1}{2} \times \frac{1}{2} =\end{array}\right] \frac{6}{16}$	0.50	0.50
$A_1 A_2 \times A_2 A_2$ $A_2 A_2 \times A_1 A_2$	$\left.\begin{array}{c}\frac{1}{2} \times \frac{1}{4} = \\[4pt] \frac{1}{4} \times \frac{1}{2} =\end{array}\right] \frac{4}{16}$	0.25	0.75
$A_2 A_2 \times A_2 A_2$	$\frac{1}{4} \times \frac{1}{4} = \frac{1}{16}$	0	1.0

Figure 34-3   Random genetic drift when only one pair of parents contributes to the next generation of a population at equilibrium containing 0.5 A_1 and 0.5 A_2.

number of fertile males. In this case, then, $N_e = 4(90)(10)/100 = 36$; the smaller this number, the larger the random genetic drift.

34.11   Genotypic variability can be maintained in a population if adaptiveness is provided by different homozygous genotypes being present in different subpopulations due to the action of random genetic drift.

As noted, genotypic heterogeneity is maintained in a population by overdominant heterotic phenotypic effects. The persistence of a variety of recessive alleles for a locus is fostered especially when optimal fitness is obtained by a single dose of a dominant allele, recessive alleles making little or no contribution to fitness. Whereas the genotypic variability in the preceding cases depends upon the fitness of heterozygosity, that of the following hypothetical example depends upon the fitness of homozygosity and the occurrence of random genetic drift.

Suppose in a given environment that two pairs of genes affect the same trait, equal numbers of uppercase and lowercase letters providing maximum fitness. In this event (Figure 34-4), $w = 1$ for $A A\ b b$, $a a\ B B$, and $A a\ B b$; $w = 0.5$ for $a a\ B b$, $A a\ b b$, $A A\ B b$, and $A a\ B B$; and $w = 0$ for $a a\ b b$ and $A A\ B B$. What will happen to the three genotypes that provide maximal fitness when the members of a population comprise a single interbreeding reproductive unit? Random genetic drift will tend to fix the entire population at $A A\ b b$ or $a a\ B B$, and genotypic variability will be lost. If, however, the population is composed of smaller subpopulations between which reproduction is limited, random genetic drift will tend to eliminate $A a\ B b$,

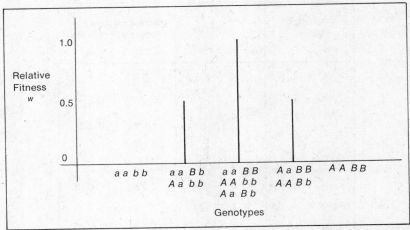

Figure 34-4 Relative fitness of genotypes. It is assumed that two pairs of genes each having two alleles affect the same trait, two uppercase letters providing maximum fitness.

and establish subpopulations with fixed genotypes, some *A A b b* and others *a a B B*, thereby maintaining the genotypic variability of the entire population.

Suppose next that the environment of one *A A b b* subpopulation changes so that fitness increases with the number of uppercase letters in the genotype. If *A A b b* individuals of this subpopulation occasionally mate with *a a B B* individuals of another subpopulation, *A a B b* progeny will result which when bred, in turn, can produce more adaptive genotypes with three and four uppercase letters. We see that subpopulations may retain genetic differences which may be combined so that with selection and genetic drift a subpopulation can reach new heights of adaptiveness, or new *adaptive peaks*. Note also, however, that the subpopulation moving off the *A A b b* adaptive peak may pass not only to a new, higher, adaptive peak but into a less adaptive state or *adaptive valley*, for example with no uppercase letters in the genotype.

SUMMARY AND CONCLUSIONS

Gene frequencies, and hence genotypic frequencies, can be shifted from their Hardy–Weinberg equilibria by selection, mutation, migration, and random genetic drift.

Selection can act differentially on homozygotes and/or heterozygotes; it can act unidirectionally or in different directions on a given genotype. Unidirectional selection will ordinarily reduce genetic variability. Selection will preserve genetic polymorphism, however, when (1) heterosis is involved, (2) opposite effects on the same genotype are favored under different circumstances, and (3) more than one genotype is favored.

Mutation is the source of the genetic variability upon which selection acts. Genetic variability is maintained when mutations occur to and from a given allele. Shifting gene frequencies will arrive at equilibrium when the net rate of increase of an allele by mutation equals its rate of loss by selection.

Although selection, mutation, and migration can change gene frequencies directionally, random genetic drift shifts gene frequencies nondirectionally by chance variations that occur in the genetic composition of finite population samples. Although genetic variability is reduced by genetic drift in a population whose members interbreed freely, it may be maintained in a population if it is adaptive for not freely inter-breeding subpopulations to have different homozygous genotypes (established by random genetic drift).

GENERAL REFERENCES

Crow, J. F., and Kimura, M. 1970. *An introduction to population genetics theory.* New York: Harper & Row, Inc.

Dobzhansky, Th. 1951. *Genetics and the origin of species,* third edition. New York: Columbia University Press.

Dobzhansky, Th. 1970. *Genetics of the evolutionary process.* New York: Columbia University Press.

Fisher, R. A. 1930. *The genetical theory of natural selection.* Oxford: Clarendon Press.

Lerner, I. M. 1968. *Heredity, evolution, and society.* San Francisco: W. H. Freeman and Company, Publishers.

Li, C. C. 1955. *Population genetics.* Chicago: University of Chicago Press.

Population genetics: the nature and causes of genetic variability in populations. 1955. Cold Spring Harbor Sympos. Quant. Biol., 20.

Spiess, E. B. (Editor), 1962. *Papers on animal population genetics.* Boston: Little, Brown and Company.

Volpe, E. P. 1970. *Understanding evolution,* second edition. Dubuque, Iowa: William C. Brown Company.

Wright, S. 1932. The roles of mutation, inbreeding, crossbreeding and selection in evolution. Proc. 6th Intern. Congr. Genet., Ithaca, pp. 356–366. Reprinted in *Evolution,* Brousseau, G. E., Jr., Dubuque, Iowa: William C. Brown Company, 1967, pp. 68–78.

Wright, S. 1951. The genetic structure of populations. Ann. Eugenics, 15: 323–354.

SPECIFIC SECTION REFERENCES

34.1   Anderson, W. W., and King, C. E. 1970. Age-specific selection. Proc. Nat. Acad. Sci., U.S., 66: 780–786. (Selection intensity depends upon age.)

Kerster, H. W., and Levin, D. A. 1970. Temporal phenotypic heterogeneity as a substrate for selection. Proc. Nat. Acad. Sci., U.S., 66: 370–376. (Selection not between individuals or populations but of a persisting population image.)

Ronald A. Fisher (1890–1962). [From Genetics, 61: 1 (1969).]

Sewall Wright in 1954. Dr. Wright is noted for his research in physiological genetics and in the mathematics of population genetics. (Photograph by The Llewellyn Studio.)

Lerner, I. M. 1958. *The genetical basis of selection*. New York: John Wiley & Sons, Inc.

Sheppard, P. M. 1959. *Natural selection and heredity*. New York: Philosophical Library, Inc.

34.3   Allison, A. C. 1956. Population genetics of abnormal human haemoglobins. Acta Genetica, 6: 430–434; reprinted in *Papers on animal population genetics*, Spiess, E. B. (Editor), pp. 165–169, 1962. Boston: Little, Brown and Company.

Allison, A. C. 1956. Sickle cells and evolution. Scient. Amer., 195: 87–94.

Crow, J. F. 1952. Dominance and overdominance. In *Heterosis*, Gowen, J. W. (Editor), Ames, Iowa: Iowa State College Press, pp. 282–297.

Parsons, P. A., and Bodmer, W. F. 1961. The evolution of overdominance: natural selection and heterozygote advantage. Nature, Lond., 190: 7–12.

Watanabe, T. K. 1969. Persistence of a visible mutant in natural populations of *Drosophila melanogaster*. Jap. J. Genet., 44: 15–22. (Single locus heterosis.)

Wills, C., and Nichols, L. 1971. Single-gene heterosis in *Drosophila* revealed by inbreeding. Nature, Lond., 233: 123–125.

34.4   Gowen, J. W. (Editor), 1952. *Heterosis*. Ames, Iowa: Iowa State College Press.

Mather, K. 1955. The genetical basis of heterosis. Proc. Roy. Soc. Lond., B144: 143–150.

Müntzing, A. 1963. A case of preserved heterozygosity in rye in spite of long-continued inbreeding. Hereditas, 50: 377–413.

34.5   Emerson, S. 1948. A physiological basis for some suppressor mutations and possibly for one gene heterosis. Proc. Nat. Acad. Sci., U.S., 34: 72–74.

Sarkissian, I. V., Kessinger, M. A., and Harris, W. 1964. Differential rates of development of heterotic and nonheterotic young maize seedlings. I. Correlation of differential morphological development with physiological differences in germinating seeds. Proc. Nat. Acad. Sci., U.S., 51: 212–218.

Srivastava, H. K., and Sarkissian, I. V. 1969. Heterosis, complementation and homeostasis in mitochondria of wheat. (Abstr.) Genetics, 61 (Suppl. 2/2): 57.

Warner, R. L., Hageman, R. H., Dudley, J. W., and Lambert, R. J. 1969. Inheritance of nitrate reductase activity in *Zea mays* L. Proc. Nat. Acad. Sci., U.S., 62: 785–792. (Heterosis involving two loci.)

34.6   Ehrman, L. 1970. Simulation of the mating advantage in mating of rare *Drosophila* males. Science, 167: 905–906.

34.7   Thoday, J. M. 1959. Effects of disruptive selection. I. Genetic flexibility. Heredity, 13: 187–203; reprinted in *Papers on animal population genetics*, Spiess, E. B. (Editor), Boston: Little, Brown and Company, pp. 25–41.

34.9 Crow, J. F., and Temin, R. G. 1964. Evidence for partial dominance of recessive lethal genes in natural populations of *Drosophila.* Amer. Nat., 98: 21–33.

Wallace, B. 1963. A comparison of the viability effects of chromosomes in heterozygous and homozygous condition. Proc. Nat. Acad. Sci., U.S., 49: 801–806.

SUPPLEMENTARY SECTION

S34.4 The increased vigor and uniformity of heterosis have important practical applications.

Breeding procedures that result in hybrid vigor have been widely applied to economically important plants and animals. For example, it has been estimated that the use of hybrid maize has enriched society by more than 1 billion dollars. We might ask: What is wrong with normal maize? The answer is that it is too variable in quality and vigor. Inbreeding decreases variability, but unfortunately inbreeding also results in loss of vigor or other desirable traits. The way to overcome this problem is to obtain inbred lines which are uniform (because they are homozygous) and carry different favorable dominant genes (yet are also homozygous for various undesirable recessive genes), and cross the different inbred lines to each other. Their F_1 will be multiply heterozygous, uniform, and more vigorous than either parental inbred line.

Consequently, hybrids are made from two selected inbred lines—of maize in this case. Although the F_1 plants are vigorous and uniform,

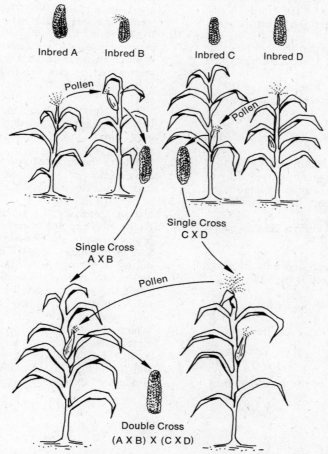

Inbred A   Inbred B   Inbred C   Inbred D

Pollen

Pollen

Single Cross
C X D

Single Cross
A X B

Pollen

Double Cross
(A X B) X (C X D)

Figure 34-5 Production of commercial hybrid maize by the "double cross" breeding procedure.

they come from kernels grown on one of the less vigorous inbred lines. For this reason, hybrid seeds are not sufficiently numerous, and consequently, are not commercially feasible. In practice this difficulty is overcome (Figure 34-5) by crossing four selected inbred lines two by two and obtaining two different *single cross hybrids*.

The two single cross hybrids are then crossed to each other. Since they are formed on a vigorous single cross hybrid plant, seeds produced by this *double cross* are plentiful and can be sold inexpensively. Heterosis is of great practical importance.

Sprague, G. F. (Editor), 1955. *Corn and corn improvement.* New York: Academic Press, Inc.

QUESTIONS AND PROBLEMS

1. Are the causes of evolution the same in populations reproducing only asexually as in those reproducing sexually? Explain.

2. Suppose, in a population obeying the Hardy–Weinberg rule, mutation occurs for only one generation and changes the composition of the gene pool. How many additional generations are required before a new genetic equilibrium is established? Explain.

3. Discuss the statement: "The Hardy–Weinberg law is the cornerstone of evolutionary genetics."

4. How can you explain that the vast majority of newly arisen mutants reduce fitness when homozygous?

5. What will happen to a gene pool of 0.9 A_1 and 0.1 A_2 that is otherwise at Hardy–Weinberg equilibrium if mutation rate from A_1 to A_2 is 10 per 10^6
   a. when there is no back mutation from A_2 to A_1?
   b. when the back-mutation rate is 4 per 10^6?

6. Explain whether the mutation frequency to a particular allele is of primary importance in shifting its frequency in the population, when this gene is
   a. a dominant lethal in early developmental stages.
   b. a recessive lethal.
   c. phenotypically expressed only after the reproductive period of the individual.
   d. very rare.
   e. present in small cross-fertilizing populations.

7. Can the adaptive value of the gene of problem 6 differ in
   a. haploids and diploids?
   b. males and females?
   c. two diploid cells of the same organism?

8. Other things being equal, what will happen to the frequency in the gene pool of a dominant mutant whose selection coefficient changes from 1 to $\frac{1}{4}$? If the mutant is completely recessive?

9. If persons carrying detrimental mutants never marry, these particular genes are removed from the gene pool. Under what conditions is the failure to marry likely to appreciably reduce the frequency of detrimental mutants in the gene pool?

10. In Thailand, heterozygotes for a mutant gene that results in the formation of hemoglobin E are more frequent in the population than would be expected from the Hardy–Weinberg rule. How can you explain this?

11. What factors determine the relative gene frequencies in a population that contains only three alleles, all having the same adaptive value?

12. What are the expected population genetics consequences of medical advances that reduce the deleteriousness of phenylketonuria or of hemophilia?

13. Heterozygotes for a certain gene develop Huntington's chorea, a nervous disease that begins to show its effect at about age 35 and is invariably lethal. Of what consequence to the population frequency of this detrimental allele is the finding that heterozygotes overcompensate by having about twice as many children as nonmutant homozygotes?

14. Which population is expected to have a more stable gene pool: A, which contains 30 ♂♂ and 30 ♀♀, or B, which contains 100 ♂♂ and 21 ♀♀, all individuals mating and fertile? Explain.

Chapter 35

The Genetic Variability
of Populations

Since the four factors—mutation, selection, migration, and random genetic drift—are the principal causes of changes in gene frequencies in a population, and the evolution of a population is based upon the history of the genotypes it contains, these four factors are the principal causes of biological evolution.

We have noted in Chapter 34 that the changes in gene frequencies caused by these factors acting individually or in combination may be accompanied by an increase or a decrease in the variability of the genotypes present in the population. The present chapter discusses the extent and adaptiveness of the genetic variability which is actually found within and between populations.

35.1 Considerable genetic variability may be present in populations that are phenotypically uniform.

When collected in the wild, almost all *Drosophila* are phenotypically alike, except for the sex differences, appearing "wild type" or normal. We cannot accept this phenotypic uniformity as evidence of genotypic uniformity, however, since a *Drosophila* population appearing wild type can conceal considerable genetic variability in the form of different but seemingly identical alleles (isoalleles; see Section S16.1b), recessive point mutants, reciprocal translocations, paracentric inversions, and so on. We would like to know the total amount of this genetic variability present in natural populations of *Drosophila*. In the next several sections we shall see how much genetic variability is revealed by studies (1) of chromosome configuration at metaphase in typical mitotic cells and at interphase in giant larval salivary cells, (2) of viability and sterility mutants, and (3) of biochemical products of gene action.

35.2 Many gross chromosomal rearrangements such as large pericentric inversions and whole-arm translocations are associated with different species of *Drosophila*.

Hundreds of different species of *Drosophila* occur in nature. These species can be compared ecologically, morphologically, physiologically, and biochemically. For those species able to interbreed, recombinational genetic properties can also be compared. Banding patterns of the salivary gland chromosomes and the appearance of chromosomes at metaphase of different species are additional areas of comparison. After all available information of this kind is gathered, it is possible to arrange the chromosomes of various species on a chart so that those closest together are more

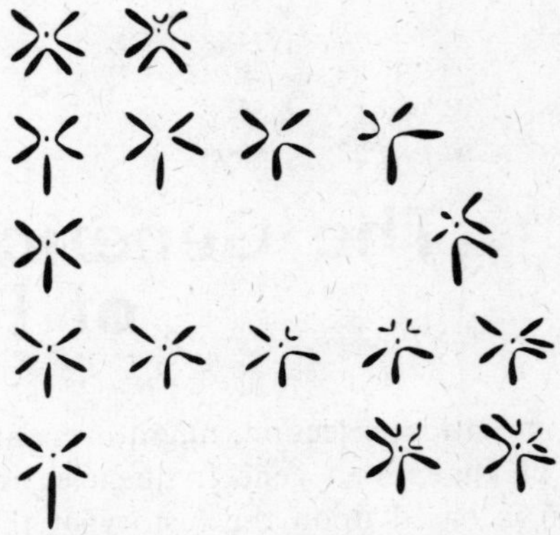

Figure 35-1 Chromosome configurations in several *Drosophila* species.

nearly related in descent—evolution—than are those farther apart. This arrangement is illustrated in Figure 35-1, which shows the *karyotype*—the types of chromosomes at metaphase—including the X but not the Y chromosome for different *Drosophila* species or groups of species. The karyotype of the *melanogaster* species group, for example, is shown in row 2, column 1; the bottom chromosome is the rod-shaped X, the two V's are the two large autosomes (II and III), and the dot represents the tiny chromosome IV. In the other karyotypes, whole chromosomes or chromosome arms judged to be homologous are placed in the same relative positions. What can be learned from a comparison of these karyotypes?

Since the amount of detail in a metaphase chromosome is limited basically to size and shape, one cannot expect to discern any small-sized rearrangements at this stage. (Accordingly, regardless of their importance, small rearrangements involving duplication, deficiency, inversion, and translocation cannot be detected on the chart.) Even a large paracentric inversion is undetected at metaphase, since it does not change the shape of the chromosome. Other gross structural changes such as large pericentric inversions and translocations involving whole chromosome arms, however, can be detected. In row 4 the chromosome patterns in columns 2 and 3 seem identical, except that a pericentric inversion has changed a rod to a V, or vice versa. (Pericentric inversions always change the relative lengths of the arms when the two breaks are different distances from the centromere.) Whole-arm translocation is indicated in the comparison of the karyotype for *melanogaster* (row 2, column 1) with the one to its right (row 2, column 2). A V-shaped autosome in *melanogaster* appears as two rods in its evolutionary relative. (Note also that the dot chromosome is missing.) In the next karyotype to the right (row 2, column 3), two rods have combined to form a V that is different from either of the two V's in *melanogaster*. Other examples in this chart indicate that two rod-shaped chromosomes have formed a V-shaped chromosome or that a V has formed two rods.[1]

---

[1] Consider how a V can originate from two rods (Figure 35-2). Recall that a rod-shaped chromosome typically has two arms, although one is very short. The short arm may not be noticeable at metaphase or anaphase; its presence may be demonstrated, however, either cytologically at an earlier or later stage of the nuclear cycle, or genetically by studying genetic recombination. Suppose two rods are broken near their centromeres, one in the long arm of one chromosome, the other in the short arm of the other chromosome. If the long acentric arm of the first chromosome becomes joined to the long centric piece of the second, a V is formed. Notice that this union involves the joining of two whole or almost-whole arms in a eucentric half-translocation. The remaining pieces may join together to form a short eucentric chromosome, thereby completing a reciprocal translocation; or they may

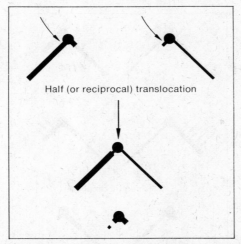

Figure 35-2 Formation of a V-shaped chromosome from two rod-shaped chromosomes. Thin arrows indicate points of chromosome breakage.

Karyotype comparisons such as those above show that whole-arm translocations are able to survive in natural populations. Such rearrangements and pericentric inversions are extremely useful in helping us establish evolutionary relationships among different species. But it should be emphasized that this kind of information by itself does not reveal whether gross chromosomal rearrangements have a primary or secondary role in causing speciation or are merely mutational events which accompany or follow speciation. (R)

35.3 The paracentric inversion polymorphism which occurs within and between populations of a single *Drosophila* species seems to be adaptive.

The fruit fly *Drosophila pseudoobscura* is commonly found in northern Mexico and the western United States. Within and between populations all the flies are very

---

not join. In either instance, if the short pieces are lost in a subsequent nuclear division and the number of genes lost is small enough, the absence of these parts may be tolerated physiologically by the organism.

The reverse process, the formation of two rods from a V, necessitates the contribution of a centromere from some other chromosome. In *Drosophila*, this second chromosome may be the Y (Figure 35-3). Suppose that the V is broken near its centromere and the Y is broken anywhere. Should a eucentric reciprocal translocation follow, two chromosomes would be produced, each having one arm derived predominantly from the Y. If subsequent paracentric deletions occur in these Y-containing arms, rod shapes will result, thereby completing the change from a V to two rods. Note that almost every part but the centromere of the Y chromosome is eventually lost in this process. But this loss may have little or no disadvantage to the *Drosophila*, since the Y carries relatively few loci and is primarily concerned with sperm motility. For example, this series of mutations may be initiated in the male germ line, producing two chromosomes—each containing part of the Y. Deletion of Y parts can occur without detriment if these chromosomes happen to enter the female germ line; they may stay in the male germ line provided that a regular Y chromosome is included in the genotype in due time. The small IV chromosome in *melanogaster*, whose monosomy is tolerated in either sex, may also contribute a centromere in the process of changing a V to two rods by an identical or similar series of mutational events.

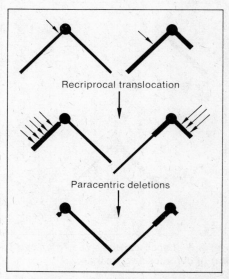

Figure 35-3 Formation of two rod-shaped chromosomes from a V-shaped chromosome and a Y chromosome. Thin arrows indicate points of chromosome breakage.

similar in appearance, being wild-type phenotypically. Nevertheless, a given population may be polymorphic with regard to gene order in a particular homolog. For example, as revealed from studies of banding sequence in the third chromosome of larval salivary nuclei, a population at Piñon Flats, California, contains three different chromosomal arrangements, of which two (called Arrowhead and Chiricahua) can be described as paracentric inversions of the third (called Standard). Although the relative frequencies of these three arrangements changes significantly during the year, all arrangements persist.

Third chromosome paracentric inversion polymorphism can also be studied in different populations of *D. pseudoobscura* in the southwestern part of the United States (Figure 35-4). California populations proved to be rich in the inversion types Standard and Arrowhead. Eastward, in nearby Arizona and New Mexico, the populations contain relatively few Standard and Pikes Peak chromosomes, most chromosomes having the Arrowhead arrangement. Finally, in still more easterly Texas, one finds almost no Standard and some Arrowhead, with most chromosomes being of the Pikes Peak type.

The shift in the frequency and type of inversions in the three different geographic regions cannot be explained as the result of differential mutation, since the spontaneous mutation rate for inversions is extremely low. Moreover, since there is no indication that the gene flow among these populations has changed appreciably in the recent past, migration rates have probably had a relatively small influence upon genotypic frequencies; there is also no indication that genetic drift has had a major role in causing the differences in inversion frequency in the three areas. These observations lead us to suppose that the primary basis for these population differences lies in the different adaptive values which different inversion types confer on individuals in different territories. Despite the absence of any obvious morphological effects, these inversions prove to have different physiological effects in laboratory tests; different

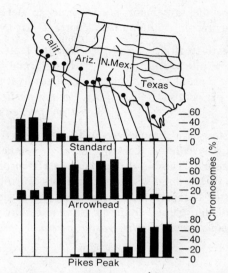

Figure 35-4   Distribution of inversion types in *D. pseudoobscura* collected in the southwestern United States. (After Th. Dobzhansky and C. Epling.)

inversion types survive best in different experimental environments. Since these inversion types show different adaptive values in the laboratory (discussed further in Section S35.3a), it is reasonably certain that they do so in nature, too. Accordingly, natural selection is primarily responsible for the inversion differences among the three geographic populations. Polymorphism for gross chromosomal changes is maintained within many other plant and animal species besides *Drosophila* (as illustrated and discussed in Section S35.3b). (R)

35.4   Natural populations of *Drosophila* carry a tremendous number of recessive detrimental mutants.

Drosophila pseudoobscura has five pairs of chromosomes—the usual X and Y sex chromosomes, three pairs of large rod-shaped autosomes (II, III, IV), and a dot-like pair of autosomes (V) (Figure 35-5). Numerous laboratory strains of this species are available whose autosomes are marked by various point and rearrangement mutants. We can, therefore, make a suitable series of crosses between laboratory strains and flies collected in the wild which will yield information on the presence of autosomal mutants in the wild-type flies. In practice, autosomes II, III, and IV

Figure 35-5   Chromosomal complement of *D. pseudoobscura*.

of individual wild-type flies are made homozygous to detect the presence of the following recessive detrimental mutants (see Figure 21-2):

1. *Lethal* (causing death to all individuals before adulthood) or *semilethal* (causing more than 90 and less than 100 per cent mortality before adulthood).

2. *Subvital* (causing significantly less than normal but greater than 10 per cent survival to adulthood).
3. *Female sterile* (sterile to females).
4. *Male sterile* (sterile to males).

The results of this study are summarized in Figure 35-6. About 25 per cent of all autosomes tested this way carry a recessive lethal or semilethal mutant. Recessive subvital mutants are found in about 40 per cent of III chromosomes tested and in more than 90 per cent of II's and IV's tested; mutants causing sterility are present in 4 to 14 per cent of tested chromosomes.[2] Obviously the natural population carries a tremendous number of detrimental mutants. Similar results have been obtained in studies of other *Drosophila* species (*melanogaster*, *persimilis*, *prosaltans*, and *willistoni*). (R)

35.5   Protein analysis also reveals that natural populations of *Drosophila* contain a large amount of genetic polymorphism.

The presence and relative amounts of certain proteins can be determined for individual fruit flies. A fly is homogenized and the resulting mixture is exposed to

Mutant Type	Per cent of Chromosomes		
	II	III	IV
Lethal or semilethal	25	25	26
Subvital	93	41	95
Female sterile	11	14	4
Male sterile	8	11	12

Figure 35-6 Recessive detrimental mutants in natural populations of *D. pseudoobscura*. (After Th. Dobzhansky.)

[2] How are these mutants distributed in the fly population? Consider first one pair of the autosomes tested. Each member has a 25 per cent chance of carrying a lethal or semilethal and a 75 per cent chance of being free of such mutants. The chance that both members of a pair of chromosomes will carry a lethal or semilethal is $(0.25)^2$, or 6.25 per cent. From the data presented we cannot tell whether all the lethals and semilethals found in a particular pair of autosomes are allelic (in which case up to 6.25 per cent of zygotes in nature would be mutant homozygotes and fail to become adults), or whether all the mutants involve different loci (in which case 6.25 per cent of zygotes would be hybrid for linked mutants of this kind), or whether some combination of these alternatives is obtained. In any case, the chance that both members of a given chromosome pair are free of lethals or semilethals is $(0.75)^2$, or 56 per cent.

What proportion of individuals in the population carry no lethal or semilethal on any member of autosomes II, III, and IV? This percentage is calculated as $(0.75)^2 \times (0.75)^2 \times (0.75)^2$, or about 17 per cent. However, if one considers the X and V chromosomes which can also carry such mutants, the frequency of lethal–semilethal–free individuals in nature is still lower. Moreover, when the subvital mutants (which comprise the most frequent mutant class detected) and the sterility mutants are also considered, it becomes clear that very few, if any, flies in natural populations are free of detrimental mutants.

an electrical field to separate compounds of different molecular weight and electrical charge. Fractions can then be tested for enzymatic activity with different substrates. If different fractions digest the same substrate, we conclude that they contain different forms of the same enzyme—*isoenzymes*, or *isozymes*. They are thought to be coded by different alleles at the same locus (or, perhaps, at duplicated loci).

If two parents each contain a different enzyme which acts on a given substrate, and each F_1 individual contains both enzymes, our simplest conclusion is that the parents are pure and their progeny are hybrids at a single locus. In some instances, an enzyme proves to be coded at two or three different loci and to exist in a half-dozen allelic forms.

Related studies can determine not only the time of enzyme formation during development, but also genetic diversity, mutation frequencies, and changes in the gene pool with respect to time. Thus, the genetics of populations can be studied by analysis of the proteins they contain. Several natural population studies, including those of *D. pseudoobscura*, *D. ananassae*, and *D. subobscura*, have detected a large amount of polymorphism among loci that specify isozymes or other proteins. For example, Finnish strains of *D. subobscura* contain two different alleles for alcohol dehydrogenase (ADH). In another investigation, 10 enzymes and 11 other proteins were studied electrophoretically in strains of *D. pseudoobscura* from five geographic localities. Nine of the 21 loci could be identified by this technique as being polymorphic; eight of these produce an esterase (6 alleles), malic dehydrogenase (4 alleles), three different alkaline phosphatases (2 alleles each), two different larval proteins (3 alleles each), and one larval protein (2 alleles). Of the loci studied, 39 per cent were polymorphic in all populations. The results indicate that the average population is polymorphic at a minimum of 30 per cent of all loci, about 12 per cent of loci in an individual being heterozygous. (R)

35.6   The natural selection associated with the large amount of genotypic variability found in natural populations is measured by the *genetic load*—the change in fitness caused by the presence and absence of factors that affect genotypic variability.

We have seen that natural populations contain a tremendous amount of genotypic variability. Since some genotypes occur which reduce the average fitness of the entire population, they are selectively disadvantageous and represent a genetic burden. Any factor that changes the relative frequencies of genotypes can theoretically increase or decrease such genetic burden, that is, can modify the average fitness of the population. The amount of change in fitness that is caused by the presence and absence of factors that affect the genotypic variability of a population is called the *genetic load*. Since there are many factors that can change genotypic variability, there are many factors that can result in a genetic load. Although any population contains several to many kinds of genetic load, several types are now briefly mentioned and exemplified individually.

1. *Mutational load*. Mutations are constantly occurring in populations. Since most mutants lower fitness this load is ordinarily detrimental.

We have already estimated (Section 35.4) the extent of this burden in natural populations of *Drosophila*. Such mutational detriment is the price paid by a population to maintain genetic variability, which, on rare occasions, may produce genotypes that are more adaptive in the old or a new environment (see Section 35.8). If a population composed of only $A_1 A_1$ genotypes undergoes mutation to A_2, genotypes $A_1 A_2$ and $A_2 A_2$ are added to the population, and genotypic variability is increased. So is the genetic (mutational) load if a change in fitness is concomitant with the change in variability. If one or both new genotypes are less fit, the increase in load was detrimental; if one or both are more fit, the increase in load was beneficial. The consequences of increasing the mutational load in somatic and germinal tissues of human beings are discussed in Section S35.6a.

2. *Segregational load.* When a locus is heterozygous $A_1 A_2$, segregation increases the genetic load if the additional $A_1 A_1$ and $A_2 A_2$ genotypes produced result in a change in population fitness. The segregational load is a balanced load in cases of single locus heterosis, $A_1 A_2$ having the highest fitness, since both alleles will be retained in the population.

3. *Inbreeding load.* We have already noted (Section 33.6) that inbreeding increases both homozygosis and genotypic variability. When the extra homozygotes produced change the average population fitness (Section 33.8), inbreeding increases the genetic load. The inbreeding load in human beings is estimated in Section S35.6b from the comparative mortality of progeny of cousin and noncousin marriages.

4. *Crossing-over load.* Another type of recombinational load (other than the segregational and inbreeding loads) involves crossing over. If linked genes have different adaptive values in $A_1 B_1$ and $A_2 B_2$ combinations than they have in $A_1 B_2$ and $A_2 B_1$ combinations, crossing over in a dihybrid will produce a genetic load.

5. *Heterogeneous environmental load.* A population may contain different genotypes each of which is adaptive in a different one of several environments being occupied. Although there is an optimal distribution of the number and kinds of different genotypes in the different environments, there will be, in fact, a departure from this ideal distribution which will constitute a genetic load.

6. *Maternal-fetal incompatibility load.* Depending on her genotype, a pregnant woman may make antibodies against antigens present on fetal red blood corpuscles that accidentally enter the maternal circulation. These antibodies can then freely enter the fetal circulation, destroy fetal blood corpuscles, and may cause fetal death.[3] Such

---

[3] For example, with respect to ABO blood types (see Section S16.1a), $I^A i \male \times i i \female$ produces a deficiency in $I^A i$ children of almost 25 per cent. In this case the $i i$ woman, who normally makes anti-A and anti-B antibodies, is stimulated by entering corpuscles of $I^A i$ fetuses to produce large additional amounts of anti-A antibodies. (The reverse mating, $i i \male \times I^A i \female$, does not show such a maternal–fetal incompatibility.) Similarly, with respect to Rhesus blood type, Rh-positive fetuses ($R r$) are less likely to survive in Rh-negative ($r r$) mothers (who will make anti-Rh antibodies in response to entering fetal Rh antigen) than they are in Rh-positive ($R R$ or $R r$) mothers (who cannot make anti-Rh antibody).

differences in compatibility that a given fetus has in genetically different mothers represents a genetic load.

7. *Genetic drift load.* Gene and genotypic frequencies have particular values in a population of infinite size. Because population size is finite, random genetic drift will cause these values to shift. If, as expected, the fitness of the population is changed by the change in genetic variability, a genetic load is produced.

8. *Migrational load.* If individuals that enter or leave a population change the average fitness of the population, a migrational genetic load is produced. (R)

35.7   The reduced fitness associated with genetic loads can be expressed in terms of the failure to reproduce, that is, *genetic death*.

The reduced fitness caused by the genetic load of an individual, can be expressed as an increased chance of *genetic death*, the failure of the individual to reproduce. Thus, a detrimental mutant in a given individual is removed from the gene pool by genetic death—the failure of the mutant individual to produce descendants carrying the mutant. All an individual's genes, whether normal or mutant, suffer genetic death if that individual fails to produce children. Since mutants are stable, they are usually removed from the gene pool by genetic death and only occasionally by mutation.

A person carrying a dominant lethal like retinoblastoma suffers genetic death (as well as physical death). In this case the mutant gene is eliminated from the population the generation in which it arises; it has, therefore, only one generation of *persistence*. A dominant detrimental mutant with a selection coefficient of 0.2 and, therefore, an adaptive value of 0.8 as compared to normal, will persist for five generations, on the average, before suffering genetic death; that is, given a population approximately the same in size for successive generations, in each generation the mutant-containing individual has a 20 per cent chance of not transmitting the mutant. After this mutant arises, it sometimes fails to be transmitted the very first generation; it may suffer genetic death at the fifth generation or at the tenth, but, on the average, the mutant persists five generations. Thus, the number of generations that a mutant persists in the population is inversely related to its selection coefficient. This principle of persistence holds even though genetic drift, migration, or other factors cause fluctuations in the frequency of the mutant.

Consider the fate in the population of a rare recessive lethal gene like the one producing juvenile amaurotic idiocy. Each time homozygosis for this gene occurs, it results in genetic death, and two mutant genes are eliminated from the gene pool. But recall that (1) heterozygotes are 600 times more frequent (Figure 34-2) and carry 300 times as many of these genes as do homozygotes, and (2) more of these genes probably are eliminated by genetic death of heterozygotes than homozygotes (Section 34.9).

In terms of biological fitness, each rare detrimental mutant is equally harmful to a constant-sized population in that each eventually causes a genetic death. Thus, a gross chromosomal abnormality which acts as a dominant lethal persists only one generation before it causes a genetic death; a rare point mutant whose reproductive disadvantage is only $\frac{1}{10}$ per cent will persist, on the average, 1,000 generations before causing genetic death.[4] (R)

35.8 Despite the typical reduction in fitness which a mutational load produces currently, the genetic variability it provides is adaptive for the evolution of the population in the future.

In view of the preceding discussion, we can assume that it is primarily the euploid or nearly euploid mutants that persist in the gene pool and are mainly responsible for changes in its composition during the course of evolution. By far the most common and most important class of such mutants is the point mutant.

For a given genotype under a given set of environmental conditions the great majority of point mutants are detrimental; perhaps only 1 point mutant in 1,000 minutely increases the reproductive potential of its carrier. Yet, provided the mutation rate is not too large and there is sufficient genetic recombination, these rare beneficial mutants offer the population the opportunity to become better adapted. Moreover, mutants that lower biological fitness under one set of environmental conditions may be more advantageous than the normal genes under different environmental circumstances. For example, several decades ago the environment was DDT-free, and mutants that confer immunity to DDT were undoubtedly less adaptive than the normal genetic alternatives present. But once DDT was introduced into the insect environment, such mutants—even if detrimental in other respects—provided such a tremendous reproductive advantage over their alternatives that they became established in the population as the new wild-type genes. Other examples can be cited in microorganisms, involving antibiotic-resistant mutants which in an antibiotic-free environment are less adaptive than the genes normally present.

It becomes clear, then, that mutation provides the opportunity for a population to become better adapted to its existing environment. It also provides the raw

[4] In general, speaking not in terms of biological fitness but in terms of the total amount of suffering to which a human population is subject, point mutants with the smallest heterozygous detriment are the most harmful type of mutant. We can appreciate this by considering, on the one hand, the heterozygous gross chromosomal abnormality which kills *in utero*, destroying a life early. Neither the individual involved nor its parents suffer very long, since such deaths may occur as abortions that pass unnoticed. On the other hand, the heterozygous point mutants in individuals who are past the reproductive age—and, therefore, already have or have not suffered genetic death—will continue to subject these people to the previously and newly produced, small phenotypic detriment of heterozygosity which adds to their aches, pains, and disease susceptibility. In this respect, then, the mutant with a small effect on reproductive potential can cause more suffering than one with a large effect, for the longer the persistence, the more the damage in postreproductive life.

From the standpoint of the affected person, the amount of gene-caused suffering is now being reduced by medical science. This is true, for example, for an individual such as the diabetic who takes insulin; no doubt he is better off than he would be without medicine. But remember that such medicine does not cure the genetic defect. (We are excluding from consideration presently unavailable "medicine" that will replace the mutant by a normal allele via genetic transformation, transduction, or mutation.) By increasing the diabetic's reproductive potential, however, the medicine serves to increase the persistence of the mutants involved, and the genetic death that must eventually occur is only postponed to a later generation—each intervening generation requiring the same medication. Moreover, since genes have pleiotropic effects and all currently used medicines act later than the transcription–translation stage of gene action, they serve to alleviate only some detrimental effects, and by increasing persistence, cause an increase in the total amount of suffering the population will experience.

materials needed to extend the population's range to different environments, either those already existing elsewhere or those that will arise through changes. A population that is already very well adapted to its present environment is appreciably harmed by the occurrence of mutation. But environments differ, and any given environment will eventually change, so a nonmutating population, although successful at one time, will, in the normal course of events, eventually face extinction. Mutation, therefore, is the price paid by a population for future adaptiveness to the same or different environments. We can now appreciate that mutation and selection, together with genetic drift and migration, are primarily responsible for the origin of more adaptive genotypes. We can also better appreciate the advantage of genetic recombination in speeding up the production of adaptive genotypes and the importance of the genetic mechanisms which regulate mutation frequency.

SUMMARY AND CONCLUSIONS

Natural populations contain a great deal of genetic variability. This is true even when the population seems phenotypically uniform, and is manifested by the presence in the population of (1) gross chromosomal changes, (2) recessive mutants detrimental to viability or fertility, and (3) polymorphism for proteins.

Such genotypic variability means that natural selection will favor some genotypes more than others. Since numerous factors can affect genotypic variability, each can produce a change in the fitness of the population; that is, each can produce a genetic load. The origin of all genetic loads is, of course, mutation; since most mutations are detrimental, the mutational load is usually a detrimental one. Natural selection operates to remove the detrimental mutants from the gene pool by genetic death, after they have persisted for a number of generations, which is inversely related to their chance of causing genetic death.

Despite the detriment of the mutational load, successful species retain a great deal of genetic variability because (1) heterosis makes the segregational load a balanced load which retains genetic polymorphism, (2) different genotypes are adaptive in different environments currently inhabited by different populations of a species, and (3) genetic polymorphism provides adaptiveness for future survival in new environments.

GENERAL REFERENCES

Crow, J. F., and Kimura, M. 1970. *An introduction to population genetics theory*. New York: Harper & Row, Inc.

Dobzhansky, Th. 1955. *Evolution, genetics, and man*. New York: John Wiley & Sons, Inc.

Timoféeff-Ressovsky, N. W., Vorontsov, N. N., and Yablokov, A. V. 1969. *An outline of evolutionary concepts*. Moscow: Nauka Publishing House. (In Russian.)

SPECIFIC SECTION REFERENCES

35.2   Patterson, J. T., and Stone, W. S. 1952. *Evolution in the genus* Drosophila. New York: The Macmillan Company.

White, M. J. D. 1969. Chromosomal rearrangements and speciation in animals. Ann. Rev. Genet., 3: 75–98.

35.3   Dobzhansky, Th. 1947. Adaptive changes induced by natural selection in wild populations of *Drosophila*. Evolution, 1: 1–16. Reprinted in *The biological perspective: introductory readings*, Laetsch, W. M. (Editor), Boston: Little, Brown and Company, 1969, pp. 437–455.

Dobzhansky, Th., and Epling, C. C. 1944. Taxonomy, geographic distribution, and ecology of *Drosophila pseudoobscura* and its relatives. Carneg. Inst. Wash. Publ., No. 554: 1–46.

John, B., and Lewis, K. R. 1966. Chromosomal variability and geographic distribution in insects. Science, 152: 711–721. Reprinted in *Papers on evolution*, Ehrlich, P. R., Holm, R. W., and Raven, P. H. (Editors), Boston: Little, Brown and Company, 1969, pp. 292–313.

35.4 Allison, A. C. 1965. Polymorphism and natural selection in human populations. Cold Spring Harbor Sympos. Quant. Biol., 29: 137–149.

Allison, A. C., and Blumberg, B. S. 1965. *Polymorphism in man*. Boston: Little, Brown and Company.

Gershenson, S. 1934. Mutant genes in a wild population of *Drosophila obscura* Fall. Amer. Nat., 68: 569–571. Reprinted in *Evolution*, Brousseau, G. E., Jr. (Editor), Dubuque, Iowa: William C. Brown Company, 1967, pp. 80–82.

Krimbas, C. B. 1959. Comparison of the concealed variability in *Drosophila willistoni* with that in *D. prosaltans*. Genetics, 44: 1359–1369.

35.5 Ayala, F. J., Mourão, C. A., Pérez-Salas, S., Richmond, R., and Dobzhansky, Th. 1970. Enzyme variability in the *Drosophila willistoni* group, I. Genetic differentiation among sibling species. Proc. Nat. Acad. Sci., U.S., 67: 225–232. (The large amount of genetic polymorphism found contrasts with the morphological similarity of the four species studied.)

Lakovaara, S., and Saura, A. 1970. Isoenzymes of alcohol dehydrogenase in the species of the *Drosophila obscura* group. Ann. Acad. Sci. fenn, A, IV Biologica, 163: 10 pp.

Lewontin, R. C., and Hubby, J. L. 1966. A molecular approach to the study of genic heterozygosity in natural populations. II. Amount of variation and degree of heterozygosity in natural populations of *Drosophila pseudoobscura*. Genetics, 54: 595–609.

35.6 Dobzhansky, Th. 1964. How do the genetic loads affect the fitness of their carriers in *Drosophila* populations? Amer. Nat., 98: 151–166.

Morton, N. E. 1960. The mutational load due to detrimental genes in man. Amer. J. Human Genet., 12: 348–364.

Sutter, J., and Goux, J. M. 1965. Lethal equivalents and demographic measures of mortality. Cold Spring Harbor Sympos. Quant. Biol., 29: 41–50.

Hugo De Vries (1848–1935). pioneer in the study of mutation and *Oenothera* genetics. [From Genetics, 4: 1 (1919.)]

Wills, C. 1970. Genetic load. Scient. Amer., 222 (No. 3): 98–107, 146.

Yamaguchi, M., Yanase, T., Nagano, H., and Nakamoto, N. 1970. Effects of inbreeding on mortality in Fukuoka population. Amer. J. Human Genet., 22: 145–159.

35.7   Muller, H. J. 1948. Mutational prophylaxis. Bull. N.Y. Acad. Med., 2nd Ser., 24: 447–469.

35.8   Crow, J. F. 1957. Genetics of insect resistance to chemicals. Ann. Rev. Entomol., 2: 227–246.

SUPPLEMENTARY SECTIONS

S35.3a   Certain paracentric inversions in *Drosophila* are heterotic in laboratory tests.

Natural populations of *Drosophila pseudoobscura* contain about 20 different paracentric inversions of chromosome III. Laboratory populations can be started with some individuals carrying the Standard chromosome arrangement and others, a particular one of these inversions. After a number of generations has passed, in some cases the population comes to contain only Standard chromosomes, because the inversion chromosome behaves like a detrimental gene which provides no advantage when heterozygous and is eliminated from the gene pool. When other particular inversions are tested this way, however, an equilibrium is reached—both the Standard and inverted chromosomes are retained in the gene pool. In these cases, the inversion heterozygote is adaptively superior to either homozygote, showing heterosis.

Although the genetic basis for heterosis in such cases could be (1) the genes gained or lost at the time the inversion was initially produced, (2) the new arrangement of the inverted genes, or (3) the types of genes or groups of genes contained within the inversion, evidence favors the last possibility. Recall that individuals with paracentric inversions are not at a reproductive disadvantage in *Drosophila* and suppose a heterotic system exists or develops in *Drosophila* heterozygous for a paracentric inversion. When the heterosis is due to the action of several specific genes within the inverted region, this adaptively favorable gene content tends to remain intact in the inversion heterozygote because of the failure of single crossovers within the inverted region to enter the haploid egg nucleus.

Vann, E. 1966. The fate of X-ray induced chromosomal rearrangements introduced into laboratory populations of *Drosophila melanogaster*. Amer. Nat., 100: 425–449. (Evidence that heterosis is due not to heterozygous rearrangements but to the genes they contain.)

S35.3b   Gross chromosomal polymorphism is maintained in many species.

Gross chromosomal differences are maintained within many other plant and animal species besides *Drosophila*. Some examples include

1. *Inversions* in plants such as tulips and *Paris quadrifolia*.
2. *Extra chromosomes* in animals such as flatworms, shrews, and insects; in plants such as maize and rye.
3. *Reciprocal translocations* in animals such as grasshoppers and snails; in plants such as the pea *Pisum*, the Jimson weed *Datura*, *Rhoeo*, *Campanula*, *Clarkia*, and the evening primrose *Oenothera*.

In many of the above cases it is not clear what factors are responsible for the maintenance of chromosomal polymorphism. Considerable information is known about *Oenothera*, however, so this example is discussed in some detail.

Oenothera (Figure 35-7) is a common weed found along roadsides, railway embankments, and in abandoned fields. It exists in nature in a number of pure breeding, self-fertilizing strains —each with a characteristic phenotype. The strain *Lamarckiana* is heterozygous for a single pair of genes, self-fertilization producing the two homozygotes, both of which are lethal. The two different alleles are, therefore, recessive lethals. Thus, in nature *Lamarckiana* is a permanent heterozygote in this respect, with a balanced lethal system. In this case both lethals kill at the time of fertilization or very soon thereafter, being in effect *zygotic lethals* (Figure 35-8).

Recall that some plants, including *Oenothera*, have a haploid gemetophyte generation. Permanent heterozygosis is maintained also, when one allele is lethal to the male gametophyte and the other to the female (Figure 35-8). Consequently, *gametophytic lethals* can also provide a balanced lethal system which prevents half the ovules from producing seeds. In general, all strains of *Oenothera* found in nature have *enforced heterozygosity*

Figure 35-7 *Oenothera*. (Courtesy of R. E. Cleland.)

due to the zygotic and gametophytic lethals which produce balanced lethal systems.

All the *Oenothera* strains discussed here have seven pairs of chromosomes. The typical self-fertilizing *Oenothera* in nature does not form seven separate bivalents during meiosis as expected, but, as seen clearly at metaphase I, forms a closed circle of 14 chromosomes synapsed end to end (Figure 35-9, upper cell). At anaphase I, moreover, adjacent chromosomes in the circle go to opposite poles of the spindle, so that at the start of the separation the chromosomes assume a zigzag arrangement (Figure 35-9, lower

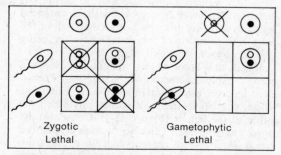

Figure 35-8 Balanced lethal systems that enforce heterozygosity.

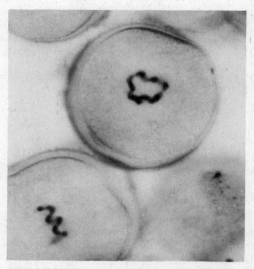

Figure 35-9 Meiosis in *Oenothera*. Upper cell shows a circle of 14 chromosomes synapsed end to end at metaphase I; lower cell shows the zig-zag chromosomal arrangement at anaphase I. (Courtesy of R. E. Cleland.)

cell). Here paternal and maternal chromosomes alternate in the circle, all paternal chromosomes go to one pole and all maternal chromosomes to the other. Since crossing over is apparently rare, the gametes produced by an individual are identical to those which united to form it (Figure 35-10). Since all genes in the paternally derived genome are completely recombinationally linked as are those in the maternally derived genome, a strain behaves as though it is composed of two *gene complexes*. The balanced lethal system kills or prevents the occurrence of homozygotes for paternal or maternal genomes.

The presence in heterozygous condition of six reciprocal translocations involving all seven different homologs explains the formation of the circle of 14 chromosomes. This can be understood with the aid of Figure 35-11. All *Oenothera* chromosomes are small, are roughly the same size, and have median centromeres. To identify homologous chromosomes, the ends of non-homologs in a genome are given different numbers. Suppose, at some time in the past, a eucentric reciprocal translocation occurred between the tips marked 2 and 3 (Figure 35-11A, B). This rearrangement in heterozygous condition (B) would produce an X-shaped configuration at the time of synapsis in prophase I (C) and a circular appearance at metaphase I–early anaphase I (D). In this way a circle of four chromosomes would be produced.

If a second reciprocal translocation occurs

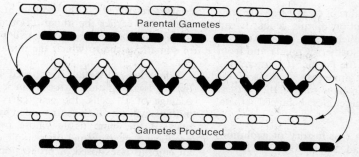

Parental Gametes

Gametes Produced

Figure 35-10   Manner of chromosome segregation during meiosis of *Oenothera*.

between any chromosome arm in a circle of four and an arm of some other pair of chromosomes, a circle of six chromosomes will form in the individual heterozygous for both reciprocal translocations. This type of formation is illustrated in Figure 35-11D, E; D shows the configuration before arms 4 and 5 have exchanged, E shows the circle of six produced in meiosis after this exchange. Still larger circles can be formed by successive interchanges of this type; six such interchanges are required to form the circle of 14 chromosomes.

Almost all the different strains of *Oenothera* found in nature form a circle of 14. Are the six translocations involved the same in all strains? No. In fact, of 350 complexes analyzed, more than 160 different segmental arrangements have been found. All results are consistent with the hypothesis that during the course of evolution, the ends of *Oenothera* chromosomes have been

shuffled many times in different ways by reciprocal translocation.

Three aspects of the cytogenetic behavior of *Oenothera* are disadvantageous under many circumstances: reciprocal translocations, recessive lethals, and self-fertilization. By combining all three of these disadvantages in one plant, however, *Oenothera*'s survival value is probably greater than it would be without them. The self-fertilization mechanism involves bringing the stigma down to the level of the anther, so that a much heavier pollination is attained than would be likely were the plant pollinated by insects. This self-fertilization mechanism offsets the 50 per cent mortality due to balanced lethals. These lethals, together with the reciprocal translocations and alternative segregation, prevent the homozygosity usually consequent to self-fertilization, enforce heterozygosity, and produce maximum hybrid vigor.

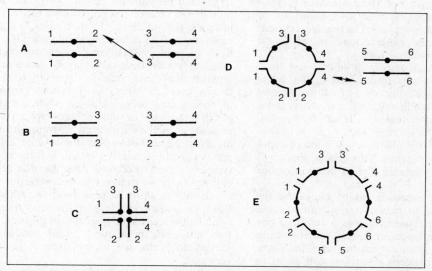

Figure 35-11   Heterozygous reciprocal translocations and circle formation. Chromatids are not shown.

The great survival value of *Oenothera* is demonstrated by the distribution of this genus; it can be found from the southern tip of South America to the far reaches of Northern Canada and from the Atlantic Ocean to the Pacific. It is interesting to note that the most numerous sections of the genus and those which have ranged the farthest are the ones with large circles, balanced lethals, and self-pollination.

Cleland, R. E. 1960. A case history of evolution. Proc. Indiana Acad. Sci. (1959), 69: 51–64.
Cleland, R. E. 1962. The cytogenetics of Oenothera. Adv. in Genet., 11: 147–237.
Lubs, H. A., and Ruddle, F. H. 1971. Chromosomal polymorphism in American Negro and White populations. Nature, Lond., 233: 134–136.
Vorontsov, N. N. (Editor) 1969. *The mammals —evolution, karyology, taxonomy, fauna.* Novosibirsk: Acad. Sci. USSR, Siberian Branch. (In Russian.) (Examples of gross chromosomal polymorphism in various species.)
White, M. J. D. 1963. Cytogenetics of the grasshopper *Moraba scurra*, VIII. Chromosoma, 14: 140–145.

S35.6a The mutational load occurs in both somatic and germinal tissues. Increasing this load in human beings has important consequences.

All types of genetic load depend upon mutation as the primary source of genetic variability. Since almost all mutants are detrimental in homozygous condition and many of these are also harmful when heterozygous, genetic load seems to be maintained in the population largely by recurrent mutation, that is, genetic load seems to be primarily a mutational load.

Present-day man carries a mutational load. Some of the mutants transmitted to him arose in his parents (probably two of each five zygotes carry a newly arisen mutant), and others arose in his more remote ancestry. It has been calculated that, on the average, each of us is heterozygous for what is probably a minimum of about eight such mutant genes. This genetic load does not include the mutants carried in homozygous condition.

Consider the consequences of increasing the mutational load in human beings, an increase that doubtlessly is occurring as a result of our exposure to man-made penetrating radiations and certain reactive chemical substances. Man-made as well as spontaneous mutations can occur in either the somatic line or the germ line. We will discuss mutations in these lines separately.

Somatic mutations. Somatic mutants are, of course, restricted to the person in which they occur. The earlier the mutation occurs in a person's development, the larger will be the sector of somatic tissue to which the mutant cell gives rise.

When an individual is exposed to an agent that causes mutation to occur in a certain percentage of all cells, the cells carrying induced mutants will usually be surrounded by nonmutant ones of the same tissue whose overall action produces a near-normal phenotypic effect. When an embryo is exposed, a proportionally smaller number of its cells will mutate. Mutant embryonic cells can, however, give rise later to whole tissues or organs which are defective; in such cases there is no compensatory action of normal tissue. Furthermore, since many mutants affect the rate of cell division, the earlier in development they occur, the more abnormal the size of the resulting structure will be. It is understandable, then— assuming that cells at all life stages are equally mutable—that the earlier somatic mutations occur in the development of an individual, the more damaging they will be to him.

Newly arisen mutants produce almost all their somatic damage when heterozygous, since mutation involves loci that are usually nonmutant in the other genome. Although somatic mutants cannot be transmitted to the next generation, they can lower the reproductive potential of their carriers, thus affecting the gene pool of the next generation.

The damage that new mutants produce in a somatic cell depends upon whether or not the cell subsequently divides. Certain highly differentiated cells in the human body, like nerve cells or the cells of the inner lining of the small intestine, do not divide. In such cases, it is ordinarily difficult to detect mutations since the cells have no progeny classifiable as mutant or nonmutant. Nondividing cells may be more or less mutable than those retaining the ability to divide. In any event, a variety of mutations can occur in nondividing cells, including point mutations which inactivate or change the type of allele present, as well as structural rearrangements of all sizes. Nevertheless, the nondividing cell remains euploid or nearly euploid, and the phenotypic detriment produced must be due almost entirely to point mutants in heterozygous condition and to shifts in gene position. Although this may considerably impair the functioning of nondividing cells and give the impression that they are aging prematurely, their sudden and immediate death due to mutation is probably very rare.

Although the same kinds of mutations occur in somatic cells that subsequently divide and in those that do not, nuclear division can result in gross aneuploidy (Chapter 18). Accordingly, most of the phenotypic damage of induced mutants in dividing cells is the result of aneuploidy—mostly the consequence of single breakages that fail to restitute. It should be noted that all known agents causing point mutation also break chromosomes.

Germinal mutations.   Consider next, in a general way, the consequences of increasing the frequency of mutations in the human germ line. The earlier that mutation occurs in the germ line, the greater the portion of all germ cells carrying the new mutant will be. Of course, the upper limit of gametes carrying a particular induced mutant is usually 50 per cent. Consider the effect of exposing the gonads of each generation to an additional constant amount of high-energy radiation (Figure 35-12). The load of mutants produced spontaneously is presumably at equilibrium—the rate of mutant origin equals the rate of mutant loss. Beginning with the first generation to receive the additional radiation exposure, the mutant load increases with each generation until a new equilibrium is reached; at this point the higher number of mutants lost per generation equals the higher number of new mutants produced each generation. If the additional radiation exposure ceases at some still later generation, the mutational load will decrease via mutant losses, until the old spontaneous equilibrium is reached again.

At present, human populations are exposed to an average amount of high-energy radiation that is not likely to be calamitous to their gene pools. The very high radiation doses from a nuclear war could be disastrous, however, for if the whole body receives 500 r in a short period of time, the chance is 50 per cent that the affected person will die in a few months. If the person survives this period, his life expectancy is reduced by some years, probably because of somatic mutations, and children conceived after exposure will be handicapped by many detrimental mutants. It is even possible, but not probable, that in a nuclear war enough radiation would be released to destroy the human species.

Finally, it should be realized that we are being

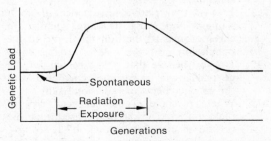

Figure 35-12   Genetic load and exposure to radiation.

constantly exposed to man-made mutagenic chemical substances. Although it is very probable that we are getting fewer germ-line mutations from chemical substances than from radiation, more somatic mutants may be produced by chemical substances than by our present exposure to radiation.

The biological effects of atomic radiation, summary reports. 1956, 1960. Washington, D.C.: National Academy of Sciences–National Research Council. (See Reports of the Genetics Committee.)

Chu, E. H. Y., Giles, N. H., and Passano, K. 1961. Types and frequencies of human chromosome aberrations induced by X-rays. Proc. Nat. Acad. Sci., U.S., 47: 830–839.

Crow, J. F. 1959. Ionizing radiation and evolution. Scient. Amer., 201: 138–160.

Hungerford, D. A., Taylor, K. M., Shagrass, C., LaBadie,. G. U., Balaban, G. B., and Paton, G. R. 1969. Cytogenetic effects of LSD 25 therapy in man. J. Amer. Med. Assoc., 206 (No. 10): 2287–2291. (Somatic gross chromosomal changes.)

Muller, H. J. 1950. Radiation damage to the genetic material. Amer. Scient., 38: 33–59, 126, 399–425.

Report of the United Nations Scientific Committee on the Effects of Atomic Radiation. 1958. New York: General Assembly Official Records: 13th Session, Suppl. 17 (A/3838), Chaps. 5–6, Annexes G–I.

S35.6b   The inbreeding load in man can be estimated by comparing the progeny of inbreeding and noninbreeding segments of a population.

A comparison of the detriment produced in an inbreeding segment with that in a noninbreeding segment of a human population provides us with an estimate of the inbreeding load. From the population records of a rural French population during the last century listing fetal deaths and all childhood and very early adult deaths we can compare the frequency of death to offspring of unrelated parents with that of cousin marriages. The frequency of death to progeny from unrelated parents was 0.12, whereas it was 0.25 from cousin marriages. We are not concerned here with establishing the genetic or nongenetic cause of death in the normal outcrossed human population; however, it can be assumed that the extra mortality of 0.13 (0.25 minus 0.12) has a genetic basis in the extra homozygosity resulting from cousin marriage. This assumption is reasonable in the absence of any known nongenetic factor that tends to cause death to more or fewer offspring from marriages between cousins than from marriages between unrelated parents.

Apparently, then, 13 per cent more offspring died because their parents were cousins. The total amount of recessive lethal effect present in the population in heterozygous condition (some of this being expressed as segregational load, some as inbreeding load) can be calculated as follows: recall (Chapter 33) that of all heterozygous genes, an extra $\frac{1}{16}$ become homozygous in offspring of cousin marriages. In the model, half of the $\frac{1}{16}$, or $\frac{1}{32}$, must have become homozygous for the normal genes and half of $\frac{1}{16}$, or $\frac{1}{32}$, for their abnormal alleles. Therefore, to estimate the total heterozygous content of mutants that would have been lethal if homozygous, it is necessary to multiply 0.13 by 32. The resultant value of about 4 represents a 400 per cent chance that the ordinary individual carried in heterozygous condition a genetic load of detrimental mutants that would have been lethal if homozygous. In other words, on the average, each person carried four *lethal equivalents* in heterozygous condition, or four times the number of detrimentals required to kill an individual if the genes involved somehow became homozygous.

The preceding analysis does not reveal the number of genes involved in the production of the four lethal equivalents. These lethal equivalents might have been due to the presence in heterozygous condition of four recessive lethals, or 8 mutants producing 50 per cent viability, or 16 mutants with 25 per cent viability, or any combination of detrimental mutants whose total was four lethal equivalents. Because of environmental improvements (better housing, nutrition, and medical care) since the last century, it is likely that the effect of the same mutants in present-day society would be expressed by somewhat less than four lethal equivalents. For the same reason, the detrimental effects of these mutants in heterozygous condition are expected to be somewhat less at present than they were a century ago. For example, in the last century a particular hypothetical homozygous combination having variable penetrance and expressivity would have produced no detectable effect 25 per cent of the time; a detrimental effect—but not death before maturity—15 per cent of the time; and death before maturity 60 per cent of the time; today, the respective values would be 50 per cent; 10 per cent; 40 per cent. A century ago this combination would have produced 0.6 of a lethal equivalent; at present, the portion is 0.4. Notice, also, that the detriment not lethal before maturity would also have been reduced during this period from 15 to 10 per cent or, speaking in terms of *detrimental equivalents*, what had been 0.15 would now be 0.10. Apparently the genes responsible for lethal equivalents and for detrimental equivalents must be the same, at least in part.

QUESTIONS AND PROBLEMS

1. Can a circle contain an odd number of chromosomes? Explain.
2. Curly-winged *Drosophila* mated together always produce some noncurly offspring. Plum eye-colored flies mated together always produce some nonplum offspring. But, when flies that are both curly and plum are mated together, only flies of this type occur among the offspring. Explain all three kinds of results and define your symbols.
3. a. Draw a diagram representing a heterozygous whole-arm translocation in *Drosophila* at the time of synapsis. Number all chromosome arms involved.
   b. What would be required for a mating between two flies with this constitution to produce offspring flies only of this type?
4. Do you suppose that the preservation of heterozygosity has an adaptive advantage in *Oenothera*? In other organisms? Why?
5. Is the balanced lethal system in *Oenothera* part of its genetic load? Explain. If so, are the lethals components of a balanced load or a mutational load? Explain.
6. Compare the genetic effects of ionizing radiation on populations of *Oenothera* and *Drosophila*.
7. Do you suppose that the mutations which occur in man serve a useful function? Why?
8. Compare the fate of a mutational load in asexually reproducing populations that are haploid, diploid, and autotetraploid.
9. Give examples of balanced and unbalanced polymorphism in the genetics of man.
10. What is the relation between phenotypic detriment, genetic death, and genetic persistence?
11. Discuss the relative importance of point mutants and gross structural changes in chromosomes to the individual and to the population.
12. Do you believe that it is essential for the general public to become acquainted with the genetic effects of radiation? Why?
13. What are some of the beneficial uses of radiation? Are any of these based upon the genetic effects of the radiation? If so, give one or more examples.
14. Susceptibility to leprosy may be due to a

single irregularly dominant gene. S. G. Spickett notes that leprosy is increasing in some human populations that have been free of it for many generations. List some factors that may be responsible for this finding.

15. Would a genotype adaptive in man today have been adaptive 2,000 or 20,000 years ago? Explain.

16. "The danger of mutation lies primarily in the rate with which it occurs." Criticize this statement.

17. How can you explain the finding that in the genus *Drosophila* apparently the heaviest genetic loads occur in common and in ecologically most versatile species, whereas the lightest loads are found in rare and in specialized species and in marginal colonies of common species?

18. How would you go about determining the mutation frequency of a locus from a population study of its protein product? What could you conclude from such work about the total mutation frequency at this locus?

19. Which do you suppose has been more important in speciation, the accumulation of many mutations, each of which produces a small change in protein composition, or the occurrence of relatively few mutations, each of which produces gross changes in protein composition? Justify your answer.

20. In *Oenothera*, complexes A, B, and C each form a circle of four chromosomes (and five pairs of chromosomes) with a standard complex; complex B forms two circles of four (and three pairs) with complex A but a circle of six (and four pairs) with complex C. What can you conclude about the reciprocal translocations differentiating these complexes?

Chapter 36

Races and the Origin of Species

We saw in Chapter 35 that a great deal of genotypic variability occurs within a cross-fertilizing species and that this variation has both disadvantages and advantages. This chapter presents additional examples of the genotypic variability of natural populations; the adaptiveness and the fate of old and new genotypic variability are discussed with respect to the original species as well as the formation of new species.

36.1 Populations of the same species that have characteristic gene pools are called races.

In reaching genetic equilibrium, all the members of cross-fertilizing populations do not eventually become homozygotes, nor do they all become heterozygotes. Such populations, therefore, do not become either genetically pure or uniform with the passage of time. Although any given population is polymorphic for some genes, it is not necessarily polymorphic with regard to a particular gene. Moreover, an allele may be rare or absent in one population and be relatively frequent in the gene pool of another population of the same species. Thus, populations located in different parts of the world may differ both in the types and frequencies of genetic alternatives carried in their gene pools. For example, as can be seen in Figure 35-4, California populations of *D. pseudoobscura* have both different types and frequencies of inversions than Texas populations. The gene pools of the flies in these two states are different, therefore. We can call the two populations different *races*, a term used for populations of the same species that have characteristic gene pools.

Accordingly, because a race has no average genotype, it is defined by the relative frequency of genetic alternatives contained in its gene pool. (Without an average genotype, a race cannot have an average phenotype; accordingly, it is futile to try to picture a typical or average member of any race.) In practice, the number of races recognized is a matter of convenience. Regardless of the number of races defined, however, each is characterized by its gene pool. In the case of human beings, present races, based on genes for blood types, have probably originated principally through migration and random genetic drift (as discussed in Section S36.1).

36.2   The genetic polymorphism that differentiates different races is often adaptive.

We have already noted (Section 35.3) that the paracentric inversion polymorphism that differentiates different races of *D. pseudoobscura* is probably adaptive and maintained by natural selection. Two other examples now follow, one animal, one plant, of the adaptiveness of different races.

1. The British peppered moth, *Biston betularia*, can be divided into two races, a light-colored one and a dark-colored one, the extra pigmentation being due to a single allele whose dominance is modified by the action of nonalleles. The dark-colored race is prevalent in the middle of England, which is highly industrialized and pollutes the air with soot, as well as in eastern England, which is downwind. In the less industrial North and South of England the light race predominates. In the absence of soot, the coloration of the light moth is very much like that of lichens growing on tree trunks; in its presence, the coloration of the dark form is very much like that of the soot-covered tree trunks minus the lichens that were killed by the pollution. When body color matches the tree background, the moth is protected from bird predators. This is substantiated by releasing equal numbers of light and dark moths in unpolluted and soot-polluted woods, and (a) making visual observations of predation, and (b) scoring the moths later recaptured. As expected, the frequency of the dark race increases with industrialization; for example, in the Manchester area, the dark race was less than 1 per cent of the population about 1850 but was more than 99 per cent in 1900. Recent smoke control in Manchester has been correlated with an increase in the frequency of the light race.

2. Three California races of the cinquefoil plant species, *Potentilla glandulosa*, live at sea level, midelevation, and the alpine zone. The sea-level race is killed when grown in the alpine environment, whereas the alpine race grown at lower elevations proves less resistant to rust fungi than the lower-elevation races.

The studies just described show that different races are adapted to their own habitats but not to others. The inorganic and organic environment—including its organisms—is different in different parts of the territory occupied by a species. Clearly, then, no single genotype will be equally well adapted to all the different environments encountered within a particular territory. One way in which a cross-fertilizing species can attain maximal biological fitness as a whole is to remain genetically polymorphic and separate into geographical populations or races which differ genetically. (R)

36.3   Different races of one species may lose or retain their identity.

Whenever, as in all of the examples discussed so far, different races of a cross-fertilizing species occupy geographically separate territories, they are said to be *allopatric*; different races occupying the same territory are said to be *sympatric*.

As long as allopatric races are kept apart, they cannot influence each other's identity via interbreeding. Under some circumstances, however, allopatric races can become sympatric, and can crossbreed to become a single race. For example, although several thousand years ago different allopatric populations of human beings were definitely different races (which might have formed different species had the same conditions of life continued), some of these races subsequently merged into one race because civilization and migration facilitated cross breeding.

Under other circumstances allopatric races that become sympatric are kept from hybridizing to become one race. Consider again the case of man in which many allopatric races have become sympatric in the past 1,000 years. Gene exchange in the now-sympatric races, however, is sometimes inhibited by social and economic forces, so that some of these races continue to maintain their identity. Domesticated plants and animals provide another example of what can happen when allopatric races become sympatric. Many different breeds, or races, of dogs originally allopatric are now found living in the same locality. Yet these now-sympatric races do not exchange genes with sufficient frequency to form a single mongrel breed, or race, because their reproduction is controlled by man.

36.4   Different races within a species may differentiate genetically and become partially reproductively isolated from each other.

A species of cross-fertilizing organisms usually consists of a number of allopatric races adapted to the different environments of the territories they occupy. All these races are kept in genetic continuity by interracial breeding and hybrid race types, so that the species, as a whole, has a single gene pool containing no portion completely isolated from any other. Nevertheless, since each race occupies its own territory, most of the mating is intraracial. In the course of time the differences in the gene subpools of different races can increase more and more because of mutation, natural selection, and genetic drift.

As this differentiation process continues, the genes that make each of the races adaptive in their own territories may, by their manifold phenotypic effects, make matings between two races still less likely to occur or may cause the hybrids of such matings to be less adaptive than the members of either parent race. Accordingly, partial reproductive isolation may be initially an accidental or an incidental by-product of the adaptability of genotypes to a given environment. The less adaptive the hybrids between two races are, however, the greater will be the force of natural selection in favor of genotypes that reproductively isolate the races, that is, in favor of intraracial mating.

36.5 A variety of barriers to gene exchange can lead to genetically based reproductive isolation between races.

Gene exchange between races can be hindered in several ways. Those barriers leading to reproductive isolation include the following:

1. *Geographical.* Water, ice, mountains, wind, earthquakes, and volcanic activity may separate races.
2. *Ecological.* Changes in temperature, humidity, sunlight, food, predators, and parasites may alter or completely change a race's habitat.
3. *Seasonal.* Seasonal changes may cause different races to become fertile at different times even if their territories overlap, or if they are sympatric.
4. *Sexual or behavioral.* Intrarace mating, resulting from preference or domestication effected by man.
5. *Morphological.* Incompatibility of the sex organs between some races.
6. *Physiological.* Failure of a race's sex cells to fertilize those of another, so that the hybrid zygote is formed infrequently, or not at all.
7. *Hybrid inviability.* Even when formed, the development of hybrid zygotes may be so abnormal that it cannot be completed.
8. *Hybrid sterility.* A possibility even if hybrids complete development and are hardy.

Although geographical, ecological, and seasonal differences do not automatically initiate genotypic differences, they furnish the environmental variations that select from the available genotypes those which are adaptive; that is, those with the greatest reproductive potential under the given conditions. Of course, mutation must provide the raw materials for natural selection; since no single genotype is equally well adapted to all conditions, different races come to contain different genotypes. The remaining barriers listed can increase reproductive isolation until it is complete.

The many genes by which two races may come to differ can produce seasonal, sexual, morphological, and physiological barriers. Hybrid inviability can result from developmental disharmony caused by the presence of either a paternal genome in a strange maternal cytoplasm, or two genetically different genomes in each cell. Besides being caused by such genetic action, hybrid sterility can also result when two races become quite different with respect to gene arrangement because of gross structural changes within and between chromosomes. During meiosis, in such cases, synapsis between the two different genomes in the hybrid is irregular; improper pairing causes abnormal segregation, which results in aneuploid meiotic products. Recall that aneuploid gametes in animals usually result in dominant lethality of the zygotes they form. Consequently, reproductive isolation can be based upon either genetic activity or chromosomal behavior, or both.

36.6   Different races become different species when reproductive isolation is complete enough to irreversibly separate their gene pools.

If races continue to diverge genetically so that they are more and more reproductively isolated, they would eventually form separate and different gene pools, and instead of being two races of the same species would become two different species. We can define a *species* as the total of all potentially interbreeding populations that maintains a discrete gene pool via gene-based reproductive isolation. Since species is defined in relation to populations, which are composed of cross-fertilizing organisms (Section 33.1), the term cannot be applied directly to organisms that only reproduce asexually. Note that species formation, or *speciation*, is an irreversible process; once a gene pool has reached the species level it can never lose its identity via cross breeding with another species.

In the next two sections we will illustrate how certain of the reproductive isolating mechanisms listed in the preceding section have been involved in actual cases of speciation. The examples will deal with closely related species which apparently formed from different races of the same species—the assumption being made that the mechanisms and principles which apply to races that are forming species still apply to the species after they are formed. This assumption is reasonable in view of the fact that speciation from races is a gradual, not clearly demarcated, process; and that many of the points to be made can be illustrated comparing *D. pseudoobscura* and *D. persimilis*, which were formerly considered to be different races of the same species; or six distinct races of *D. paulistorum*, which are apparently in the process of forming different species. (R)

36.7   Closely related species provide examples of various mechanisms that produce reproductive isolation.

Although cross breeding may occur naturally or experimentally between closely related species, each maintains its unique gene pool via reproductive isolation. Various isolating mechanisms are manifested between such species.

1. *Ecological.* Two related species of cypress occur in California—the Monterey cypress, which grows along the coast on the rocks, and the Gowen cypress, which grows 2 miles inland in the sand barrens. Although the two species are interfertile experimentally, their hybrid would have no chance in nature.

2. *Seasonal.* Two species of pine live near each other on Evolution Hill in the Monterey region of California. The Monterey pine sheds its pollen before March, the bishop pine sometime later. Although hybrids can be obtained experimentally, none are found in nature.

3. *Sexual.* Feather color is the basis for mating preference in different species of birds. In the case of different species of pheasants, females are quite similar, whereas the males are very different. Females seem to be stimulated only by males of the same species, so that interspecific hybrids are rare. Color in fishes is also a basis for mating preference.

4. *Physiological.* When certain interspecific crosses occur in *Drosophila*, females have an insemination reaction. This involves the swelling of the vagina and the clumping of the sperm, both of which may result in failure of normal fertilization of the egg. In plants, pollen grains may not be able to grow tubes down the styles of other species.

5. *Hybrid inviability.* When five species of the frog genus *Rana* are mated with each other in the laboratory, almost all the interspecific hybrids fail to survive to the adult stage. In some crosses, development stops before cleavage; in others, however, it proceeds until gastrulation, and in still others until later developmental stages. Dogs and coyotes are separate species whose hybrids often die before maturity.

6. *Hybrid sterility.* Genic action is the cause of sterility when the hybrid fails to show proper secondary sex characters. For example, the interspecific hybrid between the turkey and pheasant shows neither the wattle of the male turkey nor the ring or long tail of the male pheasant. Chromosomal imbalance is the cause of the sterility of interspecific hybrids of *Crepis neglecta* (N = 4) × *C. fuliginosa* (N = 3). During meiosis in the hybrid, besides chromosomes that are paired, others occur unpaired and in groups of 3 and 4, resulting in nonfunctional pollen.

Of all isolating mechanisms, only the last three discussed above occur after mating. These three mechanisms involve a loss of reproductive fitness due to the *wastage of gametes* that could have been used in intraspecific matings. It is expected, therefore, that natural selection would favor isolating mechanisms that operate prior to mating; and it is no surprise that these are the most common types found between species in nature. (R)

36.8   Various principles involved in speciation via reproductive isolation of races can be demonstrated in closely related species.

The discussion in Section 36.4 dealt in a generalized way with the reproductive isolation of races by genetic means. We shall now illustrate various principles involved when speciation has this mode of origin (apparently the one most common), using information from closely related species.

Phenotypes do not provide a reliable index of degree of reproductive isolation when groups are closely related in descent

It seems reasonable that the more morphologically divergent two forms are, the more likely it is that they will differ physiologically and that these differences will have originated in very different and isolated gene pools. Simply by comparing horse and mouse morphologies, one certainly expects them to be different species; thus the occurrence of morphological differences is sometimes a good index of species difference. When the groups being compared are closely related in descent, however, one finds that morphology is not well correlated with reproductive isolation. For example, European cattle and the Tibetan yak are quite different in appearance and usually are placed in different genera, but these two species can be crossed. Moreover, in Tibet, many cattle have yak-like traits, so that widely different phenotypes do not necessarily result in complete reproductive isolation between closely related species. On the other hand, consider *D. persimilis* and *D. pseudoobscura*. These two species are so similar morphologically that they can be differentiated by their genitalia only if very careful measurements are made. Nevertheless, these two species have completely isolated gene pools in nature, even where their territories overlap. Such morphologically similar species are called *sibling species*, having originated from different races of the same species. Sibling species are found in mosquitoes and other insects besides *Drosophila*; they are also found in plants—among the tarweeds of the aster family and in the blue wild rye.

Any particular reproductive barrier usually has a multiple genic or chromosomal basis

When *D. pseudoobscura* ♀ is crossed with *D. persimilis* ♂ in the laboratory, vigorous but sterile males are produced in F_1. If suitable marker genes for the different chromosomes are employed, the chromosomal basis for this sterility can be investigated using the F_1 females, which are partly fertile. These F_1 females backcrossed to *pseudoobscura* males provide 16 types of male offspring, each with a different combination of the chromosomes of the two species (Figure 36-1). The length of the testis in males of each type is determined as an index of fertility. The figure shows that when the X is from *pseudoobscura*, the testis is essentially normal in length; when the X is from *persimilis*, however, testis length is shorter. Thus, the X contains one or more genes affecting sterility. Moreover, testis length becomes even more abnormal when the X is from *persimilis*, as more and more of the autosomes come from *pseudoobscura*, demonstrating the location of genes affecting sterility on each of the autosomes, also. We conclude, therefore, that the sterility of the interspecific male hybrid has a multigenic and multichromosomal basis.

The sterility of hybrids between plant species of the *Galeopsis* genus also has a multichromosomal basis.

Any two species are separated by several to many reproductive barriers

The study of *D. pseudoobscura* and *D. persimilis* illustrates another principle relating to species formation, for example any two species are separated not by one but by a number of reproductive barriers. Although each of the barriers involved is incomplete, together they result in complete reproductive isolation—there being no stream of genes between the two gene pools in nature. The known differences between these two particular sibling species include

1. *Pseudoobscura* lives in drier, warmer, and lower regions than *persimilis*.
2. Females accept the mating advances of males of their own species more often than that of males of the other species (the courtship songs of the males being species-specific).
3. *Pseudoobscura* usually mates in the evening, *persimilis* in the morning.
4. Interspecific hybrids are relatively inviable, and when viable, they are mostly sterile.

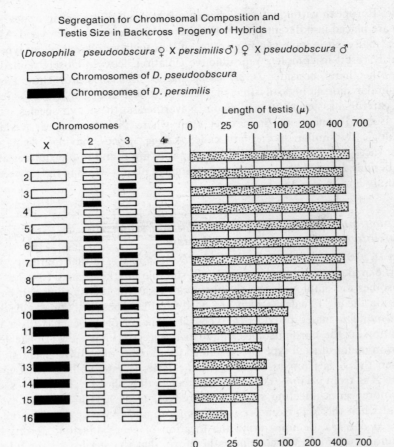

Segregation for Chromosomal Composition and
Testis Size in Backcross Progeny of Hybrids

(*Drosophila pseudoobscura* ♀ X *persimilis* ♂) ♀ X *pseudoobscura* ♂

☐ Chromosomes of *D. pseudoobscura*
■ Chromosomes of *D. persimilis*

Figure 36-1 Multigenic and multichromosomal basis for an isolating mechanism, male sterility, between *D. pseudoobscura* and *D. persimilis*. See the text for details.

Natural selection avoids gametic wastage by aiding the accumulation of genetic factors responsible for premating reproductive isolation of races and species

The nature and origin of the reproductive isolation mechanisms involved in forming new species from races shows that valid species originate not by a single or simple mutation, but as the result of many different, independently occurring genetic changes. Moreover, as already noted, speciation is accomplished not merely by an accumulation of mutants which distinguish races, but also by those which contribute to reproductive isolation. Usually populations are physically separated while reproductive barriers are being built up; otherwise, hybridization would break down these barriers. Experimental evidence also supports our expectation that natural selection acts to further the accumulation of the genetic factors promoting premating reproductive isolation between races or species which have become sympatric at least partially.

1. In the plant genus *Gilia* some species are sympatric, others allopatric. As expected, if natural selection helps to accumulate genetic

factors that increase premating isolating barriers to a greater extent in sympatric than in allopatric species, interspecific hybridization is more difficult with sympatric than allopatric species.

2. Sexual isolation between *D. pseudoobscura* and *D. miranda* is greater when the flies tested are sympatric than when they are allopatric.

3. *Drosophila pseudoobscura* and *D. persimilis* cultured together in the laboratory in the same population cage at a relatively low temperature are not isolated from each other reproductively. Under these conditions about 33 per cent of all offspring are interspecific hybrids.

If each species carries a different homozygous recessive genetic marker, interspecific hybrids can be readily identified. Natural selection is aided experimentally by removing all F_1 hybrids each generation, thereby penalizing females that accept males of the wrong species. After five generations the percentage of hybrids produced is usually less than 5 per cent, demonstrating that artificial selection quickly increased reproductive isolation between the two species. Separate tests of population cage and control flies showed that intraspecific mating preference increased as the artificial selection was continued. (R)

36.9   Speciation can occur by means of autopolyploidy.

Not all species of cross-fertilizing organisms arise from the differentiation of populations into races, then species. Under special circumstances some species are founded by one or a few individuals (as described in Section S36.9).

One species can also give rise to another via *autopolyploidy*—an increase in the number of genomes normally present in a cross-fertilizing species. Mechanisms for the production of autopolyploid cells, tissues, and organisms have already been described in Section 18.3. In the genus *Chrysanthemum*, species occur with chromosome numbers of 18, 36, 54, 72, and 90. Thus, it appears that nine is the basic number of chromosomes in a genome. In the genus *Solanum* (the nightshades, including the potato), the basic genome or N number seems to be 12, since species of this genus are known having 24, 36, 48, 60, 72, 96, 108, and 144 chromosomes. These two examples suggest that autopolyploidy has played a role in the speciation of these two genera. Autopolyploidy, however, is not considered an important mechanism of speciation in forms reproducing primarily by sexual means, since autopolyploids having more than two genomes tend to form multivalents at meiosis and, therefore, numerous aneuploid gametes. Autopolyploids can succeed, though, if they are propagated asexually, by budding or grafting, as in the case of the triploid apples—Gravenstein and Baldwin. Triploid tulips are also propagated asexually. (R)

36.10   Speciation can also occur by three mechanisms that involve interspecific hybrids.

Many new cross-fertilizing species originate not only from races or individuals of a single species, but—in relatively recent times—from hybridization between two or more different species, that is, via *interspecific hybridization*. Although interspecific hybrids pose no threat to the isolation of the gene pools of their parental species, they may form a successful, sexually reproducing population that has its own closed gene pool. Interspecific hybrids, particularly of plants, can be converted into stable, intermediate types isolated from their parental species by three methods.

Amphiploidy (allopolyploidy)

The first method involves *amphiploidy* (*allopolyploidy*, see Section 18.2). If one species has $2N = 4$ and another has $2N = 6$, their F_1 hybrid will have five chromosomes (Figure 18-1). If the hybrid survives, it may be sterile because each chromosome has no homolog and, therefore, no partner at meiosis. As a result, meiosis proceeds as if the organism were a haploid and produces mostly aneuploid gametes. If, however, the chromosome number of the F_1 hybrid is doubled—either artificially (via colchicine) or spontaneously—the individual or sector will be $2N = 10$; each chromosome will have a meiotic partner; and euploid gametes of $N = 5$ can be formed. Upon uniting, such gametes produce $2N = 10$ progeny, which are fertile and more or less phenotypically intermediate to and isolated from both parental species.

When each chromosome contributed to an interspecific hybrid is different and the hybrid's chromosome number doubles, each chromosome has just one partner at meiosis, and segregation is normal. The breeding success of the amphiploid is enhanced, therefore, the greater the differences between the chromosomes of the two species that contribute haploid genomes to the interspecific hybrid. It is not surprising, then, that meiosis of an amphiploid derived from two chromosomally similar species contains trivalents and quadrivalents leading to abnormal segregation and sterility.

It has been estimated that 20 to 25 per cent of the present flowering plant species originated as interspecific hybrids whose chromosomes doubled in number (therefore being "doubled hybrids" or amphiploids). Moreover, in the past as many (or more) species originated in this way, then diverged to form different genera. Naturally occurring amphiploidy was involved in the origin of cotton in the New World and in the appearance of new species of goatsbeard during the present century. Additional examples of amphiploidy, some occurring naturally and others artificially, are well known.[1]

Stabilizing recombinations

Although amphiploidy is not successful for hybrids between similar species, there is a second way interspecific hybrids can become stabilized as a new species, provided that the two hybridizing species are very similar chromosomally. If the two species have the same haploid number, their F_1 hybrid may have all chromosomes synapsed

[1] In the early 1800's the American marsh grass *Spartina alterniflora* ($2N = 70$) was accidentally transported by ship to France and England and became established alongside the European marsh grass, *S. stricta* ($2N = 56$). By the early 1900's a new marsh grass, *S. townsendii* ($2N = 126$), appeared and largely crowded out the two older species. Since *S. townsendii* has a chromosome number equal to the sum of the diploid numbers of the older species, is fertile, breeds true, and has an appearance intermediate between the two older forms, this species is undoubtedly an amphiploid of *S. alterniflora* and *S. stricta*. *Spartina townsendii* is so hardy that it has been purposely introduced into Holland (to support the dikes) and other localities.

Amphiploidy also can be produced artificially. For example, in the greenhouse it is possible to cross radish ($2N = 18$) with cabbage ($2N = 18$) (Figure 36-2), thus producing an F_1 hybrid with 18 unpaired chromosomes at meiosis. If, however, the chromosome number of the hybrid doubles early enough in development, it can produce amphiploid progeny with $2N = 36$ chromosomes (containing nine pairs each from radish and cabbage). Since the amphiploid is fertile and genetically isolated from both radish and cabbage, it constitutes a new species which, unfortunately, has a shoot like a radish and a root like a cabbage.

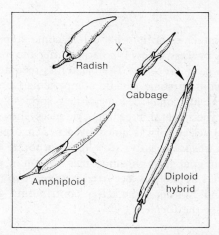

Figure 36-2   Seed pods of cabbage and radish, of their hybrid and amphiploid. (After G. D. Karpechenko.)

in pairs at meiosis. Segregation, independent segregation, and crossing over may yield progeny of the *hybrid whose recombinations can become stabilized* in nature yet are isolated from both parental species.

Consider certain species in the larkspur genus, *Delphinium*: *D. gypsophilum* is morphologically intermediate between *D. recurvatum* and *D. hesperium*; all three species have 2N = 16; and the "parent" species, *recurvatum* and *hesperium*, can be crossed to produce an F_1 hybrid. When the F_1 hybrid is crossed to *gypsophilum*, the offspring are more regular and more fertile than those produced by crossing either the F_1 hybrid or *gypsophilum* with either parental species. These results provide good evidence that *gypsophilum* arose as the hybrid between *recurvatum* and *hesperium*. Figure 36-3 shows the distribution of these species in California.

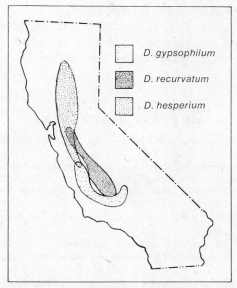

Figure 36-3   Distribution of *Delphinium* species in California. Each species has a unique habitat.

Introgression

The third way that interspecific hybrids can become stabilized as new species is by *introgression*. In this process a new type arises after the interspecific hybrid backcrosses with one of the parental types. The backcross recombinant types favored by natural selection may contain some genetic components from both species, may be true-breeding and, eventually, may become a new species.

Archeological and experimental breeding evidences show that the evolution of maize through artificial selection was aided by genes incorporated by introgression from teosinte, *Zea mexicana*. It is possible to incorporate into wheat by artificial introgression segments of goat grass chromosomes containing genes for rust resistance. Natural introgression has apparently occurred between two genera of shrubs of the rose family, *Purshia* and *Cowania*, the latter contributing genes that changed the appearance and range of the former.

SUMMARY AND CONCLUSIONS

Races are populations of the same species that have characteristic gene pools. The genetic differences between races are often associated with adapting them to different territories. Allopatric races that become sympatric may lose their identity by cross breeding or retain it by not cross breeding. Different races may differentiate genetically (especially if they remain allopatric) and will become different species when reproductive isolation is complete enough to irreversibly separate their gene pools. When species evolve from races (1) phenotypes do not provide a reliable index of degree of reproductive isolation for groups that are closely related in descent, (2) any two species are separated by several to many reproductive barriers, (3) any particular reproductive barrier usually has a multiple genic or chromosomal basis, and (4) natural selection favors the accumulation of genetic factors that produce premating reproductive isolation.

Although most species have a racial origin, some are founded by one or a few individuals, and others result from autopolyploidy.

Speciation can also occur by three mechanisms that involve interspecific hybrids. An interspecific hybrid can form a new species via amphiploidy, by selection of recombinants among its progeny, or by selection of individuals produced after introgression.

GENERAL REFERENCES

Dobzhansky, Th. 1951. *Genetics and the origin of species*, third edition. New York: Columbia University Press.

Dunn, L. C., and Dobzhansky, Th. 1957. *Heredity, race, and society*, third edition. New York: The New American Library, Inc.

Ehrlich, P. R., and Holm, R. W. 1963. *The process of evolution*. New York: McGraw-Hill Book Company.

Ehrlich, P. R., Holm, R. W., and Raven, P. H. (Editors) 1969. *Papers on evolution*. Boston: Little, Brown and Company.

Mayr, E. 1963. *Animal species and evolution*. Cambridge: Harvard University Press.

Stebbins, G. L. 1950. *Variation and evolution in plants*. New York: Columbia University Press.

Timoféeff-Ressovsky, N. W., Vorontsov, N. N., and Yablokov, A. V. 1969. *An outline of evolutionary concepts*. Moscow: Nauka Publishing House. (In Russian.)

Theodosius Dobzhansky (1900–   ).

SPECIFIC SECTION REFERENCES

36.2   Clausen, J. 1949. Genetics of climatic races of *Potentilla glandulosa*. Proc. 8th Intern.
        Congr. Genet., Lund, pp. 162–172. Reprinted in *Evolution*, Brousseau, G. E., Jr.
        (Editor). Dubuque, Iowa: William C. Brown Company, 1967, pp. 164–174.

        Cook, L. M., Askew, R. R., and Bishop, J. A. 1970. Increasing frequency of the
        typical form of the peppered moth in Manchester. Nature, Lond., 227: 1155.
        (Correlated with the introduction of smoke control.)

        Kettlewell, H. B. D. 1961. The phenomenon of industrial melanism in *Lepidoptera*.
        Ann. Rev. Entomol., 6: 245–262.

36.6   Dobzhansky, Th., Ehrman, L., Pavlovsky, O., and Spassky, B. 1964. The superspecies
        Drosophila paulistorum. Proc. Nat. Acad. Sci., U.S., 51: 3–9.

36.7   Denis, H., and Brachet, J. 1969. Gene expression in interspecific hybrids. II. RNA
        synthesis in the lethal cross *Arbacia luxula* ♂ × *Paracentrotus lividus* ♀. Proc. Nat.
        Acad. Sci., U.S., 62: 438–445. (Transcription of the paternal genome is favored.)

        Panov, E. N. 1969. Ethological mechanisms of isolation. Problems of Evolution,
        1: 142–169. (In Russian with English summary.) (Review of sexual isolation
        mechanisms.)

36.8   Bennett-Clark, H. C., and Ewing, A. W. 1970. The love song of the fruit fly. Scient.
        Amer., 223 (No. 1): 84–92, 136. (Courtship song as a reproductive isolating
        mechanism.)

        Dobzhansky, Th., and Pavlovsky, O. 1971. Experimentally created incipient species
        of *Drosophila*. Nature, Lond., 230: 289–292. (Sexual isolation observed after
        selection between two laboratory strains of *D. paulistorum*.)

        Grant, V. 1965. Evidence for the selective origin of incompatibility barriers in the
        leafy-stemmed Gilias. Proc. Nat. Acad. Sci., U.S., 54: 1567–1571.

36.9   Müntzing, A. 1936. The evolutionary significance of autopolyploidy. Hereditas,
        21: 263–278.

36.10   Chu, Y.-E., and Oka, H.-I. 1970. Introgression across isolating barriers in wild and
        cultivated *Oryza* species. Evolution, 24: 344–355. (Introgression in rice.)

        Karpechenko, G. D. 1927. Polyploid hybrids of *Raphanus sativus* × *Brassica oleracea*.
        Zeit. f. Indukt. Abst. u. VererbLehre, 48: 1–85. (Radish × cabbage.)

        Sears, E. R. 1956. Transfer of leaf-rust resistance from *Aegilops umbellulata* to wheat.
        Brookhaven Sympos. Biol., 9: 1–22.

SUPPLEMENTARY SECTIONS

S36.1 The present racial distribution of the genes for ABO blood type is probably due mainly to past genetic drift and migration.

An investigator may choose to define races of mankind according to the distribution of the I^B gene for ABO blood type only, considering populations that do or do not contain I^B in their gene pool as different races. On this basis, there would be only two races of man, the South American Indians, who are almost all of O blood type (without I^B), and all the other people (with I^B) in their gene pool.

On the other hand, an investigator may decide to define races on the basis of the relative frequency of i and I^B in the population. The frequency of these alleles in the gene pool has been determined for many populations all over the world. The results show that in western Europe, Iceland, Ireland, and parts of Spain, three fourths of the gene pool is i, but this frequency begins to decrease as one proceeds eastward from these regions. On the other hand, I^B is most frequent in central Asia and some populations of India, but becomes gradually less and less frequent as one gets farther away from this center. Since the change in frequency of these alleles is gradual, any attempt to sharply separate people into races having different gene frequencies would be arbitrary. For some purposes separating mankind into only 2 races is adequate; for other reasons, as many as 200 have been recognized. As a rule, most anthropologists recognize about 6 basic races but may increase the number to about 30 when considering finer population details.

Knowledge of the distribution of genes for ABO blood types in different populations provides important information to geneticists, anthropologists, and other scientists. To what can the different distributions be attributed? Since people do not choose their marriage partners on the basis of their ABO blood type, and since there does not seem to be any pleiotropic effect making persons of one blood type sexually more attractive than those of another, it is very likely that mating is at random with respect to ABO genotype. However, in other respects some evidence indicates that different ABO genotypes do not have the same biological fitness (see the footnote to Section 35.6). Differential mutation frequencies can also explain part of the differences in gene distribution. During the past few thousand years the greatest shift in ABO gene frequencies of different populations has probably been the result of genetic drift and migration. In fact, the paths of past migrations can be traced by utilizing—along with other information—the gradual changes in the frequencies of ABO and other blood-group genes in neighboring populations.

Bodmer, W. F., and Cavalli-Sforza, L. L. 1970. Intelligence and race. Scient. Amer., 223 (No. 4): 19–29, 144. (Present data do not allow a quantitative evaluation of the contributions of nature and nurture in the case of man.)

Boyd, W. C. 1964. Modern ideas on race, in the light of our knowledge of blood groups and other characters with known mode of inheritance. In *Taxonomic biochemistry and serology*, Leone, C. A. (Editor), New York: The Ronald Press Company, pp. 119–169.

Cavalli-Sforza, L. L. 1969. "Genetic drift" in an Italian population. Scient. Amer., 222 (No. 2): 30–37, 136. (Of genes for blood groups.)

Cavalli-Sforza, L. L., Barrai, I., and Edwards, A. W. F. 1965. Analysis of human evolution under random genetic drift. Cold Spring Harbor Sympos. Quant. Biol., 29: 9–20.

S36.9 Some species are founded by one or a few individuals.

We have already described how different populations of a species which occupies a large continuous territory can become adapted to different conditions and can differentiate into different races and, subsequently, different species. In such circumstances adaptation and speciation are synchronous evolutionary processes. When a new territory is made available to the exclusive use of only one or a few individuals, however, speciation and adaptation may occur at largely separate times. This situation seems to apply to terrestrial species that have formed on oceanic islands. Studies of *Drosophila* species in the Hawaiian Islands support the view that many species on such isolated territories originated from single fertilized females. The local habitat, being permissive, seems to have allowed the new population first to swell, and later caused it to shrink due to overpopulation, a new species being produced—largely through the operation of random genetic drift on the limited (and not especially adaptive) genetic alternatives present—soon after the founder event. After speciation occurred, mutation, recombination, and selection could have increased the adaptability of the new species.

Carson, H. L. 1970. Chromosome tracers of the origin of species. Science, 168: 1414–1418 (Evidence of speciation from single founders supporting the hypothesis that speciation can precede adaptation.)

Halkka, O., Raatikainen, M., Halkka, L., and Lallukka, R. 1970. The founder principle, genetic drift and selection in isolated populations of *Philaenus spumarius* (L.) (Homoptera). Ann. Zool. Fenn., 7: 221–238. (Studies of color polymorphism in spittlebugs living on small islands in the Gulf of Finland.)

QUESTIONS AND PROBLEMS

1. Discuss the validity of the concept of a pure race.
2. What assumptions must you make to use the frequencies of ABO blood types in tracing the course of past migration?
3. Under what future circumstances would you expect the number of races of human beings to decrease? To increase?
4. Discuss the hypothesis that a new species can result from the occurrence of a single mutational event.
5. Is geographical isolation a prerequisite for the formation of a new species? Explain.
6. What is the relative importance of mutation and genetic recombination in species formation?
7. Is a species a natural biological entity, or is it—like a race—defined to suit man's convenience?
8. Does the statement, "We are all members of the human race," make biological sense? Why?
9. Suppose intelligent beings, phenotypically indistinguishable from man, arrived on Earth from another planet. Would intermarriage with Earth people be likely to produce fertile offspring? Why?
10. Invent circumstances under which the present single species of man could evolve into two or more species.
11. The cells of triploid and tetraploid autopolyploids are usually larger than those of the diploid. What importance has this fact for fruit growers?
12. H. Kihara and co-workers have produced triploid (33 chromosomes) watermelons with no seeds, and tetraploid (44 chromosomes) watermelons with seeds but larger than the diploid. How do you suppose this was accomplished? How do you suppose these types are maintained?
13. The cotton species *Gossypium barbadense* is a tetraploid (2N = 52) and phenotypically intermediate between the diploid species *G. herbaceum* and *G. raimondii* (each is 2N = 26). If cytological examination is made of meiosis in interspecific hybrids, what would the following results reveal about the origin of *G. barbadense*?
   a. *Barbadense* × *raimondii* shows 13 pairs and 13 singles.
   b. *Barbadense* × *herbaceum* shows 13 pairs and 13 singles.
   c. *Raimondii* × *herbaceum* shows 26 singles.
14. Suppose that some members of an original population had been (miraculously) preserved and were reproductively isolated from the members of the new, descendant population. Are we now dealing with two species? Explain.

Chapter 37

The Origin and Evolution of Genetic Material

The organisms of today are intricate systems of macromolecules that have evolved from simpler macromolecular systems of preceding eras. In this chapter we will consider general aspects of chemical and biological evolution and, in particular, the origin and evolution of genetic material.

37.1   The origin of genetic material was preceded by the origin of amino acids and organic bases, of polypeptides, nucleotides, and polynucleotides.

The synthesis of the first genetic material on Earth must have been preceded by a chemical evolution which produced (1) amino acids and organic bases, followed by the production of (2) polypeptides, nucleotides, and polynucleotides. These two pregenetic stages in chemical evolution are considered separately.

Origin of amino acids and organic bases

About 4 billion years ago the atmosphere of the Earth was rich in hydrogen, methane, ammonia, and water but poor in free oxygen and carbon dioxide. Laboratory experiments involving such an atmosphere have shown that large numbers of simple chemical radicals and organic molecules can be synthesized under certain conditions. With energy sources such as electrical discharges, heat, high-energy electrons, X rays, sunlight, and ultraviolet light, the following amino acids have been synthesized: Gly, Ala, Glu, and Asp (in large quantities); Thr, Ser, Pro, Val, Leu, Ile, Tyr, and Phe (in lesser quantities). Other compounds formed include adenine, uracil, phosphoric acid, acetic acid, and succinic acid, as well as some sugars and fatty acids.

On primitive Earth, radioactivity, volcanism, sunlight, and lightning might have been important energy sources for producing such molecules. Meteorites which caused some molecules to pass very rapidly through liquids and gases might also have promoted interactions among molecules. As the Earth evolved chemically, the atmosphere changed—losing most of its hydrogen to outer space, and gaining released oxygen which was converted to ozone, forming a layer above the Earth. Since ozone absorbs ultraviolet light, this layer prevented light of UV's wavelength (and energy) from reaching the Earth. Consequently, the main sources of energy from the sun thereafter were visible light and heat. As more and more synthesis took place, especially in the oceans, the products accumulated to form an "organic soup."

Origin of polypeptides, nucleotides, and polynucleotides

All the components for the synthesis of nucleotides (hence polynucleotides) and polypeptides were present in the organic soup. Each of the required syntheses—the union of base and sugar (to form the nucleoside), of nucleoside and phosphoric acid (to form the nucleotide), of nucleotides (to form the nucleic acid), and of amino acids (to form polypeptides)—is accomplished by the removal of water. Some clues as to how these dehydrations might have been accomplished on primitive Earth have been provided by laboratory experiments.

In the presence of excess aspartic and glutamic acids, for example, a mixture of amino acids has been found to form peptide bonds and polymerize into *proteinoids* at temperatures of 200°C or less in a dry heat synthesis. Nearly all amino acids common to proteins are included in these proteinoids. Linear polymers with a molecular weight of up to 10,000, proteinoids are very similar in diversity to natural proteins and polypeptides of corresponding size, and show some catalytic activity.

The surface of proteinoid macromolecules may have provided a favorable site for various reactions to take place. Thus proteinoids may have served as rudimentary catalysts in the synthesis of more complex organic compounds from the organic soup, such as nucleotides, polyphosphates, porphyrins, and pigments.

By the action of certain dehydrating agents, nucleotides have been joined non-enzymatically to form polynucleotides of appreciable length. The rate of such a synthesis of polyuridylic acid has been found to increase more than tenfold in the presence of polyadenylic acid. The poly A apparently is used as a template in the synthesis of poly U. Complementarily, poly U specifically facilitates the union of adenylic acid and adenosine. Such experiments may indicate steps in the natural origin of polynucleotides. (R)

37.2 Proteins and nucleic acids became interdependent in their evolution and existence, leading to the formation of the first organism.

We indicated in the last section that polynucleotides can serve as templates for the nonenzymatic synthesis of complementary polynucleotides, which in turn can function as templates for the nonenzymatic synthesis of their complements. Such nucleic acid functions to replicate itself via the synthesis of a complementary intermediate. Since the nucleic acid aids in the synthesis of more of itself, the synthesis is *autocatalytic*. This autocatalysis means that a pool of nucleotide raw materials will more likely be synthesized into more copies of a given polynucleotide (by complementation) than into diverse polynucleotides (for example, in a dry heat polymerization). Evolution of nucleic acids would undergo, therefore, a natural selection in which the most abundant polynucleotide was the one that combined the greatest stability with the quickest self-replication.

The evolution of the stability and replication characteristics of nucleic acid can be considered separately even though their evolution must have been concurrent. Thus, as revealed by laboratory experiments, the primordial nucleic acids may have been polyarabinonucleotides rather than polyribonucleotides, since the former (containing arabinose instead of ribose) is more stable. Note, in this connection also, that DNA is a more stable template than RNA, since the pentose in the former has one less reactive oxygen. Insofar as some sequences of polynucleotides might more readily partake in autocatalysis than others (see footnote to Section 4.7), there would be a selection in favor of quickly replicating types.

Protenoids would also be present on early Earth at the same time as nucleic acids. Since proteinoids have diverse amino acid compositions, they could serve a variety of functions, which include (1) forming structures which, by protecting nucleic acid from degradation, would increase nucleic acid stability; and (2) serving as catalysts for a variety of reactions. Although proteins are catalysts, they are poor autocatalysts, the product of protein catalysis being determined more by the amount and type of the reactants than by the nature of the catalyst. One can imagine the spontaneous occurrence of a proteinoid which catalyzes some aspect of nucleic acid replication. Obviously, the replication of nucleic acid would be enhanced, the greater the number of such proteinoid molecules. There would be, therefore, a molecular drive (natural selection) in favor of any nucleic acid that aided the synthesis of proteins which stabilize or catalyze the replication of nucleic acids.

We see, therefore, during chemical evolution on Earth, that the maintenance (protection and repair) and replication of nucleic acid came to depend upon the synthesis of protein, and that the synthesis of large quantities of particular proteins came to depend upon nucleic acids (to be discussed further in the next section). We expect, therefore, that evolution progressed from (1) nucleic acids whose self-replication was uncatalyzed by protein, to (2) nucleic acids whose self-replication was catalyzed by proteins that originated independently of nucleic acid, to (3) nucleic acids whose maintenance and replication depended upon proteins whose existence depended upon information contained in the nucleic acid. A functional biochemical unit of the last type we recognize as an *organism* containing nucleic acid genetic material.

37.3   Both the genetic code for proteins and the transcription–translation machinery have undergone evolution.

Although we know that proteins and nucleic acids underwent an evolution that made them interdependent, we have only some very general ideas as to how this dependency became established. We expect that the interactions between proteins and nucleic acids were preceded by or simultaneous with an evolution in the interactions between monomers or small polymers of the two classes of molecules. The first interactions between these smaller units of protein and nucleic acid most probably were the result of chance collisions. From the principles of thermodynamics we know that if the interaction involves a large enough net decrease in energy, the smaller units of protein and nucleic acid may form a complex with each other. For example, a complex between (one or more) nucleotides and (one or more) amino acids may be more stable than either compound separately. Because there is some kind of specificity between the parts of the complex, we might consider the amino acid portion to be a template for the nucleotide portion, or vice versa. We might even say that these two components code for each other in a primitive manner. This type of relationship persists today in the formation of specific aminoacyl-tRNA's (in a reaction that is now catalyzed enzymatically). We should note in this connection that amino acids which possess structural similarities (and which have metabolic similarities, sometimes being synthesized from a common precursor *in vivo*) often have similar codons—for example phenylalanine (UUU and UUC) and tyrosine (UAU and UAC).

The occurrence of some sort of rudimentary recognition interactions between specific amino acids and specific short sequences of nucleotides seems to have been the initial basis for establishing a genetic code, that is, a means whereby information in nucleic acid could be converted into amino acid information. The machinery first used for translation of nucleic acid information into amino acid sequence was probably relatively simple and inefficient, and made many errors. Subsequent evolution produced a highly complex but highly efficient machinery that is so similar in all present-day cellular organisms.

The early code might have been a doublet code, in which 15 amino acids were coded by 15 nucleotide doublets with the 16th doublet used as a polypeptide terminator; a triplet code evolving to accommodate 5 additional amino acids. Alternatively, the primitive code might have started as a triplet code for a small number of amino acids, some codons for a particular one of these amino acids becoming used as codons for a new metabolically related amino acid that confers a selective advantage when incorporated into protein. Whether or not the triplet code had one of these origins or some other one, it was selectively advantageous for the code and the translation machinery to reduce the likelihood of making wrong protein due either to mutations in the genetic material or to transcriptional–translational errors. Wrongly made protein would be avoided in both cases by retaining very few of the triplet codons as nonsense codons, the code being highly degenerate. For with a highly degenerate code changes can occur prior to translation which produce no change in amino acid sense, such changes having no detrimental effect on the organism. Moreover, the code and translation machinery must have evolved so that when changes did cause amino acid substitutions to occur, the chance was maximal that an amino acid was replaced by one functionally related to it, thereby minimizing detrimental phenotypic effects. Once the genetic code and translation machinery evolved to a state that produced the fewest and most tolerable errors, both became essentially stable and universal. (R)

37.4 Directed by natural selection, organisms have undergone an increase in biochemical complexity during evolution.

The evolution of different types of organisms—essentially an evolution of the maintenance and replication of genetic material by protein coded in genetic material —started (perhaps 3.5 billion years ago) in the absence of other organisms and in the presence of abundant raw materials. When, however, a required raw material (Z) in the rich organic soup became limited in supply, natural selection would have favored any genetic material that coded for an enzyme or other protein catalyzing the chemical conversion of a similar component (Y) into the required component. When, in turn, the similar component became limiting in supply, natural selection would have favored genetic material that could convert another substance, X, into Y. In this manner, biochemical sequences such as ... X → Y → Z seems to have become established, each step catalyzed enzymatically by proteins coded in genetic material.

Thus, whereas the original organisms were *heterotrophic*, obtaining from the environment all the raw materials they needed in directly usable forms, organisms were soon required to depend more and more upon their own genotypes to convert elements of the environment into the needed components. Eventually organisms were able to synthesize via genetically specific metabolic pathways all their requirements from simple and abundant substances in the environment, being *autotrophic*. When energy-containing compounds in the environment were depleted, it became selectively advantageous, about 2 billion years ago, to establish the photosynthesis of energy-containing substances on a genetic basis.

We see, therefore, that the biochemical phenotype of early organisms became more and more complex as time progressed, as they evolved from heterotrophy toward autotrophy. Natural selection must have also favored other gene-based phenotypic changes which furnished the organism protection from unfavorable features of the organismal and nonorganismal environments or the ability to reach or search for favorable environments. Such advantages were attained by compartmentalization, irritability, growth movements and motility, use of physical and chemical protective devices, etc., all of which increased the complexity of the morphological as well as the biochemical phenotype.

37.5   Genetic material has undergone a quantitative evolution.

Since the complexity of organisms has increased during the course of evolution, the amount of information (hence, the amount of genetic material) needed to specify an organism has also increased. In a significant fraction of organisms, plants especially, increases in ploidy and subsequent differentiation of genomes have resulted in greater complexity, diversity, and adaptability. We have already noted, for example, that about one fourth of the present species of flowering plants originated as allopolyploids; autopolyploidy, however, probably did not play as important a role in increasing the gene number of sexually reproducing organisms, because of the formation of multivalents during meiosis (Section 36.9). Because of the genetic imbalance which it causes, the gain of whole chromosomes likewise does not seem to be a major mechanism for increasing the amount of genetic material. The relatively small increases in gene number which can occur after chromosome breakage and reunion, however, have played a major role in increasing gene number since they produce changes small enough to be tolerated by the organism.

Short chromosome regions that are adjacent to each other in present-day species often indicate that one region originated as a repeat of the other. This is the most likely explanation of the numerous repeats of the matrix units in the nucleolus organizer; of adjacent repeated bands (doublets) in polynemic dipteran chromosomes; of chromosome regions that yield *cis-trans* position effects; and of chromosome regions where adjacent loci have similar phenotypic effects—including perhaps the different structural genes in an operon.

Changes in the number of copies of particular genes via amplification and deamplification is of interest in this connection. In the case of amphibian oocytes, the nucleolus organizer DNA contains a *master gene sequence* which is used as a template to produce identical *slave gene sequences*, whose existence is only temporary. It has been suggested that other, sometimes protein-coding, gene sequences also have such a master–slave origin, that the slaves may sometimes remain in the chromosome adjacent to their master sequences, and that some slave sequences may become permanent in the genotype. (R)

37.6   Genetic material has undergone a functional evolution.

We have recognized as genetic material any replica of nucleic acid (1) which has been (or is expected to be) replicated or transcribed, and (2) which is used for the synthesis of protein involved in the maintenance and/or replication of the nucleic acid. As the quantity of genetic material increased during evolution, point mutations modified many genes, enabling them to code for many proteins having different structural or enzymatic functions. Some of these protein-coding genes had special utility in regulating the occurrence or permanence of changes in the primary structure of the genetic material itself [such as genes for (1) mutator and antimutator DNA polymerases and metabolites, (2) repair of damaged DNA, (3) the breakages and unions involved in primary structure genetic recombination, and (4) degradation of foreign, defective, or no-longer needed genetic material via DNases and RNases]. Other protein-coding genes became involved in the regulation of replication, genetic

[handwritten marginalia:] allopolyploid : An organism (prob. plant) with 3(or greater)n, to which different species have contributed 1 or more sets of chromosomes. autopolyploid : all sets of chromosomes from same species.

recombination at the level of quaternary structure[1] (including genes coding for proteins involved in amitosis, mitosis, meiosis, and fertilization), transcription, translation (including those specifying RNases that help determine RNA longevity), and posttranslational longevity of proteins (involving for example, protease-coding genes).

Besides the genes mentioned, which function via transcripts that are used to make translation machinery or that are translated into amino acid sequences, other genes evolved which serve other functions (see the footnote to Section 26.3). These functional genes include recognition genes for the start and stop of action of DNA polymerase and of DNA-dependent RNA polymerase (including promoter and operator genes). The possibility exists that some DNA sequences have become nontranscribed spacer or gene-action regulator genes (including perhaps redundant DNA), and that other DNA sequences which are transcribed are used, not to code for amino acids, but to determine the longevity of the mRNA or the type of ribosome which can attach to it.

37.7   The comparative study of protein primary structure can reveal information about the qualitative and quantitative evolution of genetic material.

By considering the proteins of present-day organisms, we can tell a great deal about their genetic material for the following reason: such proteins are translations of genetic information according to a code which is essentially universal and whose degeneracy though considerable is limited. Furthermore, by considering the occurrence of these proteins among groups of organisms as well as individuals, we can learn much about the evolution of proteins, their genes, and populations. The methods of attack and the kinds of results obtained are illustrated in the next few sections, which deal specifically with hemoglobins, immunoglobulins, and cytochromes.

37.8   By duplications and point mutations, an ancestral gene seems to have given rise to the present genes for myoglobin and hemoglobin.

Myoglobin, a single polypeptide chain in muscle, is similar in a number of ways to a single polypeptide chain in hemoglobin. For example, it is approximately the same length, having 153 amino acids; it also has regions coiled right-handedly; and it contains a single heme group on its surface. Although the amino acids of α and β

---

[1] By providing quaternary structure genetic recombination, sexuality has the tremendous genetic advantage over asexuality of speeding up the evolution of more adaptive organisms. For example, an individual may have an adaptive genotype which results from the combination of allelic and nonallelic genes originally located in two parents who, individually, may have been less well or even poorly adapted. Since genetic recombination normally occurs each generation for each nuclear gene pair, adaptive combinations of genes originate much more rapidly by recombination than by the relatively rare event of mutation. It should be clear, therefore, that sexuality, which produces a greater variety of adaptive genotypes in a given period of time than asexuality, is primarily responsible for the great variety of adapted kinds of individuals that have appeared on the Earth in recent times.

hemoglobin chains differ at about 110 positions from myoglobin's, in about 40 positions the same amino acid occurs on both types of chain. Their similar three-dimensional structures may be related to these similarities.

The similarities in length and sequence between myoglobin and hemoglobin chains are too great to be explained fortuitously. Let us postulate, then, that a single gene, "m-α-γ-β-δ," is the common ancestor for all present-day genes coding for myoglobin and hemoglobin chains (Figure 37-1). Since today's species have separate loci for the specification of myoglobin and hemoglobin, the ancestral gene must have become duplicated in the genome. One of these genes mutated to m, which led to the present gene for myoglobin, m^p, and the other mutated to "α-γ-β-δ," the ancestral gene for hemoglobin chains. Additional support for the common-origin hypothesis for myoglobin and hemoglobin comes from the finding that the lamprey appears to have a rather primitive form of hemoglobin, a single polypeptide chain with a molecular weight of about 17,000.

The ancestral gene for hemoglobin, "α-γ-β-δ," was probably most like the present α^A gene, since all known hemoglobins of vertebrates (except the lamprey) have a chain that starts, like the α^A chain, with the Val-Leu- sequence. The ancestral α-like hemoglobin gene may later have mutated to an allele whose polypeptide product could form a dimer, thereby conferring a selective advantage, since by doubling the number of heme groups, the chain's efficiency as an oxygen carrier is increased. If the α-like locus became duplicated, mutation of one locus could produce α which could evolve to the present α^A allele; mutation of the other locus could produce "γ-β-δ" whose dimerized product might be γ_2-like, comprising a predecessor of fetal hemoglobin. Further dimerization of α_2-like and γ_2-like dimers to a tetramer would yield a fetal-type hemoglobin like $\alpha_2^A \gamma_2^F$. The tetrameric hemoglobin is thought to be more efficient than dimeric hemoglobin in carrying oxygen.

Duplication of the γ-like locus followed by mutation seems to have produced a γ locus which eventually became the present-day γ^F, and a "β-δ" locus which coded for a β-like chain. Duplication of the "β-δ," β-like, gene followed by mutation seems to have produced a β locus which became β^A, and a δ locus which became δ^{A_2}. That this last duplication occurred "recently" is suggested by the small number of differences in amino acids between the β^A and δ^{A_2} chains, by the apparent per-

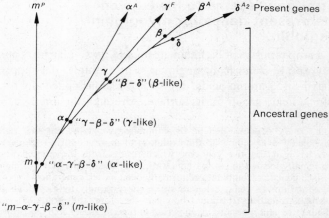

Figure 37-1 Hypothesized evolution of present genes for various chains in myoglobin (m^p) and hemoglobin (α^A, γ^F, β^A and δ^{A_2}) from ancestral genes.

sistence of linkage of the β^A and δ^{A_2} genes, and by the occurrence of A_2-like hemoglobin in primates only.

In summary, it appears that via duplications and subsequent point mutations an ancestral gene coding for a myoglobin-like polypeptide gave rise to present-day myoglobin and hemoglobin genes, the genes for the latter types of protein first appearing in evolution in the sequence α γ β δ. (R)

37.9   Internal duplications have occurred in the evolution of genes coding for proteins.

The preceding section indicated that primary structure rearrangements following duplication of genes coding for long polypeptides established new and separate loci in the evolution of myoglobin and hemoglobin. The present section mentions examples of complete or partial duplication of an ancestral gene sequence (followed by point mutations, of course)[2] that have occurred during the evolution of single polypeptide-coding loci.

1. Hemoglobin (and hence myoglobin) seems to have originated from an original globin, 21 amino acids long, which underwent successive duplications to produce the ancestral *m*-like gene.
2. Amino acid sequence studies seem to indicate that duplications containing point mutations have played an important role in the evolution of immunoglobulins. The relatively constant and relatively variable portions of an immunoglobulin chain seem to have arisen from a duplicated gene sequence. (Evidence also supports the view that heavy chain-coding genes arose as duplications of light chain-coding genes, the μ heavy chain of γM immunoglobulin being the first type of heavy chain to evolve.)
3. Cytochrome seems to contain an internal duplication of a primitive sequence of 15 amino acids.

37.10   Evolutionary trees can be constructed from the number of base substitution mutations that are detectable via amino acid changes in a given protein-coding gene in different organisms.

The preceding amino acid sequence comparisons were made either between different proteins coded at separate loci or within a protein. One can also compare the amino acid sequence of the same type of protein found in different organisms. Thus, one can compare the amino acid sequence in the α chain of hemoglobin or of cytochrome c in different organisms. Knowing the genetic code for amino acids, an evolutionary

[2] The search for repetitive homologies within a protein is complicated by the fact that many base substitutions may have occurred since the ancestral duplication. These duplications can nevertheless be detected by determining the minimum number of base changes needed to convert one amino acid sequence into another. When two unrelated proteins are compared this way, a median number of 1.40 to 1.52 base changes are usually required per amino acid codon. Accordingly, repetitive homologous sequences are indicated when they require statistically smaller numbers of mutation to be interconverted.

tree can be constructed in which the genes for a given protein in two (or more) different organisms are located at the ends of branches whose lengths are equal to the *mutational distance* between the two (or more) genes. The term "mutational distance" is defined as the minimal number of nucleotides that would need to be altered to convert the protein in one organism to the homologous protein of another organism.

Suppose the mutational distances for a given protein in species A, B, and C are

$$AB = 24$$
$$AC = 28$$
$$BC = 32.$$

Clearly, since the shortest mutational distance is between A and B, their genes must be closer to the common ancestral gene, Z, than either of them is to the common ancestral gene, Y, that both share with C. Accordingly, one can draw the evolutionary tree as in Figure 37-2, where the distances $a + b = 24$, $a + c = 28$, and $b + c = 32$. Since it takes 4 more units to get from C to B than from C to A, $b - a = 4$ and, therefore, $a = 10$ and $b = 14$; accordingly, $c = 18$.

Continuing this basic procedure one can construct a detailed, statistically optimal, evolutionary tree, for example, for cytochrome c in a large number of species (Figure 37-3). Evolutionary trees have also been made based on mutational distances for myoglobin and hemoglobin chains. The construction of detailed evolutionary trees based upon mutational distance depends, of course, upon the prior determination of the complete amino acid sequence of a protein in a wide range of organisms. (R)

37.11 Although genes for different proteins undergo adaptive amino acid changes at different rates, most surviving changes in a given protein seem to occur within a species at the same rate and to involve mutations which are adaptively neutral or near-neutral and become fixed by random genetic drift.

The evolutionary trees described in the last section do not tell us the rate at which the different mutational distances were attained. One can, however, correlate muta-

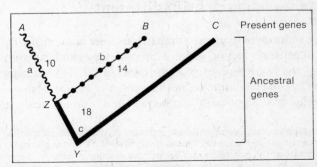

Figure 37-2   Evolutionary tree based on mutation distances (a, ∿; b, ↔; c, ━) between homologous genes in species A, B, and C. Z and Y are ancestral genes. (After W. M. Fitch and E. Margoliash, 1967.)

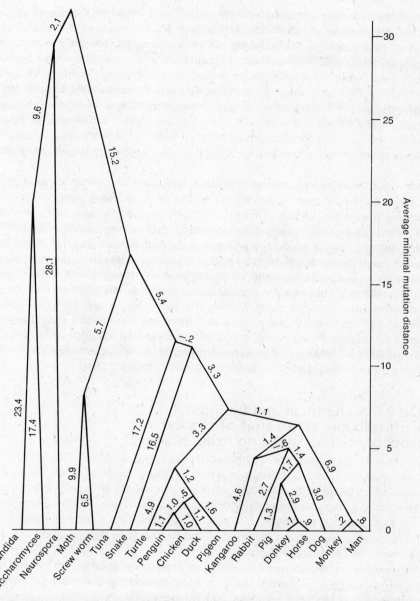

Figure 37-3 Evolutionary tree for the cytochrome c gene. Each number is the best-fitting mutation distance, each apex being placed at an ordinate value representing the average of the sums of all mutations in the lines of descent from that apex. (After W. M. Fitch and E. Margoliash, 1967.)

tional distance with geological evidence of the time of appearance of certain types of organisms. When this is done, the point-mutational rate of change for different proteins is quite different over a long period of evolution involving many species, being relatively very slow for cytochrome c (30 units on a particular scale), faster for hemoglobin (120 such units), and comparatively quick for the fibrinopeptides involved in blood clotting (900 units).

Every protein has some stretches of amino acid that are more essential for the functional success of the molecule than others. For example, of the total amino acid sequence in a chain of hemoglobin, the portion responsible for holding the heme group is doubtless most important. Mutations that change the amino acids in this region must make large changes in adaptiveness of hemoglobin. Since mutations occur with sufficient frequency, an adaptive type of hemoglobin is probably established early in the history of a species, subsequent mutations that are nonadaptive being removed by natural selection. The abovementioned differences in the rates of evolution of different proteins over long periods can be attributed, therefore, to mutations that modify the particular regions of a gene most affecting adaptiveness.

One would also expect, throughout the history of a single species, that mutations occur in functionally less important regions of a protein-coding gene—such mutations producing amino acid changes that have little or no effect on adaptive value. Accordingly, most amino acid changes in a protein that persist within single or closely related species should be due to adaptively neutral or near-neutral mutations that were retained in the population by random genetic drift. In support of this interpretation is evidence that the rate of amino acid substitution in a given protein, for example a hemoglobin chain, is remarkably similar in different species. Moreover, for proteins (like cytochrome c) which early in evolution arrived at a form that is highly adaptive in many future phyla—and, therefore, have a slow rate of evolution—the rate of change seems to be the same regardless of phylum or geological age. Such nonadaptive changes in proteins are the product of the *mutational noise* that surrounds the mutations which lead to adaptive changes. (R)

37.12 A chemical and biological evolution similar to that of the Earth is probably taking place on other planets.

The universe is thought to be about 10 billion years old, and the Earth roughly half this age. In it are an infinite number of stars, many of them, as is our sun, surrounded by planets. Surely some of these planets are of nearly the same size as the one we live on, and are equally distant from their suns. Perhaps these suns are of similar size and age as ours. The possibility, then, that a chemical and biological evolution similar to ours has occurred elsewhere seems to depend upon the chemical composition of the planets themselves.

Most matter in the universe is either hydrogen or helium, with some oxygen, nitrogen, and carbon. The universe is, in fact, richer than the Earth in carbon—the atom that has played such an important role in evolution on this planet. Since the Earth has supported a biological evolution even though it appears a relatively poor place for such a process, it is likely that the universe contains numerous planets on which a similar evolution is taking place.

We have evidence that a chemical evolution, similar to that which apparently led to the biological evolution on Earth, has also taken place elsewhere in our own solar system. Organic radicals such as CH, CN, CC, and CO are detected in comets, and extraterrestrial amino acids and hydrocarbons are apparently present in meteorites. Not only have organic molecules of an asymmetric type been detected on Mars, but laboratory experiments using a simulated Martian environment (as indicated by Mariner 6 and 7 space probes) and ultraviolet radiation have produced organic compounds such as formaldehyde, acetaldehyde, and glycolic acid. We cannot yet determine, however, whether any of the detected extraterrestrial organic matter has a preorganismal or organismal origin.

If we can investigate planets on which chemical and biological evolution are at stages different from that here, we will be a long way toward answering important questions about evolution on this planet. In whatever ways we further clarify the principles of genetics in the future, though, we can expect this science to continue its unification of the entire field of biology and, hence, to play an increasingly important role in the modern world. (R)

SUMMARY AND CONCLUSIONS

As is expected to occur on many planets in the universe, the Earth has undergone a preorganismal evolution of organic compounds which resulted in the formation of polypeptides and polynucleotides. Once these two classes of substances became so interdependent that the maintenance and replication of nucleic acid became dependent upon protein, whose existence in turn depended upon the nucleic acid it helped maintain and replicate, the first organism containing nucleic acid genetic material came into being.

Organismal (biological) evolution then proceeded in favor of organisms which most efficiently utilized the environment to perpetuate themselves. This efficiency was attained by the evolution of a genetic code for proteins and a transcription–translation machinery which became essentially universal; by increasing the quantity of genetic material; and by subsequent qualitative genetic changes which produced the structural and functional genes needed (1) to take advantage of the most abundant chemical and physical features of the environment (permitting for example, a shift from heterotrophy toward autotrophy), and (2) to regulate the organism itself (for example, by regulating the replication, transcription–translation, variation, and recombination of the genetic material).

Studies of amino acid sequence in proteins such as globins (hemo-, myo-, and immuno-) and cytochrome c in a wide range of organisms have contributed specific information on the quantitative and qualitative evolution that structural genes have undergone during biological evolution. Successive duplications of an ancestral structural gene have often occurred. After additional point mutations, the duplicated genetic material sometimes continued to function as a single structural gene (as seems to have occurred in the formation of a gene coding a 150-amino acid myoglobin-type molecule from one coding a 21-amino acid protein); other times the duplicated genetic material became separate loci (as seems to have occurred in the formation of separate loci for the different chains in hemoglobin and myoglobin). The genetically coded amino acid changes which accumulate in a protein (and are used to construct evolutionary trees via mutational distances) seem to be the result of mutations that are (1) adaptive and are fixed by natural selection and (2) adaptively neutral or near-neutral and are fixed by random genetic drift.

GENERAL REFERENCES

Bryson, V., and Vogel, H. J. (Editors) 1965. *Evolving genes and proteins.* New York: Academic Press, Inc.

Jukes, T. H. 1966. *Molecules and evolution.* New York: Columbia University Press.

SPECIFIC SECTION REFERENCES

37.1 Calvin, M. 1969. *Chemical evolution: molecular evolution towards the origin of living systems on the earth and elsewhere.* New York: Oxford University Press, Inc.

Oparin, A. I. 1964. *The chemical origin of life.* Springfield, Ill.: Charles C Thomas.

Krampitz, G., and Fox, S. W. 1969. The condensation of the adenylates of the amino acids common to protein. Proc. Nat. Acad. Sci., U.S., 62: 399–406.

37.2 Nakashima, T., and Fox, S. W. 1972. Selective condensation of aminoacyl adenylates by nucleoproteinoid microparticles. Proc. Nat. Acad. Sci., U.S., 69: 106–108. (Under certain conditions the amino acids incorporated are related to the codons in the homopolynucleotide in the particle.)

37.3 Lacey, J. C., Jr., and Pruitt, K. M. 1969. Origin of the genetic code. Nature, Lond., 223: 799–804.

Orgel, L. E. 1968. Evolution of the genetic apparatus. J. Mol. Biol., 38: 381–393.

37.5 Britten, R. J., and Davidson, E. H. 1971. Repetitive and nonrepetitive DNA sequences and a speculation on the origins of evolutionary novelty. Quart. Rev. Biol., 46: 111–133.

Edström, J. E. 1968. Masters, slaves and evolution. Nature, Lond., 220: 1196–1198.

Ohno, S. 1970. *Evolution by gene duplication.* New York: Springer Verlag.

37.8 Zuckerkandl, E. 1965. The evolution of hemoglobin. Scient. Amer. 212 (No. 5): 110–118, 152. Reprinted in *Facets of genetics*, Srb, A. M., Owen, R. D., and Edgar, R. S. (Editors). San Francisco: W. H. Freeman and Company, Publishers, 1970, pp. 256–264.

37.9 Cantor, C. R., and Jukes, T. H. 1966. The repetition of homologous sequences in the polypeptide chains of certain cytochromes and globins. Proc. Nat. Acad. Sci., U.S., 56: 177–184.

37.10 Dayhoff, M. O. 1969. Computer analysis of protein evolution. Scient. Amer., 221 (No. 1): 86–95, 140. Reprinted in *Facets of genetics*, Srb, A. M., Owen, R. D., and Edgar, R. S. (Editors). San Francisco: W. H. Freeman and Company, Publishers, 1970, pp. 265–274.

Fitch, W. M., and Margoliash, E. 1967. Construction of phylogenetic trees. Science, 155: 279–284. Reprinted in *Papers on evolution*, Ehrlich, P. R., Holm, R. W., and Raven, P. H. (Editors). Boston: Little, Brown and Company, 1969, pp. 450–462.

37.11 Ohta, T., and Kimura, M. 1971. Amino acid composition of proteins as a product of molecular evolution. Science, 174: 150–152.

Zuckerkandl, E., Derancourt, J., and Vogel, H. 1971. Mutational trends and random processes in the evolution of informational macromolecules. J. Mol. Biol., 59: 473–490.

37.12 Crick, F. 1970. Molecular biology in the year 2000. Nature, Lond., 228: 613–615. (Which problems relative to genetics will and won't be solved by then.)

Hubbard, J. S., Hardy, J. P., and Horowitz, N. H. 1971. Photocatalytic production of organic compounds from CO and H_2O in a simulated Martian atmosphere. Proc. Nat. Acad. Sci., U.S., 68: 574–578. (Apparently, formaldehyde, acetaldehyde, and glycolic acid were made.)

Kvenvolden, K., Lawless, J., Pering, K., Peterson, E., Flores, J., Ponnamperuma, C., Kaplan, I. R., and Moore, C. 1970. Evidence for extraterrestrial amino-acids and hydrocarbons in the Murchison meteorite. Nature, Lond., 228: 923–926.

QUESTIONS AND PROBLEMS

1. Why are missiles sterilized before they are sent beyond our atmosphere?
2. Give the evolutionary significance of the following observations about phage by J. W. Drake.
   a. Mutations occur in the absence of DNA replication.
   b. These mutations apparently occur in dG : dC but not dA : dT pairs.
3. The DNA of higher plants and animals is richer in dA + dT than in dC + dG. What advantage might such a base ratio confer upon an organism?
4. In what way does the table showing the DNA content of different organisms (Figure 2-11) support the view that biological evolution is closely parallel to the evolution of protein?

5. What enzymes were especially important in the first organisms? Justify your choices.

6. Do you suppose some planets have more advanced civilizations than our own? Why?

7. Can organisms without protein or nucleic acid survive? Explain.

8. What effect did the release of oxygen into the atmosphere have on mutation rate?

9. Why are most mutations harmful?

10. What are the evolutionary implications of the finding that amino acid attachment to tRNA is anomalous above 75°C?

11. What information would you seek from a landing on the moon? Mars? Venus?

12. What characteristics would you expect of genes from other planets?

13. What is your definition of a gene? Of genetics?

Appendix

Biometrics

Introduction: statistics and parameters

There are numerous occasions when one may wish to arrive at a genetic conclusion on the basis of experimental data. Whenever these data are subject to chance variation, it is necessary to make use of biometrical ideas and techniques in order to draw the most precise conclusions. Let us consider, therefore, some of the basic principles and methods which are likely to be valuable in a study of genetics. (The table of contents at the beginning of this appendix will make it easier to find the section that describes a particular biometrical technique.)

A *statistic* is a measurement obtained from a sample. A sample can be considered as having been drawn from an ideal population composed of an infinite number of measurements. Whereas the measurements of a sample are statistics, the measurements of the ideal, infinitely large, population are expressed in terms of *parameters*. The difference between a statistic and a parameter can be illustrated with a penny. Let the ideal population be composed of the results of an infinite number of tosses. In this ideal population one would expect the coin to fall heads up 50 per cent of the time, and tails up 50 per cent of the time. The population can be characterized in terms of a parameter, the probability of heads up, expressed as $p = 0.5$. If one actually takes a sample of this infinite population by tossing a penny a finite number of times, one obtains the statistic, the frequency of heads up relative to the total number of tosses.

Given a parameter, one may want to predict the range of statistics expected to comprise a sample (Figure A-1A). Alternatively, one might like to be able to determine from a statistic the range of parameters from which this statistic could have been obtained by sampling (Figure A-1B). One may want to determine the probabilities (that is, parameters) that different alternatives will occur in samples drawn from an ideal population (Figure A-1C). One may wish to compare the statistics expected (e) in a sample with those actually obtained (o) (Figure A-1D). And finally, using a parameter, one may wish to compare two groups of statistics (o1 and o2) (Figure A-1E). Methods for making these and other comparisons are presented here.

Heads vs. tails, black vs. white, smooth vs. rough, and tall vs. short all involve *discrete variables* which are measured by enumeration, since the outcomes or alter-

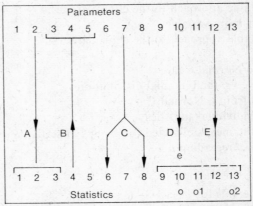

Figure A-1 Biometrical procedures to be discussed with respect to discrete variables (see the text for an explanation). o, observed; e, expected. Arrows show direction of prediction.

natives fall into discontinuous, easily distinguished and separable, classes. On the other hand, the statistics of weight, height, and intelligence are all quantitative, continuous, or *indiscrete variables*. The difference between the two lies in the number of alternatives possible in each case; there is an infinite variety of alternatives possible in the indiscrete case, but only a limited number of outcomes in the discrete one. This difference disappears, however, once the outcomes are tallied. For example, although the number of different weights possible in the range of weights between fat and skinny people is infinite, weights are scored with a scale whose number of possible readings is limited. In other words, an infinite variety of outcomes must always be scored or measured in a finite number of ways. As far as statistics are concerned, the only difference between indiscrete and discrete outcomes is the possible occurrence of a much larger number of scored outcomes in the former case. In either group of outcomes, scoring a statistic requires the use of a measuring device, be it the eye, ear, finger, etc., very often in combination with a ruler, photoelectric cell, and so forth. We will study first statistics and parameters for discrete outcomes (small number of classes) and then those for indiscrete outcomes (large number of classes).

It should be emphasized at this point that the accuracy of the conclusions reached from the use of biometrical procedures depends upon four major factors: (1) imagination and flexibility, (2) proper sampling methods, (3) accurate recording of statistics, and (4) correct choice and use of biometrical procedures. It is unreasonable to expect that good biometrical technique can overcome poor data; the biometrical analysis becomes more efficient the closer one adheres to the first three factors in carrying out experiments.

Discrete variables

Range of statistics expected from a parameter involving one variable (Figure A-1A)

One often formulates a hypothesis in terms of the probability that an event will occur. It is also often desirable to know the kind of result one would obtain were this hypothesis tested. For example, common sense suggests that "unbiased" pennies tossed in an unbiased manner have equal likelihood of falling heads up or tails up. Let heads up be considered a *success*. We can state as a *hypothesis* (Ho) that the parameter p, the *probability of success*, is 50 per cent, or 0.5, of all the times the coin falls flat. Note that there are only two alternatives involved—success and failure. Since 50 per cent of the time we would expect failure, the *probability of failure* is $1 - p$. One need only use a single variable, probability of success, to describe all the outcomes possible. (If one were to toss an unbiased die, there would be 6 different and equally possible outcomes, and 5 variables. But if one considered as a success only when the die falls "one" up, then there would be only one variable and we could state as a hypothesis that $p = \frac{1}{6}$.) What kind of statistics would one expect to obtain from actual tosses of an unbiased penny? Clearly the result will depend upon whether 1, 2, or many trials, that is, tosses, are made.

Expected range of f values. Let us represent the *number of successes* by X, the total *number of trials* or *size of sample* by N, and the *proportion of success* by f. Therefore,

$$\frac{X}{N} = f,$$

our statistic. Suppose one collected many relatively large samples. What f values would result? It has been shown that this can be determined by using the expression

$$\sqrt{\frac{p(1-p)}{N}},$$

which is called the *standard deviation* of p, or s_p. If the value of $N(p)(1-p)$ is equal to or greater than 25, it is found that 95 per cent of the f values obtained lie between $p - 1.96s_p$ and $p + 1.96s_p$.

If one stated that f can have only the values included in this 95 per cent *confidence interval*, he would be right 95 per cent of the time and wrong 5 per cent of the time. In the penny-tossing example ($p = 0.5$), if $N = 100$, s_p is approximately 0.05 and 95 per cent of the time we would expect f to be in the interval 0.4 to 0.6. If many samples of $N = 100$ are drawn, one can state that 95 per cent of all f's will lie in the interval 0.4 to 0.6. If one draws a single sample of $N = 100$, it can be stated that f will be in 0.4 to 0.6 and we would have a 95 per cent chance of being right and a 5 per cent chance of being wrong.

Why should one resign himself to the handicap of being wrong 5 per cent (or any per cent) of the time? In order to be right 100 per cent of the time one would have to admit that, 5 per cent of the time, f can lie outside the 95 per cent confidence interval. In the example this would mean that 5 per cent of the time f may lie anywhere between 0 (no successes) and 0.4 and between 0.6 and 1.0 (all successes). To be 100 per cent correct, to have 100 per cent confidence, one would have to predict f to range between 0 and 1. However, electing to be 100 per cent right also means that all other values of p would also have an expected range of f's from 0 to 1. Accordingly, the 100 per cent range does not provide different expectations of f for different values of p; it provides no power at all to discriminate between different p values. However, by being willing to be wrong 5 per cent of the time, the range of expected f's (when $p = 0.5$ and $N = 100$) can be reduced from (0 to 1) to (0.4 to 0.6). And were $p = 0.3$ and $N = 100$, f would be roughly between 0.2 and 0.4 95 per cent of the time. Accordingly, accepting a 5 per cent chance of being wrong permits one to have different statistical expectations for different p values. In genetics and biology in general, researchers usually agree to the use of the 95 per cent confidence interval both for statistics and parameters.

Using the expression given above, one can calculate the different values of s_p for numerous combinations of p and N. The 95 per cent range for f can be determined from these calculations. For convenience, the 95 per cent ranges for f for various values of p and N are plotted in Figure A-2. For values of N not shown, one can interpolate between curves. Note that if N were infinitely large, f would equal p and for any given value of p, the range would become wider as N decreased.

Range of parameters expected from a statistic involving one variable (Figure A-1B)

If one had no notion what the parameter for the chance of a successful toss of a penny should be, one could make an inference about the p value from the statistics obtained. An estimate of the unknown parameter, p, can be obtained from the statistic f. Suppose that 100 tosses of a penny yield 30 successes. The value $f = 0.30$ is a single statistic. The *single best estimate* of p is f. From the single f value, the best

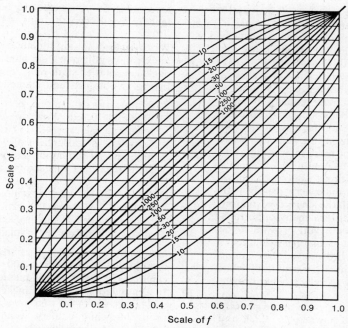

Figure A-2 Ninety-five per cent confidence limits (1) for *f* based on a single-variable parameter, *p*. To determine confidence intervals, find *p* on the vertical scale. Move right to the
intersections with the two curves indicating the sample size. Finally, read down to determine
on the horizontal scale the confidence limits of *f*. (2) For *p* based on a single-variable statistic,
f. To determine confidence intervals, find *f* on the horizontal scale. Move upward to the
intersections with the two curves indicating the sample size. Finally, read left to determine
on the vertical scale the confidence limits of *p*. (Courtesy of the Biometrika Trustees.)

estimate is $p = 0.30$. However, it should not be surprising if *p* were really 0.31, 0.29,
or some other nearby value. What would also be valuable to know is the range of
p values likely when $f = 0.3$ and $N = 100$. This range can be determined by calculating

$$\sqrt{\frac{f(1-f)}{N}},$$

which is the *standard deviation* of *f*, or s_f. The values lying between $f - 1.96s_f$ and
$f + 1.96s_f$ make up the 95 per cent confidence interval of *p*, because 95 per cent of
the time we would expect this particular sample to have a *p* value in this interval.
If we say that *p* cannot be outside this range, we will be wrong only 5 per cent of the
time. In the present case, s_f is about 0.05 and the 95 per cent confidence interval of
p is roughly 0.20 to 0.40. If one asserts that *p* must lie between 0.20 and 0.40 he will
be wrong only about 5 per cent of the time. By reading upward and then to the left,
one may use Figure A-2 to determine the 95 per cent confidence intervals of *p* for
different values of *f*.

QUESTIONS AND PROBLEMS

1. You suspect that the sex ratio of the fruit
    fly *Drosophila* is 0.5 ♂♂ and 0.5 ♀♀. Let
    success be ♂. What range of successes might
    you expect with 95 per cent confidence from
    an unbiased count of 100 flies? 250 flies?
    1,000 flies? What is happening to your

confidence limits as sample size increases? What does this mean?

2. You expect to draw a sample in which $N = 100$. What is the 95 per cent range for f when the hypothesis is $p = 0.5$? $p = 0.3$? $p = 0.1$? How does the range of f change according to the hypothesized p values?

3. You expect 8 different equally-frequent types of gametes to be produced by a certain trihybrid. Only one of these is of interest to you. If you sample 50 gametes, what range, in numbers of these interesting gametes, are you likely to obtain?

4. Under certain conditions, white-eyed *Drosophila* males do not mate very readily with red-eyed females. If the chance of mating is 10 per cent, about how many opportunities for mating should you provide to be reasonably sure that 5 matings will occur?

5. A student finds 25 brown-eyed flies among 100. Determine with 95 per cent confidence the true probability of a fly's being brown-eyed.

6. Using Figure A-2, determine the 95 per cent confidence limits of p when $f = 0.60$, and $N = 100$, 250, and 1,000.

7. After meiosis of the genotype $A\,a\,B\,b$ in *Neurospora* you obtain 100 asci. If you assume independent segregation, how many ascospores do you expect to have the following genetic constitution: $A\,B$? $A\,b$ plus $a\,B$?

8. When placed in an iodine solution, one allele causes pollen to stain blue and another allele causes it to stain red. Pollen from the hybrid is obtained and stained.

   a. Sample 1 is 100 grains, of which 30 are blue and 70 red. What do you conclude regarding the expected 1:1 ratio?
   b. Sample 2 is 150 grains, of which 81 are blue and 69 red. What are your conclusions regarding this sample and the 1:1 ratio?
   c. Combine the data in samples 1 and 2, and test against a 1:1 ratio. What do you conclude? Is this procedure permissible? Is it desirable? Explain.

9. You want to test whether a particular penny is unbiased by tossing it 100 times. How can you tell if the coin is biased?

10. In a population of 1,000 chickens, only 250 are homozygous for the gene pair $(W\,W)$ producing white feathers. Assuming genetic equilibrium, what do you calculate to be the frequency of W in the gene pool? Give (a) your best single estimate, and (b) your estimate with 95 per cent confidence.

Specific probabilities expected from parameters involving one variable (Figure A-1C)

Without tossing an unbiased penny, one can assign a value $p = 0.5$. Without recourse to trial, one can propose the hypothesis that $p = \frac{1}{8}$ that a particular side of an unbiased octahedron will fall down. Similarly, the probability that an unbiased die will fall with a given side up is $\frac{1}{6}$. In such cases one has no difficulty in deciding upon the probability of success. At other times one does not know the probability of success, and this parameter must then be determined.

Rules of Probability. *The addition rule.* Sometimes a success can occur in two or more different ways, each way excluding the others. What is the total probability of success in such cases?

If on a single toss of a die the probability of a "one" is $\frac{1}{6}$ and the probability of a "two" is $\frac{1}{6}$, then the expectation or probability of either a "one" or a "two" is $\frac{1}{6} + \frac{1}{6} = \frac{1}{3}$. In general, the probability that *one* of several mutually exclusive successes will occur is the *sum* of their individual probabilities. If the probability that an event will succeed is p, and the probability that it will fail is q, then the probability of either success or failure is $p + q$. But if it is certain that the event must either succeed or fail, then $p + q = 1$, $p = 1 - q$, and $q = 1 - p$.

The multiplication rule. Sometimes overall success depends upon the occurrence simultaneously or consecutively of two or more successes, and the occurrence (or failure) of one success in no way influences the occurrence (or failure) of the others.

If the probability of " one " in the toss of a die is $\frac{1}{6}$ and if the probability of another " one " in a second toss is also $\frac{1}{6}$, then the probability of " one " on the first and " one " on the second is $\frac{1}{6} \times \frac{1}{6} = \frac{1}{36}$. In general, the probability that *all* of several *independent* successes will occur is the *product* of their separate probabilities.

The Binomial Expression. Given a parameter involving only one variable, one can determine the exact probabilities of obtaining specific combinations of successes and failures by expanding the binomial expression $(q + p)^N$. If a " one " on a die is a success and the die is tossed 5 times, the probabilities of 0 ones, 1 one, 2 ones, 3 ones, etc., among the 5 tosses are given by successive terms of the expansion of the binomial

$$\left(\frac{5}{6} + \frac{1}{6}\right)^5.$$

In this expression $\frac{5}{6}$ represents the probability of not obtaining a one on a single trial, $\frac{1}{6}$ the probability of obtaining a one, and the exponent 5 the number of trials. The expansion is shown in Table 1. Note that each result is possible, each having its own exact probability of occurrence.

Table 1

$$\left(\frac{5}{6}\right)^5 + 5\left(\frac{5}{6}\right)^4\left(\frac{1}{6}\right) + 10\left(\frac{5}{6}\right)^3\left(\frac{1}{6}\right)^2 + 10\left(\frac{5}{6}\right)^2\left(\frac{1}{6}\right)^3 + 5\left(\frac{5}{6}\right)\left(\frac{1}{6}\right)^4 + \left(\frac{1}{6}\right)^5$$

Exact p = 0.4019	0.4019	0.1607	0.0321	0.0032	0.0001
Number of "ones" = 0	1	2	3	4	5

QUESTIONS AND PROBLEMS

11. If you roll a die three times, what is the probability of obtaining (a) three "fours" in succession? (b) "One," "two," and "three" in that order?

12. If you roll two dice at the same time in a single trial, what is the probability of obtaining a total of eleven? Two? Seven?

13. What is the chance that a simultaneous toss of a penny, a nickel, a dime, a quarter, and a half-dollar will fall:
    a. All heads or all tails?
    b. 3 heads and 2 tails?

14. What is the exact probability (using an unbiased penny) of a run of tosses which
    a. starts with 2 heads and ends with 3 tails?
    b. has 4 successive heads?
    c. has 5 successive tails?

15. What is the exact probability of 10 successes, if $p = \frac{1}{3}$ and $N = 15$?

16. How often will you expect to obtain less than 3 successes if $p = \frac{1}{4}$ and $N = 5$?

17. You have just etherized *Drosophila* which are the progeny of a cross between $ci^+ ci$ and $ci^+ ci$. What is the probability that there is only 1 $ci\ ci$ fly among the first 3 flies chosen at random? Among the first 5 flies chosen at random?

18. Following independent segregation of $A\,a$ $B\,b\ C\,c$, an ascus is formed. What is the probability that if two ascospores are chosen at random they will be $A\,B\,C$? $a\,b\,c$? Either $A\,B\,C$ or $a\,b\,c$?

19. An albino ($a\,a$) man of blood type MN marries a heterozygote for albinism ($A\,a$) also of MN blood type. They plan to have 4 children. If you assume independent segregation, what is the exact probability that they will have
    a. no albinos?
    b. 2 nonalbino children with MN blood type?
    c. 3 children with M blood type?

Comparing observed with expected statistics (Figure A-1D)

The Binomial Test of a Parameter Involving One Variable. From a certain cross, genetic theory predicts a $1:1$ ratio ($p = 0.50$) in F_1. Among 6 individuals one expects, according to the binomial expansion, to observe 3 of one type and 3 of another $\frac{5}{16}$ of the time. This is the outcome most frequently obtained, all others occurring with lower frequency. Suppose, however, that one actually observes that all 6 are of one type. Must one consider this observation of no statistical significance and due only to chance variation? Or, is the difference statistically significant, indicating that expectation and observation do not always agree? This question can be answered by considering the probability of obtaining all 6 alike on the basis of our hypothesis. According to this expectation, the probability that a single individual will be of the first type is $\frac{1}{2}$ and the probability that it will be of the second type is also $\frac{1}{2}$. The probability that all 6 will be of the first type is $(\frac{1}{2})^6$; the probability that all 6 will be of the second type is also $(\frac{1}{2})^6$. And the probability that either all 6 will be of the first type or all of the second is $(\frac{1}{2})^6 + (\frac{1}{2})^6 = 0.03$. But since the probability of this outcome, if the hypothesis holds true, is so low, one must conclude one of two things. Either the hypothesis is correct but a very improbable situation has occurred, or else the hypothesis does not fit the observations. Since an event with a probability of 0.03 is expected to occur only 3 times in a hundred trials, the latter alternative is chosen. It is concluded, therefore, that the hypothesis is probably incorrect.

In general, to test whether an observed result is consistent with a parameter, one tests the *null hypothesis*, that is, the likelihood that the statistic really has the hypothesized parameter. Accordingly, one calculates the total probability with which he would expect to obtain from the parameter a statistic which is as extreme as, or more extreme than, the observed statistic. If this probability is low (by convention, 0.05 or less), it can be concluded that observation and expectation do not agree. One rejects the hypothesis with 95 per cent confidence and at a 5 per cent level of significance (5 per cent chance of rejecting the hypothesis when it is really true). If the probability is greater than 0.05 (5 per cent), one can conclude that the observations provide no evidence against the hypothesis. This is an acceptable hypothesis. If the probability falls well below 0.05 to the 0.01 level or less, the difference is usually considered to be highly significant.

As a further example, consider finding 6 of one type and 2 of another among a group of 8 individuals. Suppose the theoretical ratio is $1:1$. The probability of obtaining a result this extreme or more extreme according to the null hypothesis is given by computing the sum of the following terms, obtained by expanding $(\frac{1}{2} + \frac{1}{2})^8$

Probability of 0 of first type	=	$(\frac{1}{2})^8$
Probability of 1 of first type	=	$8 \times (\frac{1}{2})^8$
Probability of 2 of first type	=	$28 \times (\frac{1}{2})^8$
Probability of 2 of second type	=	$28 \times (\frac{1}{2})^8$
Probability of 1 of second type	=	$8 \times (\frac{1}{2})^8$
Probability of 0 of second type	=	$(\frac{1}{2})^8$

Adding together these separate exact probabilities, one finds that the total probability of 2 or less of same type $= 74/256 = 0.29$. Since the total probability is greater than 0.05, the statistic is consistent with the hypothesis, which is consequently acceptable.

The Confidence-Interval Test of a Parameter Involving One Variable. In the examples just discussed the binomial test involved N values less than 10. The binomial test can also be used when N is larger. However, it is less cumbersome to make use of the expected range for f from an expected single-variable parameter as given in Figure A-2.

Suppose that $f = 0.3$ and $N = 100$. What could one conclude about Ho $p = 0.5$? If $p = 0.5$ and $N = 100$, 95 per cent of f's would lie between 0.4 and 0.6. Since $f = 0.3$, one may reject Ho $p = 0.5$. Had $f = 0.43$ and $N = 100$, one could accept Ho $p = 0.5$. Remember that the decisions made from Figure A-2 about a parameter are at the 5 per cent level of significance; and one can only reject or accept parameters, for these represent idealized inferences about statistics. Statistics are observations or facts, and are not subject to rejection.

Chi-square Test of a Parameter Involving One Variable. It will be useful to describe another method of testing a single-variable parameter when N is reasonably large, which differs from the expected range test. Suppose that one expects a $1:1$ ratio and hence, ideally, 50 cases of one type and 50 cases of another out of a sample of 100. But suppose one observes 55 of one type and 45 of the other. In order to judge whether the observations agree with expectation, one must find the probability of obtaining, on a null hypothesis, a result this extreme or more extreme in samples of 100 taken from an ideal population. Although the probability could be determined by summing the appropriate terms of $(\frac{1}{2} + \frac{1}{2})^{100}$, the time required is prohibitive (unless, of course, one has access to a computer). It has been found that an approximate value of the desired probability may be obtained from a quantity called *chi square* (χ^2), a comparatively easy computation:

$$\chi^2_{(1)} = \sum \frac{[(\text{observed} - \text{expected}) - \frac{1}{2}]^2}{\text{expected}}$$

The term $\frac{1}{2}$ is called Yates' correction. It may be omitted when N and the expected values are large, but it is safer to include it in a routine calculation. The formula requires that for each class (here there are only two, success and failure, and hence the χ^2 is considered to have one degree of freedom—$\chi^2_{(1)}$) one find the absolute difference between the observed and expected numbers, subtract $\frac{1}{2}$ from this remainder (making it closer to 0 by $\frac{1}{2}$), and square the result. This value is divided by the expected number. We do this for each class and sum the terms for all classes. Thus, in our case:

$$\chi^2_{(1)} = \frac{[(45 - 50) - \frac{1}{2}]^2}{50} + \frac{[(55 - 50) - \frac{1}{2}]^2}{50}$$

$$= \frac{(4\frac{1}{2})^2}{50} + \frac{(4\frac{1}{2})^2}{50} = \frac{40.5}{50} = 0.8.$$

The probability is obtained from a chart of χ^2 (Figure A-3) under one degree of freedom. (The number of degrees of freedom for such a test is one less than the number of classes; that is, it equals the number of variables.) Thus, from Figure A-3 one finds that the probability lies between 0.35 and 0.40. The difference between what is observed and what is expected according to the null hypothesis is nonsignificant. Therefore, one may accept the hypothesis.

The chi-square method is an approximation and is valid for relatively large samples only. Its use requires that no class have an expected value of less than 2 and that most of the expected values be at least 5.

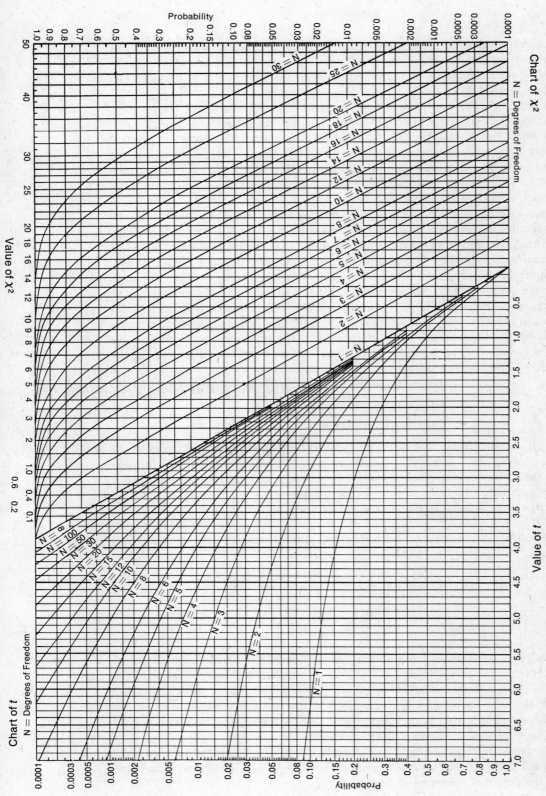

Figure A-3 Chi-square and t distributions. To read the chart with a χ^2 value of 17 based on 7 degrees of freedom, the vertical line corresponding to a χ^2 value of 17 is followed upward until it intersects the curve corresponding to $N = 7$. Directly to the left of this point the probability, 0.017, is read off. With the chart inverted, probabilities for the t distribution are read in exactly the same way. The probability given is the probability of a numerically greater deviation. (Courtesy of J. F. Crow.)

Chi-square Test of a Parameter Involving Two or More Variables. The χ^2 test is applicable to parameters involving more than two alternative outcomes, hence involving two or more variables. The chi-square test can be used to determine whether a sample is consistent with an hypothesized $9:3:3:1$ ratio, for example. If a $9:3:3:1$ ratio were being tested, the ideally expected numbers in a group of 80 individuals would be 45, 15, 15, and 5, respectively. Since there are four classes, there are three variables or degrees of freedom. If we observed 40, 20, 12, and 8, respectively, we would calculate

$$\chi^2_{(3)} = \frac{(40-45)^2}{45} + \frac{(20-15)^2}{15} + \frac{(12-15)^2}{15} + \frac{(8-5)^2}{5} = 4.6.$$

(The term $\frac{1}{2}$, the Yates correction, is not applicable if there is more than one degree of freedom.) Since the probability lies between 0.20 and 0.25, the difference is non-significant, and one accepts the null hypothesis.

It is interesting to note that the probability of obtaining a χ^2 value equal to or greater than 0.004 for one degree of freedom, 0.1 for two degrees of freedom, etc., is 0.95. It follows the probability of obtaining χ^2 values smaller than these must be 0.05. Such low values in an actual test indicate that the agreement between observation and expectation is suggestively better than expected. The question of whether the data represent authentic random samples may be legitimately raised in such cases.

QUESTIONS AND PROBLEMS

20. A person with woolly hair marries a non-woolly-haired individual; they have 8 children, 7 woolly-haired and 1 non-woolly-haired. Test the hypothesis that woolly hair is due to a rare, completely dominant gene.

21. Given the data in problem 20, test the hypothesis that woolly hair is due to a completely recessive mutant.

22. A penny is tossed seven times. One time it falls on edge, five times it falls heads, and once it falls tails. Is this an "honest" coin?

23. A test cross produces 57 individuals of A phenotype and 43 of A′ phenotype. Is one pair of genes involved?

24. Given the data in problem 23, test the hypothesis that one parent is a dihybrid and that the A phenotype is obtained only when two particular nonalleles are present.

25. In a sample of 540, $X = 90$. What is the value of chi square if you hypothesize that

$p = \frac{1}{4}$? Do you accept this hypothesis?

26. Among 64 individuals the phenotypes are 8 A, 12 B, 20 C, and 24 D. Test the hypothesis that

   a. A B C D are in the relative proportion $1:3:3:9$.

   b. all four phenotypes have an equal chance of occurring.

   c. the ideal ratio is 1A:3B:5C:7D.

27. A random sample from a natural population contains 65 *A A*, 95 *A a*, and 40 *a a* individuals. Test the hypothesis that

   a. the frequency of *a* in the population gene pool is 0.5.

   b. this sample is consistent with the population being in genetic equilibrium for this locus, if you assume that the observed gene frequency for *a* is also the population frequency.

Comparisons between statistics (Figure A-1E)

Involving One Variable. Observed difference vs. expected standard deviation. Suppose that a sample (A) provided 20 males and 30 females, whereas a different sample (B) gave 30 males and 20 females. Is there a significant difference in the frequency of males in the two samples? ($f_A = 0.40$ and $f_B = 0.60$; $N_A = 50$, $N_B = 50$.) We have no expectation as to what p_A or p_B should be. According to the null hypothesis these two samples have the same parameter, p_x. Our best estimate of p_x is f_x, obtained by pooling the results of both samples and obtaining $50/100 = 0.50$. We next calculate how large the difference between the observed f's is, relative to the total standard deviation that one would expect if f_x were obtained in each of the two samples, N_A and N_B. This calculation can be made from the expression

$$\frac{f_B - f_A}{\sqrt{\dfrac{f_x(1 - f_x)}{N_A} + \dfrac{f_x(1 - f_x)}{N_B}}}$$

$$= \frac{0.20}{\sqrt{\dfrac{0.5 \times 0.5}{50} + \dfrac{0.5 \times 0.5}{50}}} = 2.0.$$

(The subtraction in the numerator should be made to give a $+$ result, that is, one should obtain the absolute value of the remainder.) It has been shown that if N_x is greater than 30, values of 2.0 or more will occur by chance only 5 per cent of the time. We conclude, therefore, that the two samples under test are on the borderline of being statistically different at the 5 per cent level of significance.

The plus–minus test. Suppose a particular treatment is to be tested for its capacity to change a statistic. Suppose, moreover, that one does not care just how much change is being induced as compared with how much is occurring spontaneously. (The treatment might produce only a very small change; under these circumstances, two tremendously large samples, one control and the other treated, would be necessary to obtain a statistically significant difference between their measurements.) What can be done is to arrange a series of paired observations in which the members of a pair are as similar as possible in order to make the measurement of difference as sensitive as possible.

Imagine, for example, that one wishes to determine whether feeding a salt to the developing *Drosophila* male has any effect upon the sex ratio of his progeny. Each test consists of scoring the sex of the progeny of two single pair matings, in which one male has and the other has not been treated. Assume that the experiment is performed in an unbiased manner and that the results are as follows:

PAIRED OBSER- VATION	SEX RATIO ($\male\male / \female\female$)		$\pm$ TEST	
	UN- TREATED	TREATED	UN- TREATED	TREATED
1	0.47	0.46	$+$	$-$
2	0.48	0.47	$+$	$-$
3	0.49	0.48	$+$	$-$
4	0.50	0.50	No test	
5	0.46	0.44	$+$	$-$
6	0.51	0.50	$+$	$-$
7	0.48	0.47	$+$	$-$

One proceeds to test the null hypothesis that the treatment has no effect upon the F_1 sex ratio. In accordance with this view, there would be an equal chance for the untreated and treated members of a pair of observations to have the higher sex ratio (that is, to be scored $+$); consequently the Ho is $p = \frac{1}{2}$. There are only 6 tests of the Ho, since one test gave the same sex ratio for both untreated and treated. The probability that the relevant 6 untreated shall be all successes or all failures is, according to the null hypothesis, $2(\frac{1}{2})^6$, or $\frac{1}{32}$, or about 3 per cent. [The chance that the remaining 5 tests will be like the first is $(\frac{1}{2})^5$, or also about 3 per cent.] Accordingly, one rejects the null hypothesis at the 5 per cent level of significance. The statistical test indicates that the untreated and treated do not have the same parameter. Upon examining the data, one will conclude that the sex ratio is lower following salt treatment than when such a treatment is omitted. (One cannot determine from these data whether salt raises the number of females or lowers the number of males. One finds only a difference in sex ratio as a function of the presence or absence of salt, the actual mechanism of the effect remaining unknown.)

Contingency-table approach to the chi-square test. Assume that $X_A = 3$ and $N_A = 6$ in sample A, and $X_B = 5$ and $N_B = 18$ in sample B. Are these statistics different at the 5 per cent level of significance? To determine this, one tests the null hypothesis that both samples have the same parameter (p). However, the value of p is completely unknown. If a *contingency table* is constructed, it will give the most likely values of X (and hence $N - X$), a common p for both samples being understood. Having determined these ideally expected values, one can then proceed as before to calculate chi square.

The observed data are arranged as shown in Figure A-4A. The best estimates for the values expected according to the unknown p are shown in B. To obtain the value expected in the shaded box in A, for example, multiply together the totals at the end of its column and row and divide by the number $N_A + N_B$. This value ($6 \times 8/24$) is 2.

Since we are dealing with χ^2, recall that it is usually safe to require that no class have an expected frequency less than 2 and that most expected values be at least 5. Note that the other expected values in B can be obtained in a similar manner; this procedure, however, is unnecessary since all the other values are fixed by the marginal totals, which must be the same in B as in A. Accordingly, there is only one degree of freedom (one variable) in the 2×2 contingency table formed. Difference table C

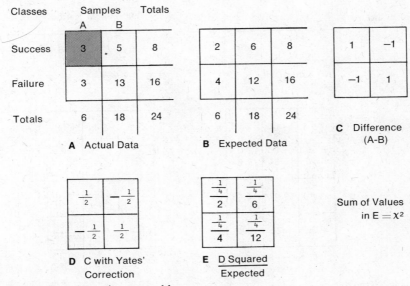

Figure A-4 A 2×2 contingency table.

is then constructed, the values of which are identical in crisscross position and always total zero. Each of the values in C is made less extreme (closer to zero) by $\frac{1}{2}$, to comply with Yates' correction. This is shown in D. Each of the corrected differences in D is squared and divided by the corresponding expected value shown in B. The sum of the four values obtained ($\frac{1}{4}/2 + \frac{1}{4}/6 + \frac{1}{4}/4 + \frac{1}{4}/12$) is chi square. In the present case chi square is less than 1 (but more than 0.004) and has a probability greater than 10 per cent. The null hypothesis is thus accepted, namely, that the two samples are not statistically different at the 5 per cent level of significance.

Involving Two or More Variables. *Contingency-table approach to the chi-square test.* Sometimes the data in a sample fall into more than two classes or outcomes, and more than two such samples are to be compared. This involves "number of classes − 1" variables as well as "number of samples − 1" variables. The total number of variables equals the product of these two sources of variability. The number of degrees of freedom is equal to the total number of variables, which is always (number of rows − 1) times (number of columns − 1) in a contingency table.

Suppose three samples were scored four alternative ways to give the results shown in Figure A-5A. The procedure followed is the same as that already described for the 2 × 2 or fourfold table (note that Yates' correction is not applicable in any larger table). There are 6 degrees of freedom. If one tests at the 5 per cent level, Figure A-3

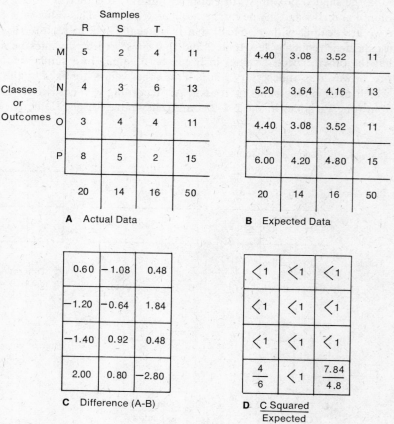

Figure A-5   A 3 × 4 contingency table.

shows that $\chi^2_{(6)}$ has to be greater than 12.5 if one is to reject the null hypothesis, namely, that all the samples and types can be represented by the same parameters. Moreover, finding that χ^2 is less than 1.6 would mean that the same parameters would produce samples varying this little from the ideally expected values only 5 per cent of the time. In that case one would reject the samples as being random, suspecting that there was some hidden bias in the collection and/or the scoring of the data. The decision that neither obtains can be seen from Figure A-5D. Consequently, one accepts the null hypothesis that these samples are not statistically different at the 5 per cent level of significance.

Assume, however, that chi square had been 14.1 in the preceding example. One would reject the null hypothesis at the 5 per cent level but could accept it at the 1 per cent level of significance (meaning that these samples have more than 1 per cent, but less than 5 per cent, chance of having the same parameters). Assuming that such a result was obtained in an unbiased manner it might be due to the fact that (a) the null hypothesis is true but one happened to collect data (as will happen by chance one time in 20) which varied at least this much from those expected, or (b) the null hypothesis is incorrect. Even if the hypothesis at the 5 per cent level is rejected, one may wish to test the data further, using smaller contingency tables to determine which samples or outcomes are consistent or inconsistent with each other according to a null hypothesis. Note here that the observed values in a contingency table furnishing the largest contributions to chi square are those most responsible for the rejection of the hypothesis.

QUESTIONS AND PROBLEMS

28. A cross yields 20 offspring of one type and 40 of another. A month later the same cross produces 15 of the first type and 15 of the second. Do these results differ significantly?

29. Ten sets of monozygotic twins are selected; only one member (the same one) of each pair is given a particular drug daily for 10 days. All individuals are weighed before and after this period. The changes to the nearest whole pound are as follows:

	TWIN	
PAIR	UNTREATED	TREATED
1	+1	+1
2	+2	+1
3	−4	−3
4	+1	+2
5	−3	−2
6	+3	+2
7	−2	+1
8	+4	+3
9	−1	0
10	+5	−4

Analyze the results of this experiment statistically.

30. Among the women of population A are 10 blondes, 5 redheads, and 15 of other hair color. In population B there are 7, 7, and 6, respectively; whereas in population C the tally is 8, 4, 8, respectively. Are these populations the same with respect to the relative frequency of these hair color types?

31. An experiment is performed four times. X is 5, 7, 10, and 11 when N is 8, 20, 20, 30, respectively. Are all four results mutually consistent?

32. Suppose the label on two packages of grass seed states that each package will germinate 40 per cent grass type A, 35 per cent grass type B, 15 per cent grass type C, and 10 per cent weeds D. A sample from package 1 germinates 400A, 400B, 50C, and 150 D. A sample from package 2 yields 390A, 410B, 70C, and 130D. Compare the contents of each package with the labeled contents and with each other. What do you conclude?

33. A drug manufacturer receives results of using or not using his product. As a check on bias in testing he scores the control and experimental group for eye color and ABO blood type and finds the results tabulated on the next page.

	AB		A	
	BLUE	BROWN	BLUE	BROWN
Control	7	6	12	10
Experimental	4	8	13	8

	B		O	
	BLUE	BROWN	BLUE	BROWN
Control	4	4	8	9
Experimental	5	2	8	12

What should he conclude about bias?

34. Suppose women were classified in two ways: hair color and temperament. Using the results listed below, test the hypothesis that there is no relation between hair color and temperament.

	BLONDE	RED	BROWN
Pugnacious	23	6	11
Quiet	26	3	31
Normal	41	9	30

Indiscrete variables

Parameters and the normal curve

Suppose a particular measurement is the result of the action of a very large number of independent variables, each of which has approximately the same magnitude of effect on the measurement. If, then, an infinitely large number of such measurements are collected, they will be expected to have a range of values which are said to be normally distributed. Figure A-6 shows the *normal distribution* or *curve* formed by plotting these measurements against the frequency with which they would be expected to occur in this infinitely large population. The *population mean*, or "*true*" *mean*, is denoted by the parameter μ. The *population standard deviation*, or "*true*" *standard deviation*, is represented by the lowercase Greek letter sigma, σ. It is known that about $\frac{3}{2}$ of all the measurements in a normal curve lie within one σ of the mean, and about 95 per cent of all measurements lie within 2σ of the mean (being in the range $\mu \pm 2\sigma$). Strictly speaking, the individual "measurements" or values which comprise the normal curve are also parameters.

The normal curve vs. the binomial distribution. Suppose that $N = 20$ and $p = \frac{1}{2}$. If an infinitely large number of samples each of $N = 20$ were obtained, the exact probabilities of obtaining different numbers of successes would be expressed in the binomial distribution plotted in histogram form in Figure A-7, where each class of success is represented by a column whose height is proportional to the frequency of

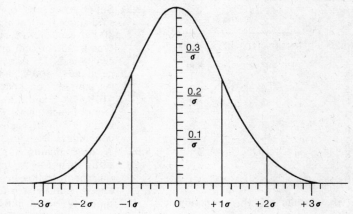

Figure A-6 The normal curve.

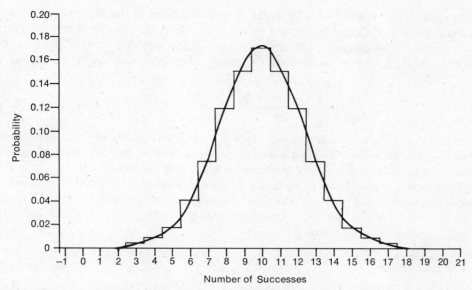

Figure A-7 Histogram of probabilities for different numbers of successes for a binomial distribution ($N = 20$, $p = \frac{1}{2}$), and a normal curve with the same μ and σ as the histogram.

the class. Note that there are only 21 ways to score the outcome of a set of 20 of these observations (from 0 to 20 successes), so we are dealing with 20 discrete variables. The smooth curve shown is the normal curve, which has the same mean and standard deviation as the histogram. The larger the sample size, if $p = \frac{1}{2}$, the larger will be the number of outcomes possible per sample, and the closer the plot of the probability of successes will approach the normal curve. Therefore, as N increases without bound, the number of possible outcomes increases to provide us with an example of a continuous variable, whose values are said to be distributed normally.

Statistics expected from a normal curve

Distribution of Individual Statistics.   If one obtains a very large number of statistics having a normal curve as a parameter, they will be distributed in a curve resembling the normal curve. The probability that any given statistic, X, is derived from the hypothetical population with mean μ and standard deviation σ_x, can be determined from the value τ calculated from the following:

$$\tau = \frac{X - \mu}{\sigma_x}.$$

When the absolute value of τ is 1.96, this probability for X is 0.05. Since exactly 5 per cent of the X values in a distribution characterized by the hypothesized μ and σ_x give absolute τ values of 1.96 or greater we reject the null hypothesis when X gives a τ value that equals or exceeds 1.96.

This equation can be rearranged $X = \mu + \tau\sigma_x$. This expression means that any given statistic is equal to the population mean plus a distance off this mean as measured by $\tau\sigma_x$, where τ is the number of σ_x's that X is away from the population mean. ($[\sigma_x]^2$ is called the *population variance*.)

Suppose one is concerned with height of corn measured to the nearest inch; hypothesize that $\mu = 50$ inches and $\sigma_x = 4$ inches. This information is completely sufficient to describe the properties of a normally distributed population. One plant is 40 inches tall, its height being considered a quantitative trait. Calculation of the value for τ yields

$$\frac{40 - 50}{4} = \frac{-10}{4},$$

which (ignoring the sign) is > 1.96. Since $p < 0.05$ one rejects the null hypothesis and may conclude that the plant measured cannot, at the 5 per cent level of significance, come from a theoretical population where $\mu = 50$ and $\sigma_x = 4$.

Distribution of the Means Expected for Groups of Statistics. The *arithmetic sample mean* or *average* of a group of statistics comprising a sample is denoted by $\bar{X}$ (read " X bar ") and is the average obtained by adding all the values of X and dividing by N. In more symbolic terms,

$$\bar{X} = \frac{1}{N} \sum X.$$

Given a population described by mean μ and standard deviation σ_x, one can predict something about the range of $\bar{X}$'s to be expected from drawing a great many samples of size N from this population. If many samples are drawn, it will be found that the $\bar{X}$ values fall into a distribution which has a theoretical mean equal to μ and which will be normally distributed with a standard deviation $\sigma_{\bar{x}}$. This

$$\sigma_{\bar{x}} = \sqrt{\frac{\sigma_x^2}{N}} = \frac{\sigma_x}{\sqrt{N}}.$$

Since $\sigma_{\bar{x}}$ is smaller than σ_x by a factor of $\sqrt{N}$, it permits greater discrimination in regard to error than does σ_x. When $N \geq 10$, $\bar{X}$ will be quite nearly normally distributed, if the distribution of X values does not differ too widely from that expected of measurements drawn from a normal curve. Accordingly, the distribution of $\bar{X}$, as measured by $\sigma_{\bar{x}}$, is usually also known by means of calculation whenever μ and σ_x are known.

In scientific papers the *standard error*, $s_{\bar{x}}$ or $\sigma_{\bar{x}}$, is often given in the form $\bar{X} \pm s_{\bar{x}}$ or $\bar{X} \pm \sigma_{\bar{x}}$, and refers to the reliability of the mean of a sample. On the other hand, s_x or σ_x are standard deviations; and when given as $X \pm s_x$ or $X \pm \sigma_x$, they refer to the variability of a single observation X.

Testing hypotheses regarding μ. The τ test. Suppose one finds for $N = 100$ that $\bar{X} = 68.03$. One may wish next to test the null hypothesis, at the 5 per cent level of significance, that $\sigma_x = 3$ and $\mu = 67.15$. In the present case

$$\sigma_{\bar{x}} = \sqrt{\frac{9}{100}} = 0.3; \qquad \tau = \frac{\bar{X} - \mu}{\sigma_{\bar{x}}}$$

$$= \frac{68.03 - 67.15}{0.3} = \frac{0.88}{0.3},$$

which is > 1.96. Consequently, one rejects the hypothesis.

The t test. Frequently one may have to test some hypothetical μ when σ_x and $\sigma_{\bar{x}}$ are unknown. In this situation, one utilizes the best available estimate of σ_x; this useful approximation is the *standard deviation of the sample*, s_x. The value for s_x can be determined from the following:

$$s_x = \sqrt{\frac{\sum(X - \bar{X})^2}{N - 1}}. \text{ Note that } s_{\bar{x}} = \sqrt{\frac{s_x^2}{N}}.$$

With $s_{\bar{x}}$ substituted for $\sigma_{\bar{x}}$, the expression

$$\frac{\bar{X} - \mu}{\sigma_{\bar{x}}} \text{ becomes } \frac{\bar{X} - \mu}{\sqrt{\dfrac{s_x^2}{N}}} = t.$$

(When $\sigma_{\bar{x}}$ is used, the final value is τ; when $s_{\bar{x}}$ is substituted, the final value is called t by convention.) If the value of t is too large, the hypothesis regarding μ will be rejected. The decision to accept or reject the null hypothesis depends upon the number of degrees of freedom, which equals $N - 1$ if one is estimating σ_x from a single sample. Figure A-3 gives the probabilities for various degrees of freedom that t differs from zero in either direction by a value equal to or greater than that observed. If $\bar{X} = 68.03$, the hypothesized $\mu = 67.15$, $s_x = 3.24$, and $N = 9$, then $t = 0.81$. With 8 degrees of freedom, $p > 0.05$. The hypothesized μ is accepted.

Confidence intervals for μ. Suppose that one chooses to work at the 5 per cent level of significance. If σ_x is known, the 95 per cent confidence interval for $\mu = X \pm 1.96\sigma_x$, or $\mu = \bar{X} \pm 1.96\sigma_{\bar{x}}$. If only s_x is known, then the 95 per cent confidence interval for μ can be determined as follows. Given, as before, that $\bar{X} = 68.03$, $s_x = 3.24$, and $N = 9$; first find the value of t which has $p = 0.05$ for $N - 1$ degrees of freedom. (For $N - 1 = 8$, this is about 2.3.) Hence,

$$\frac{\bar{X} - \mu}{\sqrt{\dfrac{s_x^2}{N}}} = 2.3.$$

One rejects all values where $\bar{X}$ differs from μ by more than $2.3s_{\bar{x}}$, and accepts all values of $\bar{X} - \mu$ with 95 per cent confidence that are less than $2.3s_{\bar{x}}$. Substituting, one finds

$$\frac{\bar{X} - \mu}{1.08} = 2.3$$

or, $\bar{X} - \mu = 2.3(1.08) = 2.48$. Finally, the 95 per cent confidence level for μ, in the present case, is $\bar{X} \pm 2.48$, or 65.55 to 70.51.

Comparison of $\bar{X}_1$ and $\bar{X}_2$. Suppose that one selects two sample sets of maize plants and then measures the height of each plant. The statistics obtained are

$$\text{Sample 1: } N_1 = 9; \quad \bar{X}_1 = 72.44$$
$$\sum(X_1 - \bar{X}_1)^2 = 65.70$$

$$\text{Sample 2: } N_2 = 10; \quad \bar{X}_2 = 70.30$$
$$\sum(X_2 - \bar{X}_2)^2 = 69.50$$

To be tested is the null hypothesis that these two samples have the same μ and the same σ_x. The best estimate of the unknown σ_x is s_x, obtained from the two samples by the following formula:

$$s_x = \sqrt{\frac{\sum(X_1 - \bar{X}_1)^2 + \sum(X_2 - \bar{X}_2)^2}{(N_1 - 1) + (N_2 - 1)}}$$

$$= \sqrt{\frac{65.70 + 69.50}{8 + 9}} = 2.82.$$

One derives a value of $s_{\bar{x}}$ in the present case equal to 1.29, since it is known that

$$s_{\bar{x}} = s_x \sqrt{\frac{1}{N_1} + \frac{1}{N_2}}.$$

The value of t is then found from

$$\frac{\bar{X}_1 - \bar{X}_2}{s_{\bar{x}}} \quad \text{to be} \quad \frac{72.44 - 70.30}{1.29} = 1.66.$$

Since each $\bar{X}$ was obtained from a single sample, the number of degrees of freedom is $(N_1 - 1) + (N_2 - 1)$, or 17. Because $p > 0.1$ one accepts the null hypothesis and may conclude that the two means are not statistically different at the 5 per cent level of significance. If one obtains a value of t inconsistent with the hypothesis, the two samples differ either in their μ's, σ_x's, or both.

The power of the test

There are two types of error involved in testing a parameter or statistic. One has already been discussed. This type of error is the rejection of the correct hypothesis 5 per cent of the time (when working at the 95 per cent confidence level, or the 5 per cent level of significance) in order to reject incorrect hypotheses. The other type of error is the incorrect acceptance of an hypothesis. Suppose that $f = 0.45$ and $N = 100$. The hypothesis that $p = \frac{1}{2}$ is tested and found acceptable at the 5 per cent level. But the real p might lie anywhere between 0.35 and 0.55 (see Figure A-2). If p is not 0.5 but somewhere between 0.35 and 0.55, one may have accepted the wrong hypothesis.

In the present case, the test is only powerful enough to reject incorrect hypotheses where $p < 0.35$ or > 0.55. Had N been 1,000 and $f = 0.45$, the discriminatory power of the test would be greater, at the 5 per cent level, causing the rejection of any hypothesis where $p < 0.42$ or > 0.47. Before collecting statistics, it is necessary to determine whether there is adequate power to discriminate against alternative hypotheses.

Suppose, for genetic reasons, one wishes to test whether some statistics obtained by experiment exhibit an expected 3:1 ratio. One may accept the hypothesis; but if a theoretical 1:1 or 2:1 ratio is also accepted, the test is rendered rather weak and is not likely to be useful in describing the nature of the genetic events involved.

One way to increase the meaningfulness of the test is to increase N. Another way is to change the level of confidence. At the 10 per cent level of significance the "power" of the test is greater than at the 5 per cent level; but there is a proportional increase in the chance of rejecting the correct hypothesis. Unless there is some special circumstance, geneticists usually work at the 5 per cent level and increase the power of the test by increasing N. Recall, however, that the size of s or σ decreases as the square root of N increases, so that a fourfold increase in N only reduces the standard deviation by a factor of 2.

QUESTIONS AND PROBLEMS

35. Given $\sigma_x = 8$, $N = 265$, $\overline{X} = 12$; test at the 5 per cent level of significance the hypothesis that $\mu = 11$.

36. Given $\sigma_x^2 = 412$, $N = 53$, $\overline{X} = 142$; test at the 5 per cent level of significance the hypothesis that $\mu = 135$.

37. What are the 95 per cent confidence limits for μ when $\sigma_x = 4$, $N = 100$, and $\overline{X} = 35$?

38. Given the statistics 1, 3, 4, 5, 5, 5, 5, 5, 6, 8, calculate $\overline{X}$, s_x, and $s_{\overline{x}}$.

39. A new antibiotic was tested on pneumonia patients with the following results: Of those treated, 64 lived and 26 died (28.9 per cent died); of those untreated, 36 lived and 24 died (40 per cent died). Test the hypothesis that the treatment is not effective.

40. A random sample of six observations drawn from a certain normal population is as follows: 0, 2, 6, 6, 8, 14. Test the hypothesis that μ, the population mean, equals 10. Use the 5 per cent level of significance.

41. Normal barley seeds are treated with X rays and planted. Of 400 seedlings examined, 55 show sectors with visible mutation. Test the hypothesis that the true mutation frequency at this dosage is 10 per cent.

42. Denote the length of an ear of corn by x inches. Explain exactly what is meant when someone says "the probability of x being less than 7 is 0.05."

43. A random sample of 25 mice is taken from a certain mutant strain. It is hypothesized that the length of these mice is approximately normally distributed. You find that $\overline{X}$ equals 60 mm and s_x is 10 mm. (a) Test the hypothesis that μ equals 61 mm at the 5 per cent level of significance. (b) Explain what is meant by "5 per cent level of significance" in this experiment.

44. Using the data of problem 43, find confidence limits for μ which provide 95 per cent confidence. Explain the practical meaning of your result.

45. Given the following data:

SAMPLE 1 $N = 10$	SAMPLE 2 $N = 10$
+3.4	+5.5
+0.7	+1.9
−1.6	+1.8
−0.2	+1.1
−1.2	+0.1
−0.1	−0.1
+3.7	+4.4
+0.8	+1.6
0.0	+4.6
+2.0	+3.4

Determine whether these two samples are statistically different.

46. Under what circumstances can one use the t table for values of τ?

GENERAL REFERENCES

Bailey, N. T. J. 1959. *Statistical methods in biology.* New York: John Wiley & Sons, Inc.

Carter, C. O. 1970. Multifactorial genetic disease. Hospital Practice, May: 45–59. (Hypothesized to include common conditions such as diabetes, heart disease, and schizophrenia.)

Crow, J. F. 1962. *Genetics notes,* fifth edition. Minneapolis: Burgess Publishing Company.

Dunn, O. J. 1964. *Basic statistics: a primer for the biomedical sciences.* New York: John Wiley & Sons, Inc.

Fried, R. 1969. *Introduction to statistics.* New York: Oxford University Press.

Kempthorne, O. 1957. *An introduction to genetic statistics.* New York: John Wiley & Sons, Inc.

Levene, H. 1958. Statistical inferences in genetics. In *Principles of genetics,* fifth edition, Sinnott, E. W., Dunn, L. C., and Dobzhansky, Th. New York: McGraw-Hill Book Company, Chap. 29, pp. 388–418.

Author Index

Subject Index